A Treasury of
WORLD
SCIENCE

Edited by Dagobert D. Runes

With an Introduction by Wernher von Braun

PHILOSOPHICAL LIBRARY
New York

Library of Congress Catalog Card No. 61-15249

Printed in the United States of America

INTRODUCTION

Long before man became a scientist he learned to write.

For about 6,000 years now he has been able to record and pass on his knowledge to others by writing.

He wrote the first classics about 2,000 years ago.

To me it is significant that so many of these first classics were written by early men of science.

Some scientific classics—like "On Floating Bodies, and Other Propositions" by Archimedes, for example—were written at least two centuries before the birth of Christ.

But science itself has been a weighty factor in determining the beliefs of educated men for only about three centuries.

So the classics, then—scientific and otherwise—have been a dominant force in guiding the thoughts and actions of mankind for much longer than science.

How does a classic become a classic? Because people read it.

Why? Because it is interesting and lucid and informative.

In my humble opinion, the classics are to science what air is to a wing. No matter how perfect the wing, it needs air to give it breadth and depth.

We owe a lot to those classical pilgrims who wrote in a language all of us can understand. They wrote with a breadth and perspective that lead us straight to the essence of a problem.

In the classics you observe proportion, balance, technical precision, simplicity, discipline, and structure. Aren't these the things you see in science?

The classics pay close attention to traditional and recognized forms. The same with science.

Classical, however, does not mean rigidity. In fact, the reflections and discussions of classical writers in the field of ideas and knowledge still are astonishingly applicable today.

Today's flourishing scientific advances and pursuit of truth bewilder and stun us. They also humble us. To understand, we must use the methods of the classicists.

By learning the techniques and disciplines practiced in the classics, we can apply them in the study of science. These same techniques and disciplines were used by writers concerned with a wide range of human interests including economics, government, religion, literature, and philosophy, as well as science.

Today, to control the tools that modern science has created, we cannot be concerned with the facts only; we must concern ourselves about values and purpose. Again, what better place to turn for true understanding of such things than the classics?

As the classicists brought order to their scientific discoveries and helped to explain the changes they wrought in the lives of men, so can we do the same—and sane—thing today.

We can't hold back progress, but with the help of the classics and the judicious use of a little common sense we can learn to live with it . . . and ourselves.

More than ever, it is true today that what has gone before is only an introduction to what is now and what is coming.

We are blessed because so many of our earlier scientific explorers could express their thoughts and write their discoveries in a simple and orderly fashion. They had to be able to write, otherwise nobody else could learn or understand what they had discovered. Classics like "Of The Revolution of Heavenly Bodies" by Copernicus or "The Elements" by Euclid are examples.

The same is true of scientists today. They have to be able to interpret their findings just as skillfully as they conduct their research. If not, a lot of priceless new knowledge will have to wait for a better man. And in the meanwhile everybody else does without.

The classics, of course, aren't everything. Neither is science or anything else.

In pursuing the study of the classics, particularly the scientific classics, we must show the same vivid curiosity possessed by that ancient flier, Icarus. It was Icarus, you remember, whose intense desire to learn about the heavens drove him to put on wings. When he soared too close to the sun the wax in his wings melted and he crashed and burned at the end of his mythical runway.

Although the classics are indispensable when it comes to stimulating our curiosity, they also provide a richer way of life through respect for truth.

But as we study our equations and sail our space ships, we must always remember that our first concern is for man himself. Our science must increase man's blessings, not drive him back in a hole.

So any scientist today who doesn't learn and practice the techniques and attitudes found in the classics is not fully equipped to do his job. As the philosopher Santayana said, he who ignores history is doomed to repeat it.

Today, as always, classical scholarship is an urgent and essential force in the education of any man or woman.

For a long time I have been distressed to see classics of all kinds pushed aside as the high school and college curricula broadened.

In my opinion, we should never discard the classics for more immediate practical training.

On the other hand, within just the past year or so, I have been somewhat encouraged to see a revival of interest in many classics. I think the publication of this anthology of scientific classics is in itself a good sign.

In fact, in writing down my personal convictions about the importance of the study of the classics in science, my own interest has been renewed to the point where I think I'll take another look at one of my favorites. It's on page 760. It was written by Sir Isaac Newton, and it is called "Principia."

For a long time this work of Newton's has steered men of science in their search for natural knowledge.

It is true that Einstein moved us substantially forward and handed us additional jewels of understanding, but the laws of Newton still remain a more comprehensive statement of truth.

Of Newton, Alexander Pope said:

"Nature and nature's laws lay hid in night:
God said, Let Newton Be! and all was light."

And so with the classics: they, too, provide light in the study of science.

WERNHER VON BRAUN

CONTENTS

GEORGIUS AGRICOLA

(1494–1555)

Trained first as a philologist, then as a physician, Agricola (the pen name of Saxon Georg Bauer) was practicing in the mining center of Joachimstal when he became interested in ores and metals and compiled *De Re Metallica* (1530 or 1556). This work has led him to be called the founder of scientific mineralogy. It also contained much new material in chemistry and medicine, and is one of the first works after the Middle Ages to return to the natural science tradition of Pliny.

ON METALS

MANY PERSONS hold the opinion that the metal industries are fortuitous and that the occupation is one of sordid toil, and altogether a kind of business requiring not so much skill as labor. But as for myself, when I reflect carefully upon its special points one by one, it appears to be far otherwise. For a miner must have the greatest skill in his work, that he may know first of all what mountain or hill, what valley or plain, can be prospected most profitably, or what he should leave alone; moreover, he must understand the veins, stringers, and seams in the rocks. Then he must be thoroughly familiar with the many and varied species of earths, juices, gems, stones, marbles, rocks, metals, and compounds. He must also have a complete knowledge of the method of making all underground works. Lastly, there are the various systems of assaying substances and of preparing them for smelting; and here again there are many altogether diverse methods. For there is one method for gold and silver, another for copper, another for quicksilver, another for iron, another for lead, and even tin and bismuth are treated differently from lead. Although

1

the evaporation of juices is an art apparently quite distinct from metallurgy, yet they ought not to be considered separately, inasmuch as these juices are also often dug out of the ground solidified, or they are produced from certain kinds of earth, and stones which the miners dig up, and some of the juices are not themselves devoid of metals. Again, their treatment is not simple, since there is one method for common salt, another for soda, another for alum, another for vitriol, another for sulphur, and another for bitumen.

Furthermore, there are many arts and sciences of which a miner should not be ignorant. First there is philosophy, that he may discern the origin, cause, and nature of subterranean things; for then he will be able to dig out the veins easily and advantageously, and to obtain more abundant results from his mining. Secondly, there is medicine, that he may be able to look after his diggers and other workmen, that they do not meet with those diseases to which they are more liable than workmen in other occupations, or if they do meet with them, that he himself may be able to heal them or may see that the doctors do so. Thirdly follows astronomy, that he may know the divisions of the heavens and from them judge the direction of the veins. Fourthly, there is the science of surveying, that he may be able to estimate how deep a shaft should be sunk to reach the tunnel which is being driven to it and to determine the limits and boundaries in these workings, especially in depth. Fifthly, his knowledge of arithmetical science should be such that he may calculate the cost to be incurred in the machinery and the working of the mine. Sixthly, his learning must comprise architecture, that he himself may construct the various machines and timberwork required underground, or that he may be able to explain the method of construction to others. Next, he must have knowledge of drawing, that he can draw plans of his machinery. Lastly, there is the law, especially that dealing with metals, that he may claim his own rights, that he may undertake the duty of giving others his opinion on legal matters, that he may not take another man's property and so make trouble for himself, and that he may fulfill his obligations to others according to the law.

2

It is therefore necessary that those who take an interest in the methods and precepts of mining and metallurgy should read these and others of our books studiously and diligently; or on every point they should consult expert mining people, though they will discover few who are skilled in the whole art. As a rule one man understands only the methods of mining, another possesses the knowledge of washing, another is experienced in the art of smelting, another has the knowledge of measuring the hidden parts of the earth, another is skillful in the art of making machines, and finally, another is learned in mining law. But as for us, though we may not have perfected the whole art of discovery and preparation of metals, at least we can be of great assistance to persons studious in its acquisition.

SMELTING IRON

VERY GOOD IRON ORE is smelted in a furnace almost like the cupellation furnace. The hearth is three and a half feet high, and five feet long and wide; in the center of it is a crucible a foot deep and one and a half feet wide, but it may be deeper or shallower, wider or narrower, according to whether more or less ore is to be made into iron. A certain quantity of iron ore is given to the master, out of which he may smelt either much or little iron. He, being about to expend his skill and labor on this matter, first throws charcoal into the crucible and sprinkles over it an iron shovelful of crushed iron ore mixed with unslaked lime. Then he repeatedly throws on charcoal and sprinkles it with ore, and continues this until he has slowly built up a heap; it melts when the charcoal has been kindled and the fire violently stimulated by the blast of the bellows, which are skillfully fixed in a pipe. He is able to complete this work sometimes in eight hours, sometimes in ten, and again sometimes in twelve. In order that the heat of the fire should not burn his face, he covers it entirely with a cap, in which, however, there are holes through which he may see and breathe. At the side of the hearth is a bar which he raises as often as is necessary, when the bellows

3

blow too violent a blast, or when he adds more ore and charcoal. He also uses the bar to draw off the slags or to open or close the gates of the sluice, through which the waters flow down onto the wheel which turns the axle that compresses the bellows. In this sensible way iron is melted out and a mass weighing two or three *centumpondia* may be made, providing the iron ore was rich. When this is done the master opens the slag vent with the tapping bar, and when all has run out he allows the iron mass to cool. Afterward he and his assistant stir the iron with the bar, and then in order to chip off the slag which had until then adhered to it and to condense and flatten it, they take it down from the furnace to the floor, and beat it with large wooden mallets having slender handles five feet long. Thereupon it is immediately placed on the anvil and repeatedly beaten by the large iron hammer that is raised by the cams of an axle turned by a water wheel. Not long afterward it is taken up with tongs and placed under the same hammer, and cut up with a sharp iron into four, five, or six pieces, according to whether it is large or small. These pieces, after they have been reheated in the blacksmith's forge and again placed on the anvil, are shaped by the smith into square bars or into plowshares or tires, but mainly into bars. Four, six, or eight of these bars weigh one fifth of a centumpondium, and from these they make various implements. During the blows from the hammer by which it is shaped by the smith, a youth pours water with a ladle onto the glowing iron, and this is why the blows make such a loud sound that they may be heard a long distance from the works. The masses, if they remain and settle in the crucible of the furnace in which the iron is smelted, become hard iron which can only be hammered with difficulty, and from these they make the iron-shod heads for the stamps, and suchlike very hard articles.

ANDRÉ MARIE AMPÈRE

(1775–1836)

This French mathematician and physicist belongs in the first rank of investigators in electricity and magnetism. From his discovery that parallel currents in the same direction attract one another, while those in opposite directions repel one another, he developed principles which became the basis of electrodynamics (the science of moving electricity). His invention of the astatic needle made possible the later astatic galvanometer. His work in electromagnetism provided the means for producing much stronger magnets than had previously been available, leading eventually to countless applications, from the electric bell to the electric locomotive. The ampere, or unit of intensity of an electric current, is named after him.

NEW NAMES

THE WORD *"electromagnetic"* which is used to characterize the phenomena produced by the conducting wires of the voltaic pile, could not suitably describe them except during the period when the only phenomena which were known of this sort were those which M. Oersted discovered, exhibited by an electric current and a magnet. I have determined to use the word *electrodynamic* in order to unite under a common name all these phenomena, and particularly to designate those which I have observed between two voltaic conductors. It expresses their true character, that of being produced by electricity in motion: while the electric attractions and repulsions, which have been known for a long time, are *electrostatic* phenomena produced by the unequal distribution of electricity at rest in the bodies in which they are observed.

5

ACTIONS BETWEEN CURRENTS

On the Mutual Action of Two Electric Currents

1. Electromotive action is manifested by two sorts of effects which I believe I should first distinguish by precise definitions.

I shall call the first *electric tension*, the second *electric current*.

The first is observed when two bodies, between which this action occurs, are separated from each other by non-conducting bodies at all the points of their surfaces except those where it is established; the second occurs when the bodies make a part of a circuit of conducting bodies, which are in contact at points on their surface different from those at which the electromotive action is produced. In the first case, the effect of the electromotive action is to put the two bodies, or the two systems of bodies, between which it exists, in two states of tension, of which the difference is constant when this action is constant, when, for example, it is produced by the contact of two substances of different sorts; this difference may be variable, on the contrary, with the cause which produces it, if it results from friction or from pressure.

The first case is the only one which can arise when the electromotive action develops between different parts of the same non-conducting body; tourmaline is an example of this when its temperature changes.

In the second case there is no longer any electric tension, light bodies are not sensibly attracted and the ordinary electrometer can no longer be of service to indicate what is going on in the body; nevertheless the electromotive action continues; for if, for example, water, or an acid or an alkali or a saline solution forms part of the circuit, these bodies are decomposed, especially when the electromotive action is constant, as has been known for some time; and furthermore as M. Oersted has recently discovered, when the electromotive action is produced by the contact of metals, the magnetic needle is turned from its direction when it is placed near any portion of the circuit; but these effects cease, water is no longer decomposed, and the needle comes back to its ordinary position as soon as the circuit is broken, when the tensions are re-established and light bodies are again attracted. This proves that the tensions are not the cause of the decomposition of water, or of the changes of direction of the magnetic needle discovered by M. Oersted. This second case is evidently the only one which can occur if the electromotive action is developed between the different parts of the same conducting body. The consequences deduced in this memoir from the experiments of M. Oersted will lead us to recognize the existence of this condition in the only case where there is need as yet to admit it.

2. Let us see in what consists the difference of these entirely different orders of phenomena, one of which consists in the tension and attractions or repulsions which have been long known, and the other, in decomposition of water and a great many other substances, in the changes of direction of the needle, and in a sort of attractions and repulsions entirely different from the ordinary electric attractions and repulsions; which I believe I have first discovered and which I have named *voltaic attractions* and *repulsions* to distinguish them from the others. When there is not conducting continuity from one of the bodies, or systems of bodies, in which the electromotive action develops, as in Volta's pile, we can only conceive this action as constantly carrying positive electricity into the one body and negative electricity into the other: in the first moment, when there is nothing opposed to the effect that it tends to produce, the two electricities accumulate, each in the part of the whole system to which it is carried, but this effect is checked as soon as the difference of electric tensions gives to their mutual attraction, which tends to reunite them, a force sufficient to make equilibrium with the electromotive action. Then everything remains in this state, except for the leakage of electricity, which may take place little by little across the non-conducting body, the air, for example, which interrupts the circuit; for it appears that there are no bodies which are perfect insulators. As this leakage takes place the tension diminishes, but since when it diminishes, the mutual attraction of the two electricities no longer makes equilibrium with the electromotive action, this last force, in case it is constant, carries anew positive electricity on one side and negative elec-

tricity on the other, and the tensions are re-established. It is this state of a system of electromotive and conducting bodies that I called *electric tension*. We know that it exists in the two halves of this system when we separate them or even in case they remain in contact after the electromotive action has ceased, provided that then it arose by pressure or friction between bodies which are not both conductors. In these two cases the tension is gradually diminished because of the leakage of electricity of which we have recently spoken.

But when the two bodies or the two systems of bodies between which the electromotive action arises are also connected by conducting bodies in which there is no other electromotive action equal and opposite to the first, which would maintain the state of electrical equilibrium, and consequently the tensions which result from it, these tensions would disappear or at least would become very small and the phenomena occur which have been pointed out as characterizing this second case. But as nothing is otherwise changed in the arrangement of the bodies between which the electromotive action develops, it cannot be doubted that it continues to act, and as the mutual attraction of the two electricities, measured by the difference in the electric tensions, which has become nothing or has considerably diminished, can no longer make equilibrium with this action, it is generally admitted that it continues to carry the two electricities in the two senses in which it carried them before; in such a way that there results a double current, one of positive electricity, the other of negative electricity, starting out in opposite senses from the points where the electromotive action arises, and going out to reunite in the parts of the circuits remote from these points. The currents of which I am speaking are accelerated until the inertia of the electric fluids and the resistance which they encounter because of the imperfection of even the best conductors make equilibrium with the electromotive force, after which they continue indefinitely with constant velocity so long as this force has the same intensity, but they always cease on the instant that the circuit is broken. It is this state of electricity in a series of electromotive and conducting bodies which I name, for brevity, the *electric current*; and as I shall frequently have to speak of

8

Plate 2

Courtesy French Embassy Press & Information Division

Marie Curie

the two opposite senses in which the two electricities move, I shall understand every time that the question arises, to avoid tedious repetition, after the words, *sense of the electric current*, these words, *of positive electricity*; so that if we are considering, for example, a voltaic pile, the expression: *direction of the electric current in the pile*, will designate the direction from the end where hydrogen is disengaged in the decomposition of water to that end where oxygen is obtained; and this expression, *direction of the electric current in the conductor which makes connection between the two ends of the pile*, will designate the direction which goes, on the contrary, from the end where oxygen appears to that where the hydrogen develops. To include these two cases in a single definition we may say that what we may call the direction of the electric current is that followed by hydrogen and the bases of the salts when water or some saline substance is a part of the circuit, and is decomposed by the current, whether, in the voltaic pile, these substances are a part of the conductor or are interposed between the pairs of which the pile is constructed. . . .

3. The ordinary electrometer indicates tension and the intensity of the tension; there was lacking an instrument which would enable us to recognize the presence of the electric current in a pile or a conductor and which would indicate the energy and the direction of it. This instrument now exists; all that is needed is that the pile, or any portion of the conductor, should be placed horizontally, approximately in the direction of the magnetic meridian, and that an apparatus similar to a compass, which, in fact, differs from it only in the use that is made of it, should be placed above the pile or either above or below a portion of the conductor. So long as the circuit is interrupted, the magnetic needle remains in its ordinary position, but it departs from this position as soon as the current is established, so much the more as the energy is greater, and it determines the direction of the current from this general fact, that if one places oneself in thought in the direction of the current in such a way that it is directed from the feet to the head of the observer and that he has his face turned toward the needle, the action of the current will always throw toward left that one of the ends of the needle

9

which points toward the north and which I shall always call the austral pole of the magnetic needle, because it is the pole similar to the southern pole of the earth. I express this more briefly by saying, that the austral pole of the needle is carried to the left of the current which acts on the needle. I think that to distinguish this instrument from the ordinary electrometer we should give it the name of *galvanometer* and that it should be used in all experiments on electric currents, as we habitually use an electrometer on electric machines, so as to see at every instant if a current exists and what is its energy.

The first use that I have made of this instrument is to employ it to show that the current in the voltaic pile, from the negative end to the positive end, has the same effect on the magnetic needle as the current in the conductor which goes on the contrary from the positive end to the negative end.

It is well to have for this experiment two magnetic needles, one of them placed on the pile and the other above or below the conductor; we see the austral pole of each needle move to the left of the current near which it is placed; so that when the second is above the conductor it is turned to the opposite side from that toward which the needle turns which has been placed on the pile, because the currents have opposite directions in these two portions of the circuit; the two needles, on the contrary, are turned toward the same side, remaining nearly parallel with each other, when the one is above the pile and the other below the conductor. As soon as the circuit is broken they come back at once in both cases to their ordinary position.

4. Such are the differences already recognized in the effects produced by electricity in the two states which I have described, of which the one consists, if not in rest, at least in a movement which is slow and only produced because of the difficulty of completely insulating the bodies in which the electric tension exhibits itself, the other, in a double current of positive and negative electricity along a continuous circuit of conducting bodies. In the ordinary theory of electricity, we suppose that the two fluids of which we consider it composed are unceasingly separated one from the other in a part of a circuit and carried

10

Courtesy British Information Se[r...]

Robert Boyle

Plate 1

Courtesy British Information Service

Robert Boyle

Plate 2

Courtesy French Embassy Press & Information Division

Marie Curie

which points toward the north and which I shall always call the austral pole of the magnetic needle, because it is the pole similar to the southern pole of the earth. I express this more briefly by saying, that the austral pole of the needle is carried to the left of the current which acts on the needle. I think that to distinguish this instrument from the ordinary electrometer we should give it the name of *galvanometer* and that it should be used in all experiments on electric currents, as we habitually use an electrometer on electric machines, so as to see at every instant if a current exists and what is its energy.

The first use that I have made of this instrument is to employ it to show that the current in the voltaic pile, from the negative end to the positive end, has the same effect on the magnetic needle as the current in the conductor which goes on the contrary from the positive end to the negative end.

It is well to have for this experiment two magnetic needles, one of them placed on the pile and the other above or below the conductor; we see the austral pole of each needle move to the left of the current near which it is placed; so that when the second is above the conductor it is turned to the opposite side from that toward which the needle turns which has been placed on the pile, because the currents have opposite directions in these two portions of the circuit; the two needles, on the contrary, are turned toward the same side, remaining nearly parallel with each other, when the one is above the pile and the other below the conductor. As soon as the circuit is broken they come back at once in both cases to their ordinary position.

4. Such are the differences already recognized in the effects produced by electricity in the two states which I have described, of which the one consists, if not in rest, at least in a movement which is slow and only produced because of the difficulty of completely insulating the bodies in which the electric tension exhibits itself, the other, in a double current of positive and negative electricity along a continuous circuit of conducting bodies. In the ordinary theory of electricity, we suppose that the two fluids of which we consider it composed are unceasingly separated one from the other in a part of a circuit and carried

the two opposite senses in which the two electricities move, I shall understand every time that the question arises, to avoid tedious repetition, after the words, *sense of the electric current*, these words, *of positive electricity*; so that if we are considering, for example, a voltaic pile, the expression: *direction of the electric current in the pile*, will designate the direction from the end where hydrogen is disengaged in the decomposition of water to that end where oxygen is obtained; and this expression, *direction of the electric current in the conductor which makes connection between the two ends of the pile*, will designate the direction which goes, on the contrary, from the end where oxygen appears to that where the hydrogen develops. To include these two cases in a single definition we may say that what we may call the direction of the electric current is that followed by hydrogen and the bases of the salts when water or some saline substance is a part of the circuit, and is decomposed by the current, whether, in the voltaic pile, these substances are a part of the conductor or are interposed between the pairs of which the pile is constructed. . . .

3. The ordinary electrometer indicates tension and the intensity of the tension; there was lacking an instrument which would enable us to recognize the presence of the electric current in a pile or a conductor and which would indicate the energy and the direction of it. This instrument now exists; all that is needed is that the pile, or any portion of the conductor, should be placed horizontally, approximately in the direction of the magnetic meridian, and that an apparatus similar to a compass, which, in fact, differs from it only in the use that is made of it, should be placed above the pile or either above or below a portion of the conductor. So long as the circuit is interrupted, the magnetic needle remains in its ordinary position, but it departs from this position as soon as the current is established, so much the more as the energy is greater, and it determines the direction of the current from this general fact, that if one places oneself in thought in the direction of the current in such a way that it is directed from the feet to the head of the observer and that he has his face turned toward the needle, the action of the current will always throw toward left that one of the ends of the needle

Plate 3

Charles Darwin

Plate 4

Portrait by Franz Hals
Courtesy French Embassy Press & Information Division

René Descartes

rapidly in contrary senses into another part of the same circuit, where they are continually reunited. Although the electric current thus defined can be produced with an ordinary machine by arranging it in such a way as to develop the two electricities and by joining by a conductor the two parts of the apparatus where they are produced, we cannot, unless we use a very large machine, obtain the current with an appreciable energy except by the use of the voltaic pile, because the quantity of electricity produced by a frictional machine remains the same in a given time whatever may be the conducting power of the rest of the circuit, whereas that which the pile sets in motion during a given time increases indefinitely as we join the two extremities by a better conductor.

But the differences which I have recalled are not the only ones which distinguish these two states of electricity. I have discovered some more remarkable ones still by arranging in parallel directions two straight parts of two conducting wires joining the ends of two voltaic piles; the one was fixed and the other, suspended on points and made very sensitive to motion by a counterweight, could approach the first or move it while keeping parallel with it. I then observed that when I passed a current of electricity in both of these wires at once they attracted each other when the two currents were in the same sense and repelled each other when they were in opposite senses. Now these attractions or repulsions of electric currents differ essentially from those that electricity produces in the state of repose; first, they cease, as chemical decompositions do, as soon as we break the circuit of the conducting bodies; secondly, in the ordinary electric attractions and repulsions the electricities of opposite sort attract and those of the same name repel; in the attractions and repulsions of electric currents we have precisely the contrary; it is when the two conducting wires are placed parallel in such a way that their ends of the same name are on the same side and very near each other that there is attraction, and there is repulsion when the two conductors, still always parallel, have currents in them in opposite senses, so that the ends of the same name are as far apart as possible. Thirdly, in

11

the case of attraction, when it is sufficiently strong to bring the movable conductor into contact with the fixed conductor, they remain attached to one another like two magnets and do not separate after a while, as happens when two conducting bodies which attract each other because they are electrified, one positively and the other negatively, come to touch. Finally, and it appears that this last circumstance depends on the same cause as the preceding, two electric currents attract or repel in vacuum as in air, which is contrary to that which we observe in the mutual action of two conducting bodies charged with ordinary electricity. It is not the place here to explain these new phenomena; the attractions and repulsions which occur between two parallel currents, according as they are directed in the same sense or in opposite senses, are facts given by an experiment which is easy to repeat. It is necessary in this experiment, in order to prevent the motions which would be given to the movable conductor by agitation of the air, to place the apparatus under a glass cover within which we introduce, through the base which carries it, those parts of the conductors which can be joined to the two ends of the pile. The most convenient arrangement of these conductors is to place one of them on two supports in a horizontal position, (Fig. 1) in which it is fixed, and to hang up the other by two metallic wires, which are joined to it, on a glass rod which is above the first conductor and which rests on two other metal supports by very fine steel points; these points are soldered to the two ends of the metallic wires of which I have spoken, in such a way that connection is established through the supports by the aid of these points.

The two conductors are thus parallel and one beside the other in a horizontal plane; one of them is movable because of the oscillations which it can make about the horizontal line passing through the ends of the two steel points and when it thus moves it necessarily remains parallel to the fixed conductor.

There is introduced above and in the middle of the glass rod a counterweight, to increase the mobility of the oscillating part of the apparatus, by raising its center of gravity.

I first thought that it would be necessary to set up the electric current in the two conductors by means of two different piles; but this is not necessary. The conductors may both make parts of the same circuit; for the electric current exists everywhere with the same intensity. We may conclude from this observation that the electric tensions of the two ends of the pile have nothing to do with the phenomena with which we are concerned; for there is certainly no tension in the rest of the circuit. This view is

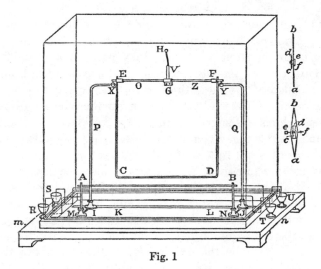

Fig. 1

confirmed by our being able to move the magnetic needle at a great distance away from the pile by means of a very long conductor, the middle of which is curved over in the direction of the magnetic meridian above or below the needle. This experiment was suggested to me by the illustrious savant to whom the physico-mathematical sciences owe so much of the great progress that they have made in our time: it has fully succeeded.

Designate by A and B the two ends of the fixed conductor, by C the end of the movable conductor which is on the side of A and by D that of the same conductor which is on the side of B; it is plain that if one of the ends of the pile is joined to A, B to C, and D to the other end of the pile, the electric current will be in the same sense in the two conductors; then we shall see them

13

attract each other; if on the other hand, while *A* always is joined to one end of the pile, *B* is joined to *D* and *C* to the other end of the pile, the current will be in opposite senses in the two conductors and then they repel each other. Further, we may recognize that since the attractions and repulsions of electric currents act at all points in the circuit we may, with a single fixed conductor, attract and repel as many conductors and change the direction of as many magnetic needles as we please. I propose to have made two movable conductors within the same glass case so arranged that by making them parts of the same circuit, with a common fixed conductor, they may be alternately both attracted or both repelled, or one of them attracted and the other repelled at the same time, according to the way in which the connections are made. Following up the success of the experiment which was suggested to me by the Marquis de Laplace, by employing as many conducting wires and magnetized needles as there are letters, by fixing each letter on a different magnet, and by using a pile at a distance from these needles, which can be joined alternately by its own ends to the ends of each conductor, we may form a sort of telegraph, by which we can write all the matters which we may wish to transmit, across whatever obstacles there may be, to the person whose duty it is to observe the letters carried by the needles. By setting up above the pile a keyboard of which the keys carry the same letters and by making connection by pressing them down, this method of correspondence could be managed easily and would take no more time than is necessary to touch the keys at one end and to read off each letter at the other.

If the movable conductor, instead of being adjusted so as to move parallel to the fixed conductor, can only turn in a plane parallel to the fixed conductor about a common perpendicular passing through their centers, it is clear, from the law that we have discovered of the attractions and repulsions of electric currents, that each half of the two conductors will attract or repel at the same time, according as the currents are in the same sense or in opposite senses; and consequently that the movable conductor will turn until it becomes parallel to the fixed conductor, in such a way that the currents are directed in the same sense: from which it follows that in the mutual action of two electric currents the directive action and the attractive or repulsive action depend on the same principle and are only different effects of one and the same action. It is no longer necessary, therefore, to set up between these two effects the distinction which it is so important to make, as we shall see very soon, when we are dealing with the mutual action of an electric current and of a magnet considered, as we ordinarily do, with respect to its axis, because in this action the two bodies tend to place themselves perpendicular to each other.

We now turn to the examination of this last action and of the action of two magnets on each other and we shall see that they both come under the law of the mutual action of two electric currents, if we conceive one of these currents as set up at every point of a line drawn on the surface of a magnet from one pole to the other, in planes perpendicular to the axis of the magnet, so that from the simple comparison of facts it seems to me impossible to doubt that there are really such currents about the axis of a magnet, or rather that magnetization consists in a process by which we give to the particles of steel the property of producing, in the sense of the currents of which we have spoken, the same electromotive action as is shown by the voltaic pile, by the oxidized zinc of the mineralogists, by heated tourmaline, and even in a pile made up of damp cardboard and discs of the same metal at two different temperatures. However, since this electromotive action is set up in the case of a magnet between the different particles of the same body, which is a good conductor, it can never, as we have previously remarked, produce any electric tension, but only a continuous current similar to that which exists in a voltaic pile re-entering itself in a closed curve. It is sufficiently evident from the preceding observations that such a pile cannot produce at any of its points either electric tensions or attractions or repulsions or chemical phenomena, since it is then impossible to insert a liquid in the circuit; but that the current which is immediately established in this pile will act to direct it or to attract or repel it either by another electric current or by a magnet, which, as we shall see, is only an assemblage of electric currents.

It is thus that we come to this unexpected result, that the phenomena of the magnet are produced by electricity and that there is no other difference between the two poles of a magnet than their positions with respect to the currents of which the magnet is composed, so that the austral pole is that which is to the right of these currents and the boreal pole that which is to the left.

THE SOLENOID

Now let us imagine in space any line MmO which is encircled by electric currents, making very small closed circuits about it, in planes infinitely near each other, which are perpendicular to it, in such a way that the areas contained by these circuits are all equal to one another, and so that their centers of gravity are on the line and so placed that there is the same distance measured on the line between two consecutive planes. If we call this distance g, which we shall consider infinitely small, the number of currents which will correspond to an element ds of the line MmO will be ds/g; and we must multiply by this number the values of A, B, C which we have found for a single circuit so as to get those values which refer to the circuits of the element ds; and finally by integrating from one end of the arc s to the other we shall obtain the values for A, B, C which hold for the assemblage of all the circuits which encircle the line. To this assemblage I have given the name *electrodynamic solenoid*, from the Greek word σωληνοειδὴς which denotes that which has the form of a canal, that is to say, the surface of this form in which all the circuits lie.

CIRCUITS AND MAGNETIC SHELLS

To justify the way in which I conceive the phenomena presented by magnets, by considering them as if they were assemblages of electric currents in very small circuits about their particles, it must be demonstrated, by starting from the formula by which I have represented the mutual action of two elements of electric current, that there shall result from certain assemblages of these small circuits forces which depend only on the positions of two definite points of this system, and which, relative to these two points, exhibit all the properties of the forces which we attribute to what we call the molecules of austral fluid and of boreal fluid, when we explain by means of these two fluids the phenomena presented by magnets, either in their mutual action or in that which they exert on the conducting wire. Now we know that the physicists who prefer the explanation in which we suppose the existence of these molecules to that which I have deduced from the properties of electric currents, assume that to each molecule of austral fluid there corresponds in each particle of the magnetized body a molecule of boreal fluid of the same intensity, and that if we give the name magnetic element to the combination of these two molecules, which we may consider to be the two poles of this element, it is necessary for the explanation of the phenomena which are presented by the two kinds of action which we are now considering: (1) That the mutual action of two magnetic elements is compounded of four forces, two attractive and two repulsive, directed along the straight lines which join the two molecules of one of these elements to the two molecules of the other, and of which the intensity is in the inverse ratio of the squares of these lines; (2) That when one of these elements acts on an infinitely small portion of the conducting wire, there result two forces perpendicular to the planes which pass through the two molecules of the element and through the direction of the small portion of the wire, and which are proportional to the sines of the angles which this direction makes with the straight lines which measure the distances to the two molecules and in the inverse ratio of the squares of these distances. So long as one does not accept the explanation which I give of the action of magnets and so long as one attributes these two sorts of forces to molecules of an austral fluid and of a boreal fluid, it is impossible to refer them to a single principle; but if one adopts my way of looking at the constitution of mag-

17

nets, one sees by the preceding calculations that both these types of action and the values of the forces which result from them are deduced immediately from my formula, and that to find these values it is sufficient to substitute for the combination of two molecules, one of them of austral fluid, and the other of boreal fluid, a solenoid whose ends, which are the two definite points on which depend the forces with which we are dealing, are situated exactly at the points where one supposes the molecules of the two fluids to be situated.

Thus two systems of very small solenoids will act on each other according to my formula like two magnets made up of as many magnetic elements as we suppose there are solenoids in these two systems; one of the same systems will act also on an element of an electric current as a magnet does; and consequently all the calculations and all the explanations based on the consideration of the attractive and repulsive forces of these molecules in the inverse ratio of the squares of their distances, and also on the consideration of the forces of rotation between one of these molecules and an element of the electric current, the law of which I have stated in the form which is adopted by the physicists who do not receive my theory, are necessarily the same whether one explains, as I do, by electric currents the phenomena which magnets present in these two cases or prefers the hypothesis of two fluids. It is therefore not in these calculations or explanations that one should seek either objections to my theory or proofs in its favor. The proof on which I rely follows altogether from this, that my theory reduces to a single principle three sorts of actions which the totality of the phenomena proves to result from a common cause and which cannot be reduced to one principle in any other way. . . .

We have now to concern ourselves with the actions that a closed circuit, whatever may be its form, its size, and its position, exerts either on a solenoid or on another circuit of any form, size and position. The principal result of these researches consists in the analogy which exists between the forces produced by this circuit, whether it acts on another closed circuit or on a solenoid, and the forces which would be exerted by points, the action of which is precisely that which is attributed to the molecules of that which we call the austral fluid and the boreal fluid; these points being distributed in the way that I have explained on surfaces bounded by these circuits and the ends of the solenoid being replaced by two magnetic molecules of opposite sort. This analogy appears at once so complete that all the electrodynamic phenomena seem to be thus referred to the theory in which we assume these two fluids; but we soon perceive that this does not hold except for voltaic conductors which form rigid closed circuits, and that only those phenomena which are produced by conductors forming such circuits can be explained in this way, and that finally the forces expressed by my formula are the only ones which agree with all the facts. . . .

Instead of replacing each circuit by two neighboring surfaces, of which one is covered with austral fluid and the other with boreal fluid, these fluids being distributed as has been said before, wo oan replace each circuit by a single surface on which are uniformly distributed magnetic elements, such as they have been defined by M. Poisson in a memoir read to the Academy of Sciences, February 2, 1824.

The author of this memoir, by calculating the formulas by which he has brought within the range of analysis all questions relative to the magnetization of bodies, whatever may be the cause which is assigned for that, has given the values of the three forces exerted by a magnetic element on a molecule of austral or boreal fluid. These values are identical with those which I have deduced from my formula for the three quantities A, B, C, in the case of a very small closed plane circuit, when we suppose that the constant coefficients are the same. It is easy to deduce from them a theorem from which we see immediately:

1. That the action of an electrodynamic solenoid, calculated from my formula, is in every case the same as that of a series of magnetic elements of the same intensity distributed uniformly along the straight or curved line which is encircled by all the small circuits of the solenoid, if we give to the axes of the elements at each point of the line the direction of the line;

2. That the action of a rigid closed voltaic circuit, calculated

from my formula, is precisely that which magnetic elements of the same intensity will exert, if they are uniformly distributed on any surface bounded by this circuit with the axes of the magnetic elements everywhere normal to this surface.

The same theorem also leads us to this consequence, that if we conceive a surface, enclosing on all sides a very small volume, and if we suppose on the one hand molecules of austral fluid and of boreal fluid distributed on this small surface in equal quantities, as they ought to be if they are to constitute a magnetic element such as M. Poisson has conceived it, and on the other hand if we suppose the same surface covered with electric currents which form on this surface small closed circuits in parallel and equidistant planes, and if we calculate the action of these currents from my formula, the forces exerted in both cases, whether on an element of the conducting wire or on a magnetic molecule, are precisely the same, are independent of the form of the small surface, and are proportional to the volume which it encloses, when the axes of the magnetic elements coincide with the perpendicular to the planes of the circuits.

When the identity of these forces has been demonstrated we may consider as simple corollaries all the results which I have given in this treatise regarding the possibility of substituting for magnets, without changing the effects produced, assemblages of electric currents forming closed circuits about their particles. I think that it will be easy for the reader to deduce this consequence, and the theorem on which it rests, from the preceding calculations.

ARCHIMEDES

(*c.* 287–*c.* 212 B.C.)

This Greek mathematician and inventor is the only scientist among the ancients who made permanent contributions in mechanics and hydrostatics. He enunciated the principle that a body immersed in liquid loses weight equivalent to the weight of the fluid displaced. According to legend, he made the discovery while trying to determine the purity of the gold in his king's crown. He is said to have rushed naked from the baths, shouting "Eureka!" ("I have found it!") Among the inventions ascribed to him are the Archimedean screw or spiral pump for raising water, the endless screw, the cogwheel and the compound pulley. During the siege of Syracuse he is reputed to have set fire to the Roman ships with concave mirrors. He was the author of a number of geometrical treatises.

ON FLOATING BODIES AND OTHER
PROPOSITIONS

On the Sphere and Cylinder

ARCHIMEDES to Dositheus greeting.

On a former occasion I sent you the investigations which I had up to that time completed, including the proofs, showing that any segment bounded by a straight line and a section of a right-angled cone [a parabola] is four-thirds of the triangle which has the same base with the segment and equal height. Since then certain theorems not hitherto demonstrated (ἀνελέγκτων) have occurred to me, and I have worked out the proofs of them. They are these: first, that the surface of any sphere is four times its greatest circle (τοῦ μεγίστου κύκλου); next, that the surface of any segment of a sphere is equal to a circle whose radius (ἡ ἐκ τοῦ κέντρου) is equal to the straight line drawn from the vertex

21

(κορυφή) of the segment to the circumference of the circle which is the base of the segment; and, further, that any cylinder having its base equal to the greatest circle of those in the sphere, and height equal to the diameter of the sphere, is itself [*i.e.* in content] half as large again as the sphere, and its surface also [including its bases] is half as large again as the surface of the sphere. Now these properties were all along naturally inherent in the figures referred to (αὐτη τη φύσει προυπῆρχεν περὶ τὰ εἰρημένα σχήματα), but remained unknown to those who were before my time engaged in the study of geometry. Having, however, now discovered that the properties are true of these figures, I cannot feel any hesitation in setting them side by side both with my former investigations and with those of the theorems of Eudoxus on solids which are held to be most irrefragably established, namely, that any pyramid is one third part of the prism which has the same base with the pyramid and equal height, and that any cone is one third part of the cylinder which has the same base with the cone and equal height. For, though these properties also were naturally inherent in the figures all along, yet they were in fact unknown to all the many able geometers who lived before Eudoxus, and had not been observed by any one. Now, however, it will be open to those who possess the requisite ability to examine these discoveries of mine. They ought to have been published while Conon was still alive, for I should conceive that he would best have been able to grasp them and to pronounce upon them the appropriate verdict; but, as I judge it well to communicate them to those who are conversant with mathematics, I send them to you with the proofs written out, which it will be open to mathematicians to examine. Farewell.

I first set out the assumptions that I have used for the proofs of my proposition.

Assumptions

1. Of all lines which have the same extremities the straight line is the least.

2. Of other lines in a plane and having the same extremities, [any two] such are unequal whenever both are concave in the same direc-

tion and one of them is either wholly included between the other and the straight line which has the same extremities with it, or is partly included by, and is partly common with, the other; and that [line] which is included is the lesser [of the two].

3. Similarly, of surfaces which have the same extremities, if those extremities are in a plane, the plane is the least [in area].

4. Of other surfaces with the same extremities, the extremities being in a plane, [any two] such are unequal whenever both are concave in the same direction and one surface is either wholly included between the other and the plane which has the same extremities with it, or is partly included by, and partly common with, the other; and that [surface] which is included in the lesser [of the two in the area].

5. Further, of unequal lines, unequal surfaces, and unequal solids, the greater exceeds the less by such a magnitude as, when added to itself, can be made to exceed any assigned magnitude among those which are comparable with [it and with] one another.

These things being premised, *if a polygon be inscribed in a circle, it is plain that the perimeter of the inscribed polygon is less than the circumference of the circle;* for each of the sides of the polygon is less than that part of the circumference of the circle which is cut off by it.

Proposition

If a polygon be circumscribed about a circle, the perimeter of the circumscribed polygon is greater than the perimeter of the circle.

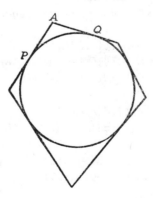

Let any two adjacent sides, meeting in A, touch the circle at P, Q respectively.

Then [*Assumptions*, 2]

$$PA + AQ > (\text{arc } PQ).$$

A similar inequality holds for each angle of the polygon; and, by addition, the required result follows.

Measurement of a Circle

Proposition 1

The area of any circle is equal to a right-angled triangle in which one of the sides about the right angle is equal to the radius, and the other to the circumference, of the circle.

Proposition 2

The area of a circle is to the square on its diameter as 11 to 14.

Proposition 3

The ratio of the circumference of any circle to its diameter is less than $3\frac{1}{7}$ but greater than $3^{10}/_{71}$.

I. Let AB be the diameter of any circle, O its center, AC the tangent at A; and let the angle AOC be one-third of a right angle. Then

$$OA:AC > 265:153 \quad \ldots \ldots \quad (1)$$

and

$$OC:CA = 306:153 \quad \ldots \ldots \quad (2).$$

First, draw OD bisecting the angle AOC and meeting AC in D.

Now

$$CO:OA = CD:DA, \qquad \text{[Eucl. VI. 3]}$$

so that

$$[CO + OA:OA = CA:DA, \text{ or}]$$
$$CO + OA:CA = OA:AD.$$

Therefore by (1) and (2)

$$OA:AD > 571:153 \quad \ldots \ldots \quad (3).$$

Hence

$$OD^2:AD^2 = (OA^2 + AD^2):AD^2$$
$$> (571^2 + 153^2):153^2$$
$$> 349450:23409,$$

so that

$$OD:DA > 591\frac{1}{8}:153 \quad \ldots \ldots \quad (4).$$

24

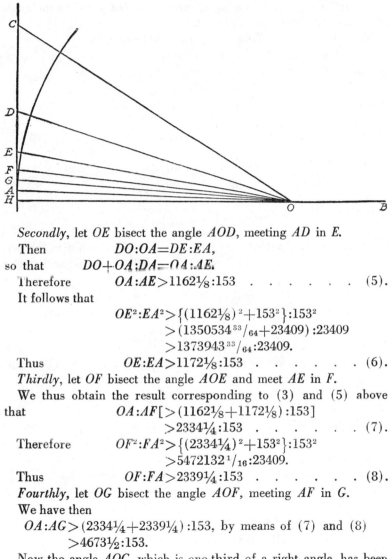

Secondly, let OE bisect the angle AOD, meeting AD in E.

Then $\qquad DO:OA=DE:EA,$

so that $\qquad DO+OA:DA=OA:AE.$

Therefore $\qquad OA:AE>1162\frac{1}{8}:153$ . . . . . . (5).

It follows that

$$OE^2:EA^2>\{(1162\tfrac{1}{8})^2+153^2\}:153^2$$
$$>(1350534\,^{33}/_{64}+23409):23409$$
$$>1373943\,^{33}/_{64}:23409.$$

Thus $\qquad OE:EA>1172\frac{1}{8}:153$ . . . . . . (6).

Thirdly, let OF bisect the angle AOE and meet AE in F.

We thus obtain the result corresponding to (3) and (5) above

that $\qquad OA:AF[>(1162\tfrac{1}{8}+1172\tfrac{1}{8}):153]$
$$>2334\tfrac{1}{4}:153 \text{ . . . . . . (7).}$$

Therefore $\qquad OF^2:FA^2>\{(2334\tfrac{1}{4})^2+153^2\}:153^2$
$$>5472132\,^1/_{16}:23409.$$

Thus $\qquad OF:FA>2339\frac{1}{4}:153$ . . . . . . (8).

Fourthly, let OG bisect the angle AOF, meeting AF in G.

We have then

$OA:AG>(2334\tfrac{1}{4}+2339\tfrac{1}{4}):153$, by means of (7) and (8)
$$>4673\tfrac{1}{2}:153.$$

Now the angle AOC, which is one-third of a right angle, has been bisected four times, and it follows that

$$\angle AOG = {}^1/_{48} \text{ (a right angle).}$$

25

Make the angle AOH on the other side of OA equal to the angle AOG, and let GA produced meet OH in H.

Then $\angle GOH = {}^1/_{24}$ (a right angle).

Thus GH is one side of a regular polygon of 96 sides circumscribed to the given circle.

And, since $\qquad OA:AG > 4673\frac{1}{2}:153$,

while $\qquad\qquad AB=2OA, \quad GH=2AG,$

it follows that

$AB:$(perimeter of polygon of 96 sides) $[>4673\frac{1}{2}:153\times96]$
$$>4673\frac{1}{2}:14688.$$

But
$$\frac{14688}{4673\frac{1}{2}}=3+\frac{667\frac{1}{2}}{4673\frac{1}{2}}$$
$$<3+\frac{667\frac{1}{2}}{4672\frac{1}{2}}$$
$$<3{}^1/_7.$$

Therefore the circumference of the circle (being less than the perimeter of the polygon) is *a fortiori* less than $3{}^1/_7$ times the diameter AB.

II. Next let AB be the diameter of a circle, and let AC, meeting the circle in C, make the angle CAB equal to one-third of a right angle. Join BC.

Then $\qquad\qquad\qquad AC:CB < 1351:780$.

First, let AD bisect the angle BAC and meet BC in d and the circle in D. Join BD.

Then $\qquad\qquad \angle BAD = \angle dAC$
$$= \angle dBD,$$

and the angles at D, C are both right angles.

It follows that the triangles ADB, $[ACd]$, BDd are similar.

Therefore $\qquad\qquad AD:DB=BD:Dd$
$$=AB:Bd \qquad \text{[Eucl. VI. 3]}$$
$$=AB+AC:Bd+Cd$$
$$=AB+AC:BC$$

or $\qquad BA+AC:BC=AD:DB.$

But $\qquad\quad AC:CB < 1351:780$, from above,

while $\qquad\quad BA:BC=2:1$
$$=1560:780.$$

Therefore $\qquad AD:DB < 2911:780 \quad . \quad . \quad . \quad . \quad . \quad . \quad (1).$

26

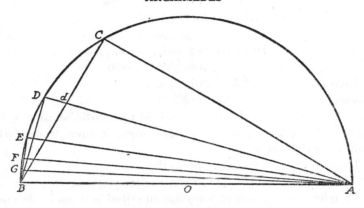

Hence $\qquad AB^2:BD^2 < (2911^2+780^2):780^2$
$$< 9082321:608400.$$

Thus $\qquad AB:BD < 3013\frac{3}{4}:780 \quad . \quad . \quad . \quad . \quad . \quad (2).$

Secondly, let AE bisect the angle BAD, meeting the circle in E; and let BE be joined.

Then we prove, in the same way as before, that
$$AE:EB=BA+AD:BD$$
$$< (3013\frac{3}{4}+2911):780, \text{ by (1) and (2)}$$
$$< 5924\frac{3}{4}:780$$
$$< 5924\frac{3}{4} \times {}^4/_{13}:780 \times {}^4/_{13}$$
$$< 1823:240 \quad . \quad . \quad . \quad . \quad . \quad . \quad (3).$$

Hence $\qquad AB^2:BE^2 < (1823^2+240^2):240^2$
$$< 3380929:57600.$$

Therefore $\qquad AB:BE < 1838\,{}^9/_{11}:240 \quad . \quad . \quad . \quad . \quad . \quad (4).$

Thirdly, let AF bisect the angle BAE, meeting the circle in F.

Thus $\qquad AF:FB=BA+AE:BE$
$$< 3661\,{}^9/_{11}:240, \text{ by (3) and (4)}$$
$$< 3661\,{}^9/_{11} \times {}^{11}/_{40}:240 \times {}^{11}/_{40}$$
$$< 1007:66 \quad . \quad . \quad . \quad . \quad . \quad . \quad (5).$$

It follows that $AB^2:BF^2 < (1007^2+66^2):66^2$
$$< 1018405:4356.$$

Therefore $\qquad AB:BF < 1009\frac{1}{6}:66 \quad . \quad . \quad . \quad . \quad . \quad (6).$

Fourthly, let the angle BAF be bisected by AG meeting the circle in G.

27

Then $\qquad AG:GB=BA+AF:BF$

$\qquad\qquad\qquad <2016\frac{1}{6}:66$, by (5) and (6).

And $\qquad AB^2:BG^2<\{(2016\frac{1}{6})^2+66^2\}:66^2$

$\qquad\qquad\qquad <4069284\frac{1}{36}:4356.$

Therefore $\qquad AB:BG<2017\frac{1}{4}:66,$

whence $\qquad BG:AB>66:2017\frac{1}{4}$ . . . . . . (7).

Now the angle BAG which is the result of the fourth bisection of the angle BAC, or of one-third of a right angle, is equal to one-forty-eighth of a right angle.

Thus the angle subtended by BG at the center is

$$\frac{1}{24} \text{ (a right angle).}$$

Therefore BG is a side of a regular inscribed polygon of 96 sides. It follows from (7) that

$\qquad$ (perimeter of polygon) $:AB[>96\times66:2017\frac{1}{4}]$

$\qquad\qquad\qquad\qquad >6636:2017\frac{1}{4}.$

And $\qquad\qquad \dfrac{6336}{2017\frac{1}{4}}>3^{10}/_{71}.$

Much more then is the circumference of the circle greater than $3^{10}/_{71}$ times the diameter.

Thus the ratio of the circumference to the diameter

$$<3^1/_7 \text{ but } >^{10}/_{71}.$$

ON THE EQUILIBRIUM OF PLANES
OR
THE CENTERS OF GRAVITY OF PLANES

I postulate the following:

1. Equal weights at equal distances are in equilibrium, and equal weights at unequal distances are not in equilibrium but incline towards the weight which is at the greater distance.

2. If, when weights at certain distances are in equilibrium, something be added to one of the weights, they are not in equilibrium but incline towards that weight to which the addition was made.

3. Similarly, if anything be taken away from one of the weights, they are not in equilibrium but incline towards the weight from which nothing was taken.

28

4. When equal and similar plane figures coincide if applied to one another, their centers of gravity similarly coincide.

5. In figures which are unequal but similar the centers of gravity will be similarly situated. By points similarly situated in relation to similar figures I mean points such that, if straight lines be drawn from them to the equal angles, they make equal angles with the corresponding sides.

6. If magnitudes at certain distances be in equilibrium, (other) magnitudes equal to them will also be in equilibrium at the same distances.

7. In any figure whose perimeter is concave in (one and) the same direction the center of gravity must be within the figure.

Proposition 1

Weights which balance at equal distances are equal.

For, if they are unequal, take away from the greater the difference between the two. The remainders will then not balance [*Post.* 3]; which is absurd.

Therefore the weights cannot be unequal.

Proposition 2

Unequal weights at equal distances will not balance but will incline towards the greater weight.

For take away from the greater the difference between the two. The equal remainders will therefore balance [*Post.* 1]. Hence, if we add the difference again, the weights will not balance but incline towards the greater [*Post.* 2].

Proposition 3

Unequal weights will balance at unequal distances, the greater weight being at the lesser distance.

Let A, B be two unequal weights (of which A is the greater) balancing about C at distances AC, BC respectively.

Then shall AC be less than BC. For, if not, take away from A the weight $(A—B)$. The remainders will then incline towards B [*Post.*

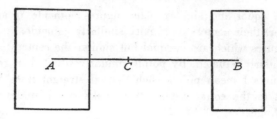

3]. But this is impossible, for (1) if $AC=CB$, the equal remainders will balance, or (2) if $AC>CB$, they will incline towards A at the greater distance [*Post.* 1].

Hence $AC<CB$.

Conversely, if the weights balance, and $AC<CB$, then $A>B$.

Proposition 4

If two equal weights have not the same center of gravity, the center of gravity of both taken together is at the middle point of the line joining their centers of gravity.

Proposition 5

If three equal magnitudes have their centers of gravity on a straight line at equal distances, the center of gravity of the system will coincide with that of the middle magnitude.

Cor. 1. *The same is true of any odd number of magnitudes if those which are at equal distances from the middle one are equal, while the distances between their centers of gravity are equal.*

Cor. 2. *If there be an even number of magnitudes with their centers of gravity situated at equal distances on one straight line, and if the two middle ones be equal, while those which are equidistant from them (on each side) are equal respectively, the center of gravity of the system is the middle point of the line joining the centers of gravity of the two middle ones.*

Proposition 6

Two magnitudes balance at distances reciprocally proportional to the magnitudes.

30

1. Suppose the magnitudes A, B to be commensurable, and the points A, B to be their centers of gravity. Let DE be a straight line so divided at C that

$$A:B=DC:CE.$$

We have then to prove that, if A be placed at E and B at D, C is the center of gravity of the two taken together.

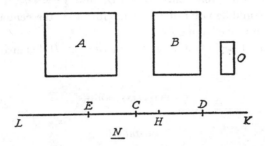

Since A, B are commensurable, so are DC, CE. Let N be a common measure of DC, CE. Make DH, DK each equal to CE, and EL (on CE produced) equal to CD. Then $EH=CD$, since $DH=CE$. Therefore LH is bisected at E, as HK is bisected at D.

Thus LH, HK must each contain N an even number of times.

Take a magnitude O such that O is contained as many times in A as N is contained in LH, whence

$$A:O=LH:N.$$

But $\qquad\qquad B:A=CE:DC$

$$=HK:LH.$$

Hence, ex aequali, $B:O=HK:N$, or O is contained in B as many times as N is contained in HK.

Thus O is a common measure of A, B.

Divide LH, HK into parts each equal to N, and A, B into parts each equal to O. The parts of A will therefore be equal in number to those of LH, and the parts of B equal in number to those of HK. Place one of the parts of A at the middle point of each of the parts N of LH, and one of the parts of B at the middle point of each of the parts N of HK.

Then the center of gravity of the parts of A placed at equal distances on LH will be at E, the middle point of LH [*Prop. 5, Cor. 2*], and the center of gravity of the parts of B placed at equal distances along HK will be at D, the middle point of HK.

Thus we may suppose A itself applied at E, and B itself applied at D.

But the system formed by the parts O of A and B together is a system of equal magnitudes even in number and placed at equal distances along LK. And, since $LE=CD$, and $EC=DK$, $LC=CK$, so that C is the middle point of LK. Therefore C is the center of gravity of the system ranged along LK.

Therefore A acting at E and B acting at D balance about the point C.

ON FLOATING BODIES

Postulate

"Let it be supposed that a fluid is of such a character that, its parts lying evenly and being continuous, that part which is thrust the less is driven along by that which is thrust the more; and that each of its parts is thrust by the fluid which is above it in a perpendicular direction if the fluid be sunk in anything and compressed by anything else."

Proposition 1

If a surface be cut by a plane always passing through a certain point, and if the section be always a circumference of a circle whose center is the aforesaid point, the surface is that of a sphere.

For, if not, there will be some two lines drawn from the point to the surface which are not equal.

Suppose O to be the fixed point, and A, B to be two points on the surface such that OA, OB are unequal. Let the surface be cut by a plane passing through OA, OB. Then the section is, by hypothesis, a circle whose center is O.

Thus $OA=OB$; which is contrary to the assumption. Therefore the surface cannot but be a sphere.

Proposition 2

The surface of any fluid at rest is the surface of a sphere whose center is the same as that of the earth.

Suppose the surface of the fluid cut by a plane through O, the center of the earth, in the curve $ABCD$.

$ABCD$ shall be the circumference of a circle.

For, if not, some of the lines drawn from O to the curve will be unequal. Take one of them, OB, such that OB is greater than some of the lines from O to the curve and less than others. Draw a circle with OB as radius. Let it be EBF, which will therefore fall partly within and partly without the surface of the fluid.

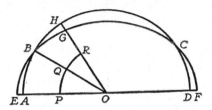

Draw OGH making with OB an angle equal to the angle EOB, and meeting the surface in H and the circle in G. Draw also in the plane an arc of a circle PQR with center O and within the fluid.

Then the parts of the fluid along PQR are uniform and continuous, and the part PQ is compressed by the part between it and AB, while the part QR is compressed by the part between QR and BH. Therefore the parts along PQ, QR will be unequally compressed, and the part which is compressed the less will be set in motion by that which is compressed the more.

Therefore there will not be rest; which is contrary to the hypothesis.

Hence the section of the surface will be the circumference of a circle whose center is O; and so will all other sections by planes through O.

Therefore the surface is that of a sphere with center O.

Proposition 3

Of solids those which, size for size, are of equal weight with a fluid will, if let down into the fluid, be immersed so that they do not project above the surface but do not sink lower.

If possible, let a certain solid *EFHG* of equal weight, volume for volume, with the fluid remain immersed in it so that part of it, *EBCF*, projects above the surface.

Draw through *O*, the center of the earth, and through the solid a plane cutting the surface of the fluid in the circle *ABCD*.

Conceive a pyramid with vertex *O* and base a parallelogram at the surface of the fluid, such that it includes the immersed portion of the solid. Let this pyramid be cut by the plane of *ABCD* in *OL*, *OM*. Also let a sphere within the fluid and below *GH* be described with center *O*, and let the plane of *ABCD* cut this sphere in *PQR*.

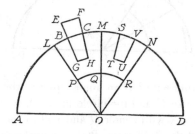

Conceive also another pyramid in the fluid with vertex *O*, continuous with the former pyramid and equal and similar to it. Let the pyramid so described be cut in *OM*, *ON* by the plane of *ABCD*.

Lastly, let *STUV* be a part of the fluid within the second pyramid equal and similar to the part *BGHC* of the solid, and let *SV* be at the surface of the fluid.

Then the pressures on *PQ*, *QR* are unequal, that on *PQ* being the greater. Hence the part at *QR* will be set in motion by that at *PQ*, and the fluid will not be at rest; which is contrary to the hypothesis.

Therefore the solid will not stand out above the surface.

Nor will it sink further, because all the parts of the fluid will be under the same pressure.

Proposition 4

A solid lighter than a fluid will, if immersed in it, not be completely submerged, but part of it will project above the surface.

In this case, after the manner of the previous proposition, we assume the solid, if possible, to be completely submerged and the fluid to be at rest in that position, and we conceive (1) a pyramid with its vertex at O, the center of the earth, including the solid, (2) another pyramid continuous with the former and equal and similar to it, with the same vertex O, (3) a portion of the fluid within this latter pyramid equal to the immersed solid in the other pyramid, (4) a sphere with center O whose surface is below the immersed solid and the part of the fluid in the second pyramid corresponding thereto. We suppose a plane to be drawn through the center O cutting the surface of the fluid in the circle ABC, the solid in S, the pyramid in OA, OB, the second pyramid in OB, OC, the portion of the fluid in the second pyramid in K, and the inner sphere in PQR.

Then the pressures on the parts of the fluid at PQ, QR are unequal, since S is lighter than K. Hence there will not be rest; which is contrary to the hypothesis.

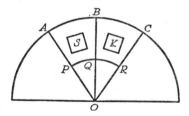

Therefore the solid S cannot, in a condition of rest, be completely submerged.

Proposition 5

Any solid lighter than a fluid will, if placed in the fluid, be so far immersed that the weight of the solid will be equal to the weight of the fluid displaced.

For let the solid be *EGHF*, and let *BGHC* be the portion of it immersed when the fluid is at rest. As in Prop. 3, conceive a pyramid with vertex *O* including the solid, and another pyramid with the same vertex continuous with the former and equal and similar to it. Suppose a portion of the fluid *STUV* at the base of the second pyramid to be equal and similar to the immersed portion of the solid; and let the construction be the same as in Prop. 3.

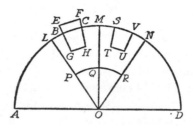

Then, since the pressure on the parts of the fluid at *PQ*, *QR* must be equal in order that the fluid may be at rest, it follows that the weight of the portion *STUV* of the fluid must be equal to the weight of the solid *EGHF*. And the former is equal to the weight of the fluid displaced by the immersed portion of the solid *BGHC*.

Proposition 6

If a solid lighter than a fluid be forcibly immersed in it, the solid will be driven upwards by a force equal to the difference between its weight and the weight of the fluid displaced.

For let *A* be completely immersed in the fluid, and let *G* represent the weight of *A*, and $(G+H)$ the weight of an equal volume of the fluid. Take a solid *D*, whose weight is *H*, and add it to *A*. Then the weight of $(A+D)$ is less than that of an equal volume of the fluid; and, if $(A+D)$ is immersed in the fluid, it will project so that its weight will be equal to the weight of the fluid displaced. But its weight is $(G+H)$.

36

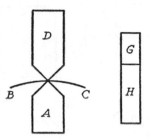

Therefore the weight of the fluid displaced is $(G+H)$, and hence the volume of the fluid displaced is the volume of the solid A. There will accordingly be rest with A immersed and D projecting.

Thus the weight of D balances the upward force exerted by the fluid on A, and therefore the latter force is equal to H, which is the difference between the weight of A and the weight of the fluid which A displaces.

Proposition 7

A solid heavier than a fluid will, if placed in it, descend to the bottom of the fluid, and the solid will, when weighed in the fluid, be lighter than its true weight by the weight of the fluid displaced.

(1) The first part of the proposition is obvious, since the part of the fluid under the solid will be under greater pressure, and therefore the other parts will give way until the solid reaches the bottom.

(2) Let A be a solid heavier than the same volume of the fluid, and let $(G+H)$ represent its weight, while G represents the weight of the same volume of the fluid.

Take a solid B lighter than the same volume of the fluid, and such that the weight of B is G, while the weight of the same volume of the fluid is $(G+H)$.

Let A and B be now combined into one solid and immersed. Then, since $(A+B)$ will be of the same weight as the same volume of fluid, both weights being equal to $(G+H)+G$, it follows that $(A+B)$ will remain stationary in the fluid.

37

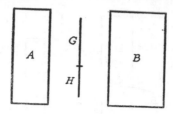

Therefore the force which causes A by itself to sink must be equal to the upward force exerted by the fluid on B by itself. This latter is equal to the difference between $(G+H)$ and G [*Prop.* 6]. Hence A is depressed by a force equal to H, i.e. its weight in the fluid is H, or the difference between $(G+H)$ and G.

THE SAND RECKONER

There are some, King Gelon, who think that the number of the sand is infinite in multitude; and I mean by the sand not only that which exists about Syracuse and the rest of Sicily but also that which is found in every region whether inhabited or uninhabited. Again there are some who, without regarding it as infinite, yet think that no number has been named which is great enough to exceed its multitude. And it is clear that they who hold this view, if they imagined a mass made up of sand in other respects as large as the mass of the earth, including in it all the seas and the hollows of the earth filled up to a height equal to that of the highest of the mountains, would be many times further still from recognizing that any number could be expressed which exceeded the multitude of the sand so taken. But I will try to show you by means of geometrical proofs, which you will be able to follow, that, of the numbers named by me and given in the work which I sent to Zeuxippus, some exceed not only the number of the mass of sand equal in magnitude to the earth filled up in the way described, but also that of a mass equal in magnitude to the universe.

Now you are aware that "universe" is the name given by most astronomers to the sphere whose center is the center of the earth and whose radius is equal to the straight line between the center of the sun and the center of the earth. This is the common account, as you have heard from astronomers. But Aristarchus of Samos brought out a book consisting of some hypotheses, in which the premises lead to the result that the universe is many times greater than that now so called. His hypotheses are that the fixed stars and the sun remain unmoved, that the earth revolves about the sun in the circumference of a circle, the sun lying in the middle of the orbit, and that the sphere of the fixed stars, situated about the same center as the sun, is so great that the circle in which he supposes the earth to revolve bears such a proportion to the distance of the fixed stars as the center of the sphere bears to its surface. Now it is easy to see that this is impossible; for, since the center of the sphere has no magnitude, we cannot conceive it to bear any ratio whatever to the surface of the sphere. We must, however, take Aristarchus to mean this: since we conceive the earth to be, as it were, the center of the universe, the ratio which the earth bears to what we describe as the "universe" is the same as the ratio which the sphere containing the circle in which he supposes the earth to revolve bears to the sphere of the fixed stars. For he adapts the proof of his results to a hypothesis of this kind, and in particular he appears to suppose the magnitude of the sphere in which he represents the earth as moving to be equal to what we call the "universe."

I say then that, even if a sphere were made up of the sand, as great as Aristarchus supposes the sphere of the fixed stars to be, I shall still prove that, of the numbers named in the *Principles*, some exceed in multitude the number of the sand which is equal in magnitude to the sphere referred to, provided that the following assumptions be made.

1. *The perimeter of the earth is about 3,000,000 stadia*[1] *and not greater.*

It is true that some have tried, as you are of course aware, to prove that the said perimeter is about 300,000 stadia. But I go

---

[1] Stadium: Greek unit of distance equal to 606.9 English feet (185 meters), which was the length of a track used for footraces. A more recent determination sets it at about 488 feet.

further and, putting the magnitude of the earth at ten times the size that my predecessors thought it, I suppose its perimeter to be about 3,000,000 stadia and not greater.

2. *The diameter of the earth is greater than the diameter of the moon, and the diameter of the sun is greater than the diameter of the earth.*

In this assumption I follow most of the earlier astronomers.

3. *The diameter of the sun is about thirty times the diameter of the moon and not greater.*

It is true that, of the earlier astronomers, Eudoxus declared it to be about nine times as great, and Pheidias, my father, twelve times, while Aristarchus tried to prove that the diameter of the sun is greater than eighteen times but less than twenty times the diameter of the moon. But I go even further than Aristarchus, in order that the truth of my proposition may be established beyond dispute, and I suppose the diameter of the sun to be about thirty times that of the moon and not greater.

4. *The diameter of the sun is greater than the side of the chiliagon[2] inscribed in the greatest circle in the [sphere of the] universe.*

I make this assumption because Aristarchus discovered that the sun appeared to be about 1/720th part of the circle of the zodiac, and I myself tried . . . to find experimentally the angle subtended by the sun and having its vertex at the eye. . . .

I conceive that these things, King Gelon, will appear incredible to the great majority of people who have not studied mathematics, but that to those who are conversant therewith and have given thought to the question of the distances and sizes of the earth the sun and moon and the whole universe the proof will carry conviction. And it was for this reason that I thought the subject would not be inappropriate for your consideration.

---

[2] Chiliagon: a polygon with 1,000 equal sides, inscribed in a circle.

ROGER BACON

(*c*. 1214–1294)

Known as the "Admirable Doctor," this English philosopher and scientist was a member of the Franciscan order at Oxford. His philosophical speculations and experimental researches led to accusations of heresy. He was "banished" to Paris for ten years, and at the close of his life imprisoned for another fourteen years. Bacon's masterwork, the encyclopedic *Opus Majus*, was written at the request of Pope Clement IV, and is a compilation of treatises on grammar, logic, philology, philosophy, mathematics and physics. Among Bacon's accomplishments was the preparation of a rectified calendar and experiments in alchemy, including the making of gunpowder. Perhaps his most advanced work was in the field of optics, where he invented the magnifying glass and developed new views on refraction.

"THIS VERY BEAUTIFUL SCIENCE"

HAVING EXPLAINED the fundamental principles of wisdom, both sacred and human, which are found in the tongues from which the sciences of the Latins have been translated, and likewise in mathematics, I now wish to discuss some principles which belong to optics. If the consideration just mentioned is noble and pleasing, the one in hand is far nobler and more pleasing, since we take especial delight in vision, and light and color have an especial beauty beyond the other things that are brought to our senses, and not only does beauty shine forth, but advantage and a greater necessity appear.

For Aristotle says in the first book of the Metaphysics that vision alone reveals the differences of things; since by means of it we search out experimental knowledge of all things that are in the heavens and in the earth. For those things that are in the

41

heavenly bodies are studied by visual instruments, as Ptolemy and the other astronomers teach. So also are those things that are generated in the air, like comets, rainbows, and the like. For their altitude above the horizon, their size, form, number, and all things that are in them, are verified by the methods of viewing them with instruments. Our experience of things here in the earth we owe to vision, because a blind man can have no experience worthy of the name concerning this world.

Hearing causes us to believe because we believe our teachers, but we cannot try out what we learn except through vision. If, moreover, we should adduce taste and touch and smell, we assume a knowledge belonging to beasts. For brutes are busied with the things pertaining to taste and touch, and exercise their sense of smell because of taste and touch, but the things are of little value, few in number, and common to us and to brutes concerning which these senses give verification, and therefore they do not rise to the rank of human wisdom.

But because of necessity, utility, and difficulty, sciences are formed, since art has to do with the difficult and with the good, as Aristotle says in the second book of the Ethics. For if what is sought is easy, there is no need for the formation of a science. Likewise although a matter be difficult yet not useful, no science is developed concerning it, because the labor would be foolish and vain. Also unless a subject were very useful and possessed many excellent truths, it does not require the formation of a separate science, but it suffices that this subject be treated in some particular book or chapter along with other matters in general science. But concerning vision alone is a separate science formed among philosophers, namely, optics, and not concerning any other sense. Wherefore there must be a special utility in our knowledge through vision which is not found in the other senses.

What I have now touched upon in general I wish to show in particular by disclosing the basic principles of this very beautiful science. It is possible that some other science may be more useful, but no other science has so much sweetness and beauty of utility. Therefore it is the flower of the whole of philosophy and through it, and not without it, can the other sciences be

Plate 5

Photo by Walter Scott Shinn

Thomas Alva **Edison**

Plate 6

Albert Einstein

Plate 7

Benjamin Franklin

Plate 8

Courtesy Archiv für Kunst und Geschichte, Berlin

Joseph von Fraunhofer

known. We must note, moreover, that Aristotle first treated this science, of which he says in the second book of the Physics that the subject is placed under another head. He also mentions it in his book on Sense and the Sensible, and has proved Democritus in error, because he did not name refractions and reflections of vision with reference to the optic and concave visual nerves. This book has been translated into Latin. After him Alhazen treats the subject more fully in a book which is extant. Alkindi also has arranged some data more fully, likewise authors of books on visions and mirrors.

EXPERIMENTAL SCIENCE

Since this experimental science is wholly unknown to the rank and file of students, I am therefore unable to convince people of its utility unless at the same time I disclose its excellence and its proper signification. This science alone, therefore, knows how to test perfectly what can be done by nature, what by the effort of art, what by trickery, what the incantations, conjurations, invocations, deprecations, sacrifices that belong to magic mean and dream of, and what is in them, so that all falsity may be removed and the truth alone of art and nature may be retained. This science alone teaches us how to view the mad acts of magicians, that they may be not ratified but shunned, just as logic considers sophistical reasoning.

This science has three leading characteristics with respect to other sciences. The first is that it investigates by experiment the notable conclusions of all those sciences. For the other sciences know how to discover their principles by experiments, but their conclusions are reached by reasoning drawn from the principles discovered. But if they should have a particular and complete experience of their own conclusions, they must have it with the aid of this noble science. For it is true that mathematics has general experiments as regards its conclusions in its figures and calculations, which also are applied to all sciences and to this kind of experiment, because no science can be known without mathematics. But if we give our attention to particular and complete experiments and such as are attested wholly by the proper method, we must employ the principles of this science which is called experimental. I give as an example the rainbow and phenomena connected with it, of which nature are the circle around the sun and the stars, the streak [*virga*] also lying at the side of the sun or of a star, which is apparent to the eye in a straight line, and is called by Aristotle in the third book of the Meteorologics a perpendicular, but by Seneca a streak, and the circle is called a corona, phenomena which frequently have the colors of the rainbow. The natural philosopher discusses these phenomena, and the writer on perspective has much to add pertaining to the mode of vision that is necessary in this case. But neither Aristotle nor Avicenna in their Natural Histories has given us a knowledge of phenomena of this kind, nor has Seneca, who composed a special book on them. But experimental science attests them.

ADOLF BAEYER

(1835–1917)

Baeyer won the right to be called one of the great organic chemists of the nineteenth century chiefly through his researches on indigo. Born in Berlin, he later taught chemistry in Berlin, Strasbourg and Munich. He produced indigo synthetically in 1870, and in 1905 received the Nobel prize for this as well as other work in synthetic chemistry, notably with arsenicals, phthaleins and uric acid compounds. He suggested the photosynthesis of formaldehyde by plants and developed the strain theory of carbon rings to account for the instability of acetylene compounds.

THEORY OF RING CLOSURE AND
THE DOUBLE BOND

RING CLOSURE is obviously the phenomenon which can give most information about the spatial arrangement of atoms. If a chain of five and six members can easily be closed and one with fewer or more members can be closed with difficulty or not at all, there must be a definite spatial basis for this fact. Any theory of the spatial arrangement of carbon compounds will naturally have to start from ring closure.

The general statements of the nature of carbon atoms which have previously been established run as follows:

1. The carbon atom is generally tetravalent.

2. The four valences are equivalent to one another. Example: there is only one monosubstitution product of methane.

3. The four valences are equally divided in space and correspond to the corners of a regular tetrahedron inscribed in a sphere.

4. The atoms or groups bound to the four valences cannot

45

exchange places with one another by themselves. Example: there are two tetrasubstitution products, abcd, of methane. Le Bel-van't Hoff law.

5. Carbon atoms can unite with one another by 1, 2, or 3 valences.

6. The compounds form open or ringlike closed chains.

To these almost universally accepted statements I might now add

7. The four valences of the carbon atom act in directions which unite the mid-point of the sphere with the corners of the tetrahedron and which make an angle of 109° 28′ with each other.

The direction of these attractions can undergo a diversion which causes a strain which increases with the size of the diversion.

The meaning of this statement can easily be explained if we start from the Kekulé spherical model and assume that the wires, like elastic springs are movable in all directions. If, now, the explanation that the direction of attraction always coincides with the direction of the wires is also assumed, a true picture is obtained of the hypothesis outlined in the seventh statement.

If, now, as can be shown clearly only by the use of a model, an attempt is made to join a greater number of carbon atoms without force, that is, in the direction of the tetrahedral axes, or the wires of the models, the result is either a zigzag line or a ring of five atoms, which is entirely comprehensible, since the angles of a regular pentagon, 108°, differ only slightly from the angle 109° 28′ which the axes of attraction make with one another. When a larger or smaller ring is formed, the wires must be bent, *i.e.*, there occurs a strain, in the sense of the seventh statement.

How well this view agrees with the facts is made clear by a consideration of rings formed from many methylene groups.

The simplest methylene ring is ethylene, which can be considered as a dimethylene. To obtain the double bond which occurs, there must be, according to the seventh statement and the hypothesis that both axes undergo an equal diversion, such a wide bending of the axes that they are parallel, *i.e.*, each axis must be diverted about ½ of 109° 44′ from their resting position. In trimethylene, which can be considered an equilateral triangle, the angle which the axes must make with one another amounts to 60°, the diversion of each of them is then ½(109° 28′ − 60°) = 24° 44′; in tetramethylene it amounts to ½(109° 28′ − 90°) = 9° 44′; in pentamethylene, which corresponds to the angle of a regular pentagon of 108°, ½(109° 28′ − 108°) = 0° 44′; in hexamethylene, corresponding to the angle of a regular hexagon of 120°, ½(109° 28′ − 120°) = −5° 16′, *i.e.*, the axes must be bent about 5° apart. The following examples will make these relations clearer:

Dimethylene is in fact the loosest ring, broken by hydrogen bromide, bromine, and even iodine. Trimethylene is split only by hydrogen bromide, not by bromine. Tetramethylene and hexamethylene, finally, are split with great difficulty or not at all. It may be added that as a point of fact six-membered rings have been very frequently found up to now, while five-membered rings occur very rarely and in complicated compounds. However, this objection has no great weight, because the six-membered ring is found almost entirely in the form of a hydrogen-poorer compound, benzene, and it may well be possible that pentamethylene itself, under the same conditions, is a little more easily formed and a little more stable than hexamethylene. I intentionally disregard the consideration of thiophene, lactones, etc., in this discussion, because there the presence of other elements must be considered.

WILLIAM BEAUMONT

(1785–1853)

One of the more curious and colorful stories in the history of medicine is that of William Beaumont's studies of the digestive processes through the open stomach wall of a Canadian Indian. Born in Connecticut, Beaumont studied medicine and eventually became a U.S. Army surgeon. His researches on the chemical nature of digestion reached their climax in his treatment of one Alexis St. Martin, whose stomach was exposed for two years by a two-inch gunshot wound. An amusing sidelight on these serious investigations is provided by the circumstance that as an Army man Beaumont was shifted from post to post, and hence was faced with the constant problem of keeping his living "laboratory" from ducking out on him! The result of his studies, published in 1833 as *Experiments and Observations on the Gastric Juice and Physiology of Digestion,* is considered the greatest single contribution ever made to our knowledge of digestion.

EXPERIMENTS AND OBSERVATIONS ON THE GASTRIC JUICE AND THE PHYSIOLOGY OF DIGESTION

ALEXIS ST. MARTIN, who is the subject of these experiments, was a Canadian, of French descent, at the above-mentioned time about eighteen years of age, of good constitution, robust and healthy. He had been engaged in the service of the American Fur Company, as a voyageur, and was accidentally wounded by the discharge of a musket, on the sixth of June 1822. . . . The whole mass of materials forced from the musket, together with fragments of clothing and pieces of fractured ribs, were driven into the muscles and cavity of the chest.

I saw him in twenty-five or thirty minutes after the accident occurred, and, on examination, found a portion of the lung, as

48

large as a turkey's egg, protruding through the external wound, lacerated and burned; and immediately below this, another protrusion, which, on further examination, proved to be a portion of the stomach, lacerated through all its coats, and pouring out the food he had taken for his breakfast, through an orifice large enough to admit the forefinger. . . .

August 1, 1825. At 12 M., I introduced through the perforation, into the stomach, the following articles of diet, suspended by a silk string, and fastened at proper distances, so as to pass in without pain, viz., a piece of high-seasoned à la mode beef; a piece of raw, salted, fat pork; a piece of raw, salted, lean beef; a piece of boiled, salted beef; a piece of stale bread; and a bunch of raw, sliced cabbage; each piece weighing about two drachms; the lad continuing his usual employment about the house.

At 1:00 P.M., withdrew and examined them. Found the cabbage and bread about half digested; the pieces of meat unchanged. Returned them into the stomach.

At 2:00 P.M., withdrew them again. Found the cabbage, bread, pork, and boiled beef all cleanly digested and gone from the string; the other pieces of meat but very little affected. Returned them into the stomach again.

At 2:00 P.M. [sic], examined again. Found the à la mode beef partly digested; the raw beef was slightly macerated on the surface, but its general texture was firm and entire. The smell and taste of the fluids of the stomach were slightly rancid; and the boy complained of some pain and uneasiness at the breast. Returned them again.

The lad complaining of considerable distress and uneasiness at the stomach, general debility and lassitude, with some pain in his head, I withdrew the string and found the remaining portions of aliment nearly in the same condition as when last examined; the fluid more rancid and sharp. The boy still complaining, I did not return them any more.

August 2. The distress at the stomach and pain in the head continuing, accompanied with costiveness, a depressed pulse, dry skin, coated tongue, and numerous white spots, or pustules, resembling coagulated lymph, spread over the inner surface of the

49

stomach, I thought it advisable to give medicine; and, accordingly, dropped into the stomach, through the aperture, half a dozen calomel pills, four or five grains each; which, in about three hours, had a thorough cathartic effect and removed all the foregoing symptoms, and the diseased appearance of the inner coat of the stomach. The effect of the medicine was the same as when administered in the usual way, by the mouth and esophagus, except the nausea commonly occasioned by swallowing pills.

This experiment cannot be considered a fair test of the powers of the gastric juice. The cabbage, one of the articles which was, in this instance, most speedily dissolved, was cut into small, fibrous pieces, very thin, and necessarily exposed on all its surfaces to the action of the gastric juice. The stale bread was porous, and of course admitted the juice into all its interstices; and probably fell from the string as soon as softened, and before it was completely dissolved. These circumstances will account for the more rapid disappearance of these substances than of the pieces of meat, which were in entire solid pieces when put in. To account for the disappearance of the fat pork, it is only necessary to remark that the fat meat is always resolved into oil by the warmth of the stomach before it is digested. I have generally observed that when he has fed on fat meat and butter the whole superior portion of the contents of the stomach, if examined a short time after eating, will be found covered with an oily pellicle. This fact may account for the disappearance of the pork from the string. I think, upon the whole, and subsequent experiments have confirmed the opinion, that fat meats are less easily digested than lean, when both have received the same advantages of comminution. Generally speaking, the looser the texture and the more tender the fiber, of animal food, the easier it is of digestion.

This experiment is important in a pathological point of view. It confirms the opinion that undigested portions of food in the stomach produce all the phenomena of fever; and is calculated to warn us of the danger of all excesses, where that organ is concerned. It also admonishes us of the necessity of a perfect comminution of the articles of diet.

JÖNS JAKOB BERZELIUS

(1779–1848)

This Swedish chemist exerted an almost unequaled influence on early nineteenth-century chemistry. It is to him that we owe our first accurate table of atomic weights and our system of symbols and formulae. Berzelius taught medicine and pharmacy at Stockholm and was made a baron for his scientific achievements. He discovered the elements cerium, selenium and thorium, and was the first to isolate silicon, calcium, barium, strontium, tantalum and zirconium as elements. He improved the analytic methods of the laboratory, especially the use of the blowpipe, filter paper and rubber tubing, and was a prolific contributor to chemical publications as well as author of a historic textbook, *Lehrbuch der Chemie* (1808). The selection here is taken from his *Essai sur la Théorie des Proportions chimique et sur l'Influence chimique de l'Électricité* (1819), expounding his "dualistic" theory which dominated chemistry for many years.

THEORY OF CHEMICAL PROPORTIONS

IN MANY carefully made experiments, Volta has observed that two metals put in contact become electric, and that this is the cause of the phenomena of the electric pile. Davy later showed that this electrical state increases due to the force of mutual affinities of the bodies used, and that this effect can be produced, and even seen, by means of certain precautions, in all bodies which have affinity for each other. It also follows from the experiments of Davy that temperature, which, as we know, increases affinity, also increases the intensity of the electrical state in bodies which are in contact, but that this mechanical contact being followed by combination, all signs of electricity immediately cease, that is to say, at the instant when, in favorable circumstances, they burst into flame, the electrical division,

51

or the charge which could be perceived, disappears. These facts agree well with the conjecture that the opposite electricities in the bodies which combine, mutually neutralize each other at the moment of combination, and then the fire is produced in the same manner as in the electric discharge.

But if these bodies, which are united and have ceased to be electric, should again be separated, and their elements restored to the isolated state with their original properties, they must recover the electrical state destroyed by the combination, or indeed, in other terms, if these combined bodies are restored for any reason to their original electrical state, which had vanished at their union, they must separate, and reappear with their original properties. Hisinger and I have observed that when the electric pile exerts its action on a conducting liquid, the elements of this liquid separate, oxygen and the acids are repelled from the negative pole toward the positive, and the combustible bodies as well as the salifiable bases from the positive pole toward the negative.

We believe we now know with certitude that bodies which are likely to combine show free, opposite electricities which increase in force as they approach the temperature at which combination occurs, until, at the instant of union, the electricity disappears with an elevation of temperature which is often so great that they burst into flame. On the other hand, we have the same certainty that combined bodies exposed in a suitable form to the action of the electric fluid, produced by discharge of a pile, are separated and regain their original chemical and electrical properties at the same time that the electricity which acted on them disappears.

In the actual state of our knowledge, the most probable explanation of combustion and the ignition which results from it is then: *that in all chemical combinations there is neutralization of opposing electricities, and that this neutralization produces fire in the same manner that it produces it in the discharge of the electric jar, the electric pile, and thunder, without being accompanied in these latter phenomenon, by chemical combination....*

The experiments made on the mutual electrical relations of bodies have taught us that they can be divided into two classes: *electropositive* and *electronegative*. The simple bodies which belong to the first class, as well as their oxides, always take up positive electricity when they meet simple bodies or oxides belonging to the second class; and the oxides of the first class always behave with the oxides of the other like salifiable bases with acids.

It has been believed that the electrical series of combustible bodies differs from that of their oxides; but although the different degrees of oxidation of several bodies present exceptions, the electrical order of combustible bodies agrees in general with that of their oxides, in such a way that the strongest degrees of oxidation in the affinity of different radicals are like those between the radicals themselves.

In arranging the bodies in the order of their electrical nature, there is formed an electro-chemical system which, in my opinion, is more fit than any other to give an idea of chemistry. I will speak more of this later.

Oxygen is, of all bodies, the most electronegative. As it is never positive relative to any other, and as, according to all chemical phenomena known up to the present it is not probable that any element of our globe can be more electronegative, we recognize in it an absolute negative. Also, in the electrochemical system, it is the only body whose electrical relations are invariable. The others vary in this sense, that one body can be negative with respect to a second, and positive with respect to a third: for example, sulphur and arsenic are positive relative to oxygen and negative relative to metals. The radicals of fixed alkalis and alkaline earths are, on the contrary, the most electropositive bodies; but they differ somewhat in degree; and at the positive extreme of the electrical series, there is no body as electropositive as oxygen is electronegative. . . .

The electrochemical properties of oxidised substances depend almost always exclusively on the unipolarity of their electropositive element, that is to say, of their radical. The oxide is ordinarily electronegative with regard to other oxides when its radical is negative with regard to their radicals, and *vice versa.* For example, sulfuric acid is electronegative with respect to all metallic oxides for the reason that sulfur is negative in relation to all metals. The oxides of potassium and zinc are, on the contrary, electropositive with regard to all oxidized substances, to the radicals of which, potassium and zinc are positive. This fact, the cause of which we are unable to explain, rectifies an inexact idea on the principle of acidity which in the antiphlogistic theory has been thought to be oxygen. We find now that it resides in the radical of the acid and that oxygen plays such an indifferent role that it enters equally into the strongest salifying bases, that is to say, the electropositive oxides and in the strongest acids or electronegative oxides. Sometimes it happens, however, that a positive oxide acquires by higher oxidation less electropositive properties, approaching electronegative, as, for example, stannic oxide and the acids of manganese. But in the strongest bases, such as potash and soda, an addition of oxygen may well destroy the positive reaction without, nevertheless, producing a negative; it is thus that the strongly salifying bases form peroxides. . . .

If these electrochemical views are correct it follows that all chemical combination depends solely on two opposing forces, positive and negative electricity, and that thus each combination should be composed of two parts united by the effect of their electrochemical reaction, provided that there exists no third force. Whence it follows that each compound substance, regardless of the number of its constituent principles, may be divided into two parts, of which one is electrically positive and the other negative. Thus, for example, sulfate of soda is not composed of sulfur, oxygen and sodium, but of sulfuric acid and soda which both may again be divided into two elements, one positive and the other negative. Similarly alum canot be considered as directly composed of its elements but should be regarded as the product of the reaction of sulfate of aluminum, a negative element, and sulfate of potash, a positive element. In this manner the electrochemical view equally well justifies what I have already detailed on particular compounds of the first, second and third orders, etc.

NIELS BOHR

(1885-   )

This pioneer of atomic physics is one of the outstanding scientific
figures of our century. Born in Copenhagen, and educated in that
city and at Cambridge, he worked with both Rutherford and Som-
merfield on the quantum theory. He became head of the Danish
Institute for Theoretical Physics in 1920, won the Nobel prize for
physics in 1922. Escaping German-occupied Denmark, he came to
America where he worked on atomic fission, returning to his own
country after the war. Bohr's greatest contribution to atomic theory
lay in his concept of atomic structure: Staged in oversimplified terms,
the atom is conceived as a system of electrons rotating in orbits
around a nucleus, from which radiation is emitted only during the
passage of an electron from an orbit of higher energy to one of
lower energy. He also developed the "correspondence principle," his
discussion of which is included here.

ON THE SPECTRUM OF HYDROGEN

HYDROGEN POSSESSES not only the smallest atomic weight of all
the elements, but it also occupies a peculiar position both with
regard to its physical and its chemical properties. One of the
points where this becomes particularly apparent is the hydrogen
line spectrum.

The spectrum of hydrogen observed in an ordinary Geissler
tube consists of a series of lines, the strongest of which lies at
the red end of the spectrum, while the others extend out into the
ultra-violet, the distance between the various lines, as well as
their intensities, constantly decreasing. In the ultraviolet the
series converges to a limit. . . .

We shall now consider the second part of the foundation on
which we shall build, namely, the conclusions arrived at from

55

experiments with the rays emitted by radioactive substances. I have previously here in the Physical Society had the opportunity of speaking of the scattering of α rays in passing through thin plates, and to mention how Rutherford (1911) has proposed a theory for the structure of the atom in order to explain the remarkable and unexpected results of these experiments. I shall, therefore, only remind you that the characteristic feature of Rutherford's theory is the assumption of the existence of a positively charged nucleus inside the atom. A number of electrons are supposed to revolve in closed orbits around the nucleus, the number of these electrons being sufficient to neutralize the positive charge of the nucleus. The dimensions of the nucleus are supposed to be very small in comparison with the dimensions of the orbits of the electrons, and almost the entire mass of the atom is supposed to be concentrated in the nucleus. . . .

Let us now assume that a hydrogen atom simply consists of an electron revolving around a nucleus of equal and opposite charge, and of a mass which is very large in comparison with that of the electron. It is evident that this assumption may explain the peculiar position already referred to which hydrogen occupies among the elements, but it appears at the outset completely hopeless to attempt to explain anything at all of the special properties of hydrogen, still less its line spectrum, on the basis of considerations relating to such a simple system.

Let us assume for the sake of brevity that the mass of the nucleus is infinitely large in proportion to that of the electron, and that the velocity of the electron is very small in comparison with that of light. If we now temporarily disregard the energy radiation, which, according to the ordinary electrodynamics, will accompany the accelerated motion of the electron, the latter in accordance with Kepler's first law will describe an ellipse with the nucleus in one of the foci.

These expressions are extremely simple and they show that the magnitude of the frequency of revolution as well as the length of the major axis depend only on W, the work which must be added to the system in order to remove the electron to an infinite distance from the nucleus; and are independent of the eccentricity of the orbit. By varying W we may obtain all possible values for the frequency of revolution and the major axis of the ellipse. This condition shows, however, that it is not possible to employ Kepler's formula directly in calculating the orbit of the electron in a hydrogen atom.

For this it will be necessary to assume that the orbit of the electron cannot take on all values, and in any event the line spectrum clearly indicates that the oscillations of the electron cannot vary continuously between wide limits. The impossibility of making any progress with a simple system like the one considered here might have been foretold from a consideration of the dimensions involved.

It can be seen that it is impossible to employ Rutherford's atomic model so long as we confine ourselves exclusively to the ordinary electrodynamics. But this is nothing more than might have been expected. As I have mentioned, we may consider it to be an established fact that it is impossible to obtain a satisfactory explanation of the experiments on temperature radiation with the aid of electrodynamics, no matter what atomic model be employed. The fact that the deficiencies of the atomic model we are considering stand out so plainly is therefore perhaps no serious drawback; even though the defects of other atomic models are much better concealed they must nevertheless be present and will be just as serious.

Quantum Theory of Spectra

Let us now try to overcome these difficulties by applying Planck's theory to the problem.

In assuming Planck's theory we have manifestly acknowledged the inadequacy of the ordinary electrodynamics and have definitely parted with the coherent group of ideas on which the latter theory is based. In fact in taking such a step we cannot expect that all cases of disagreement between the theoretical conceptions hitherto employed and experiment will be removed by the use of Planck's assumption regarding the quantum of the energy momentarily present in an oscillating system. We stand

57

here almost entirely on virgin ground, and upon introducing new assumptions we need only take care not to get into contradiction with experiment. Time will have to show to what extent this can be avoided; but the safest way is, of course, to make as few assumptions as possible.

With this in mind let us first examine the experiments on temperature radiation. The subject of direct observation is the distribution of radiant energy over oscillations of the various wave lengths. Even though we may assume that this energy comes from systems of oscillating particles, we know little or nothing about these systems. No one has ever seen a Planck's resonator, nor indeed even measured its frequency of oscillation; we can observe only the period of oscillation of the radiation which is emitted. It is therefore very convenient that it is possible to show that to obtain the laws of temperature radiation it is not necessary to make any assumptions about the systems which emit the radiation except that the amount of energy emitted each time shall be equal to hv, where h is Planck's constant and v is the frequency of the radiation.

During the emission of the radiation the system may be regarded as passing from one state to another; in order to introduce a name for these states we shall call them "stationary" states, simply indicating thereby that they form some kind of waiting places between which occurs the emission of the energy corresponding to the various spectral lines. . . .

Under ordinary circumstances a hydrogen atom will probably exist only in the state corresponding to $n=1$. For this state W will have its greatest value and, consequently, the atom will have emitted the largest amount of energy possible; this will therefore represent the most stable state of the atom from which the system cannot be transferred except by adding energy to it from without.

THE CORRESPONDENCE PRINCIPLE

So far as the principles of the quantum theory are concerned, the point which has been emphasized hitherto is the radical departure of these principles from our usual conceptions of mechanical and electrodynamical phenomena. As I have attempted to show in recent years, it appears possible, however, to adopt a point of view which suggests that the quantum theory may, nevertheless be regarded as a rational generalization of our ordinary conceptions. As may be seen from the postulates of the quantum theory, and particularly the frequency relation, a direct connection between the spectra and the motion of the kind required by the classical dynamics is excluded, but at the same time the form of these postulates leads us to another relation of a remarkable nature.

Let us consider an electrodynamic system and inquire into the nature of the radiation which would result from the motion of the system on the basis of the ordinary conceptions. We imagine the motion to be decomposed into purely harmonic oscillations, and the radiation is assumed to consist of the simultaneous emission of series of electromagnetic waves possessing the same frequency as these harmonic components and intensities which depend upon the amplitudes of the components.

An investigation of the formal basis of the quantum theory shows us now that it is possible to trace the question of the origin of the radiation processes which accompany the various transitions back to an investigation of the various harmonic components, which appear in the motion of the atom. The possibility that a particular transition shall occur may be regarded as being due to the presence of a definitely assignable "corresponding" component in the motion. This principle of correspondence at the same time throws light upon a question mentioned several times previously, namely, the relation between the number of quantum numbers, which must be used to describe the stationary states of an atom, and the types to which the orbits of the electrons belong. The classification of these types can be based very simply on a decomposition of the motion into its harmonic components. Time does not permit me to consider this question any further, and I shall confine myself to a statement of some simple conclusions, which the correspondence principle permits us to draw concerning the occurrence of transitions between various pairs of stationary states. These conclusions are of decisive importance in the subsequent argument. ...

Before I leave the interpretation of the chemical properties by means of this atomic model I should like to remind you once again of the fundamental principles which we have used. The whole theory has evolved from an investigation of the way in which electrons can be captured by an atom. The formation of an atom was held to consist in the successive binding of electrons, this binding resulting in radiation according to the quantum theory. According to the fundamental postulates of the theory this binding takes place in stages by transitions between stationary states accompanied by emission of radiation. For the problem is at what stage such a process comes to an end. As regards this point the postulates give no direct information, but here the correspondence principle is brought in. Even though it has been possible to penetrate considerably further at many points than the time has permitted me to indicate to you, still it has not yet been possible to follow in detail all stages in the formation of the atoms. We cannot say, for instance, that a given table of the atomic constitution of the inert gases may in every detail be considered as the unambiguous result of applying the correspondence principle. On the other hand, it appears that our considerations already place the empirical data in a light which scarcely permits of an essentially different interpretation of the properties of the elements based upon the postulates of the quantum theory. This applies not only to the series spectra and the close relationship of these to the chemical properties of the elements, but also to the X-ray spectra, the consideration of which leads us into an investigation of interatomic processes of an entirely different character. As we have already mentioned, it is necessary to assume that the emission of the latter spectra is connected with processes which may be described as a reorganization of the completely formed atom after a disturbance produced in the interior of the atom by the action of external forces.

LUDWIG BOLTZMANN

(1844–1906)

Known primarily for his work on the kinetic theory of gases, this Austrian physicist passed most of his life as a professor in German and Austrian universities. He was responsible for the acceptance of Maxwell's electromagnetic theory of light on the Continent, and with Stefan evolved the law named after them applying to radiation from a black body. He made contributions to the mechanical theory of heat: the Boltzmann constant is the ratio of the mean total energy of a molecule to its absolute temperature.

ENTROPY AND PROBABILITY

A RELATION between the second law of thermodynamics and the theory of probabilities was first shown when I proved that an analytical proof of that law can be erected only on a foundation which is taken from the theory of probabilities. This relation is further confirmed by the proof that an exact proof of the laws of equilibrium of heat is most easily obtained by showing that a certain quantity, which I will again designate by E, can only diminish by the exchange of kinetic energy between the molecules of the gas, and therefore will have a minimum value in the condition of equilibrium of heat. The connection between the second law and the laws of equilibrium of heat becomes clearer still by the developments in section II of my "Remarks on Some Problems of the Mechanical Theory of Heat." In that place I also first suggested the possibility of a special way of calculating the equilibrium of heat, in the following words: "It is clear that any individual uniform state which occurs after the lapse of a definite time from a definite initial state is just as improbable as any particular nonuniform state, just as in the game of lotto each individual quintern is just as improbable as the quintern 12345. It is therefore only because there are many more uniform states than nonuniform states that the probability is greater that the state becomes uniform in the progress of time"; further: "We might even calculate from the relation of the number of the different states their probability, which perhaps would lead to an interesting method of calculating the equilibrium of heat." The belief is therefore expressed that we can calculate the state of equilibrium by investigating the probability of the different possible states of the system. The initial state will in most cases be a very improbable one and from it the system will progress toward more probable states, until it at last reaches the most probable state, that is, that of equilibrium of heat. If we apply this to the second law we can identify that quantity which we commonly designate as entropy with the probability of the actual state. We think of a system of bodies which is isolated and makes no exchanges with other bodies, for example, a body of higher temperature and one of lower temperature and so called intermediate body, which permits a transfer of heat between the two; or, to choose another example, a vessel with absolutely smooth and rigid walls, one half of which is filled with air at a lower temperature or pressure while the other half is filled with air at a higher temperature or pressure. The system of bodies which we have thought of may have at the beginning of the time any state; by exchange between the bodies this state changes; in accordance with the second law this change must always occur in such a way that the total entropy of all the bodies increases; according to our present interpretation this means nothing else than that the probability of the totality of the states of all these bodies becomes greater and greater; the system of bodies goes from a more improbable to a more probable state.

GIOVANNI ALFONSO BORELLI

(1608–1679)

This Italian physicist and astronomer taught and practiced medicine at Pisa, Messina, Florence and Rome. As a friend of Galileo he wanted to reconstitute medicine in terms of Galilean physics. He is credited with the discovery of the parabolic path of comets, but his major work, *De Motu Animalium*, translated as *The Flight of Birds*, was an attempt to apply the laws of mechanics to the motions of the animal anatomy. Although Borelli concluded pessimistically that man would never fly, his work foreshadowed modern physiology in its use of mechanical and chemical terms to describe organic functioning.

THE FLIGHT OF BIRDS

Wherein are set forth the reasons for the immense power of the wings

Such excessive power of the pectoral muscles of Birds seems to arise, firstly from their large size and from the more compact and stronger organic structure of the fibres of the pectoral muscles; for these fibres are thicker and closer, forming a dense and compact fleshy structure, whereas the muscles of the legs are formed of meagre, spare flesh. By reason hereof the former can be extended more forcefully and vehemently, so that the former are able to exert more power than the latter.

Secondly, the action of the wings is increased by the decrease in resistance, for the body of a Bird is disproportionately lighter than that of man or of any quadruped; that is, the weight of a bird is in smaller proportion to the weight of the lighter animals than its mass to theirs. This is evident since the bones of a

63

Bird are porous, hollowed out to extreme thinness like the roots of the feathers, and the shoulder-bones, ribs, and wing-bones are of little substance; the breast and abdomen contain large cavities filled with air; while the feathers and the down are of exceeding lightness. Hence the power of the wings is increased in duplicate ratio: firstly, by the increase in the force of the muscles, and secondly by the decrease of the weight to be supported.

This downward pull is diminished the more as its downward movement is retarded by the spread of the wings and of the tail; hence the force of the wings can the more readily effect the leaps through the air, as the resistance of the downward pull of the Bird itself is diminished.

Thirdly, in leaping from the earth the projectile momentum is immediately extinguished so soon as the feet come into contact with the earth again; whence it follows that the momentum must forthwith be renewed. On the contrary, when a Bird is flying through the air, the projectile force is not extinguished by the fluid air, wherefore it assists the succeeding leaps which are made by the beating of the wings.

Fourthly, in effecting separate leaps from the earth, the soles of the feet come into contact with the ground not without experiencing hurt and painful injury, whence arise fatigue and weakness. But no such hurt results from leaping through the air; wherefore, since the motive force is not weakened to the same extent, longer, more powerful, and more lasting leaps may be made through the air. The various causes set forth above render the process abundantly clear.

In what manner an oblique transverse force may propel straightly a body unaffected by the motion

It is taught by the science of mechanics that the action of the wedge ABC, through which two parts EFG and LMN of the same body must be separated from one another, amounts to the forcing of the two resisting bodies DE and HM over the inclined surfaces CA and CB of the wedge, along which they seek to ascend when

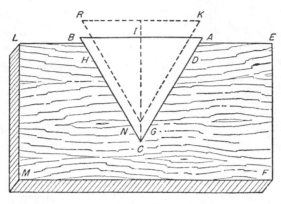

Fig. 1

the wedge is driven in a direction from I to C. And the same transverse motion over the inclined faces CA and CB must take place when the two adjacent bodies DF and HM are forced towards each other; for in this case the smooth wedge ABC seeks to escape in the opposite direction and to recoil from C to I, being expelled through the pressure of the collateral bodies, in the same manner as the smooth pips of a fruit may be projected to a long distance by being compressed between one's fingers. And this propulsion is made with the same force and momentum as that wherewith the bodies DF and HM compress the inclined faces CA and CB: the expelling force having the same proportion to their absolute force as the heights AI, BI of the planes to the lengths AC, BC of their inclination.

If a Bird suspended in the air strike with its outspread wings the undisturbed air, with a motion perpendicular to the horizon, it will fly with a transverse movement parallel to the horizon

Let the Bird RS be suspended in the air with its wings BEA and BCF expanded and its belly downwards, and the under surfaces of the wings BEA and BCF strike against the wind perpendicularly to the horizon with such force as to prevent the bird from falling, then I hold that it will be impelled horizontally

65

from S towards R. And this happens because the two osseous rods (*virgae*) BC and BE by muscular strength and on account of their hardness are able to resist the pressure of the wind, and, moreover, to retain their shape, but the afterparts of any kind of wing yield to the air pressure, as the flexible feathers are able to move about the wing bones (*manubria*) or their boney axes BC and BE; and so it follows that the ends A and F of the feathers close in towards one another, by which means the wings assume the form of a wedge with its apex towards AF. But as the surfaces

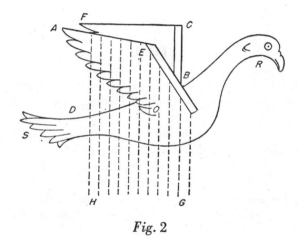

Fig. 2

of the wedge are compressed on all sides by the ascending air, the wedge is of necessity squeezed and driven towards its base CBE. And as the said wedge formed by the wings cannot move forward without taking with it, since it is attached thereto, the body of the Bird RS, which is swimming in the air and can therefore be moved freely from its position, for this reason it is able to give room to the incoming air in the place of the air driven out; and therefore the bird moves with a horizontal motion towards R.

Let us now take the case of undisturbed opposing air which is struck by the flexible portions of the wings with a movement perpendicular to the horizon. Since the sails and flexible portions

66

of the wings assume the shape of a wedge, with the apex towards the tail, when acted upon by the force and compression of the air, whether the wings strike the quiescent air beneath, or whether the air rushes up against the outstretched wings with their rigid wing-bones; in both cases the flexible feathers of each wing yield to the pressure and close in towards one another. Therefore, of necessity, as will be presently shown, the bird will be moved forwards towards R.

Wherein is explained the way in which the horizontal flight of Birds is effected

To have brought about flight, it is evident that Nature impelled birds upward and held them suspended in the air, and afterwards they were enabled by horizontal movements to be carried about. The first step could not have been accomplished except by successive leaps; next the heavy bird was carried up and its descent prevented by the beating of its wings, and then, as the downward pull of its weight is perpendicular to the horizon, beats with the flat face of its wings would be made by striking the air in the same perpendicular direction; and in this fashion has Nature brought about the suspension of the Birds in the air.

Concerning the second and transverse motion of Birds, some people do blunder strangely, for they think that it ought to be done as in Ships, which, by the exertion of a horizontal force towards the stern, through the means of oars, the while floating on the quiet and therefore resisting water beneath, recoil at the contrary motion, and so are moved forward. In the same way they affirm that the wings are flapped with a horizontal movement towards the tail and so strike against the undisturbed air, the resistance of which occasions, by the reflex action, their forward motion.

But this is repellent to the evidence of the senses and of reason, for we never see the larger Birds, such as Swans, Geese, and the like, while flying, to flap their wings toward the tail with a horizontal motion, but always to incline them downwards, describing circles set perpendicularly to the horizon. Moreover, in

67

Ships, the horizontal motion of the oars can be easily accomplished and a perpendicular stroke upon the water would be useless and unnecessary, as there is no need to prevent their descent when they are sustained by the weight and density of the water. But in the case of Birds, it would be foolish to make such a horizontal motion, which would rather hinder flight as the speedy downfall of the heavy Bird would result from it; wherefore, the Bird must be sustained by continual vibrations of the wings perpendicularly to the horizon.

Wherefore Nature was compelled to use, with remarkable shrewdness, a movement which both sustained the Bird and propelled it horizontally. . . .

How Birds, without flapping their wings, can sometimes rise in the air for a short time not only horizontally, but also obliquely upward

It is clear from what has been said that the projectile force is communicated to a Bird's body by the flapping of the wings in the same way as motion is given to a Ship by the strokes of the oars, which motion is of a constant nature.

Suppose, however, that the action of the oars stops, nevertheless the Ship proceeds upon its way until its movement is arrested by external forces.

Therefore both Bird and Ship from the motion imparted to them have the same properties as an arrow and other projectiles; and just as in a Ship in motion, if its axis is deflected from a straight course by the strength of the helm, then this same motion comes into play on the altered course, and the voyage is continued; so also in the Bird A, moving horizontally along the straight line ABC, as often as its axis is directed upward through BD by the force of its tail acting as helm, of necessity its impetus follows an upward movement through the parabolical curve BEF, but it is true that such ascent stops suddenly, the natural gravity of a Bird producing this effect and tending to bring it down. While the force of gravity is less than the velocity, the Bird rises upwards through BE, and when at F the forces equalize, the

Bird is seen to float at that point for a little while, moving with expanded wings, almost in the same plane parallel to the horizon; for a bird cannot remain entirely motionless at the same point in the air, therefore upward flight cannot be made exactly perpendicularly to the horizon, but always obliquely through the line of a parabola, as projectiles move.

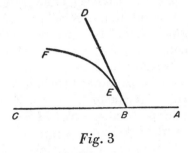

Fig. 3

Therefore, after this rise is made, either the bird continues in a horizontal course for a short time because the equalisation of the forces soon ceases, or as the projectile force is spent it descends at a constantly increasing speed until brought up by external forces. Hence the necessity arises for renewing the impulse through the air by fresh strokes of the wings. . . .

It is impossible that men should be able to fly craftly by their own strength.

Three principal points ought to be considered in flying: firstly, the motive power by which the body of the Animal may be sustained through the air; secondly, the suitable instruments, which are wings; thirdly, the resistance of the Animal's heavy body.

The degree of motive power is known by the strength and quantity of the muscles, which are designed to bend the arms or to flap the wings. And because the motive force in Birds' wings is apparently ten-thousand times greater than the resistance of their weight, and as Nature has endowed Birds with so great an excess of motive power, the Bird largely increases the

69

strength of its pectoral muscles and skilfully decreases the weight of its body, as we have hinted above.

When, therefore, it is asked whether men may be able to fly by their own strength, it must be seen whether the motive power of the pectoral muscles (the strength of which is indicated and measured by their size), is proportionately great, as it is evident that it must exceed the resistance of the weight of the whole human body ten-thousand times, together with the weight of enormous wings which should be attached to the arms. And it is clear that the motive power of the pectoral muscles in men is much less than is necessary for flight, for in Birds the bulk and weight of the muscles for flapping the wings are not less than a sixth part of the entire weight of the body. Therefore, it would be necessary that the pectoral muscles of a man should weigh more than a sixth part of the entire weight of his body; so also the arms, by flapping with the wings attached, should be able to exert a power ten-thousand times greater than the weight of the human body itself. But they are far below such excess for the aforesaid pectoral muscles do not equal a hundredth part of the entire weight of a man. Wherefore either the strength of the muscles ought to be increased or the weight of the human body must be decreased, so that the same proportion obtains in it as exists in Birds.

Hence it is deduced, that the Icarian invention is entirely mythical because impossible; for it is not possible either to increase a man's pectoral muscles or to diminish the weight of the human body; and whatever apparatus is used, although it is possible to increase the momentum, the velocity or the power employed can never equal the resistance; and therefore wing flapping by the contraction of muscles cannot give out enough power to carry up the heavy body of a man.

There only remains the diminution of the weight of the human body, not in itself, for this is impossible, its mechanism must remain intact, but especially and respectively to the aerial fluid in the same way as a strip of lead can float on water if a certain amount of cork be attached to it which causes the entire mass of lead and cork to float, being of like weight to the amount of water which it displaces, according to the law of Archimedes. And this device Nature uses in fishes. She places in their bellies a sack full of air by means of which they are able to maintain their equilibrium, so that they can remain in the same place as if they were part of the water itself.

By this same device some have lately persuaded themselves that the weight of the human body is able to be brought into equilibrium with the air, that is to say by the use of a large vessel, either a vacuum or very nearly so, of so great a size that it is possible to sustain a human body in the air together with the vessel.

But we easily perceive this to be a vain hope as it is necessary to construct the vessel of some hard metal such as brass or copper, and squeeze out and take away all the air from its interior, and it must also be of so great a size that when in the air it displaces a quantity of air of the same weight as itself, together with the man fastened to it; wherefore it would have to occupy a space of more than 22,000 cubic feet; moreover, the plates composing the sphere must be reduced to an extraordinary thinness. Furthermore, so thin a vessel of this size could not be constructed, or, if constructed, preserved intact, nor could it be exhausted by any pump, much less by mercury, of which so large a quantity is not to be found in the world, nor could be extracted from the earth, and if such a great vacuum were made the thin brass vessel could not resist the strong pressure of the air, which would break or crush it. I pass over the fact that so great a machine of the same weight as the air would not be able to keep itself in exact equilibrium with the air, and therefore would incontinently rise to the highest confines of the air like clouds, or would fall to the ground.

Again, such a large mass could not be moved in flight on account of the resistance of the air; in the same way feathers and soap bubbles can be moved only with difficulty through the air, even when they are blown by a light breeze, just as clouds, poised in the air, are driven by the wind.

At this point we cease to wonder that Nature, who is accustomed everywhere to imitate others' advantages, makes the

71

swimming of fishes in water so easy and the flying of Birds through the air so difficult, for we see whereas fishes can remain in the midst of water, being of their own accord and without effort held up and poised, and can very easily descend and ascend, and are only moved by the strength of muscles placed transversely and obliquely to the direction of motion; on the other hand, Birds are not able to float in the air but owe their sustentation to the continual exertion of strength and a projectile force, not external, but natural and intrinsic, by contracting their pectoral muscles by which they make a series of bounds through the air; and this requires enormous strength, as they are not going upon feet supported on solid ground, but on wings supported by very fluid and greatly agitated air.

ROBERT BOYLE

(1627–1691)

Sometimes called the father of modern chemistry, Boyle is known to every school child as the formulator of Boyle's law: that the volume of a gas varies inversely as the pressure. An aristocrat who lost his fortune, he spent his life investigating such fields as pneumatics, specific gravity, electricity and crystallography. He is said to have been the first chemist to collect a gas, and the first in England to use a sealed thermometer. He discovered the importance of air in the transmission of sound and believed that all substances were composed of one basic atom in different arrangements and movements. One of the original members of the Royal Society, he wrote: *New Experiments Physicomechanical Touching the Spring of the Air and Its Effects* (1660), *The Sceptical Chemist* (1661), *Origin of Forms and Qualities According to the Corpuscular Philosophy* (1666), and *Memoirs for the Natural History of the Human Blood* (1684).

NEW EXPERIMENTS PHYSICOMECHANICAL TOUCHING THE SPRING OF THE AIR AND ITS EFFECTS

Experiment XL

It may seem well worth trying, whether or no in our exhausted glass the want of an ambient body, of the wonted thickness of air, would disable even light and little animals, as bees, and other winged insects, to fly. But though we easily foresaw how difficult it would be to make such an experiment, yet not to omit our endeavours, we procured a large flesh-fly, which we conveyed into a small receiver. We also another time shut into a great receiver a humming bee, that appeared strong and lively, though we had rather have made the trial with a butterfly, if the cold

73

Plate 10

William Harvey

Plate 11

Photo by Tita Binz, Heidelberg

Werner Heisenberg

Plate 12

Portrait by Ludwig Knaus
Courtesy Archiv für Kunst und Geschichte, Berlin

Hermann von Helmholtz

we turned the stop-cock, and let in the air upon her, yet it came too late; whereupon casting our eyes upon one of those accurate dials that go with a pendulum, and were of late ingeniously invented by the noble and learned *Hugenius*, we found that the whole tragedy had been concluded within ten minutes of an hour, part of which time had been employed in cementing the cover to the receiver. Soon after we got a hen sparrow, which being caught with bird-lime was not at all hurt; when we put her into the receiver, almost to the top of which she would briskly raise herself, the experiment being tried with this bird, as it was with the former, she seemed to be dead within seven minutes, one of which were employed in cementing the cover: but upon the speedy turning of the key, the fresh air flowing in, began slowly to revive her, so that after some pantings she opened her eyes, and regained her feet, and in about ¼ of an hour after, threatened to make an escape at the top of the glass, which had been unstopped to let in the fresh air upon her: but the receiver being closed the second time, she was killed with violent convulsions within five minutes from the beginning of the pumping.

A while after we put in a mouse, newly taken, in such a trap as had rather affrighted than hurt him; whilst he was leaping up very high in the receiver, we fastened the cover to it, expecting that an animal used to live in narrow holes with very little fresh air, would endure the want of it better than the lately mentioned birds: but though, for a while after the pump was set a work, he continued leaping up as before; yet, it was not long ere he began to appear sick and giddy, and to stagger: after which he fell down as dead, but without such violent convulsions as the bird died with. Whereupon, hastily turning the key, we let in some fresh air upon him, by which he recovered, after a while, his senses and his feet, but seemed to continue weak and sick: but at length, growing able to skip as formerly, the pump was plied again for eight minutes, about the middle of which space, if not before, a little air by a mischance got in at the stop cock; and about two minutes more he fell down quite dead, yet with convulsions far milder than those wherewith the two birds expired.

75

This alacrity so little before his death, and his not dying sooner than at the end of the eighth minute, seemed ascribable to the air (how little soever) that slipt into the receiver. For the first time, those convulsions (that, if they had not been suddenly remedied, had immediately dispatched him) seized on him in six minutes after the pump began to be set a work. These experiments seemed the more strange, in regard that during a great part of those few minutes the engine could but inconsiderably rarefy the air (and that too, but by degrees) and at the end of them there remained in the receiver no inconsiderable quantity; as may appear by what we have formerly said of our not being able to draw down water in a tube, within much less than a foot of the bottom: with which we likewise considered, that by the exsuction of the air and interspersed vapours, there was left in the receiver a space some hundreds of times exceeding the bigness of the animal, to receive the fuliginous streams, from which expiration discharges the lungs; and which, in the other cases hitherto known, may be suspected, for want of room, to stifle those animals that are closely penned up in too narrow receptacles.

I forgot to mention, that having caused these three creatures to be opened, I could, in such small bodies, discover little of what we sought for, and what we might possibly have found in larger animals; for though the lungs of the birds appeared very red, and as it were inflamed, yet that colour being usual enough in the lungs of such winged creatures, deserves not so much our notice, as it doth, that in almost all the destructive experiments made in our engine, the animals appeared to die with violent convulsive motions: from which, whether physicians can gather any thing towards the discovery of the nature of convulsive distempers, I leave to them to consider.

Having proceeded thus far, though (as we have partly intimated already) there appeared not much cause to doubt, but that the death of the forementioned animals proceeded rather from the want of air, than that the air was overclogged by the steams of their bodies, exquisitely penned up in the glass; yet I, that love not to believe any thing upon conjectures, when by a not overdifficult experiment I can try whether it be true or no, thought it the safest way to obviate objections, and remove scruples, by shutting up another mouse as close as I could in the receiver; wherein it lived about three quarters of an hour, and might probably have done so much longer, had not a Virtuoso of quality, who in the mean while chanced to make me a visit, desired to see whether or no the mouse could be killed by the exsuction of the ambient air: whereupon we thought fit to open, for a little while, an intercourse betwixt the air in the receiver, and that without it, that the mouse might hereby (if it were needful for him) be refreshed; and yet we did this without uncementing the cover at the top, that it might not be objected, that perhaps the vessel was more closely stopped for the exsuction of the air than before.

The experiment had this event, that after the mouse had lived ten minutes (which we ascribed to this, that the pump, for want of having been lately oiled, could move but slowly, and could not by him that managed it be made to work as nimbly as it was wont) at the end of that time he died with convulsive fits, wherein he made two or three bounds into the air, before he fell down dead.

Nor was I content with this, but for your Lordship's farther satisfaction, and my own, I caused a mouse, that was very hungry, to be shut in all night, with a bed of paper for him to rest upon: and to be sure that the receiver was well closed, I caused some air to be drawn out of it, whereby, perceiving that there was no sensible leak, I presently readmitted the air at the stopcock, lest the want of it should harm the little animal; and then I caused the engine to be kept all night by the fire-side, to keep him from being destroyed by the immoderate cold of the frosty night. And this care succeeded so well, that the next morning I found that the mouse was not only alive, but had devoured a good part of the cheese that had been put in with him. And having thus kept him alive full twelve hours, or better, we did, by sucking out part of the air, bring him to droop, and to appear swelled; and by letting in the air again, we soon reduced him to his former liveliness.

A Digression Containing Some Doubts Touching Respiration

I fear your Lordship will now expect, that to these experiments I should add my reflections on them, and attempt, by their assistance, to resolve the difficulties that occur about respiration; since at the beginning I acknowledged a farther enquiry into the nature of that, to have been my design in the related trials. But I have yet, because of the inconvenient season of the year, made so few experiments, and have been so little satisfied by those I have been able to make, that they have hitherto made respiration appear to me rather a more, than a less mysterious thing, than it did before. But yet, since they have furnished me with some such new considerations, concerning the use of the air, as confirms me in my diffidence of the truth of what is commonly believed touching that matter; that I may not appear sullen or lazy, I am content not to decline employing a few hours in setting down my doubts, in presenting your Lordship some hints, and in considering whether the trials made in our engine will at least assist us to discover wherein the deficiency lies that needs to be supplied. . . .

For first, many there are, who think the chief, if not sole use of respiration, to be the cooling and tempering of that heat in the heart and blood, which otherwise would be immoderate; and this opinion not only seems to be most received amongst scholastic writers, but divers of the new philosophers, Cartesians and others, admitted with some variation; teaching, that the air is necessary, by its coldness to condense the blood that passeth out of the right ventricle of the heart into the lungs, that thereby it may contain such a consistence as is requisite to make it fit fewel for the vital fire or flame, in the left ventricle of the heart. And this opinion seems favoured by this, that fishes, and other cold creatures, whose hearts have but one cavity, are also unprovided of lungs, and by some other considerations. But though it need not be denied, that the inspired air may sometimes be of use by refrigerating the heart, yet (against the opinion that makes this refrigeration the most genuine and constant use of the air) it may be objected, that divers cold creatures (some of which, as particularly frogs, live in the water) have yet need of respiration; which seems not likely to be needed for refrigeration by them that are destitute of any sensible heat, and besides, live in the cold water: that even decrepit old men, whose natural heat is made very languid, and almost extinguished by reason of age, have yet a necessity of frequent respiration: that a temperate air is fittest for the generality of breathing creatures; and as an air too hot, so also an air too cold may be inconvenient for them (especially if they be troubled with an immoderate degree of the same quality which is predominant in the air:) that in some diseases the natural heat is so weakened, that in case the use of respiration were too cool, it would be more hurtful than beneficial to breathe; and the suspending of the respiration may supply the place of those very hot medicines that are wont to be employed in such distempers: that nature might better have given the heart but a moderate heat, than such an excessive one, as needs to be perpetually cooled, to keep it from growing destructive; which the gentle, and not the burning heat of an animal's heart, seems not intense enough so indispensably to require. These, and other objections might be opposed, and pressed against the recited opinion; but we shall not insist on them, but only add to them, that it appears not by our foregoing experiments that in our exhausted receiver, where yet animals die so suddenly for want of respiration, the ambient body is sensibly hotter than the common air.

Other learned men there are, who will have the very substance of the air to get in by the vessels of the lungs, to the left ventricle of the heart, not only to temper its heat, but to provide for the generation of spirits. And these alledge for themselves the authority of the ancients, among whom *Hippocrates* seems manifestly to favour their opinion; and both *Aristotle* and *Galen* do sometimes (for methinks they speak doubtfully enough) appear inclinable to it. But for aught ever I could see in dissections, it is very difficult to make out, how the air is conveyed into the left ventricle of the heart, especially the systole and the diastole of the heart and lungs being very far from being synchronical: besides, that the spirits seeming to be but the most subtile and unctuous particles of the blood appear to be of a very differing nature from that of the lean and incombustible corpuscles of air. Other objections against this opinion have been proposed, and pressed by that excellent Anatomist, and my industrious friend Dr. *Highmore,* to whom I shall therefore refer you.

Another opinion there is touching respiration, which makes the genuine use of it to be ventilation not of the heart, but of the blood, in its passage through the lungs; in which passage it is disburthened of those excrementitious steams preceding for the most part, from the superfluous serosities of the blood (we may add) and of the chyle too, which (by those new conduits of late very happily detected by the famous *Pecquet*) hath been newly mixed with it in the heart. And this opinion is that of the industrious, *Moebius,* and is said to have been that of that excellent philosopher *Gassendus;* and hath been, in part, an opinion almost vulgar. But this hypothesis may be explicated two ways: for first, the necessity of the air in respiration may be supposed to proceed from hence; that as a flame cannot long burn in a narrow and close place, because the fulginous steams it incessantly throws out, cannot be long received into the ambient body; which, after a while, growing too full of them to admit any more, stifles the flame: so that the vital fire in the heart requires an ambient body of a yielding nature, to receive into it the superfluous serosities, and other recrements of the blood, whose seasonable expulsion is requisite to depurate the mass of blood and make it fit, both to circulate and to maintain the vital heat residing in the heart. The other way of explicating the above-mentioned hypothesis is, by supposing, that the air doth not only, as a receptacle, admit into its pores the excrementitious vapours of the blood, when they are expelled through the wind-pipe, but doth also convey them out of the lungs, in regard that the inspired air reaching to all the ends of the *aspera arteria,* doth there associate itself with the exhalations of the circulating blood, and when it is exploded, carries them away with itself: as we see that winds speedily dry up the surfaces of wet bodies, not to say any thing of what we formerly observed touching our liquor, whose fumes were strangely elevated upon the ingress of the air.

Now, of these two ways of explicating the use of respiration, our engine affords us this objection against the first; that upon the exsuction of the air, the animal dies a great deal sooner than if it were left in the vessel; though by that exsuction, the ambient space is left much more free to receive the steams that are either breathed out of the lungs of the animal, or discharged by insensible transpiration through the pores of his skin.

But if the hypothesis proposed be taken in the other sense, it seems congruous enough to that grand observation, which partly the phaenomena of our engine, and partly the relations of travellers, have suggested to us; namely, that there is certain consistence of air requisite to respiration: so that if it be too thick, and already over-charged with vapours, it will be unfit to unite with, and carry off those of the blood, as water will dissolve and associate to itself but a certain proportion of saline corpuscles; and if it be too thin or rarefied, the number or size of the aerial particles is too small to be able to carry off the halituous excrements of the blood, in such plenty as is requisite.

Now that air too much thickened (and as it were clogged) with steams, is unfit for respiration, may appear by what is wont to happen in the lead mines of *Devonshire* and for aught I know, in those too of other countries (though I have seen mines where no such thing was complained of) for I have been informed by more than one credible person (and particularly by an ingenious man that hath often, for curiosity, digged in those mines and been employed about them) that there often riseth damps (as retaining the German word by which we call them) which doth so thicken the air, that, unless the workmen speedily make signs to them that are above, they would (which also sometimes happens) be presently stifled for want of breath: and though their companions do make haste to draw them up, yet frequently, by that time they come to the free air, they are, as it were, in a swoon, and are a good while before they come to themselves again. And that this swooning seems not to proceed from any arsenical or poisonous exhalation contained in the damp, as from its over much condensing the air, seems probable from hence; that the same damps oftentimes leisurely extinguish the flames of their candles or lamps; and from hence also that it appears (by many relations of authentical authors) that in those cellars where great store of new wine is set to work, men have been suffocated by the too great plenty of the steams exhaling from the must, and too much thickening the air: as may be gathered from the custom that is now used in some hot countries, where those that have occasion to go into such cellars, carry with them a quantity of well-kindled coals, which they hold near their faces; whereby it comes to pass, that the fire discussing the fumes, and rarefying the air reduceth the ambient body to a consistence fit for respiration.

We will add (by way of confirmation) the following experiment: in such a small receiver, as those wherein we killed divers birds, we carefully closed up one who though for a quarter of an hour he seemed not much prejudiced by the closeness of his prison, afterwards began first to pant very vehemently, and keep his bill very open, and then to appear very sick; and last of all, after some long and violent strainings, to cast up some little matter out of his stomach; which he did several times, till growing so sick that he staggered and gasped, as being just ready to die. We perceived, that within about three quarters of an hour from the time that he was put in, he had so thickened and tainted the air with the steams of his body, that it was become altogether unfit for the use of respiration: which he will not much wonder at, who hath taken notice in *Sanctorius* his *Statica Medicina,* how much that part of our aliments which goeth off by insensible transpiration, exceeds in weight all the visible and grosser excrements both solid and liquid.

That (on the other side) an air too much dilated is not serviceable for the ends of respiration, the hasty death of the animal we killed in our exhausted receiver seems sufficiently to manifest. And it may not irrationally be doubted, whether or no, if a man were raised to the very top of the atmosphere, he would be able to live many minutes, and would not quickly die for want of such air as we are wont to breathe here below. And that this conjecture may not appear extravagant, I shall, on this occasion, subjoin a memorable relation that I have met with in the learned *Josephus Acosta,* who tells us, that when he himself passed the high mountains of *Peru* (which they call *Pariacaca*) to which, he says, that the *Alps* themselves seemed to them but as ordinary houses in regard of high towers, he and his companions were surprized with such extreme pangs of straining and vomiting (not without casting up blood too) and with so violent a distemper, that he concludes he should undoubtedly have died, but that this lasted not above three or four hours, before they came into a more convenient and natural temperature of air: to which our learned author adds an inference, which being the principal thing I designed in mentioning the narrative, I shall set down in his own words: *I therefore* (says he) *persuade myself, that the element of the air is there so subtle and delicate, as it is not proportionable with the breathing of man, which requires a more gross and temperate air; and I believe it is the cause that doth so much alter the stomach, and trouble all the disposition.* Thus far our author, whose words I mention, that we may guess, by what happens somewhat near the confines of the atmosphere (though probably far from the surface of it) what would happen beyond the atmosphere. That, which some of those that treat of the height of mountains, relate out of *Aristotle*, namely, that those that ascend to the top of the mountain *Olympus*, could not keep themselves alive, without carrying with them wet spunges, by whose assistance they could respire in that air, otherwise too thin for respiration (that relation, I say, concerning this mountain) would much confirm what hath been newly recited out of *Acosta*, if we had sufficient reason to believe it. But I confess I am very diffident of the truth of it; partly, because when I passed the *Alps*, I took notice of no notable change betwixt the consistence of the air at the top and the bottom of the mountain; partly, because in a punctual relation made by an English gentleman, of his ascension to the top of the pike of *Tenariff* (which is by great odds higher than *Olympus*) I find no mention of any such difficulty of breathing; and partly also, because the same author tells us out of *Aristotle*, that upon the top of *Olympus* there is no motion of the air, insomuch that letters traced upon the dust, have been, after many years, found legible and not discomposed; whereas that inquisitive *Busbequius* (who was ambassador from the German to the Turkish emperor) in one of his eloquent Epistles, tells us, upon his own knowledge, that Olympus *may be seen from* Constantinople, *blanched with perpetual snow;* which seems to argue, that the top of that, as well as of divers other tall hills, is not above that region of the air wherein meteors are formed. Though otherwise, in that memorable narrative which *David Fraelichius* made of his ascent to the top of the prodigiously high Hungarian mountain *Carpathus,* he tells us, *that when having passed through very thick clouds, he came to the very top of the hill, he found the air so calm and subtile, that not a hair of his head moved, whereas, in the lower stages of the mountain, he felt a vehement wind.* But this might well be casual, as was his having clear air where he was, though there were clouds, not only beneath him, but above him.

But, though what hath been hitherto discoursed, incline us to look upon the ventilation and the depuration of the blood, as one of the principal and constant uses of respiration; yet methinks it may be suspected that the air doth something more than barely help to carry off what is thrown out of the blood, in its passage through the lungs, from the right ventricle of the heart to the left. For we see, in phlegmatic constitutions and diseases, that the blood will circulate tolerably well, notwithstanding its being excessively serious: and in asthmatical persons, we often see that though the lungs be very much stuffed with tough phlegm, yet the patient may live some months, if not some years. So that it seems scarce probable, that either the want of throwing out the superfluous serum of the blood for a few moments, or the detaining it, during so short a while, in the lungs, should be able to kill a perfectly sound and lively animal: I say, for a few moments, because, that having divers times tried the experiment of killing birds in a small receiver, we commonly found, that within half a minute of an hour, or thereabout, the bird would be surprised by mortal convulsions, and within about a minute more would be stark dead, beyond the recovery of the air, though never so hastily let in. Which sort of experiments seem so strange, that we were obliged to make it several times, which gained it the advantage of having persons of differing qualities, professions and sexes (as not only ladies and lords, but doctors and mathematicians) to witness it. And to satisfy your Lordship that it was not the narrowness of the vessel, but the sudden exsuction of the air that dispatched these creatures so soon; we will add, that we once inclosed one of these birds in one of these small receivers, where, for a while, he was so little sensible of his imprisonment, that he eat very cheerfully certain seeds that were conveyed in with him, and not only lived ten minutes, but had probably lived much longer, had not a great person, that was spectator of some of these experiments, rescued him from the prosecution of the trial. Another bird being within about half a minute cast into violent convulsions, and reduced into a sprawling condition, upon the exsuction of the air, by the pity of some fair ladies, related to your Lordship, who made me hastily let in some air at the stopcock, the gasping animal was presently recovered, and in a condition to enjoy the benefit of the ladies compassion. And another time also, being resolved not to be interrupted in our experiment, we did at night shut up a bird in one of our small receivers, and observed that for a good while he so little felt the alteration of the air, that he fell asleep with his head under his wing; and through he afterwards awaked sick, yet he continued upon his legs between forty minutes and three quarters of an hour: after which, seeming ready to expire, we took him out, and soon found him able to make use of the liberty we gave him for a compensation of his sufferings.

If to the foregoing instances of the sudden destruction of animals, by the removal of the ambient air, we should now annex some, that we think fitter to reserve till anon; perhaps your Lordship would suspect, with me, that there is some use of the air which we do not yet so well understand, that makes it so continually needful to the life of the animals. *Paracelsus*, indeed, tells us, *that as the stomach concocts meat, and makes part of it useful to the body, rejecting the other part; so the lungs consume part of the air, and proscribe the rest.* So that, according to our Hermetic philosopher (as his followers would have him styled) it seems we must suppose, that there is in the air a little vital quintessence (if I may so call it) which serves to the refreshment and restauration of our vital spirits, for which use the grosser and incomparably greater part of the air being unserviceable, it need not seem strange, that an animal stands in need of almost incessantly drawing in fresh air. But though this opinion is not (as some of the same author) absurd, yet besides that some objections may be framed against it, out of what hath been already argued against the transmutation of air into vital spirits: besides these things, it seems not probable, that the bare want of the generation of the wonted quantity of vital spirits, for less than one minute, should, within that time, be able to kill a lively animal, without the help of any external violence at all.

But yet, on occasion of this opinion of *Paracelsus,* perhaps it will not be impertinent if, before I proceed, I acquaint your Lordship with a conceit of that deservedly famous Mechanician and Chymist, *Cornelius Drebell,* who, among other strange things that he performed, is affirmed, by more than a few credible persons, to have contrived, for the late learned *King James,* a vessel to go under water; of which, trial was made in the *Thames,* with admired success, the vessel carrying twelve rowers, besides passengers; one of which is yet alive, and related it to an excellent Mathematician that informed me of it. Now that for which I mention this story is, that having had the curiosity and opportunity to make particular enquiries among the relations of *Drebell,* and especially of an ingenious Physician that married his daughter, concerning the grounds upon which he conceived it feasible to make men unaccustomed to continue so long under water without suffocation, or (as the lately mentioned person that went in the vessel affirms) without inconvenience; I was answered, that *Drebell* conceived, that it is not the whole body of the air, but a certain quintessence (as Chymists speak) or spirituous part of it, that makes it fit for respiration; which being spent, the remaining grosser body, or carcase, if I may so call it, of the air, is unable to cherish the vital flame residing in the heart: so that, for aught I could gather, besides the mechanical contrivance of his vessel, he had a chymical liquor, which he accounted the chief secret of his submarine navigation. For when, from time to time, he perceived that the finer and purer part of the air was consumed, or overclogged by the respiration and steams of those that went in his ship, he would, by unstopping a vessel full of this liquor, speedily restore to the troubled air such a proportion of vital parts, as would make it again, for a good while, fit for respiration, and it gave us also occasion to suspect, that if insects have no lungs, nor any part analogous thereunto, the ambient air affects them, and relieves them at the pores of their skin; it not being irrational to extend to these creatures that of *Hippocrates*, who saith, that a living body is throughout perspirable; or, to use his expression, εἰσπνόιε ἐχπυου, disposed to admit and part with what is spirituous. Which may be somewhat illustrated by what we have elsewhere noted, that the moister parts of the air readily insinuate themselves into, and recede from the pores of the beards of wild oats, and those of divers other wild plants; which almost continually wreath and unwreath themselves according to, even, tho light variations of the temperature of the ambient air.

This circumstance of our experiment we particularly took notice of, that when at any time, upon the ingress of the air, the bee began to recover, the first sign of life she gave, was a vehement panting, which appeared near the tail; which we therefore mention, because we have observed the like in bees drowned in water, when they first come to be revived by a convenient heat: as if the air were in the one case as proper to set the spirits and alimental juice moving, as heat is in the other; and this may, perchance, deserve a farther consideration.

We may add, that we scarce ever saw any thing that seemed so much as this experiment to manifest, that even living creatures (man always excepted) are a kind of curious engines, framed and contrived by nature (or rather the author of it) much more skillfully than our gross tools and imperfect wits can reach to. For in our present instance we see animals, vivid and perfectly sound, deprived immediately of motion, and any discernable signs of life, and reduced to a condition that differs from death, but in that it is not absolutely irrecoverable. This (I say) we see performed without any, so much as the least external violence offered to the engine; unless it be such as is offered to a wind-mill, when the wind ceasing to blow on the sails, all the several parts remain moveless and useless, till a new breath put them into motion again.

And this was farther very notable in this experiment; that whereas it is known that bees and flies will not only walk, but fly for a great while, after their heads are off; and sometimes one half of the body will, for divers hours, walk up and down, when it is severed from the other: yet, upon the exsuction of the air, not only the progressive motion of the whole body, but the very motions of the limbs do forthwith cease; as if the presence of the air were more necessary to these animals, than the presence of their own heads.

But, it seems, that in these insects, that fluid body (whether it be juice or flame) wherein life chiefly resides, is nothing near so easy dissipable as in the perfect animals. For whereas we have above recited, that the birds we conveyed into our small receiver were within two minutes brought to be past, we were unable (though by tiring him that pumped) to kill our insects by the exsuction of the air: for though, as long as the pump was kept moving, they continued immovable, yet, when he desisted from pumping, the air that pressed in at the unperceived leaks did, though slowly, restore them to the free exercise of the functions of life.

But, my Lord, I grow troublesome, and therefore shall pass on to other experiments: yet without despairing of your pardon for having entertained you so long about the use of respiration, because it is a subject of that difficulty to be explained, and and yet of that importance to human life, that I shall not regret the trouble my experiments have cost me, if they be found in any degree serviceable to the purposes to which they were designed. And though I despair not but that hereafter our engine may furnish us with divers phenomena useful to illustrate the doctrine of respiration; yet having not, as yet, had the opportunity to make other trials, of various kinds, that I judge requisite for my information, I must confess to your Lordship, that in what I have hitherto said, I pretend not so much to establish or overthrow this or that hypothesis, as to lay together divers of the particulars, because I could add many others, but that I want time, and fear that I should need your Lordship's pardon for having been so prolix in writing; and that of Physicians (which perhaps I shall more easily obtain) for having invaded anatomy, a discipline which they challenge to themselves, and indeed have been the almost sole improvers of. Without denying then, that the inspired and exspired air may be sometimes very useful, by condensing and cooling the blood that passeth through the lungs; I hold that the depuration of the blood in that passage, is not only one of the ordinary, but one of the principal uses of respiration. But I am apt also to suspect, that the air doth something else in respiration, which hath not yet been sufficiently explained; and therefore, till I have examined the matter more deliberately, I shall not scruple to answer the questions that may be asked me, touching the genuine use of respiration, in the excellent words employed by the acute St. *Austin,* to one who asked him hard questions: *Mallem quidem* (says he) *eorum quae àme quaesivisti, habere scientiam quam ignorantiam: sed quia id nondum potui, magis eligo cautam ignorantiam consiteri, quam falsam scientiam profiteri.*

TWO NEW EXPERIMENTS TOUCHING THE MEASURE OF THE FORCE OF THE SPRING OF AIR COMPRESSED AND DILATED

WE TOOK then a long glass-tube, which, by a dexterous hand and the help of a lamp, was in such a manner crooked at the bottom, that the part turned up was almost parallel to the rest of the tube, and the orifice of this shorter leg of the siphon (if I may so call the whole instrument) being hermetically sealed, the length of it was divided into inches (each of which was subdivided into eight parts) by a streight list of paper, which containing those divisions, was carefully pasted all along it. Then putting in as much quicksilver as served to fill the arch or

89

bended part of the siphon, that the mercury standing in a level might reach in the one leg to the bottom of the divided paper, and just to the same height of horizontal line in the other; we took care, by frequently inclining the tube, so that the air might freely pass from one leg into the other by the sides of the mercury (we took, I say, care) that the air at last included in the shorter cylinder should be of the same laxity with the rest of the air about it. This done, we began to pour quicksilver into the longer leg of the siphon, which by its weight pressing up that in the shorter leg, did by degrees streighten the included air: and continuing this pouring in of quicksilver till the air in the shorter leg was by condensation reduced to take up by half the space it possessed (I say, possessed, not filled) before; we cast our eyes upon the longer leg of the glass, on which was likewise pasted a list of paper carefully divided into inches and parts, and we observed, not without delight and satisfaction, that the quicksilver in that longer part of the tube was 29 inches higher than the other. Now that this observation does both very well agree with and confirm our hypothesis, will be easily discerned by him that takes notice what we teach; and Monsieur Paschal and our English friend's experiments prove, that the greater the weight is that leans upon the air, the more forcible is its endeavour of dilatation, and consequently its power of resistance (as other springs are stronger when bent by greater weights). For this being considered, it will apear to agree rarely-well with the hypothesis, that as according to it the air in that degree of density and correspondent measure of resistance, to which the weight of the incumbent atmosphere had brought it, was able to counterbalance and resist the pressure of a mercurial cylinder of about 29 inches, as we are taught by the Torricellian experiment; so here the same air being brought to a degree of density about twice as great as that it had before, obtains a spring twice as strong as formerly. As may appear by its being able to sustain or resist a cylinder of 29 inches in the longer tube, together with the weight of the atmospherical cylinder, that leaned upon those 29 inches of mercury; and, as we just now inferred from the Torricellian experiment, was equivalent to them.

We were hindered from prosecuting the trial at that time by the casual breaking of the tube. But because an accurate experiment of this nature would be of great importance to the doctrine of the spring of the air, and has not yet been made (that I know) by any man; and because also it is more uneasy to be made than one would think, in regard of the difficulty as well of procuring crooked tubes fit for the purpose, as of making a just estimate of the true place of the protuberant mercury's surface; I suppose it will not be unwelcome to the reader to be informed, that after some other trials, one of which we made in a tube whose longer leg was perpendicular, and

A TABLE OF THE CONDENSATION OF THE AIR

A	A	B	C	D	E
48	12	00		$29\,^2/_{16}$	$29\,^2/_{16}$
46	$11^1/_2$	$01\,^7/_{16}$		$30\,^9/_{16}$	$30\,^6/_{16}$
44	11	$02^{13}/_{16}$		$31^{15}/_{16}$	$31^{12}/_{16}$
42	$10^1/_2$	$04\,^6/_{16}$		$33\,^8/_{16}$	$33^1/_7$
40	10	$06\,^3/_{16}$		$35\,^5/_{16}$	35
38	$9^1/_2$	$07^{14}/_{16}$		37	$36^{15}/_{19}$
36	9	$10\,^2/_{16}$		$39\,^5/_{16}$	$38^7/_8$
34	$8^1/_2$	$12\,^8/_{16}$		$41^{10}/_{16}$	$41\,^2/_{17}$
32	8	$15\,^1/_{16}$		$44\,^8/_{16}$	$43^{11}/_{16}$
30	$7^1/_2$	$17^{15}/_{16}$	Added to $29^1/_8$ makes	$47\,^1/_{16}$	$46^3/_5$
28	7	$21\,^3/_{16}$		$50\,^5/_{16}$	50
26	$6^1/_2$	$25\,^3/_{16}$		$54\,^5/_{16}$	$53^{10}/_{13}$
24	6	$29^{11}/_{16}$		$58^{13}/_{16}$	$58^2/_8$
23	$5^3/_4$	$32\,^3/_{16}$		$61\,^5/_{16}$	$60^{18}/_{23}$
22	$5^1/_2$	$34^{15}/_{16}$		$64\,^1/_{16}$	$63\,^6/_{11}$
21	$5^1/_4$	$37^{15}/_{16}$		$67\,^1/_{16}$	$66^4/_7$
20	5	$41\,^9/_{16}$		$70^{11}/_{16}$	70
19	$4^3/_4$	45		$74\,^2/_{16}$	$73^{11}/_{19}$
18	$4^1/_2$	$48^{12}/_{16}$		$77^{14}/_{16}$	$77^2/_3$
17	$4^1/_4$	$53^{11}/_{16}$		$82^{12}/_{16}$	$82\,^4/_{17}$
16	4	$58\,^2/_{16}$		$87^{14}/_{16}$	$87^3/_8$
15	$3^3/_4$	$63^{15}/_{16}$		$93\,^1/_{16}$	$93^1/_5$
14	$3^1/_2$	$71\,^5/_{16}$		$100\,^7/_{16}$	$99^6/_7$
13	$3^1/_4$	$78^{11}/_{16}$		$107^{13}/_{16}$	$107\,^7/_{13}$
12	3	$88\,^7/_{16}$		$117\,^9/_{16}$	$116^4/_8$

AA. The number of equal spaces in the shorter leg, that contained the same parcel of air diversely extended.

B. The height of the mercurial cylinder in the longer leg, that compressed the air into those dimensions.

C. The height of the mercurial cylinder, that counterbalanced the pressure of the atmosphere.

D. The aggregate of the two last columns, B and C, exhibiting the pressure sustained by the included air.

E. What that pressure should be according to the hypothesis, that supposes the pressures and expansions to be in reciprocal proportion.

91

the other, that contained the air, parallel to the horizon, we at last procured a tube of the figure expressed in the scheme; which tube, though of a pretty bigness, was so long, that the cylinder, whereof the shorter leg of it consisted, admitted a list of paper, which had before been divided into 12 inches and their quarters, and the longer leg admitted another list of paper of divers feet in length, and divided after the same manner. Then quicksilver being poured in to fill up the bended part of the glass that the surface of it in either leg might rest in the same horizontal line, as we lately taught, there was more and more quicksilver poured into the longer tube; and notice being watchfully taken how far the mercury was risen in that longer tube, when it appeared to have ascended to any of the divisions in the shorter tube, the several observations that were thus successively made, and as they were made set down, afforded us the table above.

. . . And to let you see, that we did not (as a little above) inconsiderately mention the weight of the incumbent atmospherical cylinder as a part of the weight resisted by the imprisoned air, we will here annex, that we took care, when the mercurial cylinder in the longer leg of the pipe was about an hundred inches high, to cause one to suck at the open orifice; whereupon (as we expected) the mercury in the tube did notably ascend. . . . And therefore we shall render this reason of it that the pressure of the incumbent air being in part taken off by its expanding itself into the sucker's dilated chest, the imprisoned air was thereby enabled to dilate itself manifestly, and repel the mercury, that comprest it, till there was an equality of force betwixt the strong spring of the comprest air on the one part, and the tall mercurial cylinder, together with the contiguous dilated air, on the other part.

Now, if to what we have thus delivered concerning the compression of the air, we add some observations concerning its spontaneous expansion, it will the better appear, how much the phaenomena of these mercurial experiments depend upon the differing measures of strength to be met with in the air's spring, according to its various degrees of compression and laxity.

A Table of the Rarefaction of the Air

A. The number of equal spaces at the top of the tube, that contained the same parcel of air.

B. The height of the mercurial cylinder, that together with the spring of the included air counterbalanced the pressure of the atmosphere.

C. The pressure of the atmosphere.

D. The complement of *B* to *C*, exhibiting the pressure sustained by the included air.

E. What that pressure should be according to the hypothesis.

A	*B*	*C*	*D*	*E*
1	$00^0/_0$		$29^3/_4$	$29^3/_4$
$1^1/_2$	$10^5/_8$		$19^1/_8$	$19^5/_6$
2	$15^3/_8$		$14^3/_8$	$14^7/_8$
3	$20^2/_8$		$9^4/_8$	$9^{15}/_{12}$
4	$22^5/_8$	Subtracted from $29^3/_4$ leaves	$7^1/_8$	$7\ ^7/_{16}$
5	$24^1/_8$		$5^5/_8$	$5^{19}/_{25}$
6	$24^7/_8$		$4^7/_8$	$4^{23}/_{24}$
7	$25^4/_8$		$4^2/_8$	$4^1/_4$
8	$26^0/_0$		$3^6/_8$	$3^{23}/_{32}$
9	$26^3/_8$		$3^3/_8$	$3^{11}/_{36}$
10	$26^6/_8$		$3^0/_0$	$2^{39}/_{40}$
12	$27^1/_8$		$2^5/_8$	$2^{23}/_{48}$
14	$27^4/_8$		$2^2/_8$	$2^1/_8$
16	$27^6/_8$		$2^0/_0$	$1^{55}/_{64}$
18	$27^7/_8$		$1^7/_8$	$1^{47}/_{72}$
20	$28^0/_0$		$1^6/_8$	$1^9/_{80}$
24	$28^2/_8$		$1^4/_8$	$1^{23}/_{96}$
28	$28^3/_8$		$1^3/_8$	$1\ ^1/_{16}$
32	$28^4/_8$		$1^2/_8$	$0^{119}/_{128}$

CONDITIONS AT THE BOTTOM OF THE SEA

Another thing observed in the bottom of the sea is the tranquillity of the water there, if it be considerably distant from the surface. For though the winds have power to produce vast waves in that upper part that is exposed to their violence; yet the vehement agitation diminishes by degrees as the parts of the sea, being deeper and deeper, lie more and more remote from the superficies of the water.

The above-mentioned calmness of the sea at the bottom, will (I doubt not) appear strange to many, who admiring the force of the stormy winds and the vastness of the waves they raise, do not, at the same time, consider the almost incomparably greater quantity and weight of water that must be moved to make any great commotion at the bottom of the sea, upon which so great a mass of salt-water, which is heavier than fresh, is constantly incumbent. Wherefore, for the proof of the proposed paradox, I will set down a memorable relation, which my inquiries got me from the diver, elsewhere mentioned, who by the help of an engine could stay some hours under water.

This person then being asked, whether he observed any operation of the winds at the bottom of the sea, where it was of any considerable depth? answered me to this purpose, the wind being stiff, so that the waves were manifestly six or seven feet high above the surface of the water, he found no sign of it at 15 fathom deep; but if the blasts continued long, then it moved the mud at the bottom, and made the water thick and dark. And I remember he told me, which was the circumstance I chiefly designed, that staying once at the bottom of the sea very long, where it was considerably deep, he was amazed at his return to the upper parts of the water to find a storm there, which he dreamt not of, and which was raised in his absence, having taken no notice of it below, and having left the sea calm enough when he descended into it.

JAMES BRADLEY

(1693–1762)

This English astronomer, friend of Newton and Halley, made some 60,000 observations on the positions of the stars, which fill two large volumes. After studying theology at Oxford, Bradley became professor of astronomy there, and was later made Royal Astronomer of the Greenwich Observatory. His major discoveries were of the aberration of light due to the earth's motion during the year (announced in 1729) and the nutation of the earth's axis (announced in 1748). Besides leaving valuable work on the compilation of astronomical tables, he also stated the laws of refraction.

THE DISCOVERY OF THE ABERRATION OF LIGHT

You having been pleased to express your satisfaction with what I had an opportunity sometime ago of telling you in conversation, concerning some observations that were making by our late worthy and ingenious friend, the honourable Samuel Molyneux, esq. and which have since been continued and repeated by myself, in order to determine the parallax of the fixed stars; I shall now beg leave to lay before you a more particular account of them. . . .

Mr. Molyneux's apparatus was completed and fitted for observation about the end of November, 1725, and on the third day of December following, the bright star in the head of Draco (marked γ by Bayer) was for the first time observed as it passed near the zenith, and its situation carefully taken with the instrument. The like observations were made on the 5th, 11th, and 12th days of the same month, and there appearing no material difference in the place of the star, a farther repetition of them at this season seemed needless, it being a part of the year wherein no sensible alteration of parallax in this star could soon be expected. It was chiefly, therefore, curiosity that tempted me (being then at Kew, where the instrument was fixed) to prepare for observing the star on December 17th, when having adjusted the instrument as usual, I perceived that it passed a little more southerly this day than when it was observed before. Not suspecting any other cause of this appearance, we first concluded that it was owing to the uncertainty of the observations, and that either this or the foregoing were not so exact as we had before supposed; for which reason we purposed to repeat the observation again, in order to determine from whence this difference proceeded; and upon doing it on December 20th, I found that the star passed still more southerly than in the former observations. This sensible alteration the more surprised us, in that it was the contrary way from what it would have been had it proceeded from an annual parallax of the star: but being now pretty well satisfied that it could not be entirely owing to the want of exactness in the observations, and having no notion of any thing else that could cause such an apparent motion as this in the star, we began to think that some change in the materials etc. of the instrument itself might have occasioned it. Under these apprehensions we remained some time, but being at length fully convinced, by several trials, of the great exactness of the instrument and finding by the gradual increase of the star's distance from the pole, that there must be some regular cause that produced it; we took care to examine nicely, at the time of each observation, how it was: and about the beginning of March, 1726, the star was found to be 20″ more southerly than at the time of the first observation. It now indeed seemed to have arrived at its utmost limit southward, because in several trials made about this time, no sensible difference was observed in its situation. By the middle of April it appeared to be returning back again towards the north; and about the beginning of June, it passed at the same distance from the zenith as it had done in December, when it was first observed.

From the quick alteration of the star's declination about this time (it increasing a second in three days), it was concluded that it would now proceed northward, as it before had gone

southward of its present situation; and it happened as was conjectured: for the star continued to move northward till September
following, when it again became stationary, being then near 20″
more northerly than in June, and no less than 39″ more northerly
than it was in March. From September the star returned towards the south, till it arrived in December to the same situation
it was in at that time twelve months, allowing for the difference
of declination on account of the precession of the equinox.

This was a sufficient proof that the instrument had not been the
cause of this apparent motion of the star, and to find one adequate
to such an effect seemed a difficulty. A nutation of the earth's
axis was one of the first things that offered itself upon this occasion, but it was soon found to be insufficient; for though it
might have accounted for the change of declination in γ
Draconis, yet it would not at the same time agree with the
phænomena in other stars; particularly in a small one almost opposite in right ascension to γ Draconis, at about the same distance from the north pole of the equator: for though this star
seemed to move the same way as a nutation of the earth's axis
would have made it, yet, it changing its declination but about
half as much as γ Draconis in the same time (as appeared upon
comparing the observations of both made upon the same days, at
different seasons of the year), this plainly proved that the apparent motion of the stars was not occasioned by a real nutation,
since, if that had been the cause, the alteration in both stars
would have been near equal.

The great regularity of the observations left no room to doubt
but that there was some regular cause that produced this unexpected motion, which did not depend on the uncertainty or
variety of the seasons of the year. Upon comparing the observations with each other, it was discovered that in both the forementioned stars, the apparent difference of declination from the
maxima was always nearly proportional to the versed sine of the
sun's distance from the equinoctial points. This was an inducement to think that the cause, whatever it was, had some relation
to the sun's situation with respect to those points. But not being
able to frame any hypothesis at that time sufficient to solve all

the phænomena, and being very desirous to search a little farther into this matter, I began to think of erecting an instrument for myself at Wansted, that, having it always at hand, I might with the more ease and certainty inquire into the laws of this new motion. The consideration likewise of being able by another instrument to confirm the truth of the observations hitherto made with Mr. Molyneux's was no small inducement to me, but the chief of all was, the opportunity I should thereby have of trying in what manner other stars were affected by the same cause, whatever it was. For Mr. Molyneux's instrument, being originally designed for observing γ Draconis (in order, as I said before, to try whether it had any sensible parallax), was so contrived as to be capable of but little alteration in its direction, not above seven or eight minutes of a degree: and there being few stars within half that distance from the zenith of Kew bright enough to be well observed, he could not, with his instrument, thoroughly examine how this cause affected stars differently situated with respect to the equinoctial and solstitial points of the ecliptic. . . .

My instrument being fixed, I immediately began to observe such stars as I judged most proper to give me light into the cause of the motion already mentioned. There was variety enough of small ones; and not less than twelve that I could observe through all the seasons of the year; they being bright enough to be seen in the day-time, when nearest the sun. I had not been long observing, before I perceived that the notion we had before entertained of the stars being farthest north and south, when the sun was about the equinoxes, was only true of those that were near the solstitial colure: and after I had continued my observations a few months, I discovered what I then apprehended to be a general law, observed by all the stars, *viz.* that each of them became stationary, or was farthest north or south, when they passed over my zenith at six of the clock either in the morning or evening. I perceived likewise, that whatever situation the stars were in with respect to the cardinal points of the ecliptic, the apparent motion of every one tended the same way, when they passed my instrument about the same hour of the day or night; for they all moved southward, while they passed in the day, and northward in the night; so that each was farthest north when it came about six in the morning.

Though I have since discovered that the maxima in most of these stars do not happen exactly when they come to my instrument at those hours, yet not being able at that time to prove the contrary, and supposing that they did, I endeavoured to find out what proportion the greatest alterations of declination in different stars bore to each other; it being very evident that they did not all change their declination equally. I have before taken notice that it appeared from Mr. Molyneux's observations, that γ Draconis altered its declination about twice as much as the forementioned small star almost opposite to it; but examining the matter more particularly, I found that the greatest alteration of declination in these stars was as the sine of the latitude of each respectively. This made me suspect that there might be the like proportion between the maxima of other stars; but finding that the observations of some of them would not perfectly correspond with such an hypothesis, and not knowing whether the small difference I met with might not be owing to the uncertainty and error of the observations, I deferred the farther examination into the truth of this hypothesis, till I should be furnished with a series of observations made in all parts of the year; which might enable me not only to determine what errors the observations are liable to, or how far they may safely be depended upon; but also to judge whether there had been any sensible change in the parts of the instrument itself.

Upon these considerations I laid aside all thoughts at that time about the cause of the forementioned phænomena, hoping that I should the easier discover it, when I was better provided with proper means to determine more precisely what they were.

When the year was completed, I began to examine and compare my observations, and having pretty well satisfied myself as to the general laws of the phænomena, I then endeavoured to find out the cause of them. I was already convinced that the apparent motion of the stars was not owing to a nutation of the earth's axis. The next thing that offered itself was an alteration in the direction of the plumb-line, with which the instrument was constantly rectified; but this upon trial proved insufficient. Then I considered what refraction might do; but here also nothing satisfactory occurred. At last I conjectured that all the phænomena, hitherto mentioned, proceeded from the progressive motion of light and the earth's annual motion in its orbit. For I perceived that, if light was propagated in time, the apparent place of a fixed object would not be the same when the eye is at rest, as when it is moving in any other direction than that of the line passing through the eye and object; and that when the eye is moving in different directions, the apparent place of the object would be different. . . .

I must confess to you, that the agreement of the observations with each other, as well as with the hypothesis, is much greater than I expected to find before I had compared them; and it may possibly be thought to be too great by those who have been used to astronomical observations, and know how difficult it is to make such as are in all respects exact. But if it would be any satisfaction to such persons (till I have an opportunity of describing my instrument and the manner of using it), I could assure them, that in above seventy observations which I made of this star in a year, there is but one (and that is noted as very dubious on account of clouds) which differs from the foregoing hypothesis, more than 2″, and this does not differ 3″.

This, therefore, being the fact, I cannot but think it very probable that the phænomena proceed from the cause I have assigned, since the foregoing observations make it sufficiently evident, that the effect of the real cause, whatever it is, varies in this star, in the same proportion that it ought according to the hypothesis . . .

I think it needless to give you the comparison between the hypothesis and the observations of any more stars; since the agreement in the foregoing is a kind of demonstration (whether it be allowed that I have discovered the real cause of the phænomena or not) that the hypothesis gives at least the true law of the different situations and aspects with the sun. And if this is the case, it must be granted that the parallax of the fixed stars is much smaller than hath been hitherto supposed by those who have pretended to deduce it from their observations. I believe that I may venture to say, that in either of the two stars last mentioned it does not amount to 2″. I am of opinion, that if it were 1″ I should have perceived it, in the great number of observations that I made, especially of γ Draconis; which agreeing with the hypothesis (without allowing any thing for parallax) nearly as well when the sun was in conjunction with, as in opposition to, this star, it seems very probable that the parallax of it is not so great as one single second; and consequently that it is above 400,000 times farther from us than the sun.

There appearing, therefore, after all no sensible parallax in the fixed stars, the Anti-Copernicans have still room on that account to object against the motion of the earth; and they may have (if they please) a much greater objection against the hypothesis by which I have endeavoured to solve the forementioned phænomena, by denying the progressive motion of light, as well as that of the earth.

But as I do not apprehend that either of these postulates will be denied me by the generality of the astronomers and philosophers of the present age; so I shall not doubt of obtaining their assent to the consequences which I have deduced from them, if they are such as have the approbation of so great a judge of them as yourself.

TYCHO BRAHE

(1546–1601)

Although this Danish astronomer made the error of rejecting the
Copernican system and holding that planets and sun revolve around
the earth, the accuracy of his measurements contributed to the advancement of astronomy, and were of special value to Kepler in the
formulation of his laws. Brahe found a new star in Cassiopeia in
1572, and meticulously recorded the positions of sun, moon, stars
and planets. He founded an observatory in the island of Hven, and
worked with Kepler in Bohemia at the end of his life. He is the
author of *Astronomiae Instauratae Mechanica* (1598), which describes his discoveries and instruments, and *Astronomiae Instauratae
Progymnasmata* (1602-3), edited by Kepler after his death.

On a New Star, Not Previously Seen within the Memory
of Any Since the Beginning of the World

Its First Appearance in 1572.—Last year [1572], in the month
of November, on the eleventh day of that month, in the evening,
after sunset, when, according to my habit, I was contemplating
the stars in a clear sky, I noticed that a new and unusual star,
surpassing the other stars in brilliancy, was shining almost directly above my head; and since I had, almost from boyhood,
known all the stars of the heavens perfectly (there is no great difficulty in attaining that knowledge), it was quite evident to me
that there had never before been any star in that place in the sky,
even the smallest, to say nothing of a star so conspicuously bright
as this. I was so astonished at this sight that I was not ashamed to
doubt the trustworthiness of my own eyes. But when I observed that others, too, on having the place pointed out to them,
could see that there was really a star there, I had no further

doubts. A miracle indeed, either the greatest of all that have occurred in the whole range of nature since the beginning of the world, or one certainly that is to be classed with those attested by the Holy Oracles, the staying of the Sun in its course in answer to the prayers of Joshua, and the darkening of the Sun's face at the time of the Crucifixion. For all philosophers agree, and facts clearly prove it to be the case, that in the ethereal region of the celestial world no change, in the way either of generation or of corruption, takes place; but that the heavens and the celestial bodies in the heavens are without increase or diminution, and that they undergo no alteration, either in number or in size or in light or any other respect; that they always remain the same, like unto themselves in all respects, no years wearing them away. Furthermore, the observations of all the founders of the science, made some thousands of years ago, testify that all the stars have always retained the same number, position, order, motion, and size as they are found, by careful observation on the part of those who take delight in heavenly phenomena, to preserve even in our day. Nor do we read that it was ever before noted by any one of the founders that a new star had appeared in the celestial world, except only by Hipparchus, if we are to believe Pliny. For Hipparchus, according to Pliny (Book II of his Natural History) noticed a star different from all others previously seen, one born in his own age . . .

Its Position with Reference to the Diameter of the World and its Distance from the Earth, the Center of the Universe.—It is a difficult matter, and one that requires a subtle mind, to try to determine the distances of the stars from us, because they are so incredibly far removed from the earth; nor can it be done in any way more conveniently and with greater certainty than by the measure of the parallax [diurnal], if a star have one. For if a star that is near the horizon is seen in a different place than when it is at its highest point and near the vertex, it is necessarily found in some orbit with respect to which the Earth has a sensible size. How far distant the said orbit is, the size of the parallax compared with the semidiameter of the Earth will make clear. If, however, a [circumpolar] star, that is as near to the horizon [at

103

lower culmination], as to the vertex [at upper culmination], is seen at the same point of the Primum Mobile, there is no doubt that it is situated either in the eighth sphere or not far below it, in an orbit with respect to which the whole Earth is as a point.

In order, therefore, that I might find out in this way whether this star was in the region of the Element or among the celestial orbits, and what its distance was from the Earth itself, I tried to determine whether it had a parallax, and, if so, how great a one; and this I did in the following way: I observed the distance between this star and Schedir of Cassiopeia (for the latter and the new star were both nearly on the meridian), when the star was at its nearest point to the vertex, being only 6 degrees removed from the zenith itself (and for that reason, though it were near the Earth, would produce no parallax in that place, the visual position of the star and the real position then uniting in one point, since the line from the center of the Earth and that from the surface nearly coincide). I made the same observation when the star was farthest from the zenith and at its nearest point to the horizon, and in each case I found that the distance from the above-mentioned fixed star was exactly the same, without the variation of a minute: namely 7 degrees and 55 minutes. Then I went through the same process, making numerous observations with other stars. Whence I conclude that this new star has no diversity of aspect, even when it is near the horizon. For otherwise in its least altitude it would have been farther away from the above-mentioned star in the breast of Cassiopeia than when in its greatest altitude. Therefore, we shall find it necessary to place this star, not in the region of the Element, below the Moon, but far above, in an orbit with respect to which the Earth has no sensible size. For if it were in the highest region of the air, below the hollow region of the Lunar sphere, it would, when nearest the horizon, have produced on the circle a sensible variation of altitude from that which it held when near the vertex.

To make the proof clearer, let a circle be drawn representing the meridian, or some other vertical circle of the Primum Mobile, in which the places of all the stars are held to be, and let this circle be *CBDE*, with its center at *A*. Let the diameter *BE* indicate the vertex, and *CD* the horizon. Furthermore, let there be described with the same center a circle *MKL,* which shall indicate the circumference of the Earth. Between these let there be drawn another circle *GHFI,* to represent the lowest circle of the Lunar

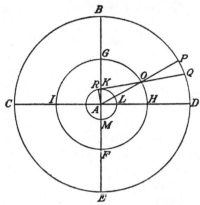

sphere and the one nearest the Earth, in which we are to imagine this star to be. And let it first be in its greatest altitude, near the point *G*: it is clear that it is entirely without diversity of aspect; for the two lines, one drawn from the center of the Earth, and the other drawn from the eye placed on the surface of the Earth, unite in one and the same point of the circle of the Primum Mobile *CBDE,* that is, in the point *B,* or near it if the star is not exactly at G. For this star is removed 6 degrees from the vertex, when it is for us at its highest point; which distance, however, produces no sensible variation from the vertex itself. But let this star be placed in the same circle *GHFI* at its lowest altitude, which is the point *O,* and, if the eye is placed at *K* on the surface of the Earth, the star will necessarily be seen in another place on the outermost circle from what it will if the eye is at A, the center of the Earth. For, if lines are drawn from *K* on the surface, and *A,* the center of the Earth, through *O,* which is the position of the star, to the outermost orbit *BDEC,* the line from *A* through *O* will fall in *P,* while the line from *K* through the same point *O* will fall in *Q. PQ,* therefore, is the arc of the Primum Mobile showing the diversity of aspect of the star.

105

I will try to determine, therefore, the length of the arc PQ, so that we may learn how great is the diversity of aspect which this star has when it is at its nearest point to the horizon, if it is placed in the circle $IGHF$, immediately below the orbit of the Moon, at the point O. That this may be done more conveniently, let the line QOK be produced until another line drawn from the center A meets it perpendicularly, and let the point of meeting be R. Since the angle BKO is known by observation—for it is the complement of the least altitude of the star itself, namely 62 degrees, 5 minutes—its vertical angle RKA will be known, being its equal. Furthermore, the angle KRA is by hypothesis a right angle; and the side KA is known by some measurement or other, for it is the semidiameter of the Earth itself. AR will be found by Proposition 29 of Regiomontanus concerning plane triangles. If, therefore, we give to the semidiameter of the Earth, KA, as being the whole sine, since it is the side opposite the right angle R, the length of 100,000 units, the side AR proves to be 88,363 units. Now at last I form my concept of the triangle ROA, two sides of which, RA and AO, are known. For AO is the distance from the center of the Earth to the lowest surface of the orbit of the Moon, which distance, with Copernicus, I have set at 5,200,000 of the same units in which the semidiameter of the Earth, AK, was reckoned at 100,000 (for I find it best to make use of larger numbers in this computation, that the calculation may be carried on more conveniently and the result be given more exactly); and since in the afore-mentioned triangle the angle ORA is by hypothesis a right angle, the angle ROA will be found by the 27th Proposition of Regiomontanus on plane triangles. For by multiplying the side AR into the whole sine, we get 8,836,300,000, which number, being divided by the side AO, gives 1699 units, the sine, namely, of the angle ROA, whose arc is 0 degrees, 58½ minutes; and this number determines the size of the required angle. To this angle, ROA, the angle POQ is equal, since it is its vertical angle, as is manifest from the principles of geometry. Therefore, the arc PQ, which is the measure of this angle (for, owing to the immense distance between the Lunar sphere and the Primum Mobile, the arc PQ does not differ sensi-

Plate 13

Courtesy Archiv für Kunst und Geschichte

Heinrich Hertz

Plate 14

Courtesy Archiv für Kunst und Geschichte, Berlin

Johannes Kepler

Plate 15

Jean Baptiste Lamarck

Plate 16

Antoine Lavoisier

bly from the arc of the circle intercepted by the same lines at the distance OP) and indicates the parallax of the star, will be 58½ minutes, which was what we had to find. So great, therefore, would have been the diversity of aspect of this star in the position O, as between that place which it held near the vertex and that in which it was seen when nearest the horizon. But after making many careful observations, as I said above, with a most delicate and accurate instrument, I found that this was not the case. Whence I concluded that this star which has recently become visible is not in the circle $IGHF$, in the uppermost region, that is, of the air, immediately below the orbit of the Moon, nor in any place yet nearer the Earth—for in the latter case the arc PQ would have produced a greater length, and the diversity of aspect would be greater—but that it is situated far above the Lunar sphere, in the heaven itself, and in fact in some orbit so far removed from the Earth that the line KA, the semidiameter of the Earth, has no sensible size in respect to it, but that the whole Earth, when compared to it, is observed to be no more than a point; and this has been found by the founders of the science to be in the eighth sphere or not far from it, in the higher orbits of the three superior planets. Whence this star will be placed in the heavens themselves, either in the eighth orbit with the other fixed stars or in the spheres which are immediately beneath it. That it is not in the orbit of Saturn, however, or in that of Jupiter, or in that of Mars, or in that of any one of the other planets, is clear from this fact: after the lapse of six months it had not advanced by its own motion a single minute from that place in which I first saw it; and this it must have done if it were in some planetary orbit. For, unlike the Primum Mobile, it would be moved by the peculiar motion of the orbit itself, unless it were at rest at one or the other pole of the orbits of the Secundum Mobile; from which, however, as I have shown above, it is removed 28 degrees. For the entire orbits, revolving on their own poles, carry along their own stars, or (as I see Pliny and some others hold) are carried along by them; unless, indeed one would deny the belief accepted by philosophers and mathematicians, and assert (what is absurd) that the stars alone revolve, while the orbits are fixed. Therefore, if this star were placed in some one of the orbits of the seven wandering stars, it would necessarily be carried around with the orbit itself to which it were affixed, in the opposite direction to the daily revolution. And, furthermore, this motion, even in the case of the orbit which moves the slowest, that of Saturn, would, after such a length of time, be noticed, though one were to make his observation without any instrument at all.

Therefore, this new star is neither in the region of the Element, below the Moon, nor among the orbits of the seven wandering stars, but it is in the eighth sphere, among the other fixed stars, which was what we had to prove. Hence it follows that it is not some peculiar kind of comet or some other kind of fiery meteor become visible. For none of these are generated in the heavens themselves, but they are below the Moon, in the upper region of the air, as all philosophers testify; unless one would believe with Albategnius that comets are produced, not in the air, but in the heavens. For he believes that he has observed a comet above the Moon, in the sphere of Venus. That this can be the case, is not yet clear to me. But, please God, sometime, if a comet shows itself in our age, I will investigate the truth of the matter. Even should we assume that it can happen (which I, in company with other philosophers, can hardly admit), still it does not follow that this star is a kind of comet; first, by reason of its very form, which is the same as the form of the real stars and different from the form of all the comets hitherto seen, and then because, in such a length of time, it advances neither latitudinally nor longitudinally by any motion of its own, as comets have been observed to do. For, although these sometimes seem to remain in one place several days, still, when the observation is made carefully by exact instruments, they are seen not to keep the same position for so very long or so very exactly. I conclude, therefore, that this star is not some kind of comet or a fiery meteor, whether these be generated beneath the Moon or above the Moon, but that it is a star shining in the firmament itself—one that has never previously been seen before our time, in any age since the beginning of the world.

108

EDUARD BUCHNER

(1860–1917)

The pioneer work of Buchner consisted of his demonstration that the alcoholic fermentation of sugars is due to the action of enzymes in yeast and not to physiological processes in the living yeast cells, as Pasteur and previous chemists had assumed. This opened the way to the chemical study of enzymes, and to all the subsequent developments in their field. Buchner, a German chemist who was killed in the First World War, was awarded the Nobel prize in chemistry in 1907 for this discovery.

ALCOHOLIC FERMENTATION WITHOUT YEAST

A SEPARATION of the fermentative action of living yeast cells has not previously been successful; in the following, a procedure is described which solves this problem.

One thousand grams of brewers' yeast, purified for the preparation of pressed yeast but still not treated with potato starch, is carefully mixed and then rubbed with an equal weight of quartz sand and 250 grams of kieselguhr, until the mass becomes moist and plastic. The paste is then treated with 100 grams of water and, wrapped in a press cloth is placed gradually under a pressure of 400 to 500 atmospheres: 300 cubic centimeters of press juice result. The residual cake is again rubbed, sieved and treated with 100 grams of water; treated once more in the hydraulic press with the same pressure, it gives another 150 cubic centimeters of press juice. From 1 kilo of yeast there is thus obtained 500 cubic centimeters of press juice which contains about 300 cubic centimeters of substances which are cell contents. To remove traces of cloudiness, the press juice is finally shaken with 4 grams of kieselguhr and filtered through a paper filter with repeated refiltrations of the first filtrate.

The press juice thus obtained is a clear, slightly opalescent, yellow liquid with a pleasant yeastlike odor. The specific gravity was once found to be 1.0416 (17°C.). When this is heated, a strong separation of coagulum occurs, so that the liquid almost completely solidifies: the formation of insoluble flakes begins at about 35 to 40 degrees; even before this, bubbles of gas, evidently carbonic acid, were seen rising, for the liquid itself is saturated with this gas.[1] The press juice contains over 10 per cent dry substance. In an earlier, less well-prepared press juice there were 6.7 per cent dry substance, 1.15 per cent ash, and according to nitrogen content, 3.7 per cent protein substances.

The most interesting property of the press juice lies in this, that it can cause fermentation of a carbohydrate. By mixing it with an equal volume of a concentrated raw-sugar solution, there occurs after one-quarter to one hour a regular evolution of carbon dioxide which lasts for a day. Grape, fruit, and malt sugar behave in the same way, but no appearance of fermentation occurs in mixtures of the press juice with saturated milk sugar or mannite solutions, just as these bodies are also not fermented by living brewers' yeast cells. Mixtures of press juice and sugar solution which have been fermenting for several days, when set in the icebox, usually grow turbid without the appearance of microscopic organisms, but at 700 times magnification they show a rather considerable number of protein curds, whose separation apparently depends upon the acids resulting from the fermentation. Saturation of the mixture of press juice and saccharose solution with chloroform does not hinder the fermentation but leads to an early precipitation of proteins. Filtration of the press juice through a sterilized Berkefeldt kieselguhr filter, which safely holds back all yeast cells, has just as slight an effect on the strength of fermentation; the mixture of the entirely clear filtrate with sterilized raw-sugar solution at the temperature of the icebox undergoes fermentation, somewhat delayed, after about a day. If a parchment-paper bag is filled with press juice in a 37 per cent raw-sugar solution, the surface of the bag after some

---

[1] Plant physiologists must decide whether this carbonic acid has some connection with oxidation processes related to respiration.

hours is covered with numerous small gas bubbles; naturally lively gas evolution was observed inside the bag, also due to diffusion of the sugar solution inward. Further studies must determine whether the bearer of the fermenting action can actually diffuse through the parchment paper, as it seems. The fermenting power of the press juice is usually lost with time: five days in ice water in a half-filled flask of preserved press juice leads to inactivity toward saccharose. However, it is noteworthy that when treated with raw-sugar solution, this fermentatively active press juice retains its fermenting power at least two weeks in the icebox. A favorable action must be assumed from this for the action of the carbonic acid formed in the reaction in holding off the oxygen of the air; but the easily assimilable sugar could also contribute to obtaining the agent.

Too few studies have yet been made to enable a conclusion to be drawn as to the nature of the active substance in the press juice. When the press juice is warmed to 40 to 50 degrees, carbon dioxide evolution first occurs, then general separation of coagulated protein. After an hour this was filtered, with numerous refilterings. The clear filtrate still had weak fermenting power toward raw sugar in one study, but in a second, none; the active substance therefore appears either to lose its action at this surprisingly low temperature or to coagulate and precipitate. Further, 20 cubic centimeters of the press juice was put into triple its volume of absolute alcohol and the precipitate sucked off and dried over sulfuric acid in a vacuum; 2 grams of dry substance resulted, and upon digestion of this with 10 cubic centimeters of water, only the smallest part again dissolved. The filtrate from this had no fermenting action on raw sugar. This experiment must be repeated; especially the isolation of the active substance by ammonium sulfate will be attempted.

Up to now, the following conclusions have been drawn for the theory of fermentation. First, it is recognized that to conduct the fermentation process, such a complicated apparatus as the yeast cell presents it is not required. It is considered that the bearer of the fermenting action of the press juice is much more probably

111

a dissolved substance, doubtless a protein; this will be called *zymase*.

The view that a protein especially formed from the yeast cell causes fermentation was expressed as long ago as 1858 by M. Traube as the enzyme or ferment theory, and it was later specially defended by F. Hoppe-Seyler. The separation of such an enzyme from yeast cells, however, had not so far been successful.

It still remains questionable also whether the zymase can be considered an addition to the enzymes already longer known. As C. v. Nägeli has already mentioned, there are important differences between fermenting action and the action of ordinary enzymes. The latter are solely hydrolytic and can be imitated by the simplest chemical media. A. v. Baeyer has recently increased our understanding of the chemical processes in alcoholic fermentation when he related them to relatively simple principles, but the decomposition of sugar to alcohol and carbon dioxide still is one of the more complicated reactions; the breakdown of carbon compounds in this manner has not been accomplished by any other method. There is also an important difference in the heat of the reaction.

Invertin can be extracted with water from yeast cells killed by dry heat (heated one hour at 150 degrees), and by precipitation with alcohol it can easily be isolated as a water-soluble powder. The substance active in fermentation cannot be obtained in a similar way. It is no longer present as a rule in yeast cells heated so high; alcoholic precipitation of the product of an attempt such as the above leads only to a water-insoluble modification. It can hardly be doubted, therefore, that zymase belongs to the true proteins and stands closer to the living protoplasm of the yeast cell than does invertin.

The French bacteriologist, Miguel, has similar views as to urase which is separated from bacteria and shows the so-called "urea fermentation"; he calls this protoplasm which acts directly outside the cell walls, lacking the protection of these, and which differs from that of the cell contents essentially only in this.[2]

[2] It must be noted here that the so-called "urea fermentation," the decom-

The experiments of E. Fisher and P. Lindner on the action of the yeast *Monilia candida* on raw sugar also belong here. This yeast ferments saccharose; but neither Ch. E. Hansen nor the authors mentioned could extract from fresh or dried yeast with water an enzyme like invertin which could cause the splitting into grape and fruit sugars. The study went entirely otherwise when Fisher and Lindner used Monilia yeast in which, by careful grinding with glass powder, a part of the cells were first opened. The inverting action was now unrecognizable. "The inverting agent seemed here truly not to be a water-stable, soluble enzyme but seemed to be a part of the living protoplasm."

The fermentation of sugars by zymase can occur within the yeast cells, [3] but apparently the yeast cells separate this protein out into the sugar solution, where it causes fermentation.[4] The occurrences in alcoholic fermentation are, then, perhaps to be considered a physiological act only as far as the separation of the zymase by the living yeast cells. Nägeli and Löw have show that the nutrient solution from yeast cells, which is originally weakly alkaline (from K_3PO_4), later becomes neutral at 30 degrees, and even after fifteen hours, a considerable amount of protein coagulable by heating has diffused out. Actually, it appears, as the above study shows, that zymase can pass through parchment paper.

---

position of urea into ammonia and carbon dioxide, is chemically very different from the usual fermentation process and therefore in general cannot be considered much like alcoholic fermentation. It is a simple hydrolysis, obtained with water even at 120 degrees.

[3] The diosmotic properties make this seem possible.

[4] This also seems to clarify the study of J. de Rey-Pailhade, who prepared a weak alcoholic extract (22 per cent) from fresh brewers' yeast with the addition of some grape sugar. After being freed from microorganisms by filtering through a sterile Arsonval candle, this extract, which contained sugar, spontaneously developed carbonic acid in the absence of oxygen.

ROBERT WILHELM BUNSEN

(1811–1899)

Professor of chemistry at Heidelberg for many years, this great German chemist shares with Kirchhoff credit for developing spectrum analysis. His inventions were many: the well-known Bunsen burner, the charcoal pile, an ice calorimeter, the filter pump, the Bunsen disk photometer, the Bunsen cell and the magnesium light. With Roscoe he formulated the reciprocity law, aand with Kirchhoff discovered the elements cesium and rubidium. He wrote on many subjects in chemistry, physics and geology, including hygrometry, gasometry, the analysis of ashes and mineral waters, etc.

GENETIC RELATIONS OF IGNEOUS ROCKS

THE ROCKS of Iceland present such a variety that at first it does not seem possible to discover the law which governed their origin. On examining them more closely, however, one soon finds a character common to all these eruptive masses, whatever their age, however varied their mineralogical constitution may be.

There are in Iceland, and probably in almost all the great volcanic systems as well, two principal groups of rocks that are easy to recognize when they are isolated, which unite with each other in all possible proportions. These are the *normal trachytic* rocks on the one side and the *normal pyroxenic* rocks on the other. The minerals peculiar to each of these types of rock, although varying greatly, nevertheless do not alter the general composition. . . .

The ratio existing [in the trachytes] between the silicic acid and the lime, as well as the magnesia, is nearly always constant, whereas that of the aluminium oxide to the iron oxide varies

114

greatly. It is easy to explain this fact by known phenomena. When an alloy of lead and silver cools, the silver found in each of the layers amounts in proportion to the order of solidification. Likewise, alloys of gold and silver are never homogeneous. Facts of the same nature are encountered in the cooling of the silicates, inasmuch as the least fusible of their elements solidified first, then those which were more so, and finally those which were fusible to the highest degree. The form of crystallization does not enter, in this case. Therefore, there is no reason to be surprised that a homogeneous rock in a melted state first permits the solidification of silicates rich in iron oxide and last, of those rich in aluminium oxide. Field observation, moreover, confirms this.

In Iceland, a notable difference is found in the composition of the two extremities of a trachytic column intact in the body of a vast rock . . .

If these variations in the composition are really due to differential solidification as an effect of temperature and pressure, it is easy to understand that inasmuch as one of the constituent parts of the mixture takes the place of the other in proportion as it diminishes, the sum of the two ought not to vary greatly. . . .

Taking the average of each of these two groups of analyses, numbers but slightly different from those of the individual specimens are obtained. This permits the general composition of the two great sources of normal trachytic and pyroxenic rocks— that is, the most acid and most basic rocks that Iceland has—to be determined; here it is:

	Composition of normal trachytic rocks	Composition of normal pyroxenic rocks
Silicic acid	76,67	48,47
Aluminium and iron oxide	14,23	30,16
Calcium oxide	1,44	11,87
Magnesium oxide	0,28	6,89
Potassium oxide	3,20	0,65
Sodium oxide	4,18	1,96
	100,00	100,00

According to these analyses, the ratio of oxygen of the acid to that of the bases is, on the average, ::3:0,596 for the trachytic rocks and ::3:1,998 for the pyroxenic rocks. All the other, unmodified rocks of Iceland which do not belong to one of these two groups have such a composition that the oxygen of their acid is to that of their base ::3:0,596 to 1,998. Therefore, it is probable that the rocks are born of the mixture of the two principal species. In view of this fact, one wonders whether all the unmetamorphosed rocks of Iceland were born of this fusion, or rather, in other words, if there were not but two great volcanic centers responsible for the formation of Iceland from most distant times to our day.

. . . To cite but one example, there is, opposite Masfell, in one of the valleys which cuts the chain of Esja in the southeast, a dike of trachyte which cuts the pyroxenic conglomerate. This trachyte, which is white at the center, becomes darker and richer in iron as it approaches the surrounding mass. . . .

Consulting the average analyses given above suffices to show that the interior part of the dike presents the composition of the normal trachytic mass, whereas the rock which encloses it has that of the normal pyroxenic mass, and that the periphery of the dike is formed by the fusion of the two rocks in the ratio of 0,5923 of pyroxenic mass to 1 of trachytic. . . .

For the rest on examining this dike closely, it is easy to see that it has melted the surrounding rock at all the points where it has touched it. The amount of mixing varies with proximity to the contact, but never reaches the center of the dike. All of these analyses, as well as the field observations, prove that the rocks with composition intermediate between that of the acid and the basic rocks of Iceland cannot be regarded as having been formed all at the same time; instead, they have been formed at any time when there was an injection of one of these rocks through an old mass of the other.

JEAN DOMINIQUE CASSINI

(1625–1712)

Jean Dominique (or Giovanni Domenico) Cassini was but one member of a family of French astronomers of Italian descent. Among his discoveries were four satellites of Saturn, the division in Saturn's ring which has since carried his name, the tables of Jupiter's moons, the zodiacal light and the obliquity of the ecliptic. He also enlarged our knowledge of the parallax of the sun, the rotation periods of Venus, and the eccentricity of the earth's orbit.

THE DISCOVERY OF THE DIVISION IN SATURN'S RING

AFTER THE discoveries which have been made at different times concerning the globe of Saturn, its ring and its satellites, in part by Huyghens who discovered one of the satellites which revolves around Saturn in 16 days less 47 minutes, and in part by Cassini who discovered two others of which we will give the history at an early date, it seemed that there was nothing more to discover concerning the planet; however, the latest observations that Cassini has made concerning the body of Saturn and its ring, show that in the Heavens as well as on the Earth, something new to observe always appears.

After the emergence of Saturn from the rays of the Sun as a morning star in the year 1675, the globe of the planet appeared with a dark band, similar to those of Jupiter, extending the length of the ring from East to West, as it is nearly always shown by the 34-foot telescope, and the breadth of the ring was divided by a dark line into two equal parts, of which the interior and nearer one to the globe was very bright, and the exterior part slightly dark. There was about the same difference between

117

the colors of these two parts that there is between dull silver, and burnished silver, which had never before been observed but which has since been seen in the same telescope, more clearly at twilight and in moonlight than on a darker night.

This appearance gave an impression of a double ring, of which the *inferior* ring, being larger and darker, had superposed upon it another that is narrower and brighter, and reminds one that in the year 1671, when the extensions of Saturn were on the verge of disappearing they contracted beforehand, perhaps because the outer part of the ring which was single and dark, disappeared before the inner part, which was double and brighter.

In the same year, 1671, the shorter diameter of the ring was still less than the diameter of the globe which extended outside the ring on the North and South sides, and this phase lasted until the immersion of Saturn in the rays of the Sun in the year 1676. But after its emersion, which took place last summer, the shorter diameter of the ring exceeded that of the globe. There is an observation by Hevelius in the English Journal, which corresponds to the first of these two phases; but as he has noted neither the band of Saturn, nor the distinction which can be seen in the ring, one has reason to judge that the telescopes which he uses are much inferior to those of the Royal Observatory.

HENRY CAVENDISH

(1731–1810)

Although his name is associated primarily with the chemistry of gases, Cavendish also made important discoveries in physics. Something of an eccentric, he lived the life of a pathologically shy recluse, with a great library located four miles from his home, and left over a million pounds at his death. His major discovery was that of hydrogen (1766), then known as inflammable air, which he identified as an element and determined its specific gravity. He made water synthetically for the first time (*c.* 1783), and analyzed the composition of nitric acid and the atmosphere. He anticipated some of Faraday's researches in electricity, and devised the so-called Cavendish experiment (1798), an ingenious apparatus for measuring the density of the earth.

THREE PAPERS, CONTAINING EXPERIMENTS ON FACTITIOUS AIR

(Read May 29, Nov. 6 and Nov. 13, 1766)

BY FACTITIOUS air, I mean in general any kind of air which is contained in other bodies in an unelastic state, and is produced from thence by art.

By fixed air, I mean that particular species of factitious air, which is separated from alcaline substances by solution in acids or by calcination; and to which Dr. Black has given that name in his treatise on quick lime.

As fixed air makes a considerable part of the subject of the following papers, and as the name might incline one to think, that it signified any sort of air which is contained in other bodies in an unelastic form; I thought it best to give this explanation before I went any farther. . . .

Part I

Containing Experiments on Inflammable Air

I know of only three metallic substances, namely, zinc, iron and tin, that generate inflammable air by solution in acids; and these only by solution in the diluted vitriolic acid, or spirit of salt.

Zinc dissolves with great rapidity in both these acids; and unless they are very much diluted, generates a considerable heat. One ounce of zinc produces about 356 ounce measures of air: the quantity seems just the same whichsoever of these acids it is dissolved in. Iron dissolves readily in the diluted vitriolic acid, but not near so readily as zinc. One ounce of iron wire produces about 412 ounce measures of air: the quantity was just the same, whether the oil of vitriol was diluted with 1½, or 7 times its weight of water: so that the quantity of air produced seems not at all to depend on the strength of acid.

Iron dissolves but slowly in spirit of salt while cold: with the assistance of heat it dissolves moderately fast. The air produced thereby is inflammable, but I have not tried how much it produces.

Tin was found to dissolve scarce at all in oil of vitriol diluted with an equal weight of water, while cold: with the assistance of a moderate heat it dissolved slowly, and generated air, which was inflammable: the quantity was not ascertained.

Tin dissolves slowly in strong spirit of salt while cold: with the assistance of heat it dissolves moderately fast. One ounce of tinfoil yields 202 ounce measures of inflammable air.

These experiments were made, when the thermometer was at 50° and the barometer at 30 inches.

All these three metallic substances dissolve readily in the nitrous acid, and generate air; but the air is not at all inflammable. They also unite readily, with the assistance of heat, to the undiluted acid of vitriol; but very little of the salt, formed by their union with the acid, dissolves in the fluid. They all unite to the acid with a considerable effervescence, and discharge plenty of vapours, which smell strongly of the volatile sul-

120

phureous acid, and which are not at all inflammable. Iron is not sensibly acted on by this acid, without the assistance of heat; but zinc and tin are in some measure acted on by it, while cold.

It seems likely from hence, that, when either of the above-mentioned metallic substances are dissolved in spirit of salt, or the diluted vitriolic acid their phlogiston flies off, without having its nature changed by the acid, and forms the inflamable air; but that, when they are dissolved in the nitrous acid, or united by heat to the vitriolic acid, their phlogiston unites to part of the acid used for their solution, and flies off with it in fumes, the phlogiston losing its inflammable property by the union. The volatile sulphureous fumes, produced by uniting these metallic substances by heat to the undiluted vitriolic acid, shew plainly, that in this case their phlogiston unites to the acid; for it is well known, that the vitriolic sulphureous acid consists of the plain vitriolic acid united to phlogiston.[1] It is highly probable too, that the same thing happens in dissolving these metallic substances in the nitrous acid; as the fumes produced during the solution appear plainly to consist in great measure of the nitrous acid, and yet it appears, from their more penetrating smell and other reasons, that the acid must have undergone some change in its nature, which can hardly be attributed to anything else than its union with the phlogiston. As to the inflammable air, produced by dissolving these substances in spirit of salt or the diluted vitriolic acid, there is great reason to think, that it does not contain any of the acid in its composition; not only because it seems to be just the same whichsoever of these acids it is produced by; but also because there is an inflammable air, seemingly much of the same kind as this, produced from animal substances in putrefaction, and from vegetable substances in distillation, as will be shewen hereafter; though there can be no reason to suppose, that this kind of inflammable air owes its

[1] Sulphur is allowed by chymists, to consist of the plain vitriolic acid united to phlogiston. The volatile sulphureous acid appears to consist of the same acid united to a less proportion of phlogiston than what is required to form sulphur. A circumstance which I think shews the truth of this, is that if oil of vitriol be be distilled, from sulphur, the liquor, which comes over, will be the volatile sulphureous acid.

121

production to any acid. I now proceed to the experiments made on inflammable air.

I cannot find that this air has any tendency to lose its elasticity by keeping, or that it is all absorbed, either by water, or by fixed or volatile alcalies; as I have kept some by me for several weeks in a bottle inverted into a vessel of water, without any sensible decrease of bulk; and as I have also kept some for a few days, in bottles inverted into vessels of sope leys and spirit of sal ammoniac, without perceiving their bulk to be at all diminished.

It has been observed by others, that, when a piece of lighted paper is applied to the mouth of a bottle, containing a mixture of inflammable and common air, the air takes fire, and goes off with an explosion. In order to observe in what manner the effect varies according to the different proportions in which they are mixed, the following experiment was made.

Some of the inflammable air, produced by dissolving zinc in diluted oil of vitriol, was mixed with common air in several different proportions, and the inflammability of these mixtures tried one after the other in this manner. A quart bottle was filled with one of these mixtures. . . . The bottle was taken out of the water, set upright on a table, and the flame of a lamp or piece of lighted paper applied to its mouth. But, in order to prevent the included air from mixing with the outward air, before the flame could be applied, the mouth of the bottle was covered while under water, with a cap made of a piece of wood covered with a few folds of linen; which cap was not removed till the instant that the flame was applied. The mixtures were all tried in the same bottle; and, as they were all ready prepared, before the inflammability of any of them was tried, the time elapsed between each trial was but small: by which means I was better able to compare the loudness of the sound in each trial. The result of the experiment is as follows.

With one part of inflammable air to 9 of common air, the mixture would not take fire, on applying the lighted paper to the mouth of the bottle; but, on putting it down into the belly of the bottle, the air took fire, but made very little sound.

With 2 parts of inflammable to 8 of common air, it took fire immediately, on applying the flame to the mouth of the bottle, and went off with a moderately loud noise.

With 3 parts of inflammable air to 7 of common air, there was a very loud noise.

With 4 parts of inflammable to 6 of common air, the sound seemed very little louder.

With equal quantities of inflammable and common air, the sound seemed much the same. In the first of these trials, namely, that with one part of inflammable to 9 of common air, the mixture did not take fire all at once, on putting the lighted paper into the bottle; but one might perceive the flame to spread gradually through the bottle. In the three next trials, though they made an explosion, yet I could not perceive any light within the bottle. In all probability, the flame spread so instantly through the bottle, and was so soon over, that it had not time to make any impression on my eye. In the last mentioned trial, namely, that with equal quantities of inflammable and common air, a light was seen in the bottle, but which quickly ceased.

With 6 parts of inflammable to 4 of common air, the sound was not very loud: the mixture continued burning a short time in the bottle, after the sound was over.

With 7 parts of inflammable to 3 of common air, there was a very gentle bounce or rather puff: it continued burning for some seconds in the belly of the bottle.

A mixture of 8 parts of inflammable to 2 of common air caught fire on applying the flame, but without any noise: it continued burning for some time in the neck of the bottle, and then went out, without the flame ever extending into the belly of the bottle.

It appears from these experiments, that this air, like other inflammable substances, cannot burn without the assistance of common air. It seems too, that, unless the mixture contains more common than inflammable air, the common air therein is not sufficient to consume the whole of the inflammable air; whereby part of the inflammable air remains, and burns by means of the common air, which rushes into the bottle after the explosion.

In order to find whether there was any difference in point of inflammability between the air produced from different metals by different acids, five different sorts of air, namely: 1. Some produced from zinc by diluted oil of vitriol, and which had been kept about a fortnight; 2. Some of the same kind of air fresh made; 3. Air produced from zinc by spirit of salt; 4. Air from iron by the vitriolic acid; 5. Air from tin by spirit of salt; were each mixed separately with common air in the proportion of 2 parts of inflammable air to $7^7/_{10}$ of common air, and their inflammability tried in the same bottle, that was used for the former experiment, and with the same precautions. They each went off with a pretty loud noise, and without any difference in the sound that I could be sure of. Some more of each of the above parcels of air were then mixed with common air, in the proportion of 7 parts of inflammable air to $3\frac{1}{5}$ of common air, and tried in the same way as before. They each of them went off with a gentle bounce, and burnt some time in the bottle, without my being able to perceive any difference between them.

In order to avoid being hurt, in case the bottle should burst by the explosion, I have commonly, in making these sort of experiments, made use of an apparatus contrived in such manner, that, by pulling a string, I drew the flame of a lamp over the mouth of the bottle, and at the same time pulled off the cap, while I stood out of the reach of danger. I believe, however, that this precaution is not very necessary; as I have never known a bottle to burst in any of the trials I have made.

The specific gravity of each of the above-mentioned sorts of inflammable air, except the first, was tried in the following manner. A bladder holding about 100 ounce measures was filled with inflammable air, . . . and the air pressed out again as perfectly as possible. By this means the small quantity of air remaining in the bladder was almost intirely of the inflammable kind. 80 ounce measures of the inflammable air, produced from zinc by the vitriolic acid, were then forced into the bladder in the same manner: after which, the pewter pipe was taken out of the wooden cap of the bladder, the orifice of the cap stopt up with a bit of lute, and the bladder weighed. A hole was then made in the lute, the air pressed out as perfectly as possible, and

124

the bladder weighed again. It was found to have increased in weight 40¾ grains. Therefore the air pressed out of the bladder weighs 40¾ grains less than an equal quantity of common air: but the quantity of air pressed out of the bladder must be nearly the same as that which was forced into it, i.e. 80 ounce measures: consequently 80 ounce measures of this sort of inflammable air weigh 40¾ grains less than an equal bulk of common air. The three other sorts of inflammable air were then tried in the same bladder, immediately one after the other. In the trial with air from zinc by spirit of salt, the bladder increased 40½ grains on forcing out the air. In the trial with the air from iron, it increased 41½ grains, and in that with the air from tin, it increased 41 grains. The heat of the air, when this experiment was made, was 50°; the barometer stood at 29¾ inches.

There seems no reason to imagine, from these experiments, that there is any difference in point of specific gravity between these four sorts of inflammable air; as the small difference observed in these trials is in all probability less than what may arise from the unavoidable errors of the experiment. Taking a medium therefore of the different trials, 80 ounce measures of inflammable air weigh 41 grains less than an equal bulk of common air.

Therefore, if the density of common air, at the time when this experiment was tried, was 800 times less than that of water, which, I imagine, must be near the truth, inflammable air must be 5490 times lighter than water, or near 7 times lighter than common air. But if the density of common air was 850 times less than that of water, then would inflammable air be 9200 times lighter than water, or $10^{8}/_{10}$ lighter than common air.

This method of finding the density of factitious air is very convenient and sufficiently accurate, where the density of the air to be tried is not much less than that of common air, but cannot be much depended on in the present case, both on account of the uncertainty in the density of common air, and because we cannot be certain but what some common air might be mixed with the inflammable air in the bladder, notwithstanding the precautions used to prevent it; both which causes may produce a considerable error, where the density of the air to be tried is many times less than that of common air. For this reason, I made the following experiments.

I endeavoured to find the weight of the air discharged from a given quantity of zinc by solution in the vitriolic acid. . . . A is a bottle filled near full with oil of vitriol diluted with about six times its weight of water: B is a glass tube fitted into its mouth, and secured with lute: C is a glass cylinder fastened on the end of the tube, and secured also with lute. The cylinder has a small hole at its upper end to let the inflammable air escape, and is filled with dry pearl-ashes in coarse powder. The whole apparatus, together with the zinc, which was intended to put in, and the lute which was to be used in securing the tube to the neck of the bottle, were first weighed carefully; its weight was 11930 grains. The zinc was then put in, and the tube put in its place. By this means, the inflammable air was made to pass through the dry pearl-ashes; whereby it must have been pretty effectually deprived of any acid or watery vapours that could have ascended along with it. The use of the glass tube B was to collect the minute jets of liquor, that were thrown up by the effervescence, and to prevent their touching the pearl-ashes; for which reason, a small space was left between the glass-tube and the pearl-ashes in the cylinder. When the zinc was dissolved, the whole apparatus was weighed again, and was found to have lost 11¾ grains in weight;[2] which loss is principally owing to the weight of the inflammable air discharged. But it must be observed, that, before the effervescence, that part of the bottle and cylinder, which was not occupied by other more solid matter, was filled with common air; whereas, after the effervescence, it was filled with inflammable air; so that, upon that account alone, supposing no more inflammable air to be discharged than what was sufficient to fill that space, the weight of the apparatus

[2] As the quantity of lute was but small, and as this kind of lute does not lose a great deal of its weight by being kept in a moderately dry room, no sensible error could arise from the drying of the lute during the experiment.

would have been diminished by the difference of the weight of that quantity of common air and inflammable air. The whole empty space in the bottle and cylinder was about 980 grain measures, there is no need of exactness; and the difference of the weight of that quantity of common and inflammable air is about one grain: therefore the true weight of the inflammable air discharged, is 10¾ grains. The quantity of zinc used was 254 grains, and consequently the weight of the air discharged is 1/23 or 1/24 of the weight of the zinc.

It was before said, that one grain of zinc yielded 356 grain measures of air: therefore 254 grains of zinc yield 90427 grain measures of air; which we have just found to weigh 10¾ grains; therefore inflammable air is about 8410 times lighter than water, or 10½ times lighter than common air.

The quantity of moisture condensed in the pearl-ashes was found to be about 1¼ grains.

By another experiment, tried exactly in the same way, the density of inflammable air came out 8300 times less than that of water.

The specific gravity of the air, produced by dissolving zinc in spirit of salt, was tried exactly in the same manner. 244 grains of zinc being dissolved in spirit of salt diluted with about four times its weight of water, the loss in effervescence was 10¾ grains; the empty space in the bottle and cylinder was 914 grain measures; whence the weight of the inflammable air was 9¾ grains, and consequently its density was 8910 times less than that of water.

By another experiment, its specific gravity came out 9030 times lighter than water.

A like experiment was tried with iron. 250½ grains of iron being dissolved in oil of vitriol diluted with four times its weight of water, the loss in effervescence was 13 grains, the empty space 1420 grain measures. Therefore the weight of the inflammable air was 11⅜ grains, i.e. about 1/22 of the weight of the iron, and its density was 8973 times less than that of water. The moisture condensed was 1¼ grains.

127

A like experiment was tried with tin. 607 grains of tinfoil being dissolved in strong spirit of salt, the loss in effervescence was 14¾ grains, the empty space 873 grain measures: therefore the weight of the inflammable air was 13¾ grains, i.e. 1/44 of the tin, and its density 8918 times less than that of water. The quantity of moisture condensed was about three grains.

It is evident, that the truth of these determinations depend[s] on a supposition, that none of the inflammable air is absorbed by the pearl-ashes. In order to see whether this was the case or not, I dissolved 86 grains of zinc in diluted acid of vitriol, and received the air in a measuring bottle in the common way. Immediately after, I dissolved the same quantity of zinc in the same kind of acid, and made the air to pass into the same measuring bottle, through a cylinder filled with dry pearl-ashes. . . . I could not perceive any difference in their bulks.

It appears from these experiments, that there is but little, if any, difference in point of density between the different sorts of inflammable air. Whether the difference of density observed between the air procured from zinc, by the vitriolic and that by the marine acid is real, or whether it is only owing to the error of the experiment, I cannot pretend to say. By a medium of the experiments, inflammable air comes out 8760 times lighter than water, or eleven times lighter than common air.

In order to see whether inflammable air, in the state in which it is, when contained in the inverted bottles, where it is in contact with water, contains any considerable quantity of moisture dissolved in it, I forced 192 ounce measures of inflammable air, through a cylinder filled with dry pearl-ashes, by means of the same apparatus, which I used for filling the bladders with inflammable air. . . . The cylinder was weighed carefully before and after the air was forced through; whereby it was found to have increased 1 grain in weight. The empty space in the cylinder was 248 grains, the difference of weight of which quantity of common and inflammable air is ¼ of a grain. Therefore the real quantity of moisture condensed in the pearl-ashes is 1¼ grain. The weight of 192 ounce measures of inflammable air deprived of its moisture appears from the former experiments to be 10½ grains; therefore its weight when saturated with moisture would be 11¾ grains. Therefore, inflammable air, in that state in which it is in, when kept under the inverted bottles, contains near 1/9 its weight of moisture; and its specific gravity in that state is 7840 times less than that of water.

THOMAS CROWDER CHAMBERLIN

(1843–1928)

As a teacher of geology at the universities of Wisconsin and Chicago, and founder of the *Journal of Geology*, Chamberlin exerted an influence on more than a generation of geologists. As geologist with the United States Geological Survey, his work dealt with the Pleistocene glacial phenomena of the Mississippi Valley. With F. R. Moulton, he formulated the spiral-nebula hypothesis to account for the origin of the earth, and devoted the latter years of his life to research in the fundamental geology of the solar system, including comets and meteorites. His works include *General Treatise on Geology* (1906), *The Origin of the Earth* (1916), *The Two Solar Families* (1928), and *The Sun's Children* (1928).

THE METHOD OF MULTIPLE WORKING HYPOTHESES

THERE ARE two fundamental modes of study. The one is an attempt to follow by close imitation the processes of previous thinkers and to acquire the results of their investigations by memorizing. It is study of a merely secondary, imitative, or acquisitive nature. In the other mode the effort is to think independently, or at least individually. It is primary or creative study. The endeavor is to discover new truth or to make a new combination of truth or at least to develop by one's own effort an individualized assemblage of truth. The endeavor is to think for one's self, whether the thinking lies wholly in the fields of previous thought or not. It is not necessary to this mode of study that the subject-matter should be new. Old material may be reworked. But it is essential that the process of thought and its results be individual and independent, not the mere following of previous lines of thought ending in predetermined

130

results. The demonstration of a problem in Euclid precisely as laid down is an illustration of the former; the demonstration of the same proposition by a method of one's own or in a manner distinctively individual is an illustration of the latter, both lying entirely within the realm of the known and old.

Creative study however finds its largest application in those subjects in which, while much is known, more remains to be learned. The geological field is preeminently full of such subjects, indeed it presents few of any other class. There is probably no field of thought which is not sufficiently rich in such subjects to give full play to investigative modes of study.

Three phases of mental procedure have been prominent in the history of intellectual evolution thus far. What additional phases may be in store for us in the evolutions of the future it may not be prudent to attempt to forecast. These three phases may be styled the method of the ruling theory, the method of the working hypothesis, and the method of multiple working hypotheses.

In the earlier days of intellectual development the sphere of knowledge was limited and could be brought much more nearly than now within the compass of a single individual. As a natural result those who then assumed to be wise men, or aspired to be thought so, felt the need of knowing, or at least seeming to know, all that was known, as a justification of their claims. So also as a natural counterpart there grew up an expectancy on the part of the multitude that the wise and the learned would explain whatever new thing presented itself. Thus pride and ambition on the one side and expectancy on the other joined hands in developing the putative all-wise man whose knowledge boxed the compass and whose acumen found an explanation for every new puzzle which presented itself. Although the pretended compassing of the entire horizon of knowledge has long since become an abandoned affectation, it has left its representatives in certain intellectual predilections. As in the earlier days, so still, it is a too frequent habit to hastily conjure up an explanation for every new phenomenon that presents itself. Interpretation leaves its proper place at the end of the intellectual

131

procession and rushes to the forefront. Too often a theory is promptly born and evidence hunted up to fit in afterward. Laudable as the effort at explanation is in its proper place, it is an almost certain source of confusion and error when it runs before a serious inquiry into the phenomenon itself. A strenuous endeavor to find out precisely what the phenomenon really is should take the lead and crowd back the question, commendable at a later stage, "How came this so?" First the full facts, then the interpretation thereof, is the normal order.

The habit of precipitate explanation leads rapidly on to the birth of general theories. When once an explanation or special theory has been offered for a given phenomenon, self-consistency prompts to the offering of the same explanation or theory for like phenomena similar to the original one. . . . For a time these hastily born theories are likely to be held in a tentative way with some measure of candor or at least some self-illusion of candor. . . . It is in this tentative stage that the affections enter with their blinding influence. . . . Important as the intellectual affections are as stimuli and as rewards, they are nevertheless dangerous factors in research. All too often they put under strain the integrity of the intellectual processes. . . . Briefly summed up, the evolution is this: a premature explanation passes first into a tentative theory, then into an adopted theory, and lastly into a ruling theory.

The defects of the method are obvious and its errors grave. If one were to name the central psychological fault, it might be stated as the admission of intellectual affection to the place that should be dominated by impartial, intellectual rectitude alone.

So long as intellectual interest dealt chiefly with the intangible, so long it was possible for this habit of thought to survive and to maintain its dominance, because the phenomena themselves, being largely subjective, were plastic in the hands of the ruling idea; but so soon as investigation turned itself earnestly to an inquiry into natural phenomena whose manifestations are tangible, whose properties are inflexible, and whose laws are

132

rigorous, the defects of the method became manifest and effort at reformation ensued. The first great endeavor was repressive. The advocates of reform insisted that theorizing should be restrained and the simple determination of facts should take its place. The effort was to make scientific study statistical instead of causal. Because theorizing in narrow lines had led to manifest evils theorizing was to be condemned. The reformation urged was not the proper control and utilization of theoretical effort but its suppression. We do not need to go backward more than a very few decades to find ourselves in the midst of this attempted reformation. Its weakness lay in its narrowness and its restrictiveness. There is no nobler aspiration of the human intellect than the desire to compass the causes of things. The disposition to find explanations and to develop theories is laudable in itself. It is only its ill-placed use and its abuse that are reprehensible. The vitality of study quickly disappears when the object sought is a mere collocation of unmeaning facts.

The inefficiency of this simply repressive reformation becoming apparent, improvement was sought in the method of the working hypothesis. This has been affirmed to be *the* scientific method. But it is rash to assume that any method is *the* method, at least that it is the ultimate method. The working hypothesis differs from the ruling theory in that it is used as a means of determining facts rather than as a proposition to be established. It has for its chief function the suggestion and guidance of lines of inquiry; the inquiry being made, not for the sake of the hypothesis, but for the sake of the facts and their elucidation. The hypothesis is a mode rather than an end. Under the ruling theory, the stimulus is directed to the finding of facts for the support of the theory. Under the working hypothesis, the facts are sought for the purpose of ultimate induction and demonstration, the hypothesis being but a means for the more ready development of facts and their relations.

It will be observed that the distinction is not such as to prevent a working hypothesis from gliding with the utmost ease into a ruling theory. Affection may as easily cling about a beloved

133

intellectual child when named an hypothesis as if named a theory, and its establishment in the one guise may become a ruling passion very much as in the other. The historical antecedents and the moral atmosphere associated with the working hypothesis lend some good influence however toward the preservation of its integrity.

Conscientiously followed, the method of the working hypothesis is an incalculable advance upon the method of the ruling theory; but it has some serious defects. One of these takes concrete form, as just noted, in the ease with which the hypothesis becomes a controlling idea. To avoid this grave danger, the method of multiple working hypotheses is urged. It differs from the simple working hypothesis in that it distributes the effort and divides the affections. It is thus in some measure protected against the radical defect of the two other methods. In developing the multiple hypotheses, the effort is to bring up into view every rational explanation of the phenomenon in hand and to develop every tenable hypothesis relative to its nature, cause or origin, and to give to all of these as impartially as possible a working form and a due place in the investigation. The investigator thus becomes the parent of a family of hypotheses; and by his parental relations to all is morally forbidden to fasten his affections unduly upon any one. In the very nature of the case, the chief danger that springs from affection is counteracted. Where some of the hypotheses have been already proposed and used, while others are the investigator's own creation, a natural difficulty arises, but the right use of the method requires the impartial adoption of all alike into the working family. The investigator thus at the outset puts himself in cordial sympathy and in parental relations (of adoption, if not of authorship,) with every hypothesis that is at all applicable to the case under investigation. Having thus neutralized so far as may be the partialities of his emotional nature, he proceeds with a certain natural and enforced erectness of mental attitude to the inquiry, knowing well that some of his intellectual children (by birth or adoption) must needs perish before maturity, but yet with the hope that several of them may survive the ordeal of crucial research, since it often proves in the end that several agencies were conjoined in the production of the phenomena. Honors must often be divided between hypotheses. One of the superiorities of multiple hypotheses as a working mode lies just here. In following a single hypothesis the mind is biased by the presumptions of its method toward a single explanatory conception. But an adequate explanation often involves the coördination of several causes. This is especially true when the research deals with a class of complicated phenomena naturally associated, but not necessarily of the same origin and nature, as for example the Basement Complex or the Pleistocene drift. Several agencies may participate not only but their proportions and importance may vary from instance to instance in the same field. The true explanation is therefore necessarily complex, and the elements of the complex are constantly varying. Such distributive explanations of phenomena are especially contemplated and encouraged by the method of multiple hypotheses and constitute one of its chief merits. For many reasons we are prone to refer phenomena to a single cause. It naturally follows that when we find an effective agency present, we are predisposed to be satisfied therewith. We are thus easily led to stop short of full results, sometimes short of the chief factors. The factor we find may not even be the dominant one, much less the full complement of agencies engaged in the accomplishment of the total phenomena under inquiry. The mooted question of the origin of the Great Lake basins may serve as an illustration. Several hypotheses have been urged by as many different students of the problem as the cause of these great excavations. All of these have been pressed with great force and with an admirable array of facts. Up to a certain point we are compelled to go with each advocate. It is practically demonstrable that these basins were river valleys antecedent to the glacial incursion. It is equally demonstrable that there was a blocking up of outlets. We must conclude then that the present basins owe their origin in part to the preëxistence of river valleys and to the blocking up of their

135

outlets by drift. That there is a temptation to rest here, the history of the question shows. But on the other hand it is demonstrable that these basins were occupied by great lobes of ice and were important channels of glacial movement. The leeward drift shows much material derived from their bottoms. We cannot therefore refuse assent to the doctrine that the basins owe something to glacial excavation. Still again it has been urged that the earth's crust beneath these basins was flexed downward by the weight of the ice load and contracted by its low temperature and that the basins owe something to crustal deformation. This third cause tallies with certain features not readily explained by the others. And still it is doubtful whether all these combined constitute an adequate explanation of the phenomena. Certain it is, at least, that the measure of participation of each must be determined before a satisfactory elucidation can be reached. The full solution therefore involves not only the recognition of multiple participation but an estimate of the measure and mode of each participation. For this the simultaneous use of a full staff of working hypotheses is demanded. The method of the single working hypothesis or the predominant working hypothesis is incompetent. . . .

A special merit of the use of a full staff of hypotheses coördinately is that in the very nature of the case it invites thoroughness. The value of a working hypothesis lies largely in the significance it gives to phenomena which might otherwise be meaningless and in the new lines of inquiry which spring from the suggestions called forth by the significance thus disclosed. Facts that are trivial in themselves are brought forth into importance by the revelation of their bearings upon the hypothesis and the elucidation sought through the hypothesis. The phenomenal influence which the Darwinian hypothesis has exerted upon the investigations of the past two decades is a monumental illustration. But while a single working hypothesis may lead investigation very effectively along a given line, it may in that very fact invite the neglect of other lines equally important. Very many biologists would doubtless be disposed today to cite the hypothesis of natural selection, extraordinary as its influence for good has been, as an illustration of this. While inquiry is thus promoted in certain quarters, the lack of balance and completeness gives unsymmetrical and imperfect results. But if on the contrary all rational hypotheses bearing on a subject are worked coördinately, thoroughness, equipoise, and symmetry are the presumptive results in the very nature of the case.

NICOLAUS COPERNICUS

(1473–1543)

The Polish astronomer is regarded as the father of modern astronomy, because he established once and for all that the earth rotates daily on its axis while the planets revolve in orbits around the sun. His major work, *De Revolutionibus Orbium Celestium*, the product of thirty-six years' labor, was completed around 1530, but its printing was delayed for political and religious reasons; it finally came off the press (1543) just in time to reach Copernicus on his deathbed. Copernicus studied mathematics and optics in Cracow, canon law at Bologna, and medicine at Padua. Though he never actually became a priest, as canon of Frauenberg in his later years, he acted as bailiff, judge, tax collector, vicar-general and physician. The effects of *De Revolutionibus* were indeed revolutionary, beginning with Giordano Bruno, who was burned at the stake for his Copernican views, down through Kepler, Galileo, Huygens and Newton, to the astronomy of the present day.

OF THE REVOLUTIONS OF HEAVENLY BODIES

Chapter I. That the Universe Is Spherical

FIRST OF ALL we assert that the universe is spherical; partly because this form, being a complete whole, needing no joints, is the most perfect of all; partly because it constitutes the most spacious form, which is thus best suited to contain and retain all things; or also because all discrete parts of the world, I mean the sun, the moon and the planets, appear as spheres; or because all things tend to assume the spherical shape, a fact which appears in a drop of water and in other fluid bodies when they seek of their own accord to limit themselves. Therefore

138

Plate 17

Portrait by J. Verkolje
Courtesy Rijksmuseum, Amsterdam

Anton van Leeuwenhoek

Plate 18

Courtesy Archiv für Kunst und Geschichte

Gottfried Wilhelm Leibniz

Plate 19

Portrait by Wilhelm Trautschold
Courtesy Archiv für Kunst und Geschichte, Berlin

Justus von Liebig

Plate 20

James Clerk Maxwell

no one will doubt that this form is natural for the heavenly bodies.

Chapter II. That the Earth Is Likewise Spherical

That the earth is likewise spherical is beyond doubt, because it presses from all sides to its center. Although a perfect sphere is not immediately recognized because of the great height of the mountains and the depression of the valleys, yet this in no wise invalidates the general spherical form of the earth. This becomes clear in the following manner: To people who travel from any place to the North, the north pole of the daily revolution rises gradually, while the south pole sinks a like amount. Most of the stars in the neighborhood of the Great Bear appear not to set, and in the South some stars appear no longer to rise. Thus Italy does not see Canopus, which is visible to the Egyptians. And Italy sees the outermost star of the River, which is unknown to us of a colder zone. On the other hand, to people who travel toward the South, these stars rise higher in the heavens, while those stars which are higher to us become lower. Therefore, it is plain that the earth is included between the poles and is spherical. Let us add that the inhabitants of the East do not see the solar and lunar eclipses that occur in the evening, and people who live in the West do not see eclipses that occur in the morning, while those living in between see the former later, and the latter earlier.

That even the water has the same shape is observed on ships, in that the land which can not be seen from the ship can be spied from the tip of the mast. And, conversely, when a light is put on the tip of the mast, it appears to observers on land gradually to drop as the ship recedes until the light disappears, seeming to sink in the water. It is clear that the water, too, in accordance with its fluid nature, is drawn downwards, just as is the earth, and its level at the shore is no higher than its convexity allows. The land therefore projects everywhere only as far above the ocean as the land accidentally happens to be higher. . . .

*Chapter IV. That the Motions of the Heavenly Bodies Are
Uniform, Circular, Uninterrupted, or Are Made Up of
Combined Circular Motions*

Hereupon, we note that the motions of the heavenly bodies
are circular. When a sphere is in motion it rotates, expressing,
through this activity, its form as that of the simplest of bodies,
in which there is to be found neither a beginning nor an end;
nor can the beginning be distinguished from the end, as the
sphere achieves, through the same intermediate points, its original position. Because of the multiplicity of circles there are,
however, numerous possible motions. The best known of all is
the daily revolution which the Greeks call Nychthemeron, *i.e.*,
the period of day and night. To achieve this motion, it is believed, the whole universe with the exception of the earth, turns
from east to west. It is recognized as the common measure of
all motions, since time itself is measured chiefly by the number
of days. In addition, we see progressing other revolutions which
are apparently retrograde, *i.e.*, from west to east; namely those
of the sun, the moon, and the five planets.

By means of this motion the sun measures for us the year, the
moon the month, as the most common units of time. And thus
each of the other five planets completes its orbit. Yet they are
peculiar in many ways. First, in that they do not revolve about
the same poles around which the first motion takes place, progressing instead in the oblique path of the Zodiac; second, in that
they do not seem to move uniformly in their own orbits, for the
sun and the moon are discovered moving now with a slower, now
a faster motion. The remaining five planets, moreover, we also
see at time going backward and, in the transition, standing still.
And while the sun moves along always in its direct path, the
planets wander in various ways, roaming, now to the South,
now to the North. Wherefore they are designated *"planets."* They
have the added peculiarity that they at times come nearer to the
earth, where they are called *at perigee,* then again they recede
from it, where they are called *at apogee.* Nevertheless, it must be
admitted that the motions are circular, or are built up of many

circles; for thus such irregularities would occur according to a reliable law and a fixed period, which could not be the case if they were not circular. For the circle alone can bring back the past, as the sun, so to speak, brings back to us, through its motion made up of circles, the irregularities of the days and nights and the four seasons; in which several motions are recognized because it cannot happen that the simple heavenly bodies move irregularly in a single circle. For this would either have to be caused by an inconstancy in the nature of the moving force—whether the inconstancy be brought about by a cause from without or within—or would have to originate in an irregularity of the moving body. But as reason rebels against both, and as it is unworthy to assume such a thing concerning that which is arranged in the best of order, so one must admit that the regular motions seem irregular to us, either because the various circles have different poles, or because the earth is not situated in the center of the circles in which the planets move; and that to us who observe the motions of the stars from the earth, the planets, because of the varying distances, appear larger when near us than when they are in paths more remote; that can be proved in optics. In this way the motions which take place in equal times through equal arcs, seem to us unequal due to different distances. Therefore, I consider it above all things necessary that we investigate carefully what relation the earth has to the heavens, so that we, when we wish to investigate the most noble things in nature, do not leave out of consideration the nearest, and erroneously attribute to the heavenly bodies what belongs to the earth.

Chapter V. Whether the Earth Has a Circular Motion, and Concerning the Location of the Earth

Since it has already been proved that the earth has the shape of a sphere, I insist that we must investigate whether from its form can be deduced a motion, and what place the earth occupies in the universe. Without this knowledge no certain computation can be made for the phenomena occurring in the heavens. To be sure, the great majority of writers agree that the earth is at rest in the center of the universe, so that they consider it unbelievable and even ridiculous to suppose the contrary. Yet, when one weighs the matter carefully, he will see that this question is not yet disposed of, and for that reason is by no means to be considered unimportant. Every change of position which is observed is due either to the motion of the observed object or of the observer, or to motions, naturally in different directions, of both; for when the observed object and the observer move in the same manner and in the same direction, then no motion is observed. Now the earth is the place from which we observe the revolution of the heavens and where it is displayed to our eyes. Therefore, if the earth should possess any motion, the latter would be noticeable in everything that is situated outside of it, but in the opposite direction, just as if everything were traveling past the earth. And of this nature is, above all, the daily revolution. For this motion seems to embrace the whole world, in fact, everything that is outside of the earth, with the single exception of the earth itself. But if one should admit that the heavens possess none of this motion, but that the earth rotates from west to east; and if one should consider this seriously with respect to the seeming rising and setting of the sun, of the moon and the stars; then one would find that it is actually true. Since the heavens which contain and retain all things are the common home of all things, it is not at once comprehensible why a motion is not rather ascribed to the thing contained than to the containing, to the located rather than to the locating. This opinion was actually held by the Pythagoreans Heraklid and Ekphantus and the Syracusean Nicetas (as told by Cicero), in that they assumed the earth to be rotating in the center of the universe. They were indeed of the opinion that the stars set due to the intervening of the earth, and rose due to its receding.

From this assumption follows the other not less important doubt concerning the position of the earth, though it is assumed and believed by almost everyone that the earth occupies the center of the universe. If, therefore, one should maintain that the earth is not in the center of the universe, but that the discrepancy be-

tween the two is not great enough to be measurable on the sphere
of the fixed stars, but on the other hand noticeable and recognizable in the orbits of the sun and the planets; and if further
he were of the opinion that the motions of the latter for this reason appear irregular, just as if they were oriented with respect to
another center than that of the earth—such a person might, perhaps, have assigned the true reason for the apparently irregular
motions. For since the planets appear now nearer, now more distant from the earth, this betrays necessarily that the center of the
earth is not the center of those circular orbits. And yet it is not
determined whether the earth decreases and increases its distance
from them or they their distance from the earth.

It would thus not be strange if someone should ascribe to the
earth, in addition to its daily rotation, also another motion. However, it is said that the Pythagorean Philolaus, a not ordinary
mathematician, believed that the earth rotates, that it moves along
in space with various motions, and that it belongs to the planets;
wherefore, Plato did not delay journeying to Italy to interview
him, as is told by those who have described Plato's life. Many,
on the other hand, believed that it could be proved by mathematical calculation that the earth is situated in the center of the
universe, and since, compared with the enormous size of the
heavens, it can be considered as a point, it occupies the central
point and is for this reason immovable; because if the universe
moves, its central point must remain motionless, and that which
is nearest the central point must move most slowly.

*Chapter VII. Why the Ancients Believed That the Earth Rests
in the Middle of the Universe, as Its Central Point*

Thus for certain other reasons the ancient philosophers sought
to prove that the earth is in the center of the universe. As chief
cause, however, they cite weight and imponderability. The element earth, is, to be sure, the heaviest of all, and everything ponderable tends to move, governed by its impulse, toward the
innermost center of the earth. Now since the earth is spherical—

143

the earth, onto the surface of which heavy bodies from all sides fall perpendicularly, due to their own nature—the falling bodies would meet at its center if they were not held back on the surface; because, indeed, a straight line which is perpendicular to the tangent plane as its point of tangency leads to the center. As to those bodies which move toward the center, it seems to follow that they would come to rest at the center. All the more would the whole earth be at rest in the center, and no matter, what it might accumulate in the way of falling bodies, it would remain motionless due to its own weight.

In a similar manner the ancients support their proofs with the cause of motion and its nature. Aristotle says, for example, that a simple body has a simple motion; of possible simple motions, however, one is motion in a straight line, the other is circular motion. Of simple motions in a straight line, one is upwards, and the other is downwards. Therefore, every simple motion would be either toward the center, i.e. downward, or away from the center, i.e. upwards, or around the center, and this would be the circular motion or revolution. Only the earth and the water, which are considered heavy, move downwards, that is, tend to move towards the center. Air, however, and fire, which are endowed with imponderability, move upwards and away from the center. It seems clear that one must admit motion in a straight line for these four elements; as regards the heavenly bodies, however, one must admit motion in a circle around the center. Thus says Aristotle.

"If, therefore," says the Alexandrian Ptolemy, "the earth turns, at least in daily rotation, the opposite of all that is said above must take place; that is to say the motion which traverses throughout the whole circumference of the earth in twenty-four hours would have to be the most violent of all and its velocity would have to be transcendent. But matter which is set in violent rotation does not seem at all fit to be massed together, but rather to be dispersed, if the component parts are not held together with some firmness. And long before now, he says, the disintegrated earth would have been dissipated over the heavens themselves, which is very ridiculous; and much less would the living

144

beings and other separated masses in any way have remained unannihilated. But also the bodies falling in straight lines would not arrive on the places destined for them, as these spots would in the meantime have moved from under with such great velocity. We would also see the clouds and whatever else is floating in the air always moving toward the west."

Chapter VIII.   Refutation of the Arguments, and Their Insufficiency

From these and similar reasons it is claimed that the earth is at rest in the center of the universe and that this is undoubtedly true. But one who believes that the earth rotates will also certainly be of the opinion that this motion is natural and not violent. Whatever is in accordance with nature produces effects which are the opposite of what happens through violence. Things upon which violence or an external force is exerted must become annihilated and cannot long exist. But whatever happens in the course of nature remains in good condition and in its best arrangement. Without cause, therefore, Ptolemy feared that the earth and all earthly things if set in rotation would be dissolved by the action of nature, for the functioning of nature is something entirely different from artifice, or from that which could be contrived by the human mind. But why did he not fear the same, and indeed in much higher degree, for the universe, whose motion would have to be as much more rapid as the heavens are larger than the earth? Or have the heavens become infinite just because they have been removed from the center by the inexpressible force of the motion; while otherwise, if they were at rest, they would collapse? Certainly if this argument were true the extent of the heavens would become infinite. For the more they were driven aloft by the outward impulse of the motion, the more rapid would the motion become because of the ever increasing circle which it would have to describe in the space of 24 hours; and, conversely, if the motion increased, the immensity of the heavens would also increase. Thus velocity would augment size into infinity, and size, velocity. But according to the physical law that the infinite can neither be traversed, nor can it for any reason have motion, the heavens would, however, of necessity be at rest.

But it is said that outside of the heavens there is no body, nor place, nor empty space, in fact, that nothing at all exists, and that, therefore, there is no space in which the heavens could expand; then it is really strange that something could be enclosed by nothing. If, however, the heavens were infinite and were bounded only by their inner concavity, then we have, perhaps, even better confirmation that there is nothing outside of the heavens, because everything, whatever its size, is within them; but then the heavens would remain motionless. The most important argument, on which depends the proof of the finiteness of the universe, is motion. Now, whether the world is finite or infinite, we will leave to the quarrels of the natural philosophers; for us remains the certainty that the earth, contained between poles, is bounded by a spherical surface. Why should we hesitate to grant it a motion, natural and corresponding to its form; rather than assume that the whole world, whose boundary is not known and cannot be known, moves? And why are we not willing to acknowledge that the *appearance* of a daily revolution belongs to the heavens, its *actuality* to the earth? The relation is similar to that of which Virgil's Æneas says: "We sail out of the harbor, and the countries and cities recede." For when a ship is sailing along quietly, everything which is outside of it will appear to those on board to have a motion corresponding to the movement of the ship, and the voyagers are of the erroneous opinion that they with all that they have with them are at rest. This can without doubt also apply to the motion of the earth, and it may appear as if the whole universe were revolving.

Now what shall we say about the clouds and whatever else is somehow floating, falling or rising in the air? Except that not only does the earth move with its attached watery element but it also carries with it no small part of the air and whatever else is thus joined with the earth. It may be that the motion has been communicated to the air, the atmosphere partaking of this motion because of the contact with the earth and the resistance during the constant rotation. Again, an equally astonishing claim, namely, that the highest region of the air obeys the heavenly motion, is said to be supported by those suddenly-appearing stellar objects which are called by the Greeks comets or bearded stars, the origin of which one assigns to just that region, and which, like other constellations, rise and set. It may be said that that part of the air, due to its great remoteness from the earth, has remained immune from the earthly motion. Therefore, the air which lies nearest the earth will appear at rest, as well as those objects floating in it, when they are not driven hither and yon by the wind or by some other external force, as may happen by chance; for what is the wind in the air other than the waves in the sea? We must admit that the motion of falling and rising objects is, with respect to the universe, a double one, compounded always of rectilinear and circular motions. Since that which, due to its weight, is attracted downwards is essentially earthy, there is no doubt that these parts obey the same law as their whole—namely, the earth; and for the same reason such objects as belong to the fire class are drawn aloft with violence. Earthly fire is fed principally with earthy materials, and it is said that a flame is only burning smoke. The peculiarity of fire however, consists in expanding that which it has taken hold of; and it achieves this with such violence that it can be hindered by no method or machine from breaking down the barriers and fulfilling its work. But the expanding motion is directed from the center to the periphery. Therefore, when anything composed of earthy parts is ignited, it moves from the center upwards.

Thus, as has been claimed, a simple body has a simple motion and this proves to be preferably a circular motion as long as the simple body remains in its natural position and retains its unity. In this position its motion is merely the circular motion which, being entirely within the body, makes it seem to be at rest. Rectilinear motion, however, attacks bodies which have left or have been forced from their natural positions, or have in some manner become displaced. Nothing militates so against the

order and form of the whole world as "being-out-of-its-place."
Thus motion in a straight line enters only when things are not
in their proper relations and are not completely as they should
be, having been separated from their whole and having lost their
unity. Moreover, such bodies which are driven upwards or
downwards, disregarding the circular motion, do not describe
simple uniform and constant motion, for they cannot orient
themselves by their lightness or the pressure of their weight;
and if at the beginning of their plunge they have a slower
motion, they increase their velocity in falling. While on the
other hand we see that earthly fire (and we know of no other
kind) when driven aloft at once becomes inert, as if it showed
by this means the origin of the earthy materials. Circular
motion, on the other hand, is always uniform because it has a
cause that does not slacken. The other motions, however,
diminish during their progress, when the bodies have reached
their natural position they cease to be either imponderable or
heavy, and, therefore, their motion ceases. If, therefore, the
universe possesses circular motion and its parts possess also
rectilinear motion, then we might say that circular motion is
compatible with rectilinear motion, just as the animal with
disease. If Aristotle divided simple motions into three kinds,
away from the center, toward the center, and around the center,
that seems to be only an intellectual exercise, just as we distinguish between a line, a point, and a surface, even though
one of these cannot exist without the other, and none of them
without matter. Moreover, the condition of rest is considered
as nobler and more divine than that of change and inconstancy,
so the latter would, therefore, be more suited to the earth than
to the universe. And I add to this that it seems irrational to
ascribe a motion to that which contains and locates and not
to that which is contained and is located, namely the earth.
Finally, since the planets clearly are now nearer, now farther
from the earth, the motion of one and the same body about
the center (which is said to be the center of the earth), is also
directed away from and toward this center. It is, therefore,
necessary to have a more general conception of motion about

a center, and it should be sufficient if each single motion has its own center. It is clear, therefore, from all this, that motion of the earth is more probable than rest, especially in relation to the daily rotation, which is most characteristic of the earth.

Chapter IX. Whether the Earth Can Be Assigned Several Motions; and Concerning the Center of the Universe

Since nothing stands in the way of the movability of the earth, I believe we must now investigate whether it also has several motions, so that it can be considered one of the planets. That it is not the center of all the revolutions is proved by the irregular motions of the planets, and their varying distances from the earth, which cannot be explained as concentric circles with the earth at the center. Therefore, since there are several central points, no one will without cause be uncertain whether the center of the universe is the center of gravity of the earth or some other central point. I, at least, am of the opinion that gravity is nothing else than a natural force planted by the divine providence of the Master of the World into its parts, by means of which they, assuming a spherical shape, form a unity and a whole. And it is to be assumed that the impulse is also inherent in the sun and the moon and the other planets, and that by the operation of this force they remain in the spherical shape in which they appear; while they, nevertheless, complete their revolutions in diverse ways. If then the earth, too, possesses other motions besides that around its center, then they must be of such a character as to become apparent in many ways and in appropriate manners; and among such possible effects we recognize the yearly revolution. If one admits the motionlessness of the sun, and transfers the annual revolution from the sun to the earth, there would result, in the same manner as actually observed, the rising and setting of the constellations and the fixed stars; and it will thus become apparent that also the haltings and the backward and forward motion of the planets are not motions of these but of the earth, which lends them the appearance of being actual planetary motions. Finally, one will be convinced that the sun itself occupies the center of the universe. And all this is taught us by the law of sequence in which things follow one upon another and the harmony of the universe; that is, if we only (so to speak) look at the matter with both eyes.

MARIE and PIERRE CURIE

MARIE CURIE (1867–1934) and PIERRE CURIE (1859–1906)

Marja Sklodowska was born in Warsaw and came to Paris to study at the Sorbonne, where she became the assistant and later the wife of the professor, chemist and physicist, Pierre Curie. In 1898 Madame Curie, in her celebrated experiments on uranium, first isolated polonium from pitchblende. This was followed swiftly by the discovery of radium, climaxing the investigations into radioactive phenomena begun two years earlier by Henri Becquerel. For their discovery, the Curies and Becquerel received the Nobel prize for physics in 1903, and in 1911 Madame Curie received the Nobel prize for chemistry for her further work on radium and its compounds. When Pierre Curie was killed in an accident, his wife took over his professorship at the Sorbonne, and continued her researches until her death. The first paper below is the joint work of the Curies, announcing the discovery of polonium and radium. The second is from Marie Curie's doctoral thesis, summarizing her fundamental investigations. The third comprises selections from her last book, *Radioactivity*.

ON A NEW RACIOACTIVE SUBSTANCE CONTAINED IN PITCHBLENDE

POLONIUM

CERTAIN MINERALS containing uranium and thorium (pitch blende, chalcolite, uranite) are very active in emitting Becquerel rays. One of us has already shown that their activity is greater than that of uranium and thorium, and has expressed the opinion that this effect arises from some other very active substance contained in these minerals in small quantity.

151

The study of the compounds of uranium and of thorium has shown, in fact, that the property of emitting rays which make air conducting and which act on photographic plates, is a specific property of uranium and of thorium, which appears in all the compounds of these metals, being so much the more feeble as the proportion of the active metal in the compound is itself less. The physical state of the substances seems to be of altogether secondary importance. Various experiments have shown that if the substances are mixed with others their condition seems to have no effect except as it varies the proportion of the active body and the absorption produced by the inert substance. Certain causes, such as the presence of impurities, which have so great an effect on phosphorescence or fluorescence, are here altogether without effect. It therefore becomes very probable that if certain minerals are more active than uranium and thorium, it is because they contain a substance more active than these metals.

We have attempted to isolate this substance in pitch blende, and the experiment has confirmed our expectations.

Our chemical investigations have been guided by the tests made of the radiating activity of the products which were separated in each operation. Each product was placed on the plates of a condenser, and the conductibility acquired by the air was measured by an electrometer and a piezoelectric quartz, as in the work already referred to. We thus have not only an indication but a number which gives some measure of the richness of the product in the active substance.

The pitch blende that we analyzed was about two and a half times more active than uranium in our apparatus. . . .

By carrying on these different operations we obtained products which were more and more active. Finally, we obtained a substance whose activity is about 400 times greater than that of uranium.

We have attempted to discover among bodies which are already known if there are any which are radioactive. We have examined compounds of almost all the simple bodies; thanks to the kindness of several chemists we have received specimens of very rare substances. Uranium and thorium were the only ones which were evidently active, tantalum perhaps is very feebly so.

RADIUM

Two of us have shown that by purely chemical processes we may extract from pitch blende a strongly radioactive substance. This substance stands near bismuth in its chemical properties. We have expressed the opinion that pitch blende perhaps contains a new element, for which we proposed the name polonium.

The researches which we have since carried on are in agreement with the first results obtained; but in the course of these researches we encountered a second substance also strongly radioactive and entirely different from the first in its chemical properties. In fact, polonium is precipitated in acid solution by sulphuretted hydrogen; its salts are soluble in acids, and water precipitates them from these solutions; polonium is completely precipitated by ammonia.

The new radioactive substance that we have found presents the chemical aspects of almost pure barium; it is not precipitated either by sulphuretted hydrogen or by ammonium sulphide, or by ammonia; the sulphate is insoluble in water and in acids; the carbonate is insoluble in water; the chloride, very soluble in water, is insoluble in concentrated hydrochloric acid and in alcohol. Finally, it gives the spectrum of barium which is easy to recognize.

We believe, nevertheless, that this substance, although for the most part consisting of barium, contains in addition a new element which gives it its radioactivity and which furthermore is very near barium in its chemical properties. These are the reasons which speak in favor of this view.

(1) Barium and its compounds are not ordinarily radioactive; now, one of us has shown that radioactivity seems to be an

153

atomic property, persisting in all the chemical and physical states of matter. If we look at the thing this way, the radioactivity of our substance, which does not arise from barium, ought to be attributed to another element.

(2) The first substances which we obtained, in the state of hydrated chlorides, had a radioactivity 60 times greater than that of metallic uranium. (The radioactivity intensity is evaluated by the conductibility of the air in our apparatus). By dissolving these chlorides in water and precipitating a part of them by alcohol, the precipitated part is much more active than the part which remains dissolved. By starting with this fact we may carry out a series of fractionations, from which we may obtain more and more active chlorides. We have thus obtained chlorides which have an activity 900 times greater than that of uranium. We have been stopped by the lack of material, but from the progress of the operations we may assume that the activity would have been much more increased if we had been able to continue. These facts can be explained by the presence of a radioactive element of which the chloride is less soluble in alcoholic solution than is barium chloride.

(3) M. Demarçay has examined the spectrum of our substance, with a kindness for which we do not know how to thank him enough. The results of his observations are presented in a special note which follows ours. M. Demarçay has found in the spectrum a ray which seems not to belong to any known element. This ray, which is scarcely visible in the chloride that is 60 times more active than uranium, becomes strongly marked in the chloride that was enriched by fractionation until its activity was 900 times that of uranium. The intensity of this ray increases at the same time as the radioactivity, and this, we think, is a strong reason for attributing it to the radioactive part of our substance.

The various reasons which we have presented lead us to believe that the new radioactive substance contains a new element, to which we propose to give the name *radium*.

MARIE AND PIERRE CURIE

RESEARCHES IN RADIOACTIVE SUBSTANCES

Chapter II Method of Research

THE RESULTS of the investigation of radio-active minerals led M. Curie and myself to endeavor to extract a new radio-active body from pitchblende. Our method of procedure could only be based on radio-activity, as we know of no other property of the hypothetical substance. The following is the method pursued for a research based on radio-activity:—The radio-activity of a compound is determined, and a chemical decomposition of this compound is effected; the radio-activity of all the products obtained is determined, having regard to the proportion in which the radio-active substance is distributed among them. In this way, an indication is obtained, which may to a certain extent be compared to that which spectrum analysis furnishes. In order to obtain comparable figures, the activity of the substances must be determined in the solid form well dried.

Polonium, Radium, Actinium

The analysis of pitchblende with the help of the method just explained, led us to the discovery in this mineral of two strongly radio-active substances, chemically dissimilar:—Polonium, discovered by ourselves, and radium, which we discovered in conjunction with M. Bémont.

Polonium from the analytical point of view, is analogous to bismuth, and separates out with the latter. By one of the following methods of fractionating, bismuth products are obtained increasingly rich in polonium:—

1. Sublimation of the sulphides *in vacuo;* the active sulphide is much more volatile than bismuth sulphide.

2. Precipitation of solutions of the nitrate by water; the precipitate of the basic nitrate is much more active than the salt which remains in solution.

3. Precipitation by sulphuretted hydrogen of a hydrochloric acid solution, strongly acid; the precipitated sulphides are con-

155

siderably more active than the salt which remains in solution.

Radium is a substance which accompanies the barium obtained from pitchblende; it resembles barium in its reactions, and is separated from it by difference of solubility of the chlorides in water, in dilute alcohol, or in water acidified with hydrochloric acid. We effect the separation of the chlorides of barium and radium by subjecting the mixture to fractional crystallisation, radium chloride being less soluble than that of barium.

A third strongly radio-active body has been identified in pitchblende by M. Debierne, who gave it the name of *actinium*. Actinium accompanies certain members of the iron group contained in pitchblende; it appears in particular allied to thorium, from which it has not yet been found possible to separate it. The extraction of actinium from pitchblende is a very difficult operation, the separations being as a rule incomplete.

All three of the new radio-active bodies occur in quite in a more concentrated condition, we were obliged to treat several tons of residue of the ore of uranium. The rough treatment was carried out in the factory; and this was followed by processes of purification and concentration. We thus succeeded in extracting from thousands of kilogrms. of crude material a few decigrammes of products which were exceedingly active as compared with the ore from which they were obtained. It is obvious that this process is long, arduous, and costly. . . .

Extraction of the New Radio-active Substances

The first stage of the operation consists in extracting barium with radium from the ores of uranium, also bismuth with polonium and the rare earths containing actinium from the same. These three primary products having been obtained, the next step is in each case to endeavour to isolate the new radio-active body. This second part of the treatment consists of a process of fractionation. The difficulty of finding a very perfect means of separating closely allied elements is well known; methods of fractionation are therefore quite suitable. Besides this, when finitesimal amounts in pitchblende. In order to obtain them in a mere trace of one element is mixed with another element, no method of complete separation could be applied to the mixture, even allowing that such a method was known; in fact, one would run the risk of losing the trace of the material to be separated.

The particular object of my work has been the isolation of radium and polonium. After working for several years, I have so far only succeeded in obtaining the former.

Pitchblende is an expensive ore, and we have given up the treatment of it in large quantities. In Europe the extraction of this ore is carried out in the mine of Joachimsthal, in Bohemia. The crushed ore is roasted with carbonate of soda, and the resulting material washed, first with warm water and then with dilute sulphuric acid. The solution contains the uranium, which gives pitchblende its value. The insoluble residue is rejected. This residue contains radio-active substances; its activity is four and a half times that of metallic uranium. The Austrian Government, to whom the mine belongs, presented us with a ton of this residue for our research, and authorised the mine to give us several tons more of the material.

It was not very easy to apply the methods of the laboratory to the preliminary treatment of the residue in the factory. M. Debierne investigated this question, and organised the treatment in the factory. The most important point of his method is the conversion of the sulphates into carbonate by boiling the material with a concentrated solution of sodium carbonate. This method avoids the necessity of fusing with sodium carbonate.

The residue chiefly contains the sulphates of lead and calcium, silica, alumina, and iron oxide. In addition nearly all the metals are found in greater or smaller amount (copper, bismuth, zinc, cobalt, manganese, nickel, vanadium, antimony, thallium, rare earths, niobium, tantalum, arsenic, barium, &c.). Radium is found in this mixture as sulphate, and is the least soluble sulphate in it. In order to dissolve it, it is necessary to remove the sulphuric acid as far as possible. To do this, the residue is first treated with a boiling concentrated soda solution. The sulphuric acid combined with the lead, aluminum, and calcium passes, for the most part, into solution as sulphate of sodium,

157

which is removed by repeatedly washing with water. The alkaline solution removes at the same time lead, silicon, and aluminium. The insoluble portion is attacked by ordinary hydrochloric acid. This operation completely disintegrates the material, and dissolves most of it. Polonium and actinium may be obtained from this solution; the former is precipitated by sulphuretted hydrogen, the latter is found in the hydrates precipitated by ammonia in the solution separated from the sulphides and oxidised. Radium remains in the insoluble portion. This portion is washed with water, and then treated with a boiling concentrated solution of carbonate of soda. This operation completes the transformation of the sulphates of barium and radium into carbonates. The material is then thoroughly washed with water, and then treated with dilute hydrochloric acid, quite free from sulphuric acid. The solution contains radium as well as polonium and actinium. It is filtered and precipitated with sulphuric acid. In this way the crude sulphates of barium containing radium and calcium, of lead, and of iron, and of a trace of actinium are obtained. The solution still contains a little actinium and polonium, which may be separated out as in the case of the first hydrochloric acid solution.

From one ton of residue 10 to 20 kilogrms. of crude sulphates are obtained, the activity of which is from thirty to sixty times as great as that of metallic uranium. They must now be purified. For this purpose they are boiled with sodium carbonate and transformed into the chlorides. The solution is treated with sulphuretted hydrogen, which gives a small quantity of active sulphides containing polonium. The solution is filtered, oxidised by means of chlorine, and precipitated with pure ammonia. The precipitated hydrates and oxides are very active, and the activity is due to actinium. The filtered solution is precipitated with sodium carbonate. The precipitated carbonates of the alkaline earths are washed and converted into chlorides. These chlorides are exaporated to dryness, and washed with pure concentrated hydrochloric acid. Calcium chloride dissolves almost entirely, whilst the chloride of barium and radium remains insoluble.

Thus, from one ton of the original material about 8 kilogrms. of barium and radium chloride are obtained, of which the activity is about sixty times that of metallic uranium. The chloride is now ready for fractionation.

Polonium

As I said above, by passing sulphuretted hydrogen through the various hydrochloric acid solutions obtained during the course of the process, active sulphides are precipitated, of which the activity is due to polonium. These sulphides chiefly contain bismuth, a little copper and lead; the latter metal occurs in relatively small amount, because it has been to a great extent removed by the soda solution, and because its chloride is only slightly soluble. Antimony and arsenic are found among the oxides only in the minutest quantity, their oxides having been dissolved by the soda. In order to obtain the very active sulphides, the following process was employed:—The solutions made strongly acid with hydrochloric acid were precipitated with sulphuretted hydrogen; the sulphides thus precipitated are very active, and are employed for the preparation of polonium; there remain in the solution substances not completely precipitated in presence of excess of hydrochloric acid (bismuth, lead, antimony). To complete the precipitation, the solution is diluted with water, and treated again with sulphuretted hydrogen, which gives a second precipitate of sulphides, much less active than the first, and which have generally been rejected. For the further purification of the sulphides, they are washed with ammonium sulphide, which removes the last remaining traces of antimony and arsenic. They are then washed with water and ammonium nitrate, and treated with dilute nitric acid. Complete solution never occurs; there is always an insoluble residue, more or less considerable, which can be treated afresh if it is judged expedient. The solution is reduced to a small volume and precipitated either by ammonia or by excess of water. In both cases the lead

159

and the copper remain in solution; in the second case, a little bismuth, scarcely active at all, remains also in solution.

The precipitate of oxides or basic nitrates is subjected to fractionation in the following manner:—The precipitate is dissolved in nitric acid, and water is added to the solution until a sufficient quantity of precipitate is formed; it must be borne in mind that sometimes the precipitate does not at once appear. The precipitate is separated from the supernatant liquid, and re-dissolved in nitric acid, after which both the liquids thus obtained are re-precipitated with water, and treated as before. The different fractions are combined according to their activity, and concentration is carried out as far as possible. In this way is obtained a very small quantity of a substance of which the activity is very high, but which, nevertheless, has so far only shown bismuth lines in the spectroscope.

There is, unfortunately, little chance of obtaining the isolution of polonium by this means. The method of fractionation just described presents many difficulties, and the case is similar with other wet processes of fractionation. Whatever be the method employed, compounds are readily formed which are absolutely insoluble in dilute or concentrated acids. These compounds can only be re-dissolved by reducing them to the metallic state, e.g., by fusion with potassium cyanide. Considering the number of operations necessary, this circumstance constitutes an enormous difficulty in the progress of the fractionation. This obstacle is the greater because polonium, once extracted from the pitchblende, diminishes in activity. This diminution of activity is slow, for a specimen of bismuth nitrate containing polonium only lost half its activity in eleven months.

No such difficulty occurs with radium. The radio-activity remains throughout an accurate gauge of the concentration; the concentration itself presents no difficulty, and the progress of the work from the start can be constantly checked by spectral analysis.

When the phenomena of induced radio-activity, which will be discussed later on, were made known, it seemed obvious that polonium, which only shows the bismuth lines and whose activity diminishes with time, was not a new element, but bismuth made active by the vicinity of radium in the pitchblende. I am not sure that this opinion is correct. In the course of my prolonged work on polonium, I have noted chemical effects, which I have never observed either with ordinary bismuth or with bismuth made active by radium. These chemical effects are, in the first place, the extremely ready formation of insoluble compounds, of which I have spoken above (especially basic nitrates), and, in the second place, the color and appearance of the precipitates obtained by adding water to the nitric acid solution of bismuth containing polonium. These precipitates are sometimes white, but more generally of a more or less vivid yellow, verging on red.

The absence of lines other than those of bismuth does not necessarily prove that the substance only contains bismuth, because bodies exist whose spectrum reaction is scarcely visible.

It would be necessary to prepare a small quantity of bismuth containing polonium in as concentrated a condition as possible, and to examine it chemically, in the first place determining the atomic weight of the metal. It has not yet been possible to carry out this research on account of the difficulties of a chemical nature already mentioned.

If polonium were proved to be a new element, it would be no less true that it cannot exist indefinitely in a strongly radioactive condition, at least when extracted from the ore. There are therefore two aspects of the question:—First, whether the activity of polonium is entirely induced by the proximity of substances themselves radio-active, in which case polonium would possess the faculty of acquiring atomic activity permanently, a faculty which does not appear to belong to any substance whatever; second, whether the activity of polonium is an inherent property, which is spontaneously destroyed under certain conditions, and persists under certain other conditions, such as those which exist in the ore. The phenomenon of atomic activity induced by contact is still so little understood, that we lack the ground on which to formulate any opinion on the matter. . . .

161

Preparation of the Pure Chloride of Radium

The method by which I extracted pure radium chloride from barium chloride containing radium consists in first subjecting the mixture of the chlorides to fractional crystallisation in pure water, then in water to which hydrochloric acid has been added. The difference in solubility of the two chlorides is thus made use of, that of radium being less soluble than that of barium.

At the beginning of the fractionation, pure distilled water is used. The chloride is dissolved, and the solution raised to boiling-point, and allowed to crystallise by cooling in a covered capsule. Beautiful crystals form at the bottom, and the supernatant, saturated solution is easily decanted. If part of this solution be evaporated to dryness, the chloride obtained is found to be about five times less active than that which has crystallised out. The chloride is thus divided into two portions, A and B— portion A being more active than portion B. The operation is now repeated with each of the chlorides A and B, and in each case two new portions are obtained. When the crystallisation is finished, the less active fraction of chloride A is added to the more active fraction of chloride B, these two having approximately the same activity. Thus there are now three portions to undergo afresh the same treatment.

The number of portions is not allowed to increase indefinitely. The activity of the most soluble portion diminishes as the number of fractions has been obtained, fractionation of the least soluble portion is stopped (the richest in radium), and it is withdrawn from the remainder.

A fixed number of fractions is used in the process. After each series of operations, the saturated solution arising from one fraction is added to the crystals arising from the following fraction; but if after one of the series the most soluble fraction has been withdrawn, then, after the following series, a new fraction is made from the most soluble portion, and the crystals of the most active portion are withdrawn. By the successive alternation of these two processes, an extremely regular system of fractionation is obtained, in which the number of fractions and the activity of each remains constant, each being about five times as active as the subsequent one, and in which, on the one hand, an almost inactive product is removed, whilst, on the other, is obtained a chloride rich in radium. The amount of material contained in these fractions gradually diminishes, becoming less as the activity increases.

At first six fractions were used, and the activity of the chloride obtained at the end was only 0.1 that of uranium.

When most of the inactive matter has been removed, and the fractions have become small, one fraction is removed from the one end, and another is added to the other end consisting of the active chloride previously removed. A chloride richer in radium than the preceding is thus obtained. This system is continued until the crystals obtained are pure radium chloride. If the fractionation has been thoroughly carried out, scarcely any trace of the intermediate products remains.

At an advanced stage of the fractionation, when the quantity of material in each fraction is small, the separation by crystallisation is less efficacious, the cooling being too rapid and the volume of the solution to be decanted too small. It is then advisable to add water containing a known quantity of hydrochloric acid; this quantity may be increased as the fractionation proceeds.

The advantage gained thus consists in increasing the quantity of the solution, the solubility of the chlorides being less in water acidified with hydrochloric acid than in pure water. By using water containing much acid, excellent separations are effected, and it is only necessary to work with three or four fractions.

The crystals, which form in very acid solution, are elongated needles, those of barium chloride having exactly the same appearance as those of radium chloride. Both show double refraction. Crystals of barium chloride containing radium are colorless, but when the proportion of radium becomes greater, they have a yellow coloration after some hours, verging on orange, and sometimes a beautiful pink. This color disappears in solution. Crystals of pure radium chloride are not colored, so that the coloration appears to be due to the mixture of radium and

163

barium. The maximum coloration is obtained for a certain degree of radium present, and this fact serves to check the progress of the fractionation.

I have sometimes noticed the formation of a deposit composed of crystals of which one part remained uncolored, whilst the other was colored, and it seems possible that the colorless crystals might be sorted out.

The fractional precipitation of an aqueous solution of barium chloride by alcohol also leads to the isolation of radium chloride, which is the first to precipitate. This method, which I first employed, was finally abandoned for the one just decribed, which proceeds with more regularity. I have, however, occasionally made use of precipitation by alcohol to purify radium chloride which contains traces of barium chloride. The latter remains in the slightly aqueous alcoholic solution, and can thus be removed.

M. Giesel, who, since the publication of our first researches, has been preparing radio-active bodies, recommends the separation of barium and radium by fractional crystallisation in water from a mixture of the bromides. I can testify that this method is advantageous, especially in the first stages of the fractionation.

Determination of the Atomic Weight of Radium

In the course of my work I determined at intervals the atomic weight of the metal contained in specimens of barium chloride containing radium. With each newly obtained product I carried the concentration as far as possible, so as to have from 0.1 grm. to 0.5 grm. of material containing most of the activity of the mixture. From this small quantity I precipitated with alcohol or with hydrochloric acid some milligrms. of chloride for spectral analysis. Thanks to his excellent method, Demarçay only required this small quantity of material to obtain the photograph of the spark spectrum. I made an atomic weight determination with the product remaining.

I employed the classic method of weighing as silver chloride the chlorine contained in a known weight of the anhydrous chloride. As control experiment, I determined the atomic weight of barium by the same method, under the same conditions, and with the same quantity of material, first 0.5 grm. and then 0.1 grm. The figures obtained were always between 137 and 138. I thus saw that the method gives satisfactory results, even with a very small quantity of material.

The first two determinations were made with chlorides, of which one was 230 times and the other 600 times as active as uranium. These two experiments gave the same figure as the experiment with the pure barium chloride. There was therefore no hope of finding a difference except by using a much more active product. The following experiment was made with a chloride, the activity of which was about 3500 times as great as that of uranium; and this experiment enabled me, for the first time, to observe a small but distinct difference; I found, as the mean atomic weight of the metal contained in this chloride, the number 140, which showed that the atomic weight of radium must be higher than that of barium. By using more and more active products, and obtaining spectra of radium of increasing intensity, I found that the figures obtained rose in proportion. . . .

From its chemical properties, radium is an element of the group of alkaline earths, being the member next above barium.

From its atomic weight also, radium takes its place in Mendeleeff's table after barium with the alkaline earth metals, in the row which already contains uranium and thorium.

Characteristics of the Radium Salts

The salts of radium, chloride, nitrate, carbonate, and sulphate, resemble those of barium, when freshly prepared, but they gradually become colored.

All the radium salts are luminous in the dark.

In their chemical properties, the salts of radium are absolutely analogous to the corresponding salts of barium. However, radium chloride is less soluble than barium chloride; the solubility of the nitrates in water is approximately the same.

The salts of radium are the source of a spontaneous and continuous evolution of heat. . . .

Conclusions

I will define, in conclusion, the part I have personally taken in the researches upon radio-active bodies.

I have investigated the radio-activity of uranium compounds. I have examined other bodies for the existence of radio-activity, and found the property to be possessed by thorium compounds. I have made clear the atomic character of the radio-activity of the compounds of uranium and thorium.

I have conducted a research upon radio-active substances other than uranium and thorium. To this end I investigated a large number of substances by an accurate electrometric method, and I discovered that certain minerals possess activity which is not to be accounted for by their content of uranium and thorium.

From this I concluded that these minerals must contain a radio-active body different from uranium and thorium, and more strongly radio-active than the latter metals.

In conjunction with M. Curie, and subsequently MM. Curie and Bémont, I was able to extract from pitchblende two strongly radio-active bodies—polonium and radium.

I have been continuously engaged upon the chemical examination and preparation of these substances. I effected the fractionations necessary to the concentration of radium and I succeeded in isolating pure radium chloride. Concurrently with this work, I made several atomic weight determinations with a very small quantity of material, and was finally able to determine the atomic weight of radium with a very fair degree of accuracy. The work has proved *that radium is a new chemical element.* Thus the new method of investigating new chemical elements, established by M. Curie and myself, based upon radio-activity, is fully justified.

I have investigated the law of absorption of polonium rays, and of the absorbable rays of radium, and have demonstrated that this law of absorption is peculiar and different from the known laws of other radiations.

I have investigated the variation of activity of radium salts, the effect of solution and of heating, and the renewal of activity with time, after solution or after heating.

In conjunction with M. Curie, I have examined different effects produced by the new radio-active substances (electric, photographic, fluorescent, luminous colorations, &c.).

In conjunction with M. Curie, I have established the fact that radium gives rise to rays charged with negative electricity.

Our researches upon the new radio-active bodies have given rise to a scientific movement, and have been the starting-point of numerous researches in connection with new radio-active substances, and with the investigation of the radiation of the known radio-active bodies.

RADIOACTIVITY

The Discovery of Radioactivity and of the Radioelements

THE STUDY of radioactivity includes the study of the chemistry of the radioelements, the study of the rays emitted by these elements, and the conclusions to be drawn from such studies relative to the structure of the atom. The radioelements can be defined as particular elements from which there emanate, spontaneously and atomically, rays designated as *alpha, beta,* and *gamma*—positive corpuscular rays, negative corpuscular rays (electrons in motion), and electromagnetic radiations. The emission is accompanied by an atomic transformation. Arranged according to their respective abilities to penetrate matter, the *alpha* rays are the weakest: they are stopped by a sheet of paper or by a leaf of aluminum 0.1 mm. in thickness; they travel through air a few centimeters. The *beta* rays travel farther in air and can penetrate several millimeters of aluminum. The *gamma* rays can penetrate several centimeters of relatively opaque material such as lead.

The Rays of Uranium. The Rays of Thorium

Henri Becquerel discovered radioactivity in 1896.

After the discovery of Roentgen rays, Becquerel began his researches upon the photographic effects of phosphorescent and fluorescent substances.

The first tubes which produced Roentgen rays had no metallic anticathode. The source of the rays was the glass wall of the tube, rendered fluorescent by the action of the cathode rays. It was natural to inquire whether the emission of Roentgen rays did not necessarily accompany the production of fluorescence, whatever might be the cause of the latter. Henri Poincaré suggested that it did, and various attempts were made to obtain photographic impressions on plates shielded in black paper, using zinc sulphide and calcium sulphide previously exposed to light; the results were finally negative.

H. Becquerel made similar experiments with the salts of uranium, some of which are fluorescent. He obtained impressions on photographic plates wrapped in black paper with the double sulphate of uranyl and potassium. Subsequent experiment showed that the phenomenon observed was not linked to that of fluorescence. The salt used need not be activated by sunlight; further, uranium and all of its compounds, whether fluorescent or not, act on the photographic plate in the same way, and metallic uranium is the most active of all. Becquerel eventually discovered that compounds of uranium, placed in complete darkness, continued for a period of years to make impressions on photographic plates wrapped in black paper. He then affirmed that uranium and its compounds emit special rays: uranium rays. These rays can penetrate thin metallic screens; as they pass through gases, they ionize them and render them conductors of electricity. The radiation from uranium is spontaneous and constant; it is independent of external conditions of light and temperature.

The electrical conductivity caused in the air or other gases by the uranium rays is the same as that caused by Roentgen rays. The ions produced in both cases have the same mobility and the same coefficient of diffusion. Measurement of the current for saturation provides a convenient means of measuring the intensity of radiation under given conditions.

The Thorium Rays. Researches made simultaneously by G. Schmidt and Marie Curie have shown that the compounds of thorium emit rays like the uranium rays. Such rays are usually called *Becquerel rays.* The substances which emit Becquerel rays are called radioactive, and the new property of matter revealed by that emission has been named by Marie Curie radioactivity. The elements which so radiate are called radio-elements.

Radioactivity an Atomic Property. New Method of Chemical Analysis Based on Radioactivity. Discovery of Radium and Polonium

From Becquerel's researches, it was clear that the radiation from uranium is more intense that that from its compounds. Marie Curie made a systematic study of all known metallic elements and their compounds to investigate the radioactivity of various materials. She pulverized the various substances and spread them in uniform layers on plates of the same diameter which could be inserted into an ionization chamber. Using the piezo-electric quartz method, she measured the saturation current produced in the chamber between the plates A and B (see drawing). With plates 3 cm. in diameter, placed three centimeters apart, an even layer of uranium oxide gives a current of about 2×10^{-11} amperes, which scarcely increases as the thickness of the layer increases after it exceeds a fraction of a millimeter; the emanations are almost all alpha rays of uranium, easily absorbed. Measurements made upon the compounds of uranium have certified that the intensity of radiation increases with the uranium content. The same thing is true for the thorium compounds. The radioactivity of these elements is therefore an atomic property.

On the contrary, a substance such as phosphorus cannot be considered radioactive because to produce ionization it must be

169

in the state of white phosphorus; in the red state, or in a compound such as sodium phosphate, it does not produce ionization. Similarly, quinine sulphate, which produces ionization only while it is being heated or cooled, is not radioactive, for the emission of ions is produced here by the variation in temperature and is not an indication of radioactivity of any of the constituent elements. It is, indeed, a fundamental characteristic of radioactivity that it is a spontaneous phenomenon and an atomic property. These considerations played an important part in the discovery of radium.

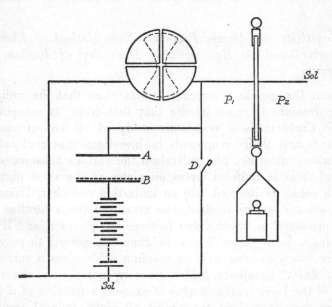

Marie Curie carried on her measurements, using both the widely distributed elements and the rare elements, and as many of their compounds as possible. In addition to pure substances, she also examined a great many samples of various rocks and ores. For simple substances and their compounds, she demonstrated that none except thorium showed an activity equal to 1% of that of uranium.

Among the ores examined, several were radioactive: pitch-

Plate 21

Portrait by Charles Jerves
Courtesy British Information Service

Sir Isaac Newton

Plate 22

Courtesy Archiv für Kunst und Geschichte, Berlin

Paracelsus
Theophrastus Bombastus von Hohenheim

Plate 23

Courtesy French Embassy Press & Information Division

Blaise Pascal

Plate **24**

Courtesy French Embassy Press & Information Division

Louis Pasteur

blende, chalcolite, autunite, thorite, and some others. Since all of these contain either uranium or thorium, it was natural to find them active; but the intensity of the phenomenon with certain minerals was unexpected. Thus some pitchblendes (oxide of uranium) were four times as active as metallic uranium. Chalcolite (copper phosphate and crystalline uranium) was twice as active as uranium. These facts did not agree with the results from the study of simple substances and their compounds, according to which none of these minerals should have shown more activity than uranium or thorium. Furthermore, double phosphate of copper and uranium, of the same formula as chalcolite, prepared from uranium salts and pure copper, showed an activity quite normal (less than half that of uranium). Marie Curie formed the hypothesis that pitchblende, chalcolite, and autunite each contain a very small quantity of a very strongly active material, different from uranium, from thorium, and from already known elements. She undertook to extract that substance from the ore by the ordinary processes of chemical analysis. The analysis of these ores, previously made in general to an accuracy of nearly 1% or 2%, did not destroy the possibility that there might occur in them, in a proportion of that order, a hitherto unknown element. Experiment verified the prophecy relative to the existence of new, powerfully radioactive radioelements; but their quantity turned out to be much smaller than had been supposed. Several years were required to extract one of them in a state of purity.

The research upon the radioelement hypothesized was made first by Pierre Curie and Marie Curie together, using pitchblende.

The research method had to be based upon radioactivity, for no other property of the hypothesized substance was known.

Radioactivity is used in a research of this kind in the following way: the activity of a product is measured: it is then subjected to chemical separation; the radioactivity of each resulting product is measured, and it is observed whether the radioactive substance now remains integrally in one of the products or is divided among them, and if so, in what proportion. The first

171

chemical operations carried out showed that an enrichment in active material was possible. The activity of the solid products— well-dried and spread in a powdered state on plates—was measured under comparable conditions. As more and more active products are obtained, it is necessary to modify the technique of measurements. Some methods of quantitative analysis for radioactive materials will be described later on in this work.

The method of analysis just described is comparable to spectrum analysis from low to high frequencies. It not only discovers a radioactive material, but also distinguishes between the various radioactive elements. For they differ from one another in the quality of their radiations and in their length of life.

The pitchblende from St. Joachimstahl which was used in the first experiment is an ore of uranium oxide. Its greatest bulk is uranium oxide, but it contains also a considerable quantity of flint, of lime, of magnesia, of iron, and of lead, and smaller quantities of some other elements: copper, bismuth, antimony, the rare earth elements, barium, silver, and so on. Analysis made by using the new method showed a concentration of the radioactive property in the bismuth and in the barium extracted from the pitchblende. Yet the bismuth and the barium in commercial use, which are extracted from non-radioactive ores, are not themselves active. In agreement with the original hypothesis, Pierre and Marie Curie concluded that there were in the pitchblende two new radioactive elements: polonium and radium. The first of these they took to be analogous in its chemical properties to bismuth, and the second to barium. They announced these conclusions in 1898. At the same time, they indicated that polonium could be separated from the bismuth by such chemical treatments as the fractional precipitation of the sulphides or the nitrites, and that radium could be separated from barium by the fractional crystallization of the chlorides in water, or their fractional precipitation by alcohol. Theoretically, they claimed, such processes should lead to the isolation of the new radioelements.

A specimen of radium-bearing barium chloride, sixty times as active as the oxide of uranium, was submitted to spectral analysis by Demarçay. He found, accompanying the spectrum of barium, a new line of 3815 Angstrom units. Later, examining a specimen nine hundred times as active as the oxide of uranium, he found the line of 3815 A. much strengthened, and two other new lines. Examination of polonium-bearing bismuth, though the specimen was very active, revealed no new lines.

It had become clear that the new elements occurred in the ore in very small proportions, and that they could be isolated only by treating hundreds or even thousands of kilograms of the ore. To accomplish this labor, it was necessary to have recourse to industrial operations, and to treat the concentrated products thus obtained. After several years, Marie Curie succeeded in obtaining several decigrams of a pure radium salt, in determining the atomic weight of that element, and in assigning to it a place in the periodic table hitherto vacant. Still later, Marie Curie and A. Debierne isolated radium in the metal state. Thus the chemical individuality of radium was established in the most complete and rigorous way.

The application of the new method of investigation later led to the discovery of other new radioelements: first, actinium (discovered by A. Debierne), than ionium (by Boltwood), then mesothorium and radiothorium (by O. Hahn), then protoactinium (by O. Hahn and L. Meitner), etc. There have also been identified radioactive gases called emanations.

Among all these substances, radium is the most widely known and most widely used. Practically unvarying because of the slowness of its transformation, it is now industrially prepared, especially because of the medical applications of the gamma radiations to which it apparently gives rise, and which are, in reality, only indirectly attributable to it. Radium produces, apparently continuously, a radioactive gas named radon, and this gas gives birth to a series of substances: radium A, radium B, radium C. The last of these emits particularly penetrating gamma rays. Radium and the derivatives which usually accompany it furnish intense sources of alpha, beta, and gamma radiations. These have been and are the principal ones used in researches upon such radiations. From the point of view of chemistry, the studies of radium have confirmed the atomic theory of radio-activity and have provided a solid foundation for a theory of radioactive transformation.

Spectrum and Atomic Weight of Radium. Metallic Radium

Since radium is an alkaline-earth metal, it is extracted from its ores simultaneously with the barium also found there, or combined with it. The mixture of radium and barium is sub-mitted to a series of operations of which the result is the separa-tion of the radium from the barium in the form of a pure salt.

As the products of these operations are successfully enriched in radium, their radioactivity increases, the intensity of the spectral lines for radium increases—as compared with the barium lines—and the mean atomic weight increases. When the radium salt is wholly pure, the photographed spark spectrum shows only the lines characteristic of radium; the strong 4554.4 Å line of barium, of such sensitivity that it is extremely hard to eliminate, is now scarcely discernible.

A radium salt introduced into a flame gives it a carmine-red color, and produces a visible spectrum composed of the charac-teristic radium lines (Giesel).

In general, the appearance of the radium spectrum resembles that of the alkaline-earth metals. It includes bright, narrow lines and also cloudy bands. The principal lines of the spark spectrum and of the flame spectrum follow:

Spark Spectrum	Flame Spectrum
4821.1 faint	6653
4682.3 very bright	6700-6530 band
4533.3 faint	6329
4340.8 bright	6330-6130 band
3814.6 very bright	4826
3649.7 bright	
2814.0 bright	
2708.6 bright	

The spark spectrum shows two bright, nebulous bands, with maximum intensity at 4627.5 and 4455.2 Å respectively.

The spectral reaction of radium is very sensitive. It makes possible the identification of radium present in a substance in the proportion of 10^{-5}. But the radioactive reaction is still more sensitive; it makes possible the identification of the radium when its concentration is no more than 10^{-12}.

The atomic weight of radium, or the mean atomic weight of a mixture of radium and barium, can be determined, as for barium, with precision. Although the radioactivity of the mixture is not less than 1000 times that of uranium, its atomic weight differs only negligibly from that of barium.

The method used to make this determination is as follows: chloride of radium, the purity of which had been certified by spectral analysis, was deprived of its water of crystallization at a temperature of about 150°C, and was carefully weighed in the state of an anhydrous salt. From a clear solution of this salt, the chlorine was precipitated as silver chloride, and the silver chloride was weighed. From the relation of that second weight to the first, supposing that the formula for anhydrous chloride of radium is $RaCl_2$—by analogy with the formula $BaCl_2$, accepted for barium chloride—and using the accepted atomic weights of chlorine and silver, the atomic weight of radium could be calculated.

The details of this technique have been explained in special reports (Marie Curie, E. Hoenigschmid). The quantities of the chloride of radium used have varied from 0.1 gm. to 1.0 gm., and the various determinations have resulted uniformly. Taking the atomic weight of silver as 107.88 and that of chlorine as 35.257, the atomic weight of radium is 226 (Hoenigschmid).

To isolate radium in its metallic state, the amalgam of radium was prepared by electrolyzing, with a cathode of mercury, a solution containing 0.1 gm. of pure radium chloride. The resulting liquid amalgam decomposes water and is modified by air. It was dried, placed in a vessel of pure iron, and distilled in an atmosphere of pure hydrogen obtained by osmosis through incandescent platinum. The amalgam solidified at about 400° C.

The metal, cleared of mercury, melts at 700° C. and begins to volatilize. Radium is a white, shining metal which rapidly alters in air, and which decomposes water energetically.

In accord with its atomic weight, radium has been placed in the periodic table of the elements as a higher homologue of barium, in the last line of the table; its atomic number is 88; its spectrum and its chemical properties accord with its position; similarly with its high-frequency spectra (value of L_1 and L_2 levels) (Maurice de Broglie).

Here is a résumé of the chemical properties of the radium salts: the sulphate is insoluble in water and the common acids (solubility in water at 20° C. is 1.4×10^{-3} gm. per liter); the carbonate is insoluble in water and in solutions of alkaline carbonates; the chloride is soluble in water (at 20° C., 245 gm. of $RaCl_2$ per liter), insoluble in concentrated hydrochloric acid and in pure alcohol; the bromide behaves similarly (at 20° C., 706 gm. of $RaBr_2$ per liter); the hydrate and the sulphide are soluble. The separation of radium from barium by fractional crystallization depends upon the fact that the chloride and the bromide of radium are less soluble than the corresponding salts of barium (at 20° C., 357 gm. of $BaCl_2$ and 1041 gm. of $BaBr_2$ per liter of water).

The Radioelements

Each radioelement undergoes a transformation consisting of the successive destruction of all its atoms, in accord with a law that half the number existing at a given moment are transformed in a time T which is characteristic of the radioelement under consideration, and which is called its *period*. Measured by the magnitude of the period, radioelements have a life which is more or less long. Some, like uranium and thorium, which have survived several geological epochs in the ores which contain them, have a very long life. Others, such as radium, actinium, polonium, mesothorium, radiothorium, and so on, would have disappeared wholly from the ores of their decay had they not been compensated for by their production from uranium and thorium.

176

These two primary elements form, therefore, the heads of series or families to which belong all the other radioelements—derivatives of the two, bound to one another by lines of descent. The quantities of the derived elements which exist in untreated ores are proportional to the quantities of the primary elements there, and to the periods of the derivatives. Each derived element with a life sufficiently long can be extracted from uranium and thorium ores, just as the primary elements are; but sometimes it can be obtained by the decay of a more or less distantly related element which has already been extracted from the ore. For the radioelements of short life, only the latter method is available. In this chapter are given descriptions of the radioelements in the order which they occupy in the several families.

The chemical properties of uranium and of thorium have been described in treatises on chemistry, and will be omitted here. There exist at least two isotopes of uranium, U_1 (period of the order of 10^9 years) and U_{11}, a derivative with a very short life, existing in small proportion along with U_1. There is probably also a third isotope, AcU.

The Derivatives of Uranium

A. The Radium Branch

Uranium X. The compounds of uranium emit alpha, beta, and gamma rays; always, the alpha rays come from the uranium itself (U_1 and U_{11}); the penetrating beta and gamma rays are emitted by a group of derivatives which together form Uranium X, discovered by Crookes. Experiments show that the alpha-radiating material cannot be separated from the uranium; but by various reactions, the material which emits the beta and gamma radiations can be separated from the uranium. The methods of operation most employed are the following: fractional crystallization of uranium nitrate, extraction of the uranium from solution by the addition of ammonium carbonate in excess, and the treatment with ether of a highly concentrated solution of uranium nitrate. In the first process, uranium X is

177

concentrated in the more soluble portions. In the second, uranium passes into solution, and the uranium X remains, with insoluble impurities such as iron, in the alkaline solution. In the third, two layers of the liquid form; the one richer in ether contains a solution of uranium without uranium X; the one richer in water contains uranium X in excess. The active material thus separated has a period of twenty-four days.

Uranium X is not simple, but is composed of several radio-elements. The substance with a period of twenty-four days, preparation of which has just been described, is an isotope of thorium (atomic number, 90), and is called Uranium X_1; it is produced by U_1, and it emits a group of beta rays only mildly penetrative.

Uranium X_1 gives rise to a derivative of very short life, uranium X_2 or brevium (Fajans and Goehring). Its period is 1.13 minutes; it is a higher homologue of tantalum (atomic number, 91); it emits a group of penetrating beta rays. Finally, there are found in uranium X, in very small proportions, two other radioelements; uranium Y (Antonoff), an isotope of thorium (atomic number, 90; period, 25 hours); and uranium Z (Hahn) (atomic number, 91; period 6.7 hours).

Ionium. Ionium, discovered by Boltwood, is the derivate of uranium which is transformed directly into radium. Its period is 83.000 years. Its chemical properties are exactly those of thorium, the two elements being isotopes (atomic number, 90). In the treatment of ores, ionium is found in the same portions as the thorium, and it is separated at the same time as that rare earth element. From the uranium ore, what is actually extracted is, therefore, a mixture of thorium-ionium; and though the proportion of ionium is generally smaller than that of thorium, it may be comparable to it.

The spectrum of a thorium-ionium mixture containing 30% of ionium is identical with that of thorium. This fact has been taken as an argument that the spectra of isotopes are identical. Later researches into the isotopes of lead have shown, however, that the identity is not complete; there are very minute differences.

Though ionium occurs in relatively important quantities in the uranium ores (perhaps 20 gm. per ton of uranium), it cannot be extracted as a pure salt because of its close association with thorium.

The radiation of ionium is simple; it is composed principally of alpha rays accompanied by a weak gamma ray of little penetrative power.

Radium and its first derivatives. The chemical individuality of radium has already been given in earlier sections. Its period is 1600 years. By radioactive transformations, radium produces a series of short-lived radioelements by which it is generally accompanied. These are a radioactive gas, or emanation from radium, called radon, and the components A,B,C,C'C'' of the active deposit. The radiation of this group is complex, and is composed of alpha, beta, and gamma rays.

Radium D. Radium E. Radium D is an isotope of lead (atomic number 82; period 22 years). It emits a beta radiation of which the ionizing power is very small; its presence is revealed by the formation of derivatives. Of these derivatives, the first, radium E (isotope of bismuth; atomic number, 83; period, 5 days), has a beta radiation; the second, radium F, identical with polonium, has an alpha radiation. Radium D can be extracted from uranium ores at the same time as the lead which they contain, and cannot be separated from this lead. This radioactive lead—or radiolead—can be used as the primary material for the preparation of polonium. Radium D can also be obtained from radium, from which it derives through the intermediary steps of radon and the materials of its active deposit.

Polonium. Polonium is the first radioactive element discovered by the new method of chemical analysis based on radioactivity. It is a derivative of uranium through the intermediary stage of radium. It is characterized by an alpha radiation, and by the

179

absence of penetrating rays. Its presence was recognized in the sulphides precipitated in an acid solution of pitchblende, and, in the analysis of these sulphides, it particularly clung to the bismuth. By means of the fractional precipitation of the bismuth salts from water, the polonium can be concentrated in the less soluble portions. Later research has shown that this element occurs in the ores in a much smaller proportion than radium, and that it decays, with a period of 140 days. Marckwald has demonstrated that in certain of its chemical properties, polonium is analogous to tellurium. It is characterized also by the ease with which certain metals (iron, copper, silver) displace it from acid solutions. It can be prepared either from ores or from radium.

The largest quantity of polonium hitherto prepared (Marie Curie and A. Debierne) consists of about 0.1 mg. mixed with several milligrams of foreign metals easily reducible. The radiation of that sample was comparable to that of 0.5 gm. of radium. Among the lines in the spark spectrum, there was one (4170.5 Å) which seems to belong to polonium. More recently, there has been announced the existence of a line of 2450 Å (A. Czapek).

To polonium, in the periodic table, has been assigned a place, hitherto vacant, beside bismuth (atomic number, 84), as a higher analogue of tellurium.

The analogy which polonium presents in part with tellurium, in part with bismuth, is explainable, apparently, on considerations of valency. For the compounds in which polonium is trivalent (sulphide), the analogy with bismuth is valid; for those in which it is tetravalent (chloride, hydroxide), the analogy with tellurium is valid (M. Guillot). Polonium is soluble in acid solutions and also in concentrated soda solutions. It can behave, then, like a metal, or it can enter, like tellurium, into an acid radical. In solutions, almost neutral, its compounds undergo hydrolysis and the radioactive material is deposited on the walls of the container; this process is hastened by centrifugation. Polonium appears to be susceptible to linkage in certain complexes such as chloropoloniate of ammonia, an isomorph of the corresponding salts of iron, lead, strontium,

180

platinum; or the diethylthiosulfocarbonate of polonium, an isomorph of the salt of cobalt having the same formula. Experiment in electrolysis points to ions of complex form.

Polonium can be volatilized, and the distilled material can be caught by a gas current. The purest preparation so far obtained upon a small surface corresponds, according to numerical evaluations, to more than fifty molecular layers, superimposed; the color is gray or black, attributable to polonium or to one of its oxides. Some polonium compounds, such as the hydride and the polonium carbonyl have been reported to be particularly volatile.

B. The Actinium Branch

The elements of the actinium family are, in all probability, derivatives of uranium; but they are not of the same linked series as radium and its derivatives. It is supposed that the isotopes of uranium give rise to two lines of derivatives, of which the radium family forms one and the actinium family the other. The first certainly known member of the latter family is protoactinium. The connection between protoactinium and uranium is probably through the intermediary UY.

Protoactinium (Hahn and Meitner, Soddy and Cranston). Protoactinium was discovered in the residue remaining from the treatment of pitchblende from St. Joachimsthal. It is the immediate parent of actinium. It emits alpha and beta rays, and it has a period of 30,000 years. In certain of its chemical properties it is analogous to tantalum, of which it is the higher homologue (atomic number, 91). But according to the experiments of Grosse, its oxide, instead of having the properties of an acid, behaves rather like a weak base. Grosse has perfected a method of fractional crystallization of the chlorides of zirconium and of protoactinium, the latter concentrating in the solution, and the solution, and has obtained several centigrams of the radioelement in a pure state. Protoactinium occurs in the ores of uranium in a proportion comparable to that of radium, and can be extracted in sufficient quantity to determine its atomic weight.

181

Like tantalum, protoactinium can easily be dissolved as an oxide or hydrate in hydrofluoric acid. The oxide (probable formula, Pa_2O_5) is a white powder with a high fusion point; calcined, it is insoluble in hydrochloric, nitric, sulphuric acids. By fusion with $NaSO_4$ and recovery by water and sulphuric acid, it can be dissolved and separated from tantalum. After fusion with K_3CO_3 and recovery by water, protoactinium remains in the insoluble residue, whereas the tantalum dissolves. In a hydrochloric, nitric, or sulphuric solution, the protoactinium can be precipitated entirely by an excess of phosphoric acid.

Actinium. Actinium (A. Debierne) belongs, according to its chemical properties, among the rare earth elements. Extracted from ore at the same time as the elements of this group, it can be separated only by laborious fractionations. Its presence is revealed by the radiation of its successive derivatives. These are formed so slowly that the activity of actinium freshly prepared increases for several months. The period of actinium being about ten years, it forms with its derivatives a relatively stable group (actinium family) with a complex alpha, beta, gamma radiation.

Like polonium and radium, actinium was first found in pitchblende. This generally contains, in a small proportion, rare earths, principally of the cerium group: cerium, lanthanum, neodymium, praseodymium, samarium; there are also always small quantities of thorium. In this mixture of substances with neighboring properties, thorium is the element most weakly basic, and lanthanum the one most strongly basic. Actinium is especially close to lanthanum and is even more strongly basic.

Actinium is precipitated with thorium and with the rare earth elements in the state of hydrates, fluorides, or oxalates (the precipitation being relatively less complete than for lanthanum). It remains with the other rare earths when thorium and cerium are separated from them by the usual methods. The rare earths can be separated from one another by the methodical fractionation of their double ammoniacal nitrates in a nitric solution. The actinium comes out at the same time as the lanthanum, in the least soluble fractions. To enrich the actinium-bearing lanthanum in actinium, there has been used successfully the fractional precipitation of the oxalate in a nitric solution; the actinium concentrates in the solution (Marie Curie and collaborators). By applying this method to the actinium-bearing lanthanum extracted from uranium ore from Haut Katanga, several grams of the oxide, containing 1 to 2 milligrams of actinium, have recently been obtained; this quantity corresponds in the ore to about ten tons of uranium.

The isomorphism of the salts of actinium and lanthanum being demonstrated by the regularity of the fractional crystallizations, it can be supposed that the chemical formulas of the actinium compounds are of the same type as the corresponding formulas for lanthanum.

In the periodic table, there has been assigned to actinium a place, hitherto vacant, in the column of the trivalent elements, in the last line of the table (atomic number, 89).

Radioactinium. Actinium X. These substances are the first derivatives of actinium and are obtained by beginning with it. Radioactinium (Hahn) is an isotope of thorium (atomic number, 90), with a period of 18.9 days; it emits an alpha radiation and also weak beta and gamma radiations. It can be separated from actinium by the same methods used to separate thorium from lanthanum. It gives rise to the formation of actinium X (Giesel, Godlewski), which has a period of 11.2 days and a radiation like that of radioactinium. Actinium X is an isotope of radium (atomic number, 88). From a solution containing actinium, radioactinium, and actinium X, the first two can be separated by precipitating them with ammonia; the actinium X remains in solution. Actinium X gives birth to *actinon* (a radioactive gas), which produces an *active deposit* from actinium composed of a number of constituents.

The Derivatives of Thorium

Mesothorium 1. This substance, discovered by O. Hahn, accompanies the radium extracted from ores which contain uranium

183

and thorium (thorianite, monazite). The beta and gamma radiations which it appears to give really come from a short-lived derivative of it, mesothorium 2. The latter can be separated from the former by precipitation by ammonia, and it immediately re-forms. Mesothorium 1 gives off no measurable radiation. It has not been separated from radium, of which it is an isotope (atomic number, 88); its period is 6.7 years. Its use in medicine is analogous to that of radium, and it has been industrially extracted as a by-product of the preparation of thorium in the incandescent-mantle industry.

Mesothorium 2 is an isotope of actinium (atomic number, 89), and though its period is only 6.2 hours, it has nevertheless been possible to study its chemical properties (Yovanovitch). Thence has been learned much about the chemical properties of actinium, the study of which, as has been observed, involves great delays. This is an example of the method of radioactive indicators.

To separate mesothorium 2 from mesothorium 1, the method is currently used of crystallization in a strongly acid hydrochloric solution in the presence of barium. This operation leaves mesothorium 2 in solution while the chloride of mesothorium 1 crystallizes with the barium-chloride.

Mesothorium is a source of radiothorium. After the solution has been for some time undisturbed, that substance accumulates, and can be separated by NH_3 after the addition of several milligrams of another reagent. In the crystallization hitherto described, radiothorium accumulates in the solution with mesothorium 1; but if the operation is repeated several times at intervals of a day, finally mesothorium 2 quite free of radiothorium collects, the speed of formation of these two being different.

Radiothorium. Thorium X. Radiothorium was found by O. Hahn in thorianite from Ceylon of which some hundreds of kilos had been submitted to treatment for the extraction of radium. This ore is composed chiefly of thorium oxide, but contains also some uranium oxide, and, consequently, some radium. When the chloride of radium-bearing barium coming from this mineral was submitted to fractional crystallization, it was remarked that at the same time that the radium concentrated in the less soluble portions. This material had the radioactive properties of thorium, but in a heightened degree; in particular, it gave off in great quantities the radioactive gas which is obtained from thorium compounds and which is called *thoron,* or *thorium emanation.* The new radioelement responsible for this release of gas has been called radiothorium. It is now known that it is present in the compounds of thorium as a derivative. Radiothorium has also been discovered in the deposits of some hot springs in Savoy (Blanc). Radiothorium is an isotope of thorium (atomic number, 90); its period is 1.9 years. Its radiation is made up chiefly of alpha rays, but it also feebly gives off beta rays. It produces a short-lived derivative, thorium X (Rutherford, Soddy) (isotope of radium, period of 3.64 days, alpha and weak beta radiation), which is used in medicine. It can be separated from a solution of radiothorium by precipitating the latter with ammonia or with oxygenated water; thorium X remains in solution. Thorium X is the direct parent of thoron, from which come other derivatives forming its active deposit.

The Radioactive Ores and the Extraction of the Radioelements

The Radioactive Ores

These ores, of which a large number are known, are all ores of uranium and thorium, containing these two elements in varying proportions, in association with inactive elements. Sought for more actively since the discovery of radium, they have been found in different parts of the globe. The radioelements, derivatives of uranium or of thorium, occur in the ores in quantities proportional to those of the primary substances, respectively. Among the exploitable ores of uranium, some are almost free of thorium and contain only the series of derivatives which begin with uranium; the radium which is extracted from them is free of mesothorium. On the contrary, the commercial ores of thorium contain an appreciable quantity of uranium; with the descendants of thorium there are also present those of uranium. The mesothorium obtained in industry is therefore always accompanied by radium. For equivalent radiation, such a mixture is less valuable than radium, for mesothorium decays in accord with its period of 6.7 years, whereas radium is practically constant, its period being 1600 years.

The radioactive ores occur sometimes in a concentrated form, but more frequently in a dispersed form. In the first case, they form crystals of considerable volume, or compact masses which are found as threads or beads embedded in massive rock. In the second case, they are intimately mixed through rock or soil which they impregnate wholly, or through which they are disseminated in the form of extremely tiny crystals. Industrially, not only the rich ores—containing 50 milligrams or more of radium per ton—but also the poorer ores—containing only a few milligrams of radium per ton—have been successfully used. In the ores, the relation between the quantity of radium and that of uranium has a constant value of 3.4×10^{-7}. Consequently, no ore can possibly contain more than 340 milligrams of radium per ton of uranium.

To recognize that an ore is radioactive, two simple processes are available: 1. A piece of the ore is placed on a photographic plate which is kept entirely in darkness for a day before it is developed. In the image obtained, the dark portions correspond to the active portions of the specimen, and the light portions to the inactive parts. 2. A piece of the ore may be pulverized, the powder so obtained placed upon a plate, and the ionization produced by the specimen measured in an electrical apparatus. Both processes are used in prospecting, and for that purpose there is available a portable electroscope. The primary, compact ores of uranium, composed of uranium oxide more or less pure, are black and dense; those in which the uranium is accompanied by acids—tantalic, niobic, titanic (samarskite, betafite, etc.)— are similarly black or dark brown. But there are also uranium ores of more recent origin, the result of the alteration of primary ores (autunite, chalcolite, curite, etc.) which are vividly colored. The thorium ores are generally of a more or less dark brown (thorite, orangite, thorianite, monazite, etc.).

Below is given a table showing a certain number of the ores, and later are recited the principal points in the treatment of first the uranium ores and then the uranium and thorium ores.

A. Ores of the oxides of uranium or of uranium and thorium:

Pitchblende (uraninite), possibly containing 30% to 80% of uranium in the form of the oxides UO_2 and UO_3, with little or almost no thorium, but with a great number of other materials in small quantities: SiO_2, Fe, Ca, Ba, Sb, Cu, Pb, Bi, etc. Compact or cryptocrystalline structure (St. Joachimsthal), England, United States, Belgian Congo, Canada).

Broggerite, cleveite, etc. Ores of crystallized uranium oxide, possibly containing thorium oxide, ThO_2, in varying proportions (Norway, United States).

Thorianite, an ore of the crystalline oxide of uranium and thorium with a great predominance of thorium (e.g., Th, 65%, U, 10%) (Ceylon).

B. Ores of hydrated deterioration:

Becquerelite ($UO_3\ 2H_2O$), 72% U (Belgian Congo).
Curite ($2PbO\ 5UO_3\ 4H_2O$), lead uranate, 55% uranium (Belgian Congo).
Kasolite ($3PbO\ 3UO_3\ 3SiO_2\ 4H_2O$), 40% uranium, silicouranate of lead (Belgian Congo).

C. Hydrated silicates:

Soddite ($12UO_2\ 5SiO_2\ 14H_2O$), 72% uranium (Belgian Congo).
Orangite, 66% thorium, 1% uranium (Norway).
Thorite, 45%-65% thorium, 9% uranium (Norway).

D. Phosphates:

Autunite ($Ca\ 2UO_4\ 2PO_4\ 8H_2O$), phosphate of calcium and uranyl, about 50% uranium, in green crystalline spangles (Portugal, Tonkin).

187

Chalcolite, torbernite (Cu $2UO_2$ $2PO_4$ $8H_2O$), phosphate of copper and uranyl, about 50% uranium, in green crystals (Cornwall, England; Portugal).

Monazite, phosphate of rare earths, principally ceric (CePO.) containing thorium (of the order of 10%) and a little uranium (of the order of 1%) (Brazil, United States, India).

E. Vanadates:

Carnotite, vanadate of UO_2 and hydrated K, about 50% uranium, in yellow crystalline powder (United States).

Ferghanite, Tuyamunite, composed of UO_3 and V_2O_5, about 50% uranium (Turkestan).

F. Niobates, tantalates, titanates:

Samarskite, niobate and tantalate of rare earths (especially the yttrium group), 3% to 15% uranium, 4% thorium (Russia, United States, India, Madagascar).

Euxenite, niobate and titanate of rare earths (yttrium), 3% to 15% uranium, 6% thorium (Norway, United States, Madagascar).

Betafite, titanoniobate and tantalate of uranium, crystallized, 25% uranium, 1% thorium (Madagascar).

Uranium Ores Containing a Little Thorium

Treatment of Pitchblende

The principal ores which the radium industry has used are pitchblende, autunite, carnotite, betafite. Some of these contain so little thorium that the Th/U ratio is of the order of 10^{-5} (pitchblendes from St. Joachimsthal and from Haut Katanga). In betafite, the ratio is higher, 1 to 4%. The Joachimsthal pitchblende is the ore in which were discovered polonium and radium; exploited first for uranium, it was later exploited for radium. It occurs in association with dolomite and quartz in veins located at great depths (500 meters and more) in the granite mass of the region. Its composition is complex and variable; here is an example:

U_3O_8	76.82
F_2O_3	4.0
PbO	4.63
Bi_2O_3	.67
As_2O_5	.82
ZnO	.22
MnO	.04
SiO_2	5.07
CaO	2.45
MgO	.19
K_2O	.28
Na_2O	1.19
Rare earths	.52
H_2O	3.25
S	1.15
Thorium	traces

The pitchblende from the Belgian Congo (Haut Katanga) occurs in nuggets within sedimentary rocks; it is accompanied by ores resulting from the alteration of pitchblende under the action of various physical and chemical agents: chalcolite, kasolite, etc. These ores are treated in the Oolen plant in Belgium and actually provide the chief source of radium. In Canada, pitchblende has been found in lengthy veins, in ancient sedimentary rock near the Arctic Circle.

The principal phases in the extraction of radium are the following: 1. Reduction of the ore to which has been added previously a proper amount of barium to serve as a radium capturer. 2. Separation of the crude sulphates containing the radium-bearing barium. 3. Purification of the crude sulphates and transformation of the radium-bearing barium into a chloride. 4. Fractional crystallization of the chloride to obtain a salt enriched in radium. 5. Purification of the enriched chloride and final fractional crystallization of the chlorides or bromides.

These operations are represented in the accompanying table with an indication of the products of the treatment in which certain radioelements are concentrated. It must be observed that this treatment is adapted to its principal objective—the

189

extraction of radium and of uranium. The other radioelements, of which less accurate account is given, are dispersed in the course of the operations. (See Table I.)

TABLE I

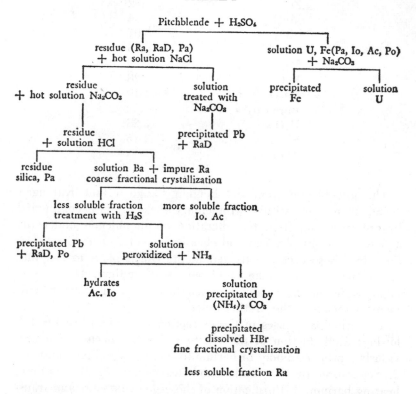

Pitchblende + H_2SO_4

residue (Ra, RaD, Pa) + hot solution NaCl

solution U, Fe(Pa, Io, Ac, Po) + Na_2CO_3

residue + hot solution Na_2CO_3

solution treated with Na_2CO_3

precipitated Fe

solution U

residue + solution HCl

precipitated Pb + RaD

residue silica, Pa

solution Ba + impure Ra coarse fractional crystallization

less soluble fraction treatment with H_2S

more soluble fraction Io. Ac

precipitated Pb + RaD, Po

solution peroxidized + NH_3

hydrates Ac. Io

solution precipitated by $(NH_4)_2 CO_3$

precipitated dissolved HBr fine fractional crystallization

less soluble fraction Ra

Pitchblende is generally reduced by the use of weak sulphuric acid; but that operation must sometimes be preceded by a preliminary treatment such as the roasting of the ore finely ground and mixed with carbonate of soda.

The fractional crystallization of the chlorides (the method originated by Marie Curie) is a fundamental step in the treatment. It is accomplished at first in an aqueous solution. As the extraction of the radium salt advances, it is desirable to crystal-

190

lize it in a solution of increasing acidity, partly to decrease its solubility, partly to aid in the elimination of various impurities (iron, calcium, rare earth elements). Generally, the fractional crystallization is not continued until a pure radium salt is obtained, but is stopped when a concentration fixed by the use to which the product is to be put (50% to 90%) has been reached. To enrich the concentrated products, fractional crystallization of bromides replaces that of chlorides (Giesel).

The method of treating pitchblende in order to obtain polonium, used in some attempts in that direction, is given in an accompanying table. The separation of polonium with lead, bismuth, and other easily reducible metals is accomplished by making use of the chemical and electrochemical properties of polonium described earlier. (See Table II.)

TABLE II

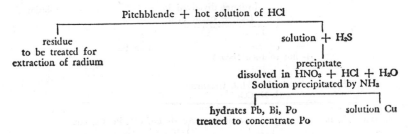

Pitchblende + hot solution of HCl

residue
to be treated for
extraction of radium

solution + H₂S

precipitate
dissolved in HNO₃ + HCl + H₂O
Solution precipitated by NH₃

hydrates Pb, Bi, Po
treated to concentrate Po

solution Cu

From Table I, it is clear that radiolead (lead + RaD) is a by-product in the preparation of radium; its separation from the ore is generally sufficiently complete, and the concentration in Radium D is greater as the ore contains less inactive lead. The radiolead may be conserved for the preparation of polonium. The method of concentration involves the following steps: 1. The precipitation of lead in a nitric solution by concentrated hydrochloric acid, leaving the polonium in solution; 2. The deposit of polonium by electrochemical means upon copper or silver leaves plunged into the solution of radiolead; 3. The capture of polonium with a precipitate of colloidal ferric hydrate.

Among the other by-products in the preparation of radium,

protoactinium occurs either with the final residue of the reduction —composed principally of silica—or in the sulphuric solution of uranium. Ionium and actinium also occur—in part in that same solution, in part in the insoluble sulphates. The accompanying table records the method used to extract that material, on one hand the mixture thorium-ionium, on the other, actinium associated with lanthanum. In this treatment, hydrofluoric acid may be substituted for the oxalic acid. (See Table III.)

TABLE III

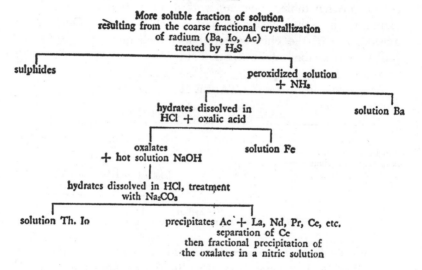

More soluble fraction of solution
resulting from the coarse fractional crystallization
of radium (Ba, Io, Ac)
treated by H₂S

sulphides

peroxidized solution
+ NH₃

hydrates dissolved in
HCl + oxalic acid

solution Ba

oxalates
+ hot solution NaOH

solution Fe

hydrates dissolved in HCl, treatment
with Na₂CO₃

solution Th. Io

precipitates Ac + La, Nd, Pr, Ce, etc.
separation of Ce
then fractional precipitation of
the oxalates in a nitric solution

Only a few indications of the treatment used for other ores which have been exploited industrially are given here. The principal phases of the treatment are the same as for pitchblende, but the processes employed for the reduction of the ore and the obtaining of the crude sulphates may vary from one ore to another.

Carnotite—a vanadate of uranium found principally in the United States—and autunite—a phosphate of uranium and lime which has been mined principally in Portugal—can both, in certain cases, be treated with weak, hot hydrochloric acid; from that solution, the crude sulphates are precipitated. In other cases there is an advantage in treating the ore with carbonate of soda prior to dissolving it in acid.

Betafite—an ore from Madagascar which contains uranium with niobic, titanic, and tantalic acids—is reduced by fusion with soda and carbonate of soda in order to cause the rare acids to pass into solution. The reduction can also be accomplished with bisulphate of soda and reclamation with water; the sulphate of radium-bearing barium then remains in the residue with the rare acids. These latter can be separated by treatment with soda or with weak hydrofluoric acid.

Ores of Thorium and Uranium

Some ores of thorium are poor in uranium, and consequently have a scientific interest from the fact that they contain almost solely the derivatives of thorium; this is the situation with certain thorites. But in the ores which have been exploited (thorianite, monazite) the proportion of uranium to thorium is sufficiently large for the derivatives of these two elements to be represented by comparable radiations.

Thorianite is an ore rich in thorium, found in the island of Ceylon in the form of small crystal cubes. By the treatment of several hundred kilograms of that ore, mesothorium and radiothorium were discovered. The proportion of thorium in this ore runs as high as 60 to 80%; that of uranium, 10 to 20%. Monazite, though it is less rich in thorium, is nevertheless regularly exploited for the incandescent-mantle industry, because it is found in great quantities in the so-called monazite sands of the United States and of Brazil.

Monazite is a rare-earth phosphate, crystallized, containing generally 6 to 12% of thorium. It is reduced with hot sulphuric acid, and all the soluble sulphates are extracted; in the insoluble sulphates, along with barium, radium and mesothorium 1 occur. The latter treatment of these crude sulphates does not differ in principle from that already described. The fractional crystallization is undertaken to separate in the less soluble portions the radium and the mesothorium 1 and, in the more soluble portions, the radiothorium—a disintegration product of mesothorium. The fractional crystallization can be continued until there is obtained a chloride or a bromide of radium quite free of barium and containing a negligible amount of mesothorium. After that, continued fractional crystallization does not alter the product thus obtained. The effect of the mesothorium is, however, so important that in certain products a month old it is estimated that about 75% of the most penetrating gamma rays are due to the mesothorium (through its derivative MThII) and about 25% of the most penetrating gamma rays to the radium (through its derivative RaC). The gamma radiation increases constantly for about three years because of the formation of radiothorium and its later derivatives. Having passed a maximum, it lessens because of the destruction of the mesothorium 1; after about fifty years, the radiation is due almost solely to radium, with a diminution of about 2% of the original quantity of radiation.

GEORGES CUVIER

(1769–1832)

Georges Cuvier, the father of comparative anatomy and paleontology, first gained attention for his natural classification of worms. Later he divided the animal kingdom into four branches: vertebrates, molluscs, articulates and radiates. At the head of the animal kingdom he placed the "only two-legged, two-handed animal: man." He investigated the comparative anatomy of fish and the osteology of mammals, and took particular interest in fossil mammals and reptiles. It is primarily Cuvier's work that led to paleontology becoming a separate science. Among his works: *Tableau élémentaire de l'Histoire Naturelle des Animaux* (1798), *Leçons d'Anatomie Comparée* (1800-05), *Mémoires sur les Espèces d'Eléphants Vivants et Fossiles* (1800), and *Histoire Naturelle des Poissons*.

THE ANIMAL KINGDOM

FIRST ORDER OF MAMMALS

THE TWO-HANDED OR HUMAN

THERE is only one genus of man and this genus is unique in its order. Since the [natural] history of man interests us most directly and should stand as the basis of comparison to which we submit the accounts of all other animals, we shall treat it in greater detail.

We shall quickly disclose those particular features of structural organization in which man differs from other mammals; we shall examine the advantages that man's peculiarities give him over other living creatures. . . .

Man's foot is very different from those of monkeys; it is large,

195

the leg drops vertically upon it; the heel bulges out underneath; the toes are short and cannot be bent very far; the great toe, longer and bigger than the others, is placed in the same line and cannot be opposed to the others. The foot is adequate to support the body, but it does not serve to grasp or hold on to [anything]. Since the hands, on their part, are of no use for walking, man is the only animal [that can be considered] truly two-legged and two-handed.

The entire human body is disposed for a vertical posture. Man's feet, as we have seen, furnish him a larger [base of support] than any other mammal has. The strongest muscles support the foot, [leg], and thigh when extended and account for the bulges in the calf and buttocks. The flexors of the leg are attached even higher, permitting the knee to be completely straightened and the calf to show off better. The pelvis, from which the legs and thighs separate, is quite large and gives the trunk a pyramidal shape favorable to equilibrium. The neck of the femur makes a [wide] angle with the shaft of the bone, augmenting still further the separation of the feet and enlarging the base of the body. In the vertical position the head is in equilibrium on the trunk, because its articulation is below its center of gravity.

Even should he want to, a man cannot walk very comfortably on all fours. His short and almost inflexible hind feet throw his knees against the ground; his wide shoulders and arms thrown far from the middle of the body offer poor support. The great striated muscle, which in quadrupeds holds the trunk up between the shoulder blades like a saddle girth, is smaller in man than in any of them. The head is too heavy because of the great size of the brain and the smallness of the sinuses or cavities in the bone. Furthermore, the means of holding [the head] up are too feeble, for man has neither the cervical ligaments nor the disposition of the vertebrae proper to keep them from flexing forward. A man [on all fours] could hold his head more or less in the line of his spine, but then his mouth and eyes would be directed toward the ground; he could not see ahead. On the other hand the position of these organs is perfect when he walks erect.

196

The blood vessels which feed the brain are not subdivided, as in most quadrupeds, and the blood necessary for so voluminous an organ being rushed there with too great extravagance, apoplexy would be the all too frequent result of the horizontal position.

Man is designed to support himself on his feet only. Thus he keeps his hands entirely free for action, and his sense organs remain in the positions most favorable for observation.

The hands, which derive great advantages from their freedom, are not without it in their structure. The thumb, longer in proportion than in monkeys, permits the greatest ease in picking up small objects. All the fingers, except the ring [third] finger, have separate movements, something which does not occur in other animals, not even monkeys. The nails adorn only one side of the ends of the fingers, permitting firmness in the sense of touch without depriving it of any of its delicacy. The arms which carry the hands have a solid attachment through the large shoulder blades and the strong collarbone.

Though favored by dexterity, man has no advantages on the side of strength. His endurance in the chase is far less than that of the other animals of his stripe; having neither protruding jaws, nor canine fangs, nor sharp claws, he is without offensive arms; and his body lacking a natural protective covering on top and on all sides, he is absolutely without defensive armor. Indeed among all the animals man is the one which has taken the longest time to acquire the powers necessary for his own preservation.

But this physical feebleness has been an advantage for him [nevertheless]. It has forced him to take recourse to his inner self and especially to the intelligence which has been vouchsafed to him in such high degree.

No quadruped approaches man in the size and folds of the hemispheres of the brain, that is, in the part of the brain which serves as the principal instrument of intellectual functions. The posterior part of the same organ extends backward in such a fashion as to cover over the cerebellum. Likewise the shape of man's skull announces the size of his brain, just as the smallness

197

of his face indicates how little predominance is accorded that part of the [central] nervous system connected by the external senses.

However, these external senses, though mediocre in man, are nevertheless rather delicate and well balanced.

The eyes look forward; man cannot see from two sides at the same time, as most quadrupeds [can do], a fact which puts more unity into the results of his sight and fixes more attention upon sensations of this kind. The globe and iris of [the human] eye are both but slightly variable, a fact which restricts vision in focus to one distance at a time and to fixed amounts of light. The external ear, neither very sensitive nor spread out, does not augment the intensity of sounds; yet man is of all animals the one which best distinguishes intonations. Man's nostrils, more complicated than those of monkeys, are of less [importance] than those of all other creatures. Nevertheless, man appears to be the only one whose sense of smell is so delicate as to be offended by bad odors. The delicacy of his sense of smell has an influence on that of taste; and man should have some advantage in this regard at least over the animals whose tongues are covered with scales. Finally, the fineness of his sense of touch results from [the sensitivity] of his skin and the absence of all insensible parts as well as from the form of his hand, better made than any other to adapt itself to the small irregularities of surfaces.

Man has a particular pre-eminence in his vocal organs. Alone among mammals he can articulate sounds. The form of his mouth and the extreme mobility of his lips are the probable causes. As a result, he has acquired a most precious means of communication, for of all the signs that might be easily used for the transmission of ideas, varied sounds are those which can be perceived at the greatest distance and in more than one direction. . . .

On account of his industry, man enjoys a uniform [year-round] nourishment. Hence he is at all times disposed to the pleasures of love without ever being overwhelmed by [seasons of animal] heat. . . .

198

GEORGES CUVIER

SECOND ORDER OF MAMMALS

THE FOUR-HANDED (QUADRUMANES)

Independently of the anatomic details which distinguish man, as we have already pointed out, the quadrumanes differ from our species by very notable characteristics; [namely], that the hind feet have big toes free to oppose the other toes; that the digits of the feet are long and flexible like those of the hand; also that all these species swing from the branches of trees with ease, including those which stand and walk erect only with difficulty, their feet touching [the ground] only on the outer edges, and their narrow pelvis being not at all favorable for equilibrium. They have intestines very like our own; eyes that look forward; breasts on their chests; a pendant verge; a brain with three lobes on each side, whose posterior part covers over the cerebellum; the temporal fossa is separated from the orbital by a bony septum. But for the rest, they depart from our form by degrees, taking on a longer and longer snout, a tail, and a more exclusively four-legged gait. Nevertheless, the freedom of their forearms and the complexity of their hands permit them a great [variety of] actions and gestures similar to those of human beings.

For a long time two divisions of genus were made, monkeys and lemurs. Today in some fashion, through the multiplication of secondary forms, they have become two small families and between them we must place a third genus, marmosets, which belongs neither to the one nor the other.

JOHN DALTON

(1766–1844)

This English chemist and physicist was color-blind, a fact which led him to give the first detailed description of this biological defect and name it Daltonism. Teacher, lecturer and private tutor, he kept a meteorological diary all his life, publishing excerpts in 1793, *Meteorological Observations and Essays,* in which he maintained the electrical origin of the aurora borealis. He is more famous, however, for his researches into the physical properties of gases. *The Absorption of Gases by Water and Other Liquids* (1803) states Dalton's law: the pressures of the saturated vapors of all liquids have the same value at temperatures equally removed from their boiling points. His main work, *A New System of Chemical Philosophy* (1808-27), contains his famous atomic theory, which is one of the foundations of modern chemistry—though Dalton still held to the idea that the atom was indivisible.

A NEW SYSTEM OF CHEMICAL PHILOSOPHY

ON THE CONSTITUTION OF BODIES

THERE ARE three distinctions in the kinds of bodies, or three states, which have more especially claimed the attention of philosophical chemists; namely, those which are marked by the terms *elastic fluids, liquids,* and *solids.* A very famous instance is exhibited to us in water, of a body, which, in certain circumstances, is capable of assuming all the three states. In steam we recognize a perfectly elastic fluid, in water a perfect liquid, and in ice a complete solid. These observations have tacitly led to the conclusion, which seems universally adopted, that all bodies of sensible magnitude, whether liquid or solid, are constituted of a vast number of extremely small particles

200

or atoms of matter bound together by a force of attraction, which is more or less powerful according to circumstances. . . .

Whether the ultimate particles of a body, such as water, are all alike, that is, of the same figure, weight, et cetera, is a question of some importance. From what is known, we have no reason to apprehend a diversity in these particulars: if it does exist in water it must equally exist in the elements constituting water, namely, hydrogen and oxygen. Now it is scarcely possible to conceive how the aggregates of dissimilar particles should be so uniformly the same. If some of the particles of water were heavier than others, if a parcel of the liquid on any occasion were constituted principally of these heavier particles, it must be supposed to affect the specific gravity of the mass, a circumstance not known. Similar observations may be made on other substances. Therefore we may conclude that *the ultimate particles of all homogeneous bodies are perfectly alike in weight, figure, et cetera.* In other words, every particle of water is like every other particle of water; every particle of hydrogen is like every other particle of hydrogen, et cetera.

ON CHEMICAL SYNTHESIS

When any body exists in the elastic state its ultimate particles are separated from each other to a much greater distance than in any other state; each particle occupies the center of a comparatively large sphere and supports its dignity by keeping all the rest which, by their gravity or otherwise, are disposed to encroach upon it at a respectful distance. When we attempt to conceive the *number* of particles in an atmosphere it is somewhat like attempting to conceive the number of stars in the universe: we are confounded with the thought. But if we limit the subject by taking a given volume of any gas, we seem persuaded that, let the divisions be ever so minute, the number of particles must be finite; just as in a given space of the universe the number of stars and planets cannot be infinite.

Chemical analysis and synthesis go no farther than to the separation of particles one from another, and to their reunion.

201

No new creation or destruction of matter is within the reach of chemical agency. We might as well attempt to introduce a new planet into the solar system, or to annihilate one already in existence, as to create or destroy a particle of hydrogen. All the changes we can produce consist in separating particles that are in a state of cohesion or combination, and joining those that were previously at a distance.

In all chemical investigations it has justly been considered an important object to ascertain the relative *weights* of the simples which constitute a compound. But unfortunately the inquiry has terminated here; whereas from the relative weights in the mass the relative weights of the ultimate particles or atoms of the bodies might have been inferred, from which their number and weight in various other compounds would appear, in order to assist and to guide future investigations, and to correct their results.

Plate 25

Courtesy Sovfoto

Ivan Pavlov

Plate 26

Max Planck

Plate 27

Joseph Priestley

Plate 28

Chandrasekhara Venkata Raman

CHARLES DARWIN

(1809–1882)

One of the more sensational landmarks in science, and one of a handful of books which have had revolutionary impact on the whole of modern culture, *On the Origin of Species by Means of Natural Selection* aroused a controversy on its publication (1859) which has not entirely ceased after a full century. For though largely accepted (with reservations and qualifications) by contemporary science, Darwin's theory of evolution is still disputed in some quarters. Almost equally startling was *The Descent of Man* (1871), which derived man from an animal of the anthropoid group and which set naturalists to searching for "the missing link." Darwin's lifelong interest in natural history bore fruit in numerous works, the most important being *Zoology of the Voyage of the Beagle* (1840), *The Variations of Animals and Plants under Domestication* (1868), and *The Expression of the Emotions in Man and Animals* (1873). Though not himself the originator of the evolution hypothesis, nor even the first to apply it to living organisms, Darwin, with his natural selection concept, supplied an explanation which lifted it from a hypothesis to a verifiable theory.

ON THE ORIGIN OF SPECIES

CREATION OR EVOLUTION?

WHEN on board H.M.S. Beagle as naturalist, I was much struck with certain facts in the distribution of the organic beings inhabiting South America, and in the geographical relations of the present to the past inhabitants of that continent. These facts, as will be seen in the latter chapters of this volume, seemed to throw some light on the origin of species—that mystery of mysteries, as it has been called by one of our greatest philoso-

203

phers. On my return home, in 1837, it occurred to me that something might perhaps be made out on this question by patiently accumulating and reflecting on all sorts of facts which could possibly have any bearing on it. After five years' work, I allowed myself to speculate on the subject, and drew up some short notes; these I enlarged in 1844 into a sketch of the conclusions which then seemed to me probable. From that period to the present day I have steadily pursued the same object. I hope that I may be excused for entering on these personal details, as I give them to show that I have not been hasty in coming to a decision.

In considering the origin of species, it is quite conceivable that a naturalist, reflecting on the mutual affinities of organic beings, on their embryological relations, their geographical distribution, geological succession, and other such facts, might come to the conclusion that species had not been independently created, but had descended, like varieties, from other species. Nevertheless, such a conclusion, even if well founded, would be unsatisfactory, until it could be shown how the innumerable species inhabiting this world have been modified so as to acquire that perfection of structure and co-adaptation which justly excites our admiration.

Naturalists continually refer to external conditions, such as climate, food, etc., as the only possible cause of variation. In one limited sense, as we shall hereafter see, this may be true; but it is preposterous to attribute to mere external conditions the structure, for instance, of the woodpecker, with its feet, tail, beak, and tongue, so admirably adapted to catch insects under the bark of trees. In the case of the mistletoe, which draws its nourishment from certain trees, which has seeds that must be transported by certain birds, and which has flowers with separate sexes absolutely requiring the agency of certain insects to bring pollen from one flower to the other, it is equally preposterous to account for the structure of the parasite, with its relations to several distinct organic beings, by the effects of external conditions, or of habit, or of the volition of the plant itself.

It is, therefore, of the highest importance to gain a clear insight into the means of modification and coadaptation. At the beginning of my observations it seemed to me probable that a careful study of domesticated animals and of cultivated plants would offer the best chance of making out this obscure problem. Nor have I been disappointed; in this and in all other perplexing cases I have invariably found that our knowledge, imperfect though it be, of variation under domestication, afforded the best and safest clue. I may venture to express my conviction of the high value of such studies, although they have been very commonly neglected by naturalists.

Although much remains obscure, and will long remain obscure, I can entertain no doubt, after the most deliberate study and dispassionate judgment of which I am capable, that the view which most naturalists until recently entertained, and which I formerly entertained—namely, that each species has been independently created—is erroneous. I am fully convinced that species are not immutable, but that those belonging to what are called the same genera are lineal descendants of some other and generally extinct species, in the same manner as the acknowledged varieties of any one species are the descendants of that species. Furthermore, I am also convinced that Natural Selection has been the most important, but not the exclusive, means of modification.

VARIATION AND SELECTION

All living beings vary more or less from one another, and though variations which are not inherited are unimportant for us, the number and diversity of inheritable deviations of structure, both those of slight and those of considerable physiological importance, are endless.

No breeder doubts how strong is the tendency to inheritance; that like produces like is his fundamental belief. Doubts have been thrown on this principle only by theoretical writers. When any deviation of structure often appears, and we see it in the father and child, we cannot tell whether it may not be due to the same cause having acted on both; but when amongst individuals, apparently exposed to the same conditions, any very rare deviation, due to some extraordinary combination of circumstances, appears in the parent—say, once amongst several million individuals—and it reappears in the child, the mere doctrine of chances almost compels us to attribute its reappearance to inheritance.

Everyone must have heard of cases of albinism, prickly skin, hairy bodies, etc., appearing in members of the same family. If strange and rare deviations of structure are really inherited, less strange and commoner deviations may be freely admitted to be inheritable. Perhaps the correct way of viewing the whole subject would be to look at the inheritance of every character whatever as the rule, and non-inheritance as the anomaly.

The laws governing inheritance are for the most part unknown. No one can say why the same peculiarity in different individuals of the same species, or in different species, is sometimes inherited and sometimes not so; why the child often reverts in certain characters to its grandfather or grandmother, or more remote ancestor; why a peculiarity is often transmitted from one sex to both sexes, or to one sex alone, more commonly but not exclusively to the like sex.

The fact of heredity being given, we have evidence derived from human practice as to the influence of selection. There are large numbers of domesticated races of animals and plants admirably suited in various ways to man's use or fancy—adapted to the environment of which his need and inclination are the most essential constituents. We cannot suppose that all the breeds were suddenly produced as perfect and as useful as we now see them; indeed, in many cases, we know that this has not been their history. The key is man's power of accumulative selection. Nature gives successive variations; man adds them up in certain directions useful to him. In this sense he may be said to have made for himself useful breeds.

The great power of this principle of selection is not hypothetical. It is certain that several of our eminent breeders have, even within a single lifetime, modified to a large extent their breeds of cattle and sheep. What English breeders have actually effected is proved by the enormous prices given for animals with a good pedigree;

206

and these have been exported to almost every quarter of the world. The same principles are followed by horticulturists, and we see an astonishing improvement in many florists' flowers, when the flowers of the present day are compared with drawings made only twenty or thirty years ago.

The practice of selection is far from being a modern discovery. The principle of selection I find distinctly given in an ancient Chinese encyclopaedia. Explicit rules are laid down by some of the Roman classical writers. It is clear that the breeding of domestic animals was carefully attended to in ancient times, and is now attended to by the lowest savages. It would, indeed, have been a strange fact had attention not been paid to breeding, for the inheritance of good and bad qualities is so obvious.

Study of the origin of our domestic races of animals and plants leads to the following conclusions. Changed conditions of life are of the highest possible importance in causing variability, both by acting directly on the organization, and indirectly by affecting the reproductive system. Spontaneous variation of unknown origin plays its part. Some, perhaps a great, effect may be attributed to the increased use or disuse of parts.

The final result is thus rendered infinitely complex. In some cases the intercrossing of aboriginally distinct species appears to have played an important part in the origin of our breeds. When several breeds have once been formed in any country, their occasional intercrossing, with the aid of selection, has, no doubt, largely aided in the formation of new sub-breeds; but the importance of crossing has been much exaggerated, both in regard to animals and to those plants which are propagated by seed. Over all these causes of change, the accumulative action of selection, whether applied methodically and quickly, or unconsciously and slowly, but more efficiently, seems to have been the predominant power.

VARIATION UNDER NATURE

Before applying these principles to organic beings in a state of nature, we must ascertain whether these latter are subject to

207

any variation. We find variation everywhere. Individual differences, though of small interest to the systematist, are of the highest importance for us, for they are often inherited; and they thus afford materials for natural selection to act and accumulate, in the same manner as man accumulates in any given direction individual differences in his domesticated productions. Further, what we call varieties cannot really be distinguished from species in the long run, a fact which we can clearly understand if species once existed as varieties, and thus originated. But the facts are utterly inexplicable if species are independent creations.

How have all the exquisite adaptations of one part of the body to another part, and to the conditions of life, and of one organic being to another being, been perfected? For everywhere we find these beautiful adaptations.

The answer is to be found in the struggle for life. Owing to this struggle, variations, however slight, and from whatever cause proceeding, if they be in any degree profitable to the individuals of a species in their infinitely complex relations to other organic beings and to their physical conditions of life, will tend to the preservation of such individuals, and will generally be inherited by the offspring. The offspring, also, will thus have a better chance of surviving, for, of the many individuals of any species which are periodically born, but a small number can survive. I have called this principle, by which each slight variation, if useful, is preserved, by the term Natural Selection, in order to mark its relation to man's power of selection. But the expression, often used by Mr. Herbert Spencer, of the Survival of the Fittest, is more accurate.

We have seen that man, by selection, can certainly produce great results, and can adapt organic beings to his own uses, through the accumulation of slight but useful variations given to him by the hand of Nature. Natural Selection is a power incessantly ready for action, and is as immeasurably superior to man's feeble efforts as the works of Nature are to those of Art.

All organic beings are exposed to severe competition. Nothing is easier than to admit in words the truth of the universal struggle for life, or more difficult—at least, I have found it so—than constantly to bear this conclusion in mind. Yet, unless it be thoroughly engrained in the mind, the whole economy of Nature, with every fact of distribution, rarity, abundance, extinction, and variation, will be dimly seen or quite misunderstood. We behold the face of Nature bright with gladness; we often see superabundance of food. We do not see, or we forget, that the birds which are idly singing round us mostly live on insects or seeds, and are thus constantly destroying life; or we forget how largely these song-sters, or their eggs, or their nestlings, are destroyed by birds or beasts of prey. We do not always bear in mind that, though food may be superabundant, it is not so at all seasons of each recurring year.

A struggle for existence, the term being used in a large, general, and metaphorical sense, inevitably follows from the high rate at which all organic beings tend to increase.

Every being, which during its natural lifetime produces several eggs or seeds, must suffer destruction during some period of its life, and during some season or occasional year; otherwise, on the principle of geometrical increase, its numbers would quickly become so inordinately great that no country could support the product. Hence, as more individuals are produced than can possibly survive, there must in every case be a struggle for existence, either one individual with another of the same species, or with the individuals of distinct species, or with the physical conditions of life. It is the doctrine of Malthus applied with manifold force to the whole animal and vegetable kingdoms; for in this case there can be no artificial increase of food, and no prudential restraint from marriage. Although some species may be now increasing, more or less rapidly, in numbers, all cannot do so, for the world would not hold them.

There is no exception to the rule that every organic being naturally increases at so high a rate that, if not destroyed, the earth would soon be covered by the progeny of a single pair. Even slow-breeding man has doubled in twenty-five years, and at this rate, in less than a thousand years, there would literally not be standing-room for his progeny. Linnaeus has calculated that if an annual plant produced only two seeds—and there is no plant so unproductive as this—and their seedlings next year produced two, and so on, then in twenty years there would be a million plants. The elephant is reckoned the slowest breeder of all known animals, and I have taken some pains to estimate its probable minimum rate of natural increase. It will be safest to assume that it begins breeding when thirty years old, and goes on breeding until ninety years old, bringing forth six young in the interval, and surviving till one hundred years old. If this be so, after a period of from 740 to 750 years there would be nearly nineteen million elephants alive, descended from the first pair.

The causes which check the natural tendency of each species to increase are most obscure. Eggs or very young animals seem generally to suffer most, but this is not invariably the case. With plants there is a vast destruction of seeds. The amount of food for each species of course gives the extreme limit to which each can increase; but very frequently it is not the obtaining food, but the serving as prey to other animals, which determines the average number of a species. Climate is important, and periodical seasons of extreme cold or drought seem to be the most effective of all checks.

The relations of all animals and plants to each other in the struggle for existence are most complex, and often unexpected. Battle within battle must be continually recurring with varying success; and yet in the long run the forces are so nicely balanced that the face of Nature remains for long periods of time uniform, though assuredly the merest trifle would give the victory to one organic being over another. Nevertheless, so profound is our ignorance, and so high our presumption, that we marvel when we hear of the extinction of an organic being; and as we do not see the cause, we invoke cataclysms to desolate the world, or invent laws on the duration of the forms of life!

The struggle for life is most severe between individuals and varieties of the same species. The competition is most severe between allied forms which fill nearly the same place in the economy of Nature. But great is our ignorance on the mutual relations of all organic beings. All that we can do is to keep steadily in mind that each organic being is striving to increase in a geometrical ratio; that each at some period of its life, during some season of the year, during each generation or at intervals, has to struggle for life and to suffer great destruction. When we reflect on this struggle, we may console ourselves with the full belief that the war of Nature is not incessant, that no fear is felt, that death is generally prompt, and that the vigorous, the healthy, and the happy survive and multiply.

THE SURVIVAL OF THE FITTEST

How will the struggle for existence act in regard to variation? Can the principle of selection, which we have seen is so potent in the hands of man, apply under Nature? I think we shall see that it can act most efficiently. Let the endless number of slight variations and individual differences occurring in our domestic productions, and, in a lesser degree, in those under Nature, be borne in mind, as well as the strength of the hereditary tendency. Under domestication, it may be truly said that the whole organization becomes in some degree plastic.

But the variability, which we almost universally meet with in our domestic productions, is not directly produced by man; he can neither originate variations nor prevent their occurrence; he can only preserve and accumulate such as do occur. Unintentionally he exposes organic beings to new and changing conditions of life, and variability ensues; but similar changes of condition might and do occur under Nature.

Let it also be borne in mind how infinitely complex and close-fitting are the mutual relations of all organic beings to each other and to their physical conditions of life, and consequently what infinitely varied diversities of structure might be of use to each being under changing conditions of life. Can it, then, be thought improbable, seeing what variations useful to man have undoubtedly occurred, that other variations, useful in some way to each being in the great complex battle of life, should occur in the course of many successive generations? If such do occur, can we doubt, remembering that many more individuals are born than

211

can possibly survive, that individuals having any advantage over others, would have the best chance of surviving and of procreating their kind? On the other hand, we may feel sure that any variation in the least degree injurious would be rigidly destroyed. This preservation of favorable individual differences and variations, and the destruction of those which are injurious, I have called Natural Selection, or the Survival of the Fittest.

The term is too frequently misapprehended. Variations neither useful nor injurious would not be affected by natural selection. It is not asserted that natural selection induces variability. It implies only the preservation of such varieties as arise and are beneficial to the being under its conditions of life. Again, it has been said that I speak of natural selection as an active Power or Deity; but who objects to an author speaking of the attraction of gravity as ruling the movements of the planets? It is difficult to avoid personifying the word Nature; but I mean by Nature only the aggregate action and product of many natural laws, and by laws the sequence of events as ascertained by us.

As man can produce, and certainly has produced, a great result by his methodical and unconscious means of selection, what may not natural selection effect? Man can act only on external and visible characters; Nature, if I may be allowed to personify the natural preservation or survival of the fittest, cares nothing for appearances, except in so far as they are useful to any being. She can act on every internal organ, on every shade of constitutional difference, on the whole machinery of life. Man selects only for his own good; Nature only for that of the being which she tends. Every selected character is fully exercised by her, as is implied by the fact of their selection. Man keeps the natives of many climates in the same country; he seldom exercises each selected character in some peculiar and fitting manner; he feeds a long and a short-beaked pigeon on the same food; he does not exercise a long-backed or long-legged quadruped in any peculiar manner; he exposes sheep with long and short wool to the same climate.

Man does not allow the most vigorous males to struggle for the females. He does not rigidly destroy all inferior animals, but protects during each varying season, as far as lies in his power, all his productions. He often begins his selection by some half-monstrous form; or at least by some modification prominent enough to catch the eye or to be plainly useful to him.

But under Nature, the slightest differences of structure or constitution may well turn the nicely-balanced scale in the struggle for life, and so be preserved. How fleeting are the wishes and efforts of man! How short his time! And, consequently, how poor will be his results compared with those accumulated by Nature during whole geological periods! Can we wonder that Nature's productions should be far "truer" in character than man's productions; that they should be infinitely better adapted to the most complex conditions of life, and should plainly bear the stamp of far higher workmanship?

It may metaphorically be said that natural selection is daily and hourly scrutinising, throughout the world, the slightest variations; rejecting those that are bad, preserving and adding up all that are good; silently and insensibly working, whenever and wherever opportunity offers, at the improvement of each organic being in relation to its organic and inorganic conditions of life. We see nothing of these slow changes in progress until the hand of time has marked the lapse of ages, and then so imperfect is our view into long-past geological ages that we see only that the forms of life are now different from what they formerly were.

Although natural selection can act only through and for the good of each being, yet characters and structures, which we are apt to consider as of very trifling importance, may thus be acted on.

Natural selection will modify the structure of the young in relation to the parent, and of the parent in relation to the young. In social animals it will adapt the structure of each individual for the benefit of the whole community, if the community profits by the selected change. What natural selection cannot do is to modify the structure of one species, without giving it any advantage, for the good of another species; and though statements to this effect may be found in works of natural history, I cannot find one case which will bear investigation.

A structure used only once in an animal's life, if of high im-

213

portance to it, might be modified to any extent by natural selection; for instance, the great jaws possessed by certain insects, used exclusively for opening the cocoon, or the hard tip to the beak of unhatched birds, used for breaking the egg. It has been asserted that of the best short-beaked tumbler pigeons a greater number perish in the egg than are able to get out of it; so that fanciers assist in the act of hatching. Now, if Nature had to make the beak of a full-grown pigeon very short for the bird's own advantage, the process of modification would be very slow, and there would be simultaneously the most rigorous selection of all the young birds within the egg, for all with weak beaks would inevitably perish; or more easily broken shells might be selected, the thickness of the shell being known to vary like every other structure.

With all beings there must be much fortuitous destruction, which can have little or no influence on the course of natural selection. For instance, a vast number of eggs or seeds are annually devoured, and these could be modified through natural selection only if they varied in some manner which protected them from their enemies. Yet many of these eggs or seeds would perhaps, if not destroyed, have yielded individuals better adapted to their conditions of life than any of those which happened to survive. So, again, a vast number of mature animals and plants, whether or not they be the best adapted to their conditions, must be annually destroyed by accidental causes, which would not be in the least degree mitigated by certain changes of structure or constitution which would in other ways be beneficial to the species.

But let the destruction of the adults be ever so heavy, if the number which can exist in any district be not wholly kept down by such causes—or, again, let the destruction of eggs or seeds be so great that only a hundredth or a thousandth part are developed—yet of those which do survive, the best adapted individuals, supposing there is any variability in a favorable direction, will tend to propagate their kind in larger numbers than the less well adapted.

On our theory the continued existence of lowly organisms offers no difficulty; for natural selection does not necessarily include

progressive development; it only takes advantage of such variations as arise and are beneficial to each creature under its complex
relations of life.

The mere lapse of time by itself does nothing, either for or
against natural selection. I state this because it has been erroneously asserted that the element of time has been assumed by me
to play an all-important part in modifying species, as if all the
forms of life were necessarily undergoing change through some
innate law.

SEXUAL SELECTION

This form of selection depends, not on a struggle for existence
in relation to other organic beings or to external conditions, but
on a struggle between the individuals of one sex, generally the
males, for the possession of the other sex. The result is not death
to the unsuccessful competitor, but few or no offspring. Sexual
selection is, therefore, less rigorous than natural selection. Generally, the most vigorous males, those which are best fitted for
their places in Nature, will leave most progeny. But, in many
cases, victory depends not so much on general vigour as on having
special weapons, confined to the male sex. A hornless stag or
spurless cock would have a poor chance of leaving numerous offspring. Sexual selection, by always allowing the victor to breed,
might surely give indomitable courage, length to the spur, and
strength to the wing to strike in the spurred leg, in nearly the same
manner as does the brutal cock-fighter by the careful selection
of his best cocks.

How low in the scale of Nature the law of battle descends I
know not. Male alligators have been described as fighting, bellow-
ing, and whirling round, like Indians in a war-dance, for the possession of the females; male salmons have been observed fighting
all day long; male stag-beetles sometimes bear wounds from the
mandibles of other males; the males of certain other insects have
been frequently seen fighting for a particular female who sits by,
an apparently unconcerned beholder of the struggle, and then
retires with the conqueror. The war is, perhaps, severest between

the males of the polygamous animals, and these seem oftenest provided with special weapons. The males of carnivorous animals are already well armed, though to them special means of defence may be given through means of sexual selection, as the mane of the lion and the hooked jaw of the salmon. The shield may be as important for victory as the sword or spear.

Amongst birds, the contest is often of a more peaceful character. All those who have attended to the subject believe that there is the severest rivalry between the males of many species to attract, by singing, the females. The rock-thrush of Guiana, birds of paradise, and some others, congregate; and successive males display with the most elaborate care, and show off in the best manner, their gorgeous plumage; they likewise perform strange antics before the females, which, standing by as spectators, at last choose the most attractive partner.

If man can in a short time give beauty and an elegant carriage to his bantams, according to his standard of beauty, I can see no good reason to doubt that female birds, by selecting, during thousands of generations, the most melodious or beautiful males, according to their standard of beauty, might produce a marked effect.

THE STRUGGLE FOR EXISTENCE

Under domestication we see much variability, caused, or at least excited, by changed conditions of life; but often in so obscure a manner that we are tempted to consider the variations as spontaneous. Variability is governed by many complex laws—by correlated growth, compensation, the increased use and disuse of parts, and the definite action of the surrounding conditions. There is much difficulty in ascertaining how largely our domestic productions have been modified; but we may safely infer that the amount has been large, and that modifications can be inherited for long periods. As long as the conditions of life remain the same, we have reason to believe that a modification, which has already been inherited for many generations, may continue to be inherited for an almost infinite number of generations. On the other hand, we have evidence that variability, when it has once come into play, does not cease under domestication for a very long period; nor do we know that it ever ceases, for new varieties are still occasionally produced by our oldest domesticated productions.

Variability is not actually caused by man; he only unintentionally exposes organic beings to new conditions of life, and then Nature acts on the organisation and causes it to vary. But man can and does select the variations given to him by Nature, and thus accumulates them in any desired manner. He thus adapts animals and plants for his own benefit or pleasure. He may do this methodically, or he may do it unconsciously by preserving the individuals most useful or pleasing to him without an intention of altering the breed.

It is certain that he can influence the character of a breed by selecting, in each successive generation, individual differences so slight as to be inappreciable except by an educated eye. This unconscious process of selection has been the agency in the formation of the most distinct and useful domestic breeds. That many breeds produced by man have to a large extent the character of natural species is shown by the inextricable doubts whether many of them are varieties or aboriginally distinct species.

There is no reason why the principles which have acted so efficiently under domestication should not have acted under Nature. In the survival of favoured individuals and races, during the constantly recurrent struggle for existence, we see a powerful and ever-acting form of selection. The struggle for existence inevitably follows from the high geometrical ratio of increase which is common to all organic beings. This high rate of increase is proved by calculation; by the rapid increase of many animals and plants during a succession of peculiar seasons and when naturalised in new countries. More individuals are born than can possibly survive. A grain in the balance may determine which individuals shall live and which shall die; which variety or species shall increase in number, and which shall decrease, or finally become extinct.

As the individuals of the same species come in all respects into

217

the closest competition with each other, the struggle will generally be most severe between them; it will be almost equally severe between the varieties of the same species, and next in severity between the species of the same genus. On the other hand, the struggle will often be severe between beings remote in the scale of Nature. The slightest advantage in certain individuals, at any age or during any season, over those with which they come into competition, or better adaptation, in however slight a degree, to the surrounding physical conditions, will, in the long run, turn the balance.

With animals having separated sexes, there will be in most cases a struggle between the males for the possession of the females. The most vigorous males, or those which have most successfully struggled with their conditions of life, will generally leave most progeny. But success will often depend on the males having special weapons, or means of defence, or charms; and a slight advantage will lead to victory.

As geology plainly proclaims that each land has undergone great physical changes, we might have expected to find that organic beings have varied under domestication. And if there has been any variability under Nature, it would be an unaccountable fact if natural selection had not come into play. It has often been asserted, but the assertion is incapable of proof, that the amount of variation under Nature is a strictly limited quantity. Man, though acting on external characters alone, and often capriciously, can produce within a short period a great result by adding up mere individual differences in his domestic productions; and everyone admits that species present individual differences. But, besides such differences, all naturalists admit that natural varieties exist, which are considered sufficiently distinct to be worthy of record in systematic works.

No one has drawn any clear distinction between individual differences and slight varieties, or between more plainly marked varieties and sub-species and species. On separate continents, and on different parts of the same continent when divided by barriers of any kind, what a multitude of forms exist which some experienced naturalists rank as varieties, others as geographical races or sub-species, and others as distinct, though closely allied species!

If, then, animals and plants do vary, let it be ever so slightly or slowly, why should not variations of individuals, differences which are in any way beneficial, be preserved and accumulated through natural selection, or the survival of the fittest? If man can, by patience, select variations useful to him, why, under changing and complex conditions of life, should not variations useful to Nature's living products often arise, and be preserved, or selected? What limit can be put to this power, acting during long ages and rigidly scrutinising the whole constitution, structure, and habits of each creature—favouring the good and rejecting the bad? I can see no limit to this power, in slowly and beautifully adapting each form to the most complex relations of life.

In the future I see open fields for far more important researches. Psychology will be based on the foundation already well laid by Mr. Herbert Spencer that of the necessary acquirement of each mental power and capacity by gradation. Much light will be thrown on the origin of man and his history.

Authors of the highest eminence seem to be fully satisfied with the view that each species has been independently created. To my mind it accords better with what we know of the laws impressed on matter by the Creator that the production and extinction of the past and present inhabitants of the world should have been due to secondary causes, like those determining the birth and death of the individual. When I view all beings not as special creations, but as the lineal descendants of some few beings which lived long before the first bed of Cambrian system was deposited, they seem to me to become ennobled. Judging from the past, we may safely infer that not one living species will transmit its unaltered likeness to a distant futurity.

Of the species now living very few will transmit progeny of any kind to a far distant futurity; for the manner in which all organic beings are grouped shows that the greater number of species in each genus, and all the species in many genera, have left no descendants, but have become utterly extinct. We can so far take a prophetic glance into futurity as to foretell that it will be the common and widely-spread species, belonging to the larger and dominant groups within each class, which will ultimately prevail and procreate new and dominant species. As all the living forms of life are the lineal descendants of those which lived long before the Cambrian epoch, we may feel certain that the ordinary succession by generation has never once been broken, and that no cataclysm has desolated the whole world. We may look with some confidence to a secure future of great length. As natural selection works solely by and for the good of each being, all corporeal and mental endowments will tend to progress towards perfection.

It is interesting to contemplate a tangled bank, clothed with many plants of many kinds, with birds singing on the bushes, with various insects flitting about, and with worms crawling through the damp earth, and to reflect that these elaborately constructed forms, so different from each other, and dependent upon each other in so complex a manner, have all been produced by laws acting around us. These laws, taken in the largest sense, being Growth with Reproduction; Inheritance, which is almost implied by reproduction; Variability from the indirect and direct action of the conditions of life, and from use and disuse; a ratio of increase so high as to lead to a struggle for life, and, as a consequence, to Natural Selection, entailing Divergence of Character and the Extinction of less improved forms. Thus, from the war of Nature, from famine and death, the most exalted object which we are capable of conceiving, namely, the production of the higher animals, directly follows. There is grandeur in this view of life, with its several powers, having been originally breathed by the Creator into a few forms, or into one; and that, whilst this planet has gone cycling on according to the fixed law of gravity, from so simple a beginning endless forms most beautiful and most wonderful have been, and are being, evolved.

WILLIAM MORRIS DAVIS

(1850–1934)

American geologist and geographer, Davis spent most of his life on the faculty of Harvard University. He served as physiographer on the Carnegie Institution's expedition to Turkestan in 1903, and was the leader of the so-called American school of physiographers. Works: *Elementary Meteorology* (1894), *Geographical Essays* (1909), and *Coral Reef Problem* (1928).

THE RIVERS AND VALLEYS OF PENNSYLVANIA

RIVERS ARE so long lived and survive with more or less modification so many changes in the attitude and even in the structure of the land, that the best way of entering on their discussion seems to be to examine the development of an ideal river of simple history, and from the general features thus discovered, it may then be possible to unravel the complex sequence of events that leads to the present condition of actual rivers of complicated history.

A river that is established on a new land may be called an original river. It must at first be of the kind known as a consequent river, for it has no ancestor from which to be derived. Examples of simple original rivers may be seen in young plains, of which southern New Jersey furnishes a fair illustration. Examples of essentially original rivers may be seen also in regions of recent and rapid displacement, such as the Jura or the broken country of southern Idaho, where the directly consequent character of the drainage leads us to conclude that, if any rivers occupied these regions before their recent deformation, they were so completely extinguished by the newly made slopes that we see nothing of them now.

221

Once established, an original river advances through its long life, manifesting certain peculiarities of youth, maturity and old age, by which its successive stages of growth may be recognized without much difficulty. For the sake of simplicity, let us suppose the land mass, on which an original river has begun its work, stands perfectly still after its first elevation or deformation, and so remains until the river has completed its task of carrying away all the mass of rocks that rise above its base level. This lapse of time will be called a cycle in the life of a great river. A complete cycle is a long measure of time in regions of great elevation or of hard rocks; but whether or not any river ever passed through a single cycle of life without interruption we need not now inquire. Our purpose is only to learn what changes it would experience if it did thus develop steadily from infancy to old age without disturbance.

In its infancy, the river drains its basin imperfectly; for it is then embarrassed by the original inequalities of the surface, and lakes collect in all the depressions. At such time, the ratio of evaporation to rainfall is relatively large, and the ratio of transported land waste to rainfall is small. The channels followed by the streams that compose the river as a whole are narrow and shallow, and their number is small compared to that which will be developed at a later stage. The divides by which the side-streams are separated are poorly marked, and in level countries are surfaces of considerable area and not lines at all. It is only in the later maturity of a system that the divides are reduced to lines by the consumption of the softer rocks on either side. The difference between constructional forms and those forms that are due to the action of denuding forces is in a general way so easily recognized, that immaturity and maturity of a drainage area can be readily discriminated. In the truly infantile drainage system of the Red River of the North, the inter-stream areas are so absolutely flat that water collects on them in wet weather, not having either original structural slope or subsequently developed denuded slope to lead it to the streams. On the almost equally young lava blocks of southern Oregon, the well-marked slopes are as yet hardly channeled by the flow of rain down them, and the depressions among the tilted blocks are still undrained, unfilled basins.

As the river becomes adolescent, its channels are deepened and all the larger ones descend close to base level. If local contrasts of hardness allow a quick deepening of the down-stream part of the channel, while the part next up-stream resists erosion, a cascade of waterfall results; but like the lakes of earlier youth, it is evanescent, and endures but a small part of the whole cycle of growth; but the falls on the small headwater streams of a large river may last into its maturity, just as there are young twigs on the branches of a large tree. With the deepening of the channels, there comes an increase in the number of gulleys on the slopes of the channel; the gulleys grow into ravines and these into side valleys, joining their master streams at right angles (La Noë and Margerie). With their continued development, the maturity of the system is reached; it is marked by an almost complete acquisition of every part of the original constructional surface by erosion under the guidance of the streams, so that every drop of rain that falls finds a way prepared to lead it to a stream and then to the ocean, its goal. The lakes of initial imperfection have long since disappeared; the waterfalls of adolescence have been worn back, unless on the still young headwaters. With the increase of the number of side-streams, ramifying into all parts of the drainage basin, there is a proportionate increase in the rate of waste under atmospheric forces; hence it is at maturity that the river receives and carries the greatest load; indeed, the increase may be carried so far that the lower trunk-stream, of gentle slope in its early maturity, is unable to carry the load brought to it by the upper branches, and therefore resorts to the temporary expedient of laying it aside in a flood-plain. The level of the flood-plain is sometimes built up faster than the small side-streams of the lower course can fill their valley, and hence they are converted for a little distance above their mouths into shallow lakes. The growth of the flood-plain also results in carrying the point of junction of tributaries farther and farther down stream, sometimes forcing them to follow independent courses to the sea (Lombardini). But although thus separated from the

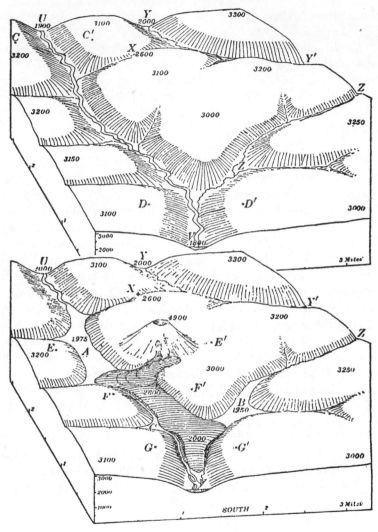

Fig. 1

main trunk, it would be no more rational to regard such streams as independent rivers than it would be to regard the branch of an old tree, now fallen to the ground in the decay of advancing

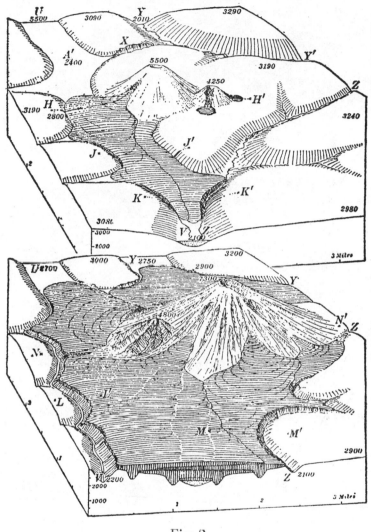

Fig. 2

age, as an independent plant; both are detached portions of a single individual, from which they have been separated in the normal processes of growth and decay.

225

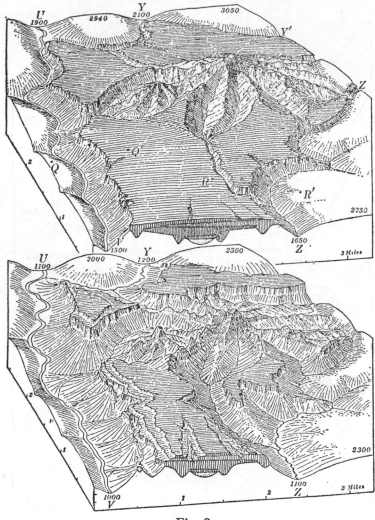

Fig. 3

In the later and quieter old age of a river system, the waste of the land is yielded slower by reason of the diminishing slopes of the valley sides; then the headwater streams deliver less detritus to the main channel, which, thus relieved, turns to its post-

226

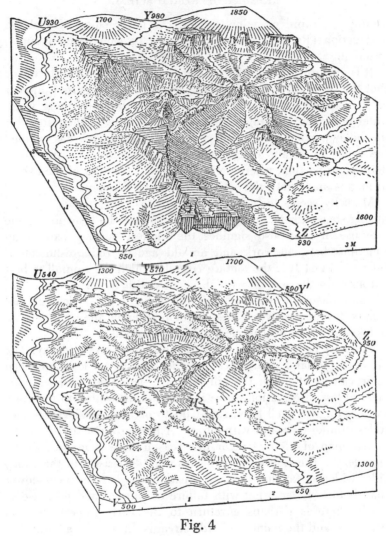

Fig. 4

poned task of carrying its former excess of load to the sea, and cuts terraces in its flood-plain, preparatory to sweeping it away. It does not always find the buried channel again, and perhaps settling down on a low spur a little to one side of its old line,

227

produces a rapid or a low fall on the lower slope of such an obstruction (Penck). Such courses may be called locally superimposed.

It is only during maturity and for a time before and afterwards that the three divisions of a river, commonly recognized, appear most distinctly; the torrent portion being the still young headwater branches, growing by gnawing backwards at their sources; the valley portion proper, where longer time of work has enabled the valley to obtain a greater depth and width; and the lower flood-plain portion, where the temporary deposition of the excess of load is made until the activity of middle life is past.

Maturity seems to be a proper term to apply to this long enduring stage; for as in organic forms, where the term first came into use, it here also signifies the highest development of all functions between work and an old age of relinquishment of fullest powers. It is the mature river in which the rainfall is best led away to the sea, and which carries with it the greatest load of land waste; it is at maturity that the regular descent and steady flow of the river is best developed, being the least delayed in lakes and least overhurried in impetuous falls.

Maturity past, and the power of the river is on the decay. The relief of the land diminishes, for the streams no longer deepen their valleys although the hill tops are degraded; and with the general loss of elevation, there is a failure of rainfall to a certain extent; for it is well known that up to certain considerable altitudes rainfall increases with height. A hyetographic and a hypsometric map of a country for this reason show a marked correspondence. The slopes of the headwaters decrease and the valley sides widen so far that the land waste descends from them slower than before. Later, what with failure of rainfall and decrease of slope, there is perhaps a return to the early imperfection of drainage, and the number of side streams diminishes as branches fall from a dying tree. The flood-plains of maturity are carried down to the sea, and at last the river settles down to an old age of well-earned rest with gentle flow and light load, little work remaining to be done. The great task that the river entered upon is completed.

RENÉ DESCARTES

(1596–1650)

Descartes was equally noted as a mathematician and a philosopher.
Indeed, the Cartesian system introduced mathematical certitude into
metaphysical speculation, discarding the diffuse subtleties of medieval
Scholasticism. Educated as a Jesuit and trained for an army career,
Descartes developed his mathematical gifts early and became not
only the father of modern philosophy but the founder of analytical
geometry—the representing of lines and curves by equations. His
theory of vortices, explaining the motions of heavenly bodies, was
accepted until replaced by Newton's theory of gravitation. He used
Snell's law of refraction of light to explain the rainbow, though here
again it was Newton who finally accounted for its colors. His philosophic masterwork, *Discours de la Méthode* was supplemented by
three scientific essays, *La Géométrie, Les Météores* and *La Dioptrique,*
from which two selections are taken here. Other works: *Meditationes
de Prima Philosophia* (1641), *Principia Philosophiae* (1644), and
De l'Homme (1664).

REFRACTION OF LIGHT

SINCE WE shall need hereafter to know exactly the quantity of
this refraction, and that it may be conveniently understood by
the comparison which I am going to use, I believe that it is
proper that I attempt here a complete explanation and that I
speak first therefore of reflection, so as to make it easier to
understand the explanation of refraction. Let us suppose therefore that a ball driven from *A* to *B* (Fig. 1) encounters at the
point *B* the surface of the earth *CBE*; which prevents its going
on and is the reason that it changes its direction. Let us see
toward what side. But first, in order that we shall not embarrass
ourselves with new difficulties, let us suppose that the earth is

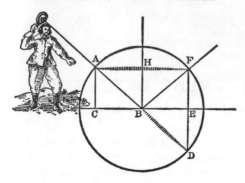

Fig. 1

perfectly flat and hard, and that the ball proceeds always with constant velocity, both as it descends and as it rises again, not inquiring in any way about the force which maintains its motion after it is no longer in contact with the racquet, and not considering any effect of its weight or its size or its shape. For there is no question here of looking so closely into the matter, and none of these things come into the action of the light, to which this motion is to be compared. It only needs to be noticed that the force, whatever it may be, which keeps up the motion of the ball, is different from that which makes it move in one direction rather than in another, as it is very easy to see from this, that it is the force by which it has been driven by the racquet on which its motion depends, and that this same force would have been able to make it move in any other direction as easily as toward B, while in fact it is the position of the racquet which makes it move toward B, and which would have been able to make it move in the same way, even if another force had moved it. This shows already that it is not impossible that the ball may be turned in its path by its encounter with the earth, and that the tendency which it had to go to B may be changed without anything being changed in the force of its motion, since they are two different things; and consequently that we should not imagine that it is necessary that it should stop for a moment at the point B, before turning toward F, as several of our philosophers

230

would have it do; for if its motion were once interrupted by this check, there would be no cause which would thereafter make it start off again. Furthermore, it must be remarked that the tendency to move itself in any direction, just as well as the motion itself, and generally as any other sort of quantity, may be divided into all the parts of which we may imagine that it is compounded, and that we may easily imagine that this motion of the ball which moves it from A to B is compounded of two others, one of which would make it descend from the line AF toward the line CE, and the other would, at the same time, make it go from the left-hand line AC toward the right-hand line FE, so that these two motions together carry it to B along the line AB. And further it is easy to understand that the encounter with the earth can only prevent one of these two motions, and cannot affect the other in any way. For it certainly ought to prevent that motion which would make the ball descend from AF toward CE, because it occupies all the space which is below CE; but why should it prevent the other motion, which would make it advance toward the right, seeing that it is not opposed in any way in that sense? Therefore, to find out correctly in what direction the ball ought to rebound, we describe a circle with the center B, which passes through the point A, and we say that, in the same time that it would take to move from A to B, it infallibly should return from B to some point of the circumference of this circle, in as much as all the points which are as distant from the center B as A is, are found in this circumference, and we suppose the motion of the ball to be always equally swift. Then finally, to find out precisely to which one of all the points of this circumference it ought to return, we draw three straight lines AC, HB, and FE, perpendicular to CE, and in such a way that there is neither more nor less distance between AC and HB than between HB and FE: and we say that in the same time that the ball has advanced toward the right from A, one of the points of the line AC, to B, one of the points of the line HB, it should also move from the line HB as far as some point of the line FE; for all the points of this line FE are as far away from the line HB in this sense on the one side as those of the line AC are on the other, and it is also as ready to

231

move in this direction as it was before. Now it cannot in the same time reach some point in the line *FE*, and also some point in the circumference of the circle *AFD*, except at the point *D*, or at the point *F*, since there are only these two points where these lines cut each other; so that since the earth prevents its passing toward *D*, we must conclude that it must go infallibly toward *F*, and so you see easily how reflection occurs, that is, with an angle equal to that which we call the angle of incidence. Thus if a ray coming from the point *A* falls at the point *B* on the surface of a plane mirror *CBE*, it is reflected toward *F* in such a way that the angle of reflection *FBE* is neither greater nor less than the angle of incidence *ABC*.

We now come to refraction. And, first, we suppose that a ball, driven from *A* to *B*, (Fig. 2) encounters at the point *B*, not now

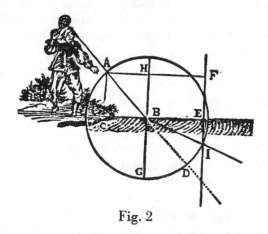

Fig. 2

the surface of the earth, but a cloth *CBE*, which is so weak and so thin that the ball can break it and pass entirely through it, losing only a part of its velocity, for example, half of it. Now, this being supposed, in order to determine what path it should follow, we notice first that its motion differs entirely from its tendency to move in one direction rather than in another; from which it follows that the quantities of these motions should be considered separately. And we notice also that of the two parts

232

of which we may imagine that this tendency is compounded, only that part which would make the ball move from above downward can be changed in any way by encountering the cloth; and that the tendency which made it move toward the right should always remain the same as it has been, because the cloth is in no way opposed to it in that sense. Then, having described from the center B the circle AFD and drawn at right angles to CBE the three straight lines AC, HB, FE, in such a way that there is twice as much distance between FE and HB as between HB and AC, we see that the ball ought to move toward the point I. For since it loses half of its velocity when it passes through the cloth CDE, it ought to take twice as long to move downward from B to some point of the circumference of the circle AFD as it has taken above it to pass from A to B. And, since it loses none of the tendency which it had previously to move toward the right, in twice the time that it has taken to pass from the line AC to HB it ought to travel twice as far in this same direction, and consequently should reach some point of the straight line FE at the same instant that it reaches also some point of the circumference of the circle AFD. This would be impossible if it did not go to I, since that is the only point below the cloth CBE where the circle AFD and the straight line FE cut each other.

Let us now think of the ball which moves from A toward D, as encountering at the point B, no longer a cloth, but water, of which the surface CBE deprives it of half of its velocity just as the cloth did. And supposing everything else to be the same as before, I say that the ball ought to pass from B in a straight line, not toward D but toward I. For, first, it is certain that the surface of the water ought to turn it toward that point in the same way that the cloth did, seeing that it deprives it of just as much of its force and is opposed to it in the same sense. Considering the body of water which fills all the space between B and I, while it may resist its motion more or less than the air did which we supposed before, we cannot say nevertheless that it ought to change its path; for it may open up to give it passage as easily in one direction as in another. At least that is so, if we suppose always, as we have done, that neither the weight nor the lightness

233

of the ball, nor its size, nor its shape, nor any other such cause changes its course. And we may here remark that it is so much more changed in direction by the surface of the water or by the cloth as it encounters it more obliquely; so that if it encounters the surface at right-angles, as when it is driven from *H* toward *B*, (Fig. 3) it ought to go on in a straight line toward *G* without

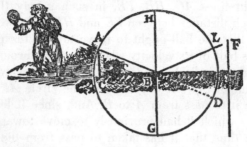

Fig. 3

turning out of it at all. But if it is driven along a line such as *AB*, which is so much inclined to the surface of the water or to the cloth *CBE*, that when the line *FE* is drawn as before it does not cut the circle *AD*, then the ball does not penetrate the surface at all but rebounds from the surface *B* toward the air *L*, just as if it had encountered the earth. This effect has sometimes produced the regrettable result that when cannon have been shot for fun toward the surface of a river, men have been wounded who were on the bank on the other side.

But now let us make here another supposition, and assume that the ball which has been first driven from *A* to *B* is driven just when it is at the point *B* by the racquet *CBE* which increases the force of its motion, for example, by a third, so that it can afterwards move over as great a distance in two moments as it did in three before. This will have the same effect as if the ball had encountered at the point *B* a body of such a nature that it passes through the surface *CBE* a third more easily than through air. It follows manifestly from that which has already been demonstrated, that if we describe the circle *AD* as before (Fig. 4)

234

Plate 29

William Conrad Roentgen

Plate **30**

Manfred Sakel

Plate 31

Baruch Spinoza

Plate 32

Leonardo da Vinci

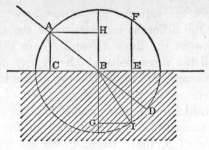

Fig. 4

and the lines *AC, HB, FE*, in such a way that there is a third less distance between *FE* and *HB* than between *HB* and *AC*, the point *I*, in which the straight line *FE* and the circular line *AD* cut each other, will determine the place toward which the ball which is at the point *B* should turn.

Now we may also take the reverse of this conclusion, and say that, since the ball which comes from *A* moves in a straight line as far as *B*, and at the point *B* turns and proceeds to the point *I*, this means that the force of facility with which it enters the body *CBEI* is to that with which it leaves the body *ACBE*, as the distance between *AC* and *HB* is to that which is between *HB* and *FI*, that is to say, as the line *CB* is to *BE*.

To conclude, inasmuch as the action of light follows in this respect the same laws as the motion of the ball, we must say that when its rays pass obliquely from one transparent body into another, which receives them more or less easily than the first body, they turn in such a way that they are always less inclined to the surface separating these bodies on the side where that body is which receives them more easily than on the side where the other body is, and this just in proportion to that which receives them more easily than the other does. Only we must take notice that this inclination should be measured by the magnitudes of the straight lines, like *CB* or *AH*, and *EB* or *IG*, and others like them, compared one to the other; not by the magnitudes of the angles, such as *ABH* or *GBI*; and much less by the magnitudes of the angles, such as *DBI*, which are called angles

235

of refraction. For the ratio or proportion between these angles changes for all the different inclinations of the rays, while that which holds between the lines *AH* and *IG*, or the like, remains the same for all the refractions which are caused by the same bodies. So, for example, (Fig. 5) if a ray passes in air from *A* to *B* and encounters at the point *B* the surface of glass *CBR*, so that it turns toward *I* in the glass; and if another one comes from *K* to *B* which turns toward *L*; and another from *P* toward *R* which turns toward *S*, there ought to be the same proportion between the lines *KM* and *LN*, or *PQ* and *ST*, as between *AH* and *IG*, but not the same proportion between the angles *KBM* and *LBN*, or *PRQ* and *SRT*, as between *ABH* and *IBG*.

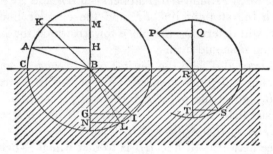

Fig. 5

Now that you see in what way refraction should be measured and further that to determine the quantity of refraction, in so far as it depends on the particular nature of the bodies in which it occurs, there is need of proceeding by experiment, there is found to be no difficulty in doing this with sufficient certainty and facility, since all refractions are thus reduced to the same measure; for it is only necessary to determine them for a single ray to determine all those which occur at the same surface, and we can avoid all error if we examine in addition some others. Thus if we wish to know the measure of the refractions which occur in the surface *CBR*, which separates air *AKP* from glass *LIS*, we have only to test the refraction of the ray *ABI*, by finding the ratio between the lines *AH* and *IG*. Then if we fear

236

we have made some mistake in this experiment, we can test
our result by using other rays, such as *KBL* or *PRS*, and when
we find the same ratio of *KL* to *LM* and of *PQ* to *ST* as that of
AH to *IG*, we shall have no further reason to question the accuracy of our experiment.

But perhaps you will be astonished when you make these
experiments to find that the rays of light are more inclined in
air than in water to the surface where the refractions occur; and
still more in water than in glass, exactly the opposite from the
course of a ball, which is more inclined to the surface in water
than in air and can not enter glass at all. For example, if a ball,
which is driven in air from *A* to *B* (Fig. 6), encounters the

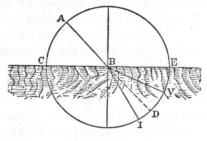

Fig. 6

surface of water *CBE* at the point *B*, it will be deflected from *B*
toward *V*; and if it is a ray of light it will go on the contrary
from *B* toward *I*. You will cease, however, to find this a strange
effect, if you recall the nature that I have attributed to light,
when I said that it is nothing other than a certain motion or an
action conceived in a very subtle matter, which fills the pores
of all other bodies; and when you consider that as a ball loses
more of its motion when it strikes against a soft body than
against a hard one, and that it rolls less easily on a table-cloth
than on a bare table; so the action of this subtle matter may be
much more restrained by the parts of the air which, being as they
are soft and loosely joined together, do not offer much resistance
to it than by the parts of the water, which offer more resistance,
and still more by the parts of the water than by those of glass

237

or crystal. Thus it happens that so much as the small parts of a transparent body are harder and firmer so much the more do they allow the light to pass more easily; for the light should not drive any of them out of their places, as a ball ought to drive out the parts of the water to find passage among them.

Further, as we now know the cause of the refractions which occur in water and in glass, and generally in all other transparent bodies which exist about us, we may remark that they should be in all respects similar when the rays come out from the bodies and when they enter them. Thus, if the ray which passes from A toward B is bent at B toward I in passing from air into glass, the ray which will come back from I toward B should also bend at B toward A. It may possibly be that other bodies may be found, principally in the skies, where refractions proceed from other causes and are not thus reciprocal. And there may also be other certain cases in which the rays ought to bend even though they pass only through a single transparent body; just as the motion of a ball is often a curved motion because it is turned in one direction by its weight, and in another by the action which has set it going; or for divers other reasons. In fact I dare to say that the three comparisons which I have just employed are so suitable that all the particularities which can be noticed are comparable with others which are found just like them in light; but I have not tried to explain those which are not of the most importance to my subject. And I shall not ask you to consider anything further except this, that the surfaces of transparent bodies which are curved bend the rays which pass at each of their points in the same way that plane surfaces would that we may imagine touching these bodies at the same points. Thus for example, the refraction of the rays AB, AC, AD, (Fig. 7) which come from the flame A and fall on the curved surface of the crystal ball BCD ought to be treated as if AB fell on the plane surface EBF and AC on GCH and AD on IDK, and so for the others. Thus you may see that these rays may be brought together or may separate in different ways, according as they fall on surfaces which are differently curved. It is time that I begin the description of the structure of the eye, that I

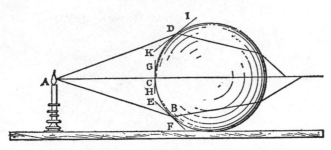

Fig. 7

may make you understand how the rays which enter within it conduct themselves so as to cause the sensation of sight.

THE RAINBOW

The rainbow is such a remarkable natural wonder and its cause has been so zealously sought by able men and is so little understood, that I thought that there was nothing I could choose which is better suited to show how, by the method which I employ, we can arrive at knowledge which those whose writings we possess have not had. In the first place, considering that this bow appears not only in the sky, but also in the air near us, wherever there are drops of water illuminated by the sun, as we can see in certain fountains, I readily decided that it arose only from the way in which the rays of light act on these drops and pass from them to our eyes. Further, knowing that the drops are round, as has been formerly proved, and seeing that whether they are larger or smaller, the appearance of the bow is not changed in any way, I had the idea of making a very large one, so that I could examine it better. For this purpose I filled with water a large glass phial, perfectly spherical in shape and very transparent, and then found that if the sunlight came, for example, from the part of the sky which is marked *AFZ* (Fig. 8), and my eye was at the point *E*, when I put the globe in the position *BCD*, its part *D* appeared all red, and much more bril-

239

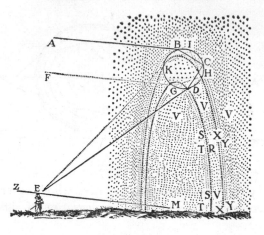

Fig. 8

liant than the rest of it; and that whether I approached it, or
receded from it, or put it on my right or my left, or even turned
it round about my head, provided that the line *DE* always made
an angle of about forty-two degrees with the line *EM*, which we
are to think of as drawn from the center of the sun to the eye,
the part *D* appeared always similarly red; but that as soon as I
made this angle *DEM* even a little smaller, the color did not
disappear so all at once, but divided itself first as if into two
parts, less brilliant, and in which I could see yellow, blue, and
other colors. Next, when I looked at that part of the globe which
is marked *K*, I saw that, if I made the angle *KEM* about fifty-two
degrees, the part *K* appeared also of a red color, but not so
bright as that at *D*; and if I made the angle a little larger, there
appeared other less brilliant colors, but if I made it even a little
smaller, or much larger, no colors at all appeared. From which I
clearly perceived that if all the air which is near *M* is filled with
such globes, or instead of them with drops of water, there ought
to appear a bright red point in every one of the drops so placed
that the lines drawn from them to the eye at *E* make an angle
of about forty-two degrees with the line *EM*, as I suppose those
do which are marked *R*; and that if we look at all these points

240

together, without any consideration of their exact position except of the angle at which they are viewed, they should appear as a continuous circle of a red color; and that something similar ought to appear at the points marked S and T, the lines drawn from which to E make more acute angles with EM, where there will be circles of less brilliant colors. This constitutes the first and principal rainbow. And further if the angle MEK is fifty-two degrees, there should appear a red circle in the drops marked X; and other circles of less brilliant colors in the drops marked Y. This constitutes the second and less important rainbow. And finally in all the other drops marked V no colors at all should appear. When I examined more particularly, in the globe BCD, what it was which made part D appear red, I found that it was the rays of the sun which, coming from A to B, bend on entering the water at the point B, and pass to C, where they are reflected to D, and bending there again as they pass out of the water, proceed to the point E; for when I put an opaque body or screen in any part of the lines AB, BC, CD, or DE, the red color disappeared. And although I covered all the globe except the two points B and D, and set up screens everywhere else, provided that I did not interfere with the rays ABCDE, the red never failed to appear. Then when I sought also for the cause of the red that appeared at K, I found that it was the rays which come from F to G, where they bend towards H, and at H are reflected to I, where they are again reflected to K, and finally bend at K and proceed to E. So that the first bow is caused by the rays which come to the eye after two refractions and one reflection, and the second by other rays which reach the eye only after two refractions and two reflections, so that it does not appear so often as the first one.

But the principal difficulty still remained, which was to determine why, since there are many other rays which can reach the eye after two refractions and one or two reflections when the globe is in some other position, it is only those of which I have spoken which exhibit the colors. And to answer that question I asked myself if there were not some other method of making the colors appear, so that by a comparison of the two I might better

241

determine the reason for them. Then remembering that a prism or triangle of glass shows similar colors, I considered such a prism as that represented at *MNP* (Fig. 9), whose two surfaces

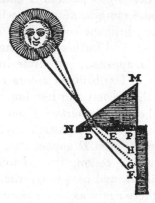

Fig. 9

MN and *NP* are plane and inclined to each other, at an angle of 30 or 40 degrees, so that if the rays of the sun *ABC* traverse *MN* perpendicularly, or almost perpendicularly, so that they experience no appreciable refraction, they will experience a considerable refraction as they pass out through *NP*. And when I covered one of these surfaces with a screen, in which there was a small opening *DE*, I observed that the rays which pass through this opening and are received on a white cloth or sheet of paper, show all the colors of the rainbow; and that the red always appears at *F* and the blue or violet at *H*. From which I learned, in the first place, that the curvature of the surface drops of water is not necessary for the production of the colors; for the surfaces of the crystal are plane; and that the size of the angle at which the colors appear is not important, since that can be changed without changing the colors; and even if we make the rays which go to *F* bend sometimes more and sometimes less than those which go to *H*, they still never fail to give red, and those which go to *H* to give blue; nor is reflection necessary, for there is none; nor finally the plurality of refractions, for in this case

242

there is only one. I decided however that at least one refraction is necessary, and one the effect of which is not destroyed by another contrary one; for experiment shows that if the surfaces *MN* and *NP* are parallel, the rays which are bent at the one surface return to their original direction at the other, and produce no colors. I had no doubt that light was necessary, for without it we should see nothing. And further I observed that a shadow or a limitation of the light was necessary; for if we remove the screen on *NP* the colors *FGH* no longer appear; and if we make the opening *DE* large enough, the red, the orange, and the yellow which go to *F* do not move farther out, nor do the green, the blue, and the violet, which go to *H*, but all the rest of the space between them at *G* remains white. . . .

However I was in doubt whether the colors of the rainbow are produced in the same way as they are in the crystal *MNP*; for I saw no shadow there to limit the light, and did not understand why the colors appeared only at certain angles; until I took my pen and made an accurate calculation of the paths of the rays which fall on the different points of a globe of water, to determine at what angles, after two refractions and one or two reflections they will come to the eye, and then I found that after one reflection or two refractions there are many more rays which can be seen at an angle of from forty-one to forty-two degrees than at any smaller angle; and that there are none which can be seen at a larger angle. I found also that, after two reflections and two refractions, there are many more rays which come to the eye at an angle of from fifty-one to fifty-two degrees than at any larger angle, and none which come at a smaller angle. Thus there is a shadow on one side and the other, which limits the light which, after having passed through an infinity of drops of rain illuminated by the sun, comes to the eye, at the angle of forty-two degrees or a little less, and thus causes the first and principal rainbow; and there is also a shadow which limits the light which comes at the angle of fifty-one degrees or a little greater, and causes the exterior bow; for to receive no rays of light in the eye, or to receive notably less light from an object than from another one which is near it, is to see a shadow. This shows clearly that the colors of these rainbows are produced by the same cause as that which produces them when we use the crystal *MNP*, and that the semi-diameter of the interior bow should not be greater than forty-two degrees or that of the exterior bow less than fifty-one degrees; and finally that the former should be more sharply limited at its outer edge than at its inner edge; and exactly the contrary with the latter, as is verified by observation.

RATIONAL BASIS FOR HYPOTHESIS OF CREATION OF SOLAR SYSTEM

I did resolve to leave all this world here to their disputes, and to speak only of that which would take place in a new, if God should now create in some region, in the imaginary spaces, enough material to compose it, and that he agitate diversely and without order the divers parts of this matter, so that he form of them a chaos as confused as the poets could imagine, and that, thereafter, he do nothing other than lend his usual aid to nature, and allow it to act according to the laws which he has established.

I shall show how the greatest part of the matter of this chaos, as result of these laws, ought to be disposed and arranged in a certain fashion which would render it similar to our heavens; how, meanwhile, some of its parts ought to compose an earth, and some, planets and comets, and some others a sun and fixed stars.

THE COMPOSITION OF THE EARTH

That the Earth and the Heaven are made of but one same matter

Finally, it is not difficult to infer from all this, that the earth and the heavens are all made of one same matter, and that although there were an infinity of worlds, they would be made only of this matter....

244

How this fourth body is broken into many pieces

But there being many crevices in the body *E*, which enlarge more and more, they are finally become so great that it cannot be longer sustained by the binding of its parts, and that the vault which it forms bursting all at once, its heaviness has made it fall in great pieces on the surface of the body *C*. But because this surface was not wide enough to receive all the pieces of this body in the same position as they were before, some fall on their sides and recline, the one upon the other. . . .

How the mountains, the plains, the seas, etc. have been produced

As a result, we may think of the bodies *B* and *F* as nothing other than air, that *D* is the water and *C*, a very solid and very heavy crust upon the earth's interior, from which come all the metals, and finally that *E* is another, less massive, crust of the earth, composed of stones, clay, sand, and mud. We see clearly the fashion in which the seas are made above the pieces 2, 3, 6, 7, and the like, and that those of the other pieces which are not

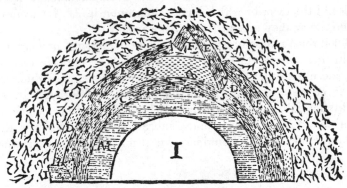

Fig. 10

Diagram used by Descartes to illustrate his ideas concerning the structure of the earth

covered with water nor much higher than the rest, have made plains; but that which has been more raised and strongly sloped, like 1, 2, and 9, 4, V, has made mountains.

245

How the metals come to be in the mines; and how vermilion is made there

Thus the vapors of the quicksilver which ascend through the small cracks and the wider pores of the inner earth, take with them also accessories of gold, silver, lead, or some other metal, which remain there thereafter, even though the quicksilver often does not stop there, because being very fluid it passes beyond, or even redescends. But it happens also that it does stop there sometimes, to wit, when it meets several exhalations of which the very loosely joined parts envelope its own and by this means change it into vermilion. For the rest, it is only the quicksilver which can carry with it the metals from the interior of the earth to the exterior, the spirits and exhalations are alike as regards some others, as those of copper, iron, and antimony.

Why metals are not found except in certain places of the earth

And it should be noted that these metals are rarely able to ascend save at those points of the inner earth, touched by the pieces of the exterior which have fallen upon it. As, for example, in the figure they ascend from 5 towards V. . . .

But it must not be hoped that, by dint of delving, one can ever attain this inner earth which I have said to be entirely metallic. For, more than that the exterior, which is above, is so thick that the force of men could hardly suffice to dig through it, one would not fail to meet various springs there, from which the water would issue with as much more impetuosity as they were opened lower; so that the miners could not avoid being drowned.

THOMAS ALVA EDISON

(1847–1931)

The most prolific of modern inventors, Edison made perhaps the largest single contribution to the industrial era which preceded the atomic age. Among his more than a thousand inventions may be mentioned the phonograph, the kinetoscope, the microphone, the incandescent electric lamp, the alkaline storage battery, the printing telegraph, the electric valve, the electric pen, mimeograph, and the carbon transmitter which enabled Bell to complete the telephone. A self-made American of the peak period of free enterprise, Edison had very little formal schooling, became a newsboy and telegraph operator at twelve, and died the director of laboratories employing thousands and organized like a modern industrial plant. The selection here describes his work on the motion picture, which he envisioned more as an education than as an entertainment medium.

THE BEGINNING OF MOTION PICTURES

IT WAS IN 1890 that we decided that we were far enough advanced in our plans for the development of animated photography to warrant a special building for our work, but it was such an ungainly looking structure when it was done, and the boys had so much sport with it, that we called it "The Black Maria."

Our studio was almost as amazing as the pictures we made in it: We were looking for service, not art. The building itself was about twenty-five by thirty feet in dimensions, and we gave a grotesque effect to the roof by slanting it up in a hunch in the center and arranging shutters that could be opened or closed with a pulley to obtain the greatest benefit from the light.

Then, in order to make certain of as long a working day as possible, we swung the whole building on pivots, like an old-

247

fashioned river bridge, so it could be turned to follow the course of the sun. We covered it with tar-paper outside, and painted it a dead black inside to bring our actors into the sharpest relief. It was a ghastly proposition for a stranger daring enough to brave its mysteries—especially when it began to turn like a ship in a gale. But we managed to make pictures there. And, after all, that was the real test.

"The Black Maria" always reminded me of an Irishman who used to work for me in my early days when we were trying out a certain variation of the railroad telegraph system; that is, sending a message from an ordinary wire to and from a moving train. We were working with our apparatus down on Staten Island at the time, and my Irish friend—his name was King—was in charge of the crew on the line.

He was a good electrician, too, but for some reason he had difficulty in making the system operate as it should. Strange to say, it worked like a charm when the train was running in one direction, but as soon as it started on its return trip troubles began. Although King would swear and tear his hair he couldn't fathom the source of the disturbance.

Finally, in disgust he wrote me that the only solution he could think of was for me to run an axle under Staten Island so the island could be turned instead of the train! This was a good deal the same kind of problem we had with our old "Black Maria." But we couldn't very well control the sun. So we had to compromise, and fix up a contrivance to turn the studio.

We didn't use artificial lights in those days. We had to depend altogether on nature. Therefore, it was a case of literally having to follow up the sun so as to extract all the benefit we could from every fugitive ray. Crude methods, the modern film producer may say, but they gave us results and fairly continuous results, too.

The phonograph first suggested the motion picture camera. I had been working for several years on my experiments for recording and reproducing sounds, and the thought occurred to me that it should be possible to devise an apparatus to do for the eye what the phonograph was designed to do for the ear.

That was the broad purpose, but how to accomplish that purpose was a problem which seemed more impossible the longer I studied it. It was in 1887 that I began my investigations, and photography, compared to what it is today, was in a decidedly crude state of development. Pictures were made by "wet" plates, operated by involved mechanism. The modern dry films were unheard of.

. I had only one fact to guide me at all. This was the principle of optics, technically called "the persistence of vision," which proves that the sensation of light lingers in the brain for anywhere from one-tenth to one-twentieth part of a second after the light itself has disappeared from the sight of the eye.

Ptolemy, the ancient Greek mathematician, first demonstrated this truth by means of a wooden wheel, painted with spots of red paint. As the wheel was whirled swiftly around, the spots on its surface apparently melted together and gave the effect of one continuous red streak, although when the wheel had stopped it was seen the spots had not changed their positions at all.

This fact served as the basic principle for various mechanical toys, creating the illusion of pictures that moved before the eyes of the beholder. A very simple contrivance of this kind was a spinning cardboard, revolving on a string. On one side was the picture of a man, and on the other side the picture of a galloping horse. As the card was spun, the man apparently leaped into the saddle of the horse, whereas what actually happened was that the revolutions of the card brought the second picture into view before the eye had lost the mental image of the first. I presume the inventor of the novelty made a good sum. He deserved to.

This same idea was later elaborated into a contrivance called the "Zoetrope" that was very popular when I was a young man. Around the inside lower rim of a cylinder affair, opened at the top, a series of related pictures was pasted, generally of a humorous character. As the cylinder was rapidly rotated, the wondering eye, glued to the opening in the top, was regaled with a succession of scenes presumed to have all of the appearance of life. The fact that most of the pictures were wood-cuts and that the action didn't always match at the right moment created at times a weird effect, but for years the Zoetrope was one of the most popular fads of the day.

The photographic art itself was beginning to languish, but even with its imperfections it remained for the camera to add the needed touch of finish and reality to the revolving pictures. The circumstances of how this came about were rather curious. Indeed, I don't think that many persons today, even connected with the film industry, are familiar with the facts of how photography contrived to introduce the semblance of motion in its product.

An Englishman of the name of Muybridge, who was an enthusiast on two subjects—cameras and race-horses—was visiting at his California farm Senator Leland Stanford, who was also something of a "crank" on the subject of blooded trotters. During the visit the merits of a certain horse, owned by the Senator, came under discussion, Stanford contending for one fact, and his guest arguing for another. To settle the dispute Muybridge conceived an ingenious plan.

Along one side of the private race-course on the farm he placed a row of twenty-four cameras. Attached to the shutter of each, he fastened a long thread, which in turn was carried across the track, and then, to make sure of obtaining sharp exposures, he erected a white screen opposite to serve as a reflector. When all was in readiness the race-horse was turned loose down the track.

As it dashed past the rows of cameras the various threads were snapped, and a series of photographs, establishing each successive point in the "action" of the horse, were automatically registered. When they were developed they revealed for the first time a complete photographic record of the minutest details of a horse in actual motion, and Muybridge had the satisfaction of using them to win his argument.

He would have laid the pictures away in his private collection, but someone suggested trying the effect on a Zoetrope apparatus. The result was so startling that it created something of a public sensation. But, except as a novelty, there was little practicable

250

benefit gained. To have made an actual motion picture, lasting even for the space of a single minute, at the rate of twelve exposures per second, the minimum for steady illusion, would have required, under the plan of Muybridge, seven hundred and twenty different cameras.

There were many problems connected with the first motion picture camera, but before everything else came the question of making a unit machine—that is, one where all of the exposures needed could be made with the same apparatus and through the same lens. And this at once brought up the second difficulty. Obviously, it was quite impossible to construct any single camera capable of the proper speed and mechanism required for the purpose, and use glass plates for the exposures. I saw at once enough for our purpose, but as soon as we undertook enlargements we saw we were stumped at the start. The bromide of these would have to be discarded entirely, and any experiments would have to start from a brand new point of departure.

We tried various kinds of mechanisms and various kinds of materials and chemicals for our negatives. The experiments of a laboratory consist mostly in finding that something won't work. The worst of it is you never know beforehand, and sometimes it takes months, even years, before you discover you have been on the wrong line all the time. First we tried making a cylindrical shell, something like an ordinary phonograph cylinder, and sensitizing the surface in the hope of obtaining microscopic photographs which could be enlarged.

These impressions would have been no larger than the point of a pin, if successful, and, of course, our plan involved a tremendous magnifying process to produce results. But we couldn't find a substance for coating the cylinder that was sensitive enough for our need. The old dry albumen that had been used by photographers we found would not do at all. Then we tried a gelatine bromide of silver emulsion, and for a little while it looked like it might work.

The first minute impressions were all right, and seemed clear enough for our purpose, but as soon as we undertook enlargements we saw we were stumped at the start. The bromide of silver was so coarse that all of the details of the negative were blotted out even in an eighth-of-an-inch size. We had to begin again, and this time we tried a different kind of mechanism with the idea of making larger pictures.

And again we found that we were wrong. Celluloid by this time was on the market—and we conceived the idea of a drum, over which a sheet of prepared celluloid was drawn, with the edges squeezed into narrow slots in the rim, like the old tin-foil phonograph. We had to take our pictures spirally, and they were so limited in size as a result that only the center of each could be brought into focus.

It was along about this point that George Eastman came into our experiments. I heard that he was working on a new kind of dry film, and asked him to come down and talk it over. The result was that his representative went back home to see what he could do in making a narrow strip of sensitized film that would operate on a roll. Without George Eastman I don't know what the result would have been in the history of the motion picture. The months that followed were a series of discouragements for all of us. While he was busy with the problem of chemicals we were busy with the problem of mechanics.

It is almost impossible for the layman to appreciate the extreme niceties of adjustment we had to overcome. Try to realize that we were dealing always with minute fractions of seconds. For instance, allowing forty-six exposures per second, as we did at first, we had to face the fact that the film had to be stopped and started again after each exposure. Now, allowing a minimum of 1/100 part of a second for every impression that was registered, you can see that practically half of our time was already gone, and in the remainder of the time we had to move the film forward the necessary distance for the next exposures.

And all this had to be done with the exactness of a watch movement. If there was the slightest variation in the movement of the film, or if it slipped at any time by so much as a hair's breadth, this fact was certain to show up in the enlargements. Finally we completed a mechanism that allowed the film to be moved in the uniform ratio of one-tenth part of the time needed for a satisfactory exposure, and permitted from twenty to forty such exposures per second.

It looked as though we were finished, and we tried the first roll of film jubilantly. Success was in our hands. But we had counted too soon.

The strips had been made in a one-half inch width that we thought was ample, but it was not enough. We had to make a larger size, allowing a one-inch surface for the emulsion, with a one-half inch margin for the perforations needed for the locking device that we used for starting and stopping the film.

This meant, of course, adjusting our mechanical apparatus also to carry the new-sized roll; but we did it at last, and soon the first of the new cameras was ready to show what it could do.

I didn't apply for the patent until two years later. I was very much occupied with other matters, and while we all congratulated ourselves on what we had accomplished, and knew we had an interesting and novel apparatus, we generally regarded it more or less as a curiosity with no very large practicable possibilities. It probably seems strange to the world now, but such was the fact, even after we had exhibited our first pictures.

These were shown originally in an apparatus that we christened "The Kinetescope," consisting of a cabinet equipped with an electrical motor and battery, and carrying a fifty-foot band of film, passed through the field of a magnifying glass. They attracted quite a lot of attention at the World's Fair in Chicago in 1893, but we didn't think much of it until we found that two Englishmen, who had been interested in the exhibit, finding that I had carelessly neglected to patent the apparatus abroad, had started an independent manufacture on a considerable scale.

Of course, it was too late then to protect myself, and I concentrated my efforts on devising a mechanism that would project the pictures on a screen before an audience. This consisted largely in reversing the action of the apparatus for taking the original pictures.

The main trouble we found here was the question of "flicker" and eye strain. It was necessary primarily to find and establish a uniform speed both for photographing and projecting the pictures. If we kept the number of exposures down too low it made the action jerky and hard to follow on the screen. Nearly all of our first pictures allowed from thirty to forty exposures per second, although the number has since been reduced down to from fifteen to twenty.

I consider that the greatest mission of the motion picture is first to make people happy . . . to bring more joy and cheer and wholesome good will into this world of ours. And God knows we need it.

Second—to educate, elevate, and inspire. I believe that the motion picture is destined to revolutionize our educational system and that in a few years it will supplant largely, if not entirely, the use of text-books in our schools. Books are clumsy methods of instruction at best, and often even the words of explanation in them have to be explained.

I should say that on the average we get only about two per cent efficiency out of school books as they are written to-day. The education of the future, as I see it will be conducted through the medium of the motion picture, a visualized education, where it should be possible to obtain a one-hundred-per-cent-efficiency.

The motion picture has tremendous possibilities for the training and development of the memory. There is no medium for memory-building as productive as the human eye.

That is another basic reason for the motion picture in the school. It will make a more alert and more capable generation of citizens and parents. You can't make a trained animal unless you start with a puppy. It is next to impossible to teach an old dog new tricks.

I do not believe that any other single agency of progress has the possibilities for a great and permanent good to humanity that I can see in the motion picture. And those possibilities are only beginning to be touched.

ALBERT EINSTEIN

(1879–1955)

This Jewish-Austrian-Swiss-American theoretical physicist effected the greatest revolution in scientific theory since Copernicus. His "special" theory of relativity (basis of the quantum theory, used in nuclear physics) was evolved while he was an examiner in the patent office at Berne (1905); his "general" theory, involving a new concept of gravitation, was completed about 1915. Deprived of citizenship, his property confiscated by the Nazis, Einstein came to America in 1933 to join the Institute for Advanced Study at Princeton, where he lived till his death. Nobel prize winner for physics in 1921, his unified field theory has reduced electromagnetism and gravity to a single set of formulae. Among other things he explained the principles of photoelectric effect, the influence of gravity on light, and the Brownian movement. A humanitarian of broad interest, he also wrote on Zionism, pacifism and general philosophical subjects. Works: *The Meaning of Relativity* (1923), *On the Method of Theoretical Physics* (1933), *Why War?* (with Freud, 1933), *The World As I See It* (1934), and *The Evolution of Physics* (1938).

THE THEORY OF RELATIVITY

MATHEMATICS DEALS exclusively with the relations of concepts to each other without consideration of their relation to experience. Physics too deals with mathematical concepts; however, these concepts attain physical content only by the clear determination of their relation to the objects of experience. This in particular is the case for the concepts of motion, space, time.

The theory of relativity is that physical theory which is based on a consistent physical interpretation of these three concepts. The name "theory of relativity" is connected with the fact that motion from the point of view of possible experience always

255

appears as the *relative* motion of one object with respect to another (e.g., of a car with respect to the ground, or the earth with respect to the sun and the fixed stars). Motion is never observable as "motion with respect to space" or, as it has been expressed, as "absolute motion." The "principle of relativity" in its widest sense is contained in the statement: The totality of physical phenomena is of such a character that it gives no basis for the introduction of the concept of "absolute motion"; or shorter but less precise: There is no absolute motion.

It might seem that our insight would gain little from such a negative statement. In reality, however, it is a strong restriction for the (conceivable) laws of nature. In this sense there exists an analogy between the theory of relativity and thermodynamics. The latter too is based on a negative statement: "There exists no perpetuum mobile."

The development of the theory of relativity proceeded in two steps, "special theory of relativity" and "general theory of relativity." The latter presumes the validity of the former as a limiting case and is its consistent continuation.

A. *Special Theory of Relativity*

Physical interpretation of space and time in classical mechanics.

Geometry, from a physical standpoint, is the totality of laws according to which rigid bodies mutually at rest can be placed with respect to each other (e.g., a triangle consists of three rods whose ends touch permanently). It is assumed that with such an interpretation the Euclidean laws are valid. "Space" in this interpretation is in principle an infinite rigid body (or skeleton) to which the position of all other bodies is related (body of reference). Analytic geometry (Descartes) uses as the body of reference, which represents space, three mutually perpendicular rigid rods on which the "coordinates" (x, y, z) of space points are measured in the known manner as perpendicular projections (with the aid of a rigid unit-measure).

Physics deals with "events" in space and time. To each event belongs, besides its place coordinates x, y, z, a time value t. The latter was considered measurable by a clock (ideal periodic process) of negligible spatial extent. This clock C is to be considered at rest at one point of the coordinate system, e.g., at the coordinate origin (x = y = z = O). The time of an event taking place at a point P(x,y,z) is then defined as the time shown on the clock C simultaneously with the event. Here the concept "simultaneous" was assumed as physically meaningful without special definition. This is a lack of exactness which seems harmless only since with the help of light (whose velocity is practically infinite from the point of view of daily experience) the simultaneity of spatially distant events can apparently be decided immediately.

The special theory of relativity removes this lack of precision by defining simultaneity physically with the use of light signals. The time t of the event in P is the reading of the clock C at the time of arrival of a light signal emitted from the event, corrected with respect to the time needed for the light signal to travel the distance. This correction presumes (postulates) that the velocity of light is constant.

This definition reduces the concept of simultaneity of spatially distant events to that of the simultaneity of events happening at the same place (coincidence), namely the arrival of the light signal at C and the reading of C.

Classical mechanics is based on Galileo's principle: A body is in rectilinear and uniform motion as long as other bodies do not act on it. This statement cannot be valid for arbitrary moving systems of coordinates. It can claim validity only for so-called "inertial systems." Inertial systems are in rectilinear and uniform motion with respect to each other. In classical physics laws claim validity only with respect to all inertial systems (special principle of relativity).

It is now easy to understand the dilemma which has led to the special theory of relativity. Experience and theory have gradually led to the conviction that light in empty space always travels with the same velocity c independent of its color and the state of motion of the source of light (principle of the constancy of the velocity of light—in the following referred to as "L-principle").

257

Now elementary intuitive considerations seem to show that the same light ray *cannot* move with respect to all inertial systems with the same velocity c. The L-principle seems to contradict the spatial principle of relativity.

It turns out, however, that this contradiction is only an apparent one which is based essentially on the prejudice about the absolute character of time or rather of the simultaneity of distant events. We just saw that x, y, z and t of an event can, for the moment, be defined only with respect to a certain chosen system of coordinates (inertial system). The transformation of the x, y, z, t of events which has to be carried out with the passage from one inertial system to another (coordinate transformation), is a problem which cannot be solved without special physical assumptions. However, the following postulate is exactly sufficient for a solution: *The L-principle holds for all inertial systems* (application of the special principle of relativity to the L-principle). The transformations thus defined, which are linear in x, y, z, t, are called Lorentz transformations. Lorentz transformations are formally characterized by the demand that the expression

$$dx^2 + dy^2 + dz^2 - c^2dt^2,$$

which is formed from the coordinate differences dx, dy, dz, dt of two infinitely close events, be invariant (i.e., that through the transformation it goes over into the *same* expression formed from the coordinate differences in the new system).

With the help of the Lorentz transformations the special principle of relativity can be expressed thus: The laws of nature are invariant with respect to Lorentz-transformations (i.e., a law of nature does not change its form if one introduces into it a new inertial system with the help of a Lorentz-transformation on x, y, z, t).

The special theory of relativity has led to a clear understanding of the physical concepts of space and time and in connection with this to a recognition of the behavior of moving measuring rods and clocks. It has in principle removed the concept of absolute simultaneity and thereby also that of instantaneous action at a distance in the sense of Newton. It has shown how the law of motion must be modified in dealing with motions that are not negligibly small as compared with the velocity of light. It has led to a formal clarification of Maxwell's equations of the electromagnetic field; in particular it has led to an understanding of the essential oneness of the electric and the magnetic field. It has unified the laws of conservation of momentum and of energy into one single law and has demonstrated the equivalence of mass and energy. From a formal point of view one may characterize the achievement of the special theory of relativity thus: it has shown generally the role which the universal constant c (velocity of light) plays in the laws of nature and has demonstrated that there exists a close connection between the form in which time on the one hand and the spatial coordinates on the other enter into the laws of nature.

B. *General Theory of Relativity*

The special theory of relativity retained the basis of classical mechanics in one fundamental point, namely the statement: The laws of nature are valid only with respect to inertial systems. The "permissible" transformations for the coordinates (i.e., those which leave the form of the laws unchanged) are *exclusively* the (linear) Lorentz-transformations. Is this restriction really founded in physical facts? The following argument convincingly denies it.

Principle of equivalence. A body has an inertial mass (resistance to acceleration) and a heavy mass (which determines the weight of the body in a given gravitational field, e.g., that at the surface of the earth). These two quantities, so different according to their definition, are according to experience measured by one and the same number. There must be a deeper reason for this. The fact can also be described thus: In a gravitational field different masses receive the same acceleration. Finally, it can also be described thus: Bodies in a gravitational field behave as in the absence of a gravitational field if, in the latter case, the system of reference used is a uniformly accelerated coordinate system (instead of an inertial system).

There seems, therefore, to be no reason to ban the following interpretation of the latter case. One considers the system as

259

being "at rest" and considers the "apparent" gravitational field which exists with respect to it as a "real" one. This gravitational field "generated" by the acceleration of the coordinate system would of course be of unlimited extent in such a way that it could not be caused by gravitational masses in a finite region; however, if we are looking for a field-like theory, this fact need not deter us. With this interpretation the inertial system loses its meaning and one has an "explanation" for the equality of heavy and inertial mass (the same property of matter appears as weight or as inertia depending on the mode of description).

Considered formally, the admission of a coordinate system which is accelerated with respect to the original "inertial" coordinates means the admission of non-linear coordinate transformations, hence a mighty enlargement of the idea of invariance, i.e., the principle of relativity.

First, a penetrating discussion, using the results of the special theory of relativity, shows that with such a generalization the coordinates can no longer be interpreted directly as the results of measurements. Only the coordinate difference together with the field quantities which describe the gravitational field determine measurable distances between events. After one has found oneself forced to admit non-linear coordinate transformations as transformations between equivalent coordinate systems, the simplest demand appears to admit all continuous coordinate transformations (which form a group), i.e., to admit arbitrary curvilinear coordinate systems in which the fields are described by regular functions (general principle of relativity).

Now it is not difficult to understand why the general principle of relativity (*on the basis of the equivalence principle*) has led to a theory of gravitation. There is a special kind of space whose physical structure (field) we can presume as precisely known on the basis of the special theory of relativity. This is empty space without electromagnetic field and without matter. It is completely determined by its "metric" property: Let dx_0, dy_0, dz_0, dt_0 be the coordinate differences of two infinitesimally near points (events); then

$$(1) \qquad ds^2 = dx_0^2 + dy_0^2 + dz_0^2 - c^2 dt_0^2$$

260

is a measurable quality which is independent of the special choice of the inertial system. If one introduces in this space the new coordinates x_1, x_2, x_3, x_4 through a general transformation of coordinates, then the quantity ds^2 for the same pair of points has an expression of the form

(2) $ds^2 = \Sigma g_{ik} dx^i dx^k$ (summed for i and k from 1 to 4)

where $g_{ik} = g_{ki}$. The g_{ik} which form a "symmetric tensor" and are continuous functions of $x_1, \ldots x_4$ then describe according to the "principle of equivalence" a gravitational field of a special kind (namely one which can be retransformed to the form [1]). From Riemann's investigations on metric spaces the mathematical properties of this g_{ik} field can be given exactly ("Riemann-condition"). However, what we are looking for are the equations satisfied by "general" gravitational fields. It is natural to assume that they too can be described as tensor-fields of the type g_{ik}, which in general do *not* admit a transformation to the form (1), i.e., which do not satisfy the "Riemann condition," but weaker conditions, which, just as the Riemann condition, are independent of the choice of coordinates (i.e., are generally invariant). A simple formal consideration leads to weaker conditions which are closely connected with the Riemann condition. These conditions are the very equations of the pure gravitational field (on the outside of matter and at the absence of an electromagnetic field).

These equations yield Newton's equations of gravitational mechanics as an approximate law and in addition certain small effects which have been confirmed by observation (deflection of light by the gravitational field of a star, influence of the gravitational potential on the frequency of emitted light, slow rotation of the elliptic circuits of planets—perihelion motion of the planet Mercury). They further yield an explanation for the expanding motion of galactic systems, which is manifested by the red-shift of the light omitted from these systems.

The general theory of relativity is as yet incomplete insofar as it has been able to apply the general principle of relativity satisfactorily only to gravitational fields, but not to the total field. We do not yet know with certainty, by what mathematical me-

261

chanism the total field in space is to be described and what the general invariant laws are to which this total field is subject. One thing, however, seems certain: namely, that the general principle of relativity will prove a necessary and effective tool for the solution of the problem of the total field.

EUCLID

(*c.* 330–*c.* 275 B.C.)

The only fact known with certainty about the world's first-known geometer is that he taught at Alexandria in the time of Ptolemy. His textbooks on geometry have been in use for two thousand years—a record unequaled by any work on any subject whatsoever. The most important of these, the 13-volume *Elements,* provided the basis for many later works. Euclid's accomplishment seems mainly to have been that of an editor—analyzing the work of his predecessors, introducing new proofs for some propositions, and contributing at least one that was definitely original: the proof of the Pythagorean theorem. Other surviving works: *Data* (geometrical theorems), *Phae-nomena* (astronomy), *Optics* and *Section of the Scale.*

THE ELEMENTS

DEFINITIONS

1. A point is that which has no parts, or which has no magnitude.
2. A line is length without breadth.
3. The extremities of a line are points.
4. A straight line is that which lies evenly between its extreme points.
5. A superficies is that which has only length and breadth.
6. The extremities of a superficies are lines.
7. A plane superficies is that in which any two points being taken, the straight line between them lies wholly in that superficies.
8. A plane angle is the inclination of two lines to one another in a plane, which meet together, but are not in the same direction.

9. A plane rectilineal angle is the inclination of two straight lines to one another, which meet together, but are not in the same straight line.

10. When a straight line standing on another straight line makes the adjacent angles equal to one another, each of the angles is called a right angle; and the straight line which stands on the other is called a perpendicular to it.

11. A term or boundary is the extremity of any thing.

12. A figure is that which is enclosed by one or more boundaries.

13. A circle is a plane figure contained by one line, which is called the circumference, and is such that all straight lines drawn from a certain point within the figure to the circumference are equal to one another:

14. And this point is called the centre of the circle.

15. A diameter of a circle is a straight line drawn through the centre, and terminated both ways by the circumference.

[A radius of a circle is a straight line drawn from the centre to the circumference.]

16. Rectilineal figures are those which are contained by straight lines:

17. Trilateral figures, or triangles, by three straight lines:

18. Quadrilateral figures by four straight lines:

19. Multilateral figures, or polygons, by more than four straight lines.

20. Of three-sided figures,
An equilateral triangle is that which has three equal sides:

21. An isosceles triangle is that which has two sides equal:

22. A scalene triangle is that which has three unequal sides:

23. A right-angled triangle is that which has a right angle:

Of four-sided figures,

24. A square is that which has all its sides equal, and all its angles right angles:

25. An oblong is that which has all its angles right angles, but not all its sides equal:

26. A rhombus is that which has all its sides equal, but its angles are not right angles:

27. A rhomboid is that which has its opposite sides equal to one another, but all its sides are not equal, nor its angles right angles:

28. All other four-sided figures besides these are called trapeziums.

29. Parallel straight lines are such as are in the same plane, and which being produced ever so far both ways do not meet.

POSTULATES

Let it be granted,

1. That a straight line may be drawn from any one point to any other point:

2. That a terminated straight line may be produced to any length in a straight line:

3. And that a circle may be described from any centre, at any distance from that centre.

AXIOMS

1. Things which are equal to the same thing are equal to one another.

2. If equals be added to equals the wholes are equal.

3. If equals be taken from equals the remainders are equal.

4. If equals be added to unequals the wholes are unequal.

5. If equals be taken from unequals the remainders are unequal.

6. Things which are double of the same thing are equal to one another.

7. Things which are halves of the same thing are equal to one another.

8. Magnitudes which coincide with one another that is, which exactly fill the same space, are equal to one another.

9. The whole is greater than its part.

10. Two straight lines cannot enclose a space.

11. All right angles are equal to one another.

12. If a straight line meet two straight lines, so as to make the two interior angles on the same side of it taken together less than two right angles, these straight lines, being continually produced, shall at length meet on that side on which are the angles which are less than two right angles.

Proposition 1.   Problem

To describe an equilateral triangle on a given finite straight line.

Let *AB* be the given straight line: it is required to describe an equilateral triangle on *AB*.

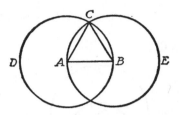

From the centre *A*, at the distance *AB*, describe the circle *BCD*.
[*Postulate* 3.
From the centre *B*, at the distance BA, describe the circle *ACE*.
[*Post.* 3.
From the point *C*, at which the circles cut one another, draw the straight lines *CA* and *CB* to the points *A* and *B*.   [*Postulate* 1.
ABC shall be an equilateral triangle.

Because the point *A* is the centre of the circle *BCD*, *AC* is equal to *AB*.   [*Definition* 13.
And because the point *B* is the centre of the circle *ACE*, *BC* is equal to *BA*.   [*Definition* 13.
But it has been shewn that *CA* is equal to *AB*; therefore *CA* and *CB* are each of them equal to *AB*.
But things which are equal to the same thing are equal to one another.   [*Axiom* 1.
Therefore *CA* is equal to *CB*.
Therefore *CA*, *AB*, *BC* are equal to one another.

Wherefore *the triangle ABC is equilateral*,   [*Definition* 20.
and it is described on the given straight line AB.   Q.E.F.

Proposition 2.   Problem

From a given point to draw a straight line equal to a given straight line.

Let *A* be the given point, and *BC* the given straight line: it is required to draw from the point *A* a straight line equal to *BC*.

From the point *A* to *B* draw the straight line *AB*;   [*Postulate* 1.
and on it describe the equilateral triangle *DAB*,   [I. 1.
and produce the straight lines *DA*, *DB* to *E* and *F*.   [*Postulate* 2.
From the centre *B*, at the distance *BC*, describe the circle *CGH*, meeting *DF* at *G*.   [*Postulate* 3.

From the centre *D*, at the distance *DG*, describe the circle *GKL*, meeting *DE* at *L*. [*Postulate* 3.
AL shall be equal to *BC*.

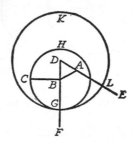

Because the point *B* is the centre of the circle *CGH*, *BC* is equal to *BG*. [*Definition* 13.
And because the point *D* is the centre of the circle *GKL*, *DL* is equal to *DG* [*Definition* 13.
and *DA*, *DB* parts of them are equal; [*Definition* 20.
therefore the remainder *AL* is equal to the remainder *BG*. [*Axiom* 3.
But it has been shewn that *BC* is equal to *BG*; therefore *AL* and *BC* are each of them equal to *BG*.
But things which are equal to the same thing are equal to one another. [*Axiom* 1.
Therefore *AL* is equal to *BC*.
Wherefore *from the given point A a straight line AL has been drawn equal to the given straight line BC.* Q.E.F.

Proposition 3. Problem

From the greater of two given straight lines to cut off a part equal to the less.

Let *AB* and *C* be the two given straight lines, of which *AB* is the greater: it is required to cut off from *AB*, the greater, a part equal to *C* the less.

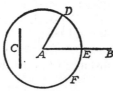

From the point A draw the straight line AD equal to C; [I. 2.
and from the centre A, at the distance AD, describe the circle DEF
meeting AB at E. [*Postulate* 3.
AE shall be equal to C.

Because the point A is the centre of the circle DEF, AE is equal to
AD. [*Definition* 13.
But C is equal to AD. [*Construction*.
Therefore AE and C are each of them equal to AD.
Therefore AE is equal to C. [*Axiom* 1.

Wherefore *from AB the greater of two given straight lines a part
AE has been cut off equal to C the less.* Q.E.F.

Proposition 4.   Theorem

*If two triangles have two sides of the one equal to two sides of the
other, each to each, and have also the angles contained by those sides
equal to one another, they shall also have their bases or third sides
equal and the two triangles shall be equal, and their other angles
shall be equal, each to each, namely those to which the equal sides
are opposite.*

Let ABC, DEF be two triangles which have the two sides AB, AC
equal to the two sides DE, DF, each to each, namely, AB to DE, and
AC to DF, and the angle BAC equal to the angle EDF: the base BC
shall be equal to the base EF, and the triangle ABC to the triangle
DEF, and the other angles shall be equal, each to each, to which the
equal sides are opposite, namely, the angle ABC to the angle DEF,
and the angle ACB to the angle DFE.

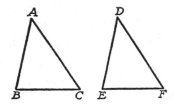

For if the triangle ABC be applied to the triangle DEF, so that
the point A may be on the point D, and the straight line AB on the

269

straight line *DE*, the point *B* will coincide with the point *E*, because *AB* is equal to *DE*. [*Hypothesis.*

And, *AB* coinciding with *DE*, *AC* will fall on *DF*, because the angle *BAC* is equal to the angle *EDF*. [*Hypothesis.*

Therefore also the point *C* will coincide with the point *F*, because *AC* is equal to *DF*. [*Hypothesis.*

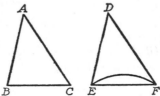

But the point *B* was shewn to coincide with the point *E*, therefore the base *BC* will coincide with the base *EF*; because, *B* coinciding with *E* and *C* with *F*, if the base *BC* does not coincide with the base *EF*, two straight lines will enclose a space; which is impossible.

[*Axiom* 10.

Therefore the base *BC* coincides with the base *EF*, and is equal to it.

[*Axiom* 8.

Therefore the whole triangle *ABC* coincides with the whole triangle *DEF*, and is equal to it. [*Axiom* 8.

And the other angles of the one coincide with the other angles of the other, and are equal to them, namely, the angle *ABC* to the angle *DEF*, and the angle *ACB* to the angle *DFE*.

Wherefore, *if two triangles* &c. Q.E.D.

Proposition 5. Theorem

The angles at the base of an isosceles triangle are equal to one another; and if the equal sides be produced the angles on the other side of the base shall be equal to one another.

Let *ABC* be an isosceles triangle, having the side *AB* equal to the side *AC*, and let the straight lines *AB*, *AC* be produced to *D* and *E*: the angle *ABC* shall be equal to the angle *ACB*, and the angle *CBD* to the angle *BCE*.

In *BD* take any point *F*, and from *AE* the greater cut off *AG* equal to *AF* the less, and join *FC*, *GB*. [I. 3.

270

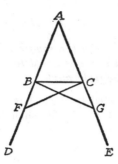

Because *AF* is equal to *AG*,   [*Construction.*
and *AB* to *AC*,   [*Hypothesis.*
the two sides *FA*, *AC* are equal to the two sides *GA*, *AB*, each to
each; and they contain the angle *FAG* common to the two triangles
AFC, *AGB*; therefore the base *FC* is equal to the base *GB*, and the
triangle *AFC* to the triangle *AGB*, and the remaining angles of the
one to the remaining angles of the other, each to each, to which the
equal sides are opposite, namely the angle *ACF* to the angle *ABG*,
and the angle *AFC* to the angle *AGB*.   [I. 4.
    And because the whole *AF* is equal to the whole *AG*, of which the
parts *AB*, *AC* are equal.   [*Hypothesis.*
the remainder *BF* is equal to the remainder *CG*.   [*Axiom* 3.
And *FC* was shewn to be equal to *GB*; therefore the two sides *BF*, *FC*
are equal to the two sides *CG*, *GB*, each to each; and the angle *BFC*
was shewn to be equal to the angle *CGB*; therefore the triangles
BFC, *CGB* are equal, and their other angles are equal, each to each,
to which the equal sides are opposite, namely the angle *FBC* to the
angle *GCB*, and the angle *BCF* to the angle *CBG*.   [I. 4.
    And since it has been shewn that the whole angle *ABG* is equal to
the whole angle *ACF*, and that the parts of these, the angles *CBG*,
BCF are also equal; therefore the remaining angle *ABC* is equal to
the remaining angle *ACB*, which are the angles at the base of the
triangle *ABC*.   [*Axiom* 3.
    And it has also been shewn that the angle *FBC* is equal to the
angle *GCB*, which are the angles on the other side of the base.
    Wherefore, *the angles* &c.   Q.E.D.
    Corollary. Hence every equilateral triangle is also equiangular.

Proposition 47. Theorem

In any right-angled triangle, the square which is described on the side subtending the right angle is equal to the squares described on the sides which contain the right angle.

Let *ABC* be a right-angled triangle, having the right angle *BAC*: the square described on the side *BC* shall be equal to the squares described on the sides *BA, AC*.

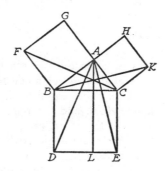

On *BC* describe the square *BDEC*, and on *BA, AC* describe the squares *GB, HC*; through *A* draw *AL* parallel to *BD* or *CE*; and join *AD, FC*.

Then, because the angle *BAC* is a right angle,   *Hypothesis.*
and that the angle *BAG* is also a right angle,   [*Definition* 24.
the two straight lines *AC, AG*, on the opposite sides of *AB*, make with it at the point *A* the adjacent angles equal to two right angles; therefore *CA* is in the same straight line with *AG*.

For the same reason, *AB* and *AH* are in the same straight line.

Now the angle *DBC* is equal to the angle *FBA*, for each of them is a right angle.   [*Axiom* 11.
Add to each the angle *ABC*.

Therefore the whole angle *DBA* is equal to the whole angle *FBC*.
    [*Axiom* 2.

And because the two sides *AB, BD* are equal to the two sides *FB, BC*, each to each;   [*Definition* 24.
and the angle *DBA* is equal to the angle *FBC*; therefore the triangle *ABD* is equal to the triangle *FBC*.   [I. 4.

Now the parallelogram *BL* is double of the triangle *ABD*, because

they are on the same base *BD*, and between the same parallels *BD*, *AL*.   [I. 41.
And the square *GB* is double of the triangle *FBC*, because they are on the same base *FB*, and between the same parallels *FB*, *GC*. [I. 41.
But the doubles of equals are equal to one another.   [*Axiom* 6.
Therefore the parallelogram *BL* is equal to the square *GB*.

In the same manner, by joining *AE*, *BK*, it can be shewn, that the parallelogram *CL* is equal to the square *CH*. Therefore the whole square *BDEC* is equal to the two squares *GB*, *HC*.   [*Axiom* 2.
And the square *BDEC* is described on *BC*, and the squares *GB*, *HC* on *BA*, *AC*.
Therefore the square described on the side *BC* is equal to the squares described on the sides *BA*, *AC*.

Wherefore, *in any right-angled triangle* &c.   Q.E.D.

GABRIEL DANIEL FAHRENHEIT

(1686-1736)

Here is the amazingly simple story of how a German instrument maker invented the mercury thermometer (1714) and the temperature scale now in use. Alcohol or wine had previously been used to measure temperature. Fahrenheit selected 32° as freezing point to avoid negative measurements. He made other discoveries about the boiling points of liquids, and was one of the first of a long line of investigators into the problem of heat.

A PERSONAL STORY OF INVENTION

ABOUT TEN YEARS AGO I read in the "History of Sciences" issued by the Royal Academy of Paris that the celebrated Amontons, using a thermometer of his own invention, had discovered that water boils at a fixed degree of heat. I was at once inflamed with a great desire to make for myself a thermometer of the same sort, so that I might with my own eyes perceive this beautiful phenomenon of nature and be convinced of the truth of the experiment.

I therefore attempted to construct a thermometer, but because of my lack of experience in its construction my efforts were in vain, though they were often repeated; and since other matters prevented my going on with the development of the thermometer I postponed any further repetition of my attempts to some more fitting time. Though my powers and my time failed me yet my zeal did not slacken and I was always desirous of seeing the outcome of the experiment. It then came into my mind what that most careful observer of natural phenomena had written about the correction of the barometer; for he had observed that the height of the column of mercury in the barometer was a little (though sensibly enough) altered by the varying temperature of

274

GABRIEL DANIEL FAHRENHEIT

the mercury. From this I gathered that a thermometer might perhaps be constructed with mercury, which would not be so hard to construct, and by the use of which it might be possible to carry out the experiment which I so greatly desired to try.

When a thermometer of that sort was made (perhaps imperfect in many ways) the result answered to my prayer; and with great pleasure of mind I observed the truth of the thing.

Three years then passed, in which I was occupied with optical and other work, when I became anxious to try by experiment whether other liquids boiled at fixed degrees of heat.

The results of my experiments are contained in the following table, of which the first column contains the liquids used, the second, their specific gravity, the third, the degree of heat which each liquid attains when boiling.

Liquids	Specific Gravity of Liquids at 48° of HEAT	Degree Attained by Boiling
Spirits of Wine or Alcohol	0.8260	176
Rain Water	1.0000	212
Spirits of Niter	1.2935	242
Lye prepared from wine lees	1.5634	240
Oil of Vitriol	1.8775	546

I thought it best to give the specific gravity of each liquid, so that, if the experiments of others already tried, or which may be tried, give different results, it might be determined whether the difference should be looked for as resulting from differences in the specific gravities or from other causes. The experiments were not made at the same time, and hence the liquids were affected by different degrees of temperature or heat, but since their gravity is altered in a different way and unequally, I reduced it by calculation to the degree 48, which in my thermometers holds the middle place between the limit of the most intense cold obtained artificially in a mixture of water, of ice, and of sal ammoniac, or even of sea salt, and the limit of the heat which is found in the blood of a healthy man.

275

MICHAEL FARADAY

(1791–1867)

A blacksmith's son, Faraday began work as a bookbinder, with science as his hobby, and eventually became professor of the Royal Institution. Although his discoveries were many and of far-reaching consequence, his fame is attached chiefly to his discovery of electromagnetic induction. His production of electromotive force by the movement of a conductor in a magnetic field led eventually to the generator. He established the identity of electricity from different sources, the relation of electric and magnetic forces, and in electrolysis discovered that the amount of liquid decomposed is proportionate to the current passing through the solution. His publications include: *Experimental Researches on Electricity* (1844-55), *Lectures on the Chemical History of a Candle* (1861), and *On the Various Forces in Nature.*

INDUCED CURRENTS

1. The power which electricity of tension possesses of causing an opposite electrical state in its vicinity has been expressed by the general term Induction; which, as it has been received into scientific language, may also, with propriety, be used in the same general sense to express the power which electrical currents may possess of inducing any particular state upon matter in their immediate neighbourhood, otherwise indifferent. It is with this meaning that I purpose using it in the present paper.

2. Certain effects of the induction of electrical currents have already been recognized and described: as those of magnetization; Ampere's experiments of bringing a copper disc near to a flat spiral; his repetition with electro-magnets of Arago's extraordinary experiments, and perhaps a few others. Still it appeared

unlikely that these could be all the effects which induction by currents could produce; especially as, upon dispensing with iron, almost the whole of them disappear, whilst yet an infinity of bodies, exhibiting definite phenomena of induction with electricity of tension, still remain to be acted upon by the induction of electricity in motion.

3. Further: Whether Ampere's beautiful theory were adopted, or any other, or whatever reservation were mentally made, still it appeared very extraordinary, that as every electric current was accompanied by a corresponding intensity of magnetic action at right angles to the current, good conductors of electricity, when placed within the sphere of this action, should not have any current induced through them, or some sensible effect produced equivalent in force to such a current.

4. These considerations, with their consequence, the hope of obtaining electricity from ordinary magnetism, have stimulated me at various times to investigate experimentally the inductive effect of electric currents. I lately arrived at positive results; and not only had my hopes fulfilled, but obtained a key which appeared to me to open out a full explanation of Arago's magnetic phenomena, and also to discover a new state, which may probably have great influence in some of the most important effects of electric currents.

5. These results I purpose describing, not as they were obtained, but in such a manner as to give the most concise view of the whole.

1. INDUCTION OF ELECTRIC CURRENTS

6. About twenty-six feet of copper wire one twentieth of an inch in diameter were wound round a cylinder of wood as a helix, the different spires of which were prevented from touching by a thin interposed twine. This helix was covered with calico, and then a second wire applied in the same manner. In this way twelve helices were superposed, each containing an average length of wire of twenty-seven feet, and all in the same direction.

The first, third, fifth, seventh, ninth, and eleventh of these helices were connected at their extremities end to end, so as to form one helix; the others were connected in a similar manner; and thus two principal helices were produced, closely interposed, having the same direction, not touching anywhere, and each containing one hundred and fifty-five feet in length of wire.

7. One of these helices was connected with a galvanometer, the other with a voltaic battery of ten pairs of plates four inches square, with double coppers and well charged; yet not the slightest sensible deflection of the galvanometer needle could be observed.

8. A similar compound helix, consisting of six lengths of copper and six of soft iron wire, was constructed. The resulting iron helix contained two hundred and fourteen feet of wire, the resulting copper helix two hundred and eight feet; but whether the current from the trough was passed through the copper or the iron helix, no effect upon the other could be perceived at the galvanometer.

9. In these and many similar experiments no difference in action of any kind appeared between iron and other metals.

10. Two hundred and three feet of copper wire in one length were coiled round a large block of wood; other two hundred and three feet of similar wire were interposed as a spiral between the turns of the first coil, and metallic contact everywhere prevented by twine. One of these helices was connected with a galvanometer, and the other with a battery of one hundred pairs of plates four inches square, with double coppers, and well charged. When the contact was made, there was a sudden and very slight effect at the galvanometer, and there was also a similar slight effect when the contact with the battery was broken. But whilst the voltaic current was continuing to pass through the one helix, no galvanometrical appearances nor any effect like induction upon the other helix could be perceived, although the active power of the battery was proved to be great, by its heating the whole of its own helix, and by the brilliancy of the discharge when made through charcoal.

11. Repetition of the experiments with a battery of one hun-

dred and twenty pairs of plates produced no other effects; but it was ascertained, both at this and the former time, that the slight deflection of the needle occurring at the moment of completing the connection, was always in one direction, and that the equally slight deflection produced when the contact was broken, was in the other direction; and also, that these effects occurred when the first helices were used (6, 8).

12. The results which I had by this time obtained with magnets led me to believe that the battery current through one wire, did, in reality, induce a similar current through the other wire, but that it continued for an instant only, and partook more of the nature of the electrical wave passed through from the shock of a common Leyden jar than of the current from a voltaic battery, and therefore might magnetize a steel needle, although it scarcely affected the galvanometer.

13. This expectation was confirmed: for on substituting a small hollow helix, formed round a glass tube, for the galvanometer, introducing a steel needle, making contact as before between the battery and the inducing wire (7, 10), and then removing the needle before the battery contact was broken, it was found magnetized.

14. When the battery contact was first made, then an unmagnetized needle introduced into the small indicating helix (13), and lastly the battery contact broken, the needle was found magnetized to an equal degree apparently as before; but the poles were of the contrary kind.

15. The same effects took place on using the large compound helices first described (6, 8).

16. When the unmagnetized needle was put into the indicating helix, before contact of the inducing wire with the battery, and remained there until the contact was broken, it exhibited little or no magnetism; the first effect having been nearly neutralized by the second (13, 14). The force of the induced current upon making contact was found always to exceed that of the induced current at breaking of contact; and if therefore the contact was made and broken many times in succession, whilst the needle remained in the indicating helix, it at last came out not unmag-

netized, but a needle magnetized as if the induced current upon making contact had acted alone on it. This effect may be due to the accumulation (as it is called) at the poles of the unconnected pile, rendering the current upon first making contact more powerful than what it is afterwards, at the moment of breaking contact.

17. If the circuit between the helix or wire under induction and the galvanometer or indicating spiral was not rendered complete *before* the connection between the battery and the inducing wire was completed or broken, then no effects were perceived at the galvanometer. Thus, if the battery communications were first made, and then the wire under induction connected with the indicating helix, no magnetizing power was there exhibited. But still retaining the latter communications, when those with the battery were broken, a magnet was formed in the helix, but of the second kind (14), i.e. with poles indicating a current in the same direction to that belonging to the battery current, or to that always induced by that current at its cessation.

18. In the preceding experiments the wires were placed near to each other, and the contact of the inducing one with the battery made when the inductive effect was required; but as the particular action might be supposed to be exerted only at the moments of making and breaking contact, the induction was produced another way. Several feet of copper wire were stretched in wide zigzag forms, representing the letter *W*, on one surface of a broad board; a second wire was stretched in precisely similar forms on a second board, so that when brought near the first, the wires should everywhere touch, except that a sheet of thick paper was interposed. One of these wires was connected with the galvanometer, and the other with a voltaic battery. The first wire was then moved towards the second, and as it approached, the needle was deflected. Being then removed, the needle was deflected in the opposite direction. By first making the wires approach and then recede, simultaneously with the vibrations of the needle, the latter soon became very extensive; but when the wires ceased to move from or towards each other, the galvanometer-needle soon came to its usual position.

280

19. As the wires approximated, the induced current was in the *contrary* direction to the inducing current. As the wires receded, the induced current was in the *same* direction as the inducing current. When the wires remained stationary, there was no induced current (54).

20. When a small voltaic arrangement was introduced into the circuit between the galvanometer (10) and its helix or wire, so as to cause a permanent deflection of 30° or 40°, and then the battery of one hundred pairs of plates connected with inducing wire, there was an instantaneous action as before (11); but the galvanometer-needle immediately resumed and retained its place unaltered, notwithstanding the continued contact of the inducing wire with the trough: such was the case in whichever way the contacts were made (33).

21. Hence it would appear that collateral currents, either in the same or in opposite directions, exert no permanent inducing power on each other, affecting their quantity or tension.

22. I could obtain no evidence by the tongue, by spark, or by heating fine wire or charcoal, of the electricity passing through the wire under induction; neither could I obtain any chemical effects, though the contacts with metallic and other solutions were made and broken alternately with those of the battery, so that the second effect of induction should not oppose or neutralize the first (13, 16).

23. This deficiency of effect is not because the induced current of electricity cannot pass fluids, but probably because of its brief duration and feeble intensity; for on introducing two large copper plates into the circuit on the induced side (20), the plates being immersed in brine, but prevented from touching each other by an interposed cloth, the effect at the indicating galvanometer or helix occurred as before. The induced electricity could also pass through a voltaic trough (20). When, however, the quantity of interposed fluid was reduced to a drop, the galvanometer gave no indication.

24. Attempts to obtain similar effects by the use of wires conveying ordinary electricity were doubtful in the results. A com-

pound helix similar to that already described, containing eight elementary helices (6), was used. Four of the helices had their similar ends bound together by wire, and the two general terminations thus produced connected with the small magnetizing helix containing an unmagnetized needle (13). The other four helices were similarly arranged, but their ends connected with a Leyden jar. On passing the discharge, the needle was found to be a magnet; but it appeared probable that a part of the electricity of the jar had passed off to the small helix, and so magnetized the needle. There was indeed no reason to expect that the electricity of a jar possessing as it does great tension, would not diffuse itself through all the metallic matter interposed between the coatings.

25. Still it does not follow that the discharge of ordinary electricity through a wire does not produce analogous phenomena to those arising from voltaic electricity; but as it appears impossible to separate the effects produced at the moment when the discharge begins to pass, from the equal and contrary effects produced when it ceases to pass (16), inasmuch as with ordinary electricity these periods are simultaneous, so there can be scarcely any hope that in this form of the experiment they can be perceived.

26. Hence it is evident that currents of voltaic electricity present phenomena of induction somewhat analogous to those produced by electricity of tension, although, as will be seen hereafter, many differences exist between them. The result is the production of other currents (but which are only momentary), parallel, or tending to parallelism, with the inducing current. By reference to the poles of the needle formed in the indicating helix (13, 14) and to the deflections of the galvanometer-needle (11), it was found in all cases that the induced current, produced by the first action of the inducing current, was in the contrary direction to the latter, but that the current produced by the cessation of the inducing current was in the same direction (19). For the purpose of avoiding periphrasis, I propose to call this action of the current from the voltaic battery *volta-electric induction*. The properties of the second wire, after induction has

developed the first current, and whilst the electricity from the battery continues to flow through its inducing neighbor (10, 18), constitute a peculiar electric condition, the consideration of which will be resumed hereafter (60). All these results have been obtained with a voltaic apparatus consisting of a single pair of plates.

2. EVOLUTION OF ELECTRICITY FROM MAGNETISM

27. A welded ring was made of soft round bar-iron, the metal being seven eighths of an inch in thickness, and the ring six inches in external diameter. These helices were put round one part of this ring, each containing about twenty-four feet of copper wire one twentieth of an inch thick; they were insulated from the iron and each other and superposed in the manner before described (6), occupying about nine inches in length upon the ring. They could be used separately or conjointly; the group may be distinguished by the letter A (Fig. 1). On the other part of the ring about sixty feet of similar copper wire in two pieces were applied in the same manner, forming a helix B, which had the same common direction with the helices of A, but being separated from it at each extremity by about half an inch of the uncovered iron.

28. The helix B was connected by copper wires with a galvanometer three feet from the ring. The helices of A were connected end to end so as to form one common helix, the extremities of which were connected with a battery of ten pairs of plates four inches square. The galvanometer was immediately affected, and to a degree far beyond what has been described when with a battery of tenfold power helices *without iron* were used (10); but though the contact was continued, the effect was not permanent, for the needle soon came to rest in its natural position, as if quite indifferent to the attached electro-magnetic arrangement. Upon breaking the contact with the battery, the needle was again powerfully deflected, but in the contrary direction to that induced in the first instance.

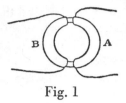

Fig. 1

29. Upon arranging the apparatus so that B should be out of use, the galvanometer be connected with one of the three wires of A (27), and the other two made into a helix through which the current from the trough (28) was passed, similar but rather more powerful effects were produced.

30. When the battery contact was made in one direction, the galvanometer-needle was deflected on the one side; if made in the other direction, the deflection was on the other side. The deflection on breaking the battery contact was always the reverse of that produced by completing it. The deflection on making a battery contact always indicated an induced current in the opposite direction to that from the battery; but on breaking the contact the deflection indicated an induced current in the same direction as that of the battery. No making or breaking of the contact at B side, or in any part of the galvanometer circuit, produced any effect at the galvanometer. No continuance of the battery current caused any deflection of the galvanometer-needle. As the above results are common to all these experiments, and to similar ones with ordinary magnets to be hereafter detailed, they need not be again particularly described.

31. Upon using the power of one hundred pairs of plates (10), with this ring, the impulse at the galvanometer, when contact was completed or broken, was so great as to make the needle spin round rapidly four or five times, before the air and terrestrial magnetism could reduce its motion to mere oscillation.

32. By using charcoal at the ends of the B helix, a minute *spark* could be perceived when the contact of the battery with A was completed. This spark could not be due to any diversion of a part of the current of the battery through the iron to the helix B; for when the battery contact was continued, the galva-

nometer still resumed its perfectly indifferent state (28). The spark was rarely seen on breaking contact. A small platina wire could not be ignited by this induced current; but there seems every reason to believe that the effect would be obtained by using a stronger original current or a more powerful arrangement of helices.

33. A feeble voltaic current was sent through the helix B and the galvanometer, so as to deflect the needle of the latter 30° or 40°, and then the battery of one hundred pairs of plates connected with A; but after the first effect was over, the galvanometer-needle resumed exactly the position due to the feeble current transmitted by its own wire. This took place in whichever way the battery contacts were made, and shows that here again (20) no permanent influence of the currents upon each other, as to their quantity and tension, exists.

34. Another arrangement was then employed connecting the former experiments on volta-electric induction (6-26) with the present. A combination of helices like that already described (6) was constructed upon a hollow cylinder of pasteboard: there were eight lengths of copper wire, containing altogether 220 feet; four of these helices were connected end to end, and then with the galvanometer (7); the other intervening four were also connected end to end, and the battery of one hundred pairs discharged through them. In this form the effect on the galvanometer was hardly sensible (11), though magnets could be made by the induced current (13). But when a soft iron cylinder seven eighths of an inch thick, and twelve inches long, was introduced into the pasteboard tube, surrounded by the helices, then the induced current affected the galvanometer powerfully, and with all the phenomena just described (30). It possessed also the power of making magnets with more energy, apparently, than when no iron cylinder was present.

35. When the iron cylinder was replaced by an equal cylinder of copper, no effect beyond that of the helices alone was produced. The iron cylinder arrangement was not so powerful as the ring arrangement already described (27).

36. Similar effects were then produced by *ordinary magnets*:

285

thus the hollow helix just described (34) had all its elementary helices connected with the galvanometer by two copper wires, each five feet in length; the soft iron cylinder was introduced into its axis; a couple of bar magnets, each twenty-four inches long, were arranged with their opposite poles at one end in contact, so as to resemble a horse-shoe magnet, and then contact made between the other poles and the ends of the iron cylinder, so as to convert it for the time into a magnet (Fig. 2): by breaking the

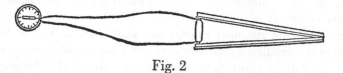

Fig. 2

magnetic contacts, or reversing them, the magnetism of the iron cylinder could be destroyed or reversed at pleasure.

37. Upon making magnetic contact, the needle was deflected; continuing the contact, the needle became indifferent, and resumed its first position; on breaking the contact, it was again deflected, but in the opposite direction to the first effect, and then it again became indifferent. When the magnetic contacts were reversed the deflections were reversed.

38. When the magnetic contact was made, the deflection was such as to indicate an induced current of electricity in the opposite direction to that fitted to form a magnet, having the same polarity as that really produced by contact with the bar magnets. Thus when the marked and unmarked poles were placed as in (Fig. 3), the current in the helix was in the direction represented, P being supposed to be the end of the wire going to the positive pole of the battery, or that end towards which the zinc

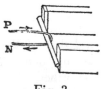

Fig. 3

plates face, and *N* the negative wire. Such a current would have converted the cylinder into a magnet of the opposite kind to that formed by contact with the poles *A* and *B*; and such a current moves in the opposite direction to the currents which in M. Ampere's beautiful theory are considered as constituting a magnet in the position figured.

39. But as it might be supposed that in all the preceding experiments of this section, it was by some peculiar effect taking place during the formation of the magnet, and not by its mere virtual approximation, that the momentary induced current was excited, the following experiment was made. All the similar ends of the compound hollow helix (34) were bound together by copper wire, forming two general terminations, and these were connected with the galvanometer. The soft iron cylinder (34) was removed, and a cylindrical magnet, three quarters of an inch in diameter and eight inches and a half in length, used instead. One end of this magnet was introduced into the axis of the helix (Fig. 4), and then, the galvanometer-needle being stationary,

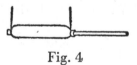

Fig. 4

the magnet was suddenly thrust in; immediately the needle was deflected in the same direction as if the magnet had been formed by either of the two preceding processes (34. 36). Being left in, the needle resumed its first position, and then the magnet being withdrawn the needle was deflected in the opposite direction. These effects were not great; but by introducing and withdrawing the magnet, so that the impulse each time should be added to those previously communicated to the needle, the latter could be made to vibrate through an arc of 180° or more.

40. In this experiment the magnet must not be passed entirely through the helix, for then a second action occurs. When the magnet is introduced, the needle at the galvanometer is deflected in a certain direction; but being in, whether it be pushed quite

through or withdrawn, the needle is deflected in a direction the reverse of that previously produced. When the magnet is passed in and through at one continuous motion, the needle moves one way, is then suddenly stopped, and finally moves the other way.

41. If such a hollow helix as that described (34) be laid east and west (or in any other constant position), and a magnet be retained east and west, its marked pole always being one way; then whichever end of the helix the magnet goes in at, and consequently whichever pole of the magnet enters first, still the needle resumed its first position, and then the magnet being the needle is deflected the same way: on the other hand, whichever direction is followed in withdrawing the magnet, the deflection is constant, but contrary to that due to its entrance.

42. These effects are simple consequences of the *law* hereafter to be described (114)....

114. The relation which holds between the magnetic pole, the moving wire or metal, and the direction of the current evolved, i.e. *the law* which governs the evolution of electricity by magneto-electric induction, is very simple, although rather difficult to express. If in (Fig. 5) *PN* represent a horizontal wire passing by a

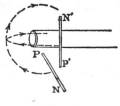

Fig. 5

marked magnetic pole, so that the direction of its motion shall coincide with the curved line proceeding from below upwards; or if its motion parallel to itself be in a line tangential to the curved line, but in the general direction of the arrows; or if it pass the pole in other direction, but so as to cut the magnetic curves in the same general direction, or in the same side as they would be cut by the wire if moving along the dotted curved line;—then the current of electricity in the wire is from *P* to *N*. If it be carried in the reverse directions, the electric current will be from N to P. Or if the wire be in the vertical position, figured $P'N'$, and it be carried in similar directions, coinciding with the dotted horizontal curve so far as to cut the magnetic curves on the same side with it, the current will be from P' to N'. If the wire be considered a tangent to the curved surface of the cylindrical magnet, and it be carried round that surface into any other position, or if the magnet itself be revolved on its axis, so as to bring any part opposite to the tangential wire,—still, if afterwards the wire be moved in the directions indicated, the current of electricity will be from P to N; or if it be moved in the opposite direction, from N to P; so that as regards the motions of the wire past the pole, they may be reduced to two, directly opposite to each other, one of which produces a current from P to N, and the other from N to P.

115. The same holds true of the unmarked pole of the magnet, except that if it be substituted for the one in the figure, then, as the wires are moved in the direction of the arrows, the current of electricity would be from N to P, and when they move in the reverse direction, from P to N.

116. Hence the current of electricity which is excited in metal when moving in the neighborhood of a magnet, depends for its direction altogether upon the relation of the metal to the resultant of magnetic action, or to the magnetic curves, and may be expressed in a popular way thus: Let AB (Fig. 6) represent a cylinder magnet, A being the marked pole, and B the unmarked pole; let PN be a silver knife-blade resting across the magnet with its edge upward, and with its marked or notched side to-

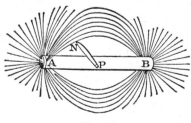

Fig. 6

wards the pole A; then in whatever direction or position this knife be moved edge foremost, either about the marked or the unmarked pole, the current of electricity produced will be from P to N, provided the intersected curves proceeding from A abut upon the notched surface of the knife, and those from B upon the unnotched side. Or if the knife be moved with its back foremost, the current will be from N to P in every possible position and direction, provided the intersected curves abut on the same surfaces as before. A little model is easily constructed, by using a cylinder of wood for a magnet, a flat piece for the blade, and a piece of thread connecting one end of the cylinder with the other, and passing through a hole in the blade, for the magnetic curves: this readily gives the result of any possible direction.

117. When the wire under induction is passing by an electromagnetic pole, as for instance one end of a copper helix traversed by the electric current (34), the direction of the current in the approaching wire is the same with that of the current in the parts or sides of the spirals nearest to it, and in the receding wire the reverse of that in the parts nearest to it.

118. All these results show that the power of inducing electric currents is circumferentially exerted by a magnetic resultant or axis of power, just as circumferential magnetism is dependent upon and is exhibited by an electric current.

119. The experiments described combine to prove that when a piece of metal (and the same may be true of all conducting matter) (213) is passed either before a single pole, or between the opposite poles of a magnet, or near electro-magnetic poles, whether ferruginous or not, electrical currents are produced across the metal transverse to the direction of motion; and which therefore, in Arago's experiments, will approximate towards the direction of radii. If a single wire be moved like the spoke of a wheel near a magnetic pole, a current of electricity is determined through it from one end towards the other. If a wheel be imagined, constructed of a great number of these radii, and this revolved near the pole, in the manner of the copper disc (85), each radius will have a current produced in it as it passes by the pole. If the radii be supposed to be in contact laterally, a copper

disc results, in which the directions of the currents will be generally the same, being modified only by the coaction which can take place between the particles, now that they are in metallic contact.

EXPERIMENTAL RESEARCHES IN ELECTRICITY

ATMOSPHERIC MAGNETISM

It is to me an impossible thing to perceive that two-ninths of the atmosphere by weight is a highly magnetic body, subject to great changes in its magnetic character, by variations in its temperature and condensation or rarefaction, without being persuaded that it has much to do with the variable disposition of the magnetic forces upon the surface of the earth.

The earth is a spheroidal body consisting of paramagnetic and diamagnetic substances irregularly disposed and intermingled; but for the present the whole may be considered a mighty compound magnet. The magnetic force of this great magnet is known to us only on the surface of the earth and water of our planet, and the variations in the magnetic lines of force which pass in or across this surface can be measured by their action on small standard magnets; but these variations are limited in their information, and do not tell us whether the cause is in the air above or the earth beneath.

The lines of force issue from the earth in the northern and southern parts and coalesce with each other over the equatorial, as would be the case in a globe having one or two short magnets adjusted in relation to its axis, and it is probable that the lines of force in their circuitous course may extend through space to tens of thousands of miles. The lines proceed through space with a certain degree of facility, but there may be variations in space, e.g., variations in its temperature which affect its power of transmitting the magnetic influence.

Between the earth and space, however, is interposed the at-

291

mosphere, and at the bottom of the atmosphere we live. The atmosphere consists of four volumes of nitrogen and one of oxygen uniformly mixed and acting magnetically as a single medium. The *nitrogen* of the air is, as regards the magnetic force, neither paramagnetic nor diamagnetic, whether dense or rare, or at high or low temperatures.

The *oxygen* of the air, on the other hand, is highly paramagnetic, being, bulk for bulk, equivalent to a solution of protosulphate of iron, containing of the crystallized salt seventeen times the weight of the oxygen. It becomes less paramagnetic, volume for volume, as it is rarefied, and apparently in the simple proportion of its rarefaction, the temperature remaining the same. When its temperature is raised—the expansion consequent thereon being permitted—it loses very greatly its paramagnetic force, and there is sufficient reason to conclude that when its temperature is lowered its paramagnetic condition is exalted. These characters oxygen preserves even when mingled with the nitrogen in the air.

Hence the atmosphere is a highly magnetic medium, and this medium is changed in its magnetic relations by every change in its density and temperature, and must affect both the intensity and direction of the magnetic force emanating from the earth, and may account for the variations which we find in terrestrial magnetic power.

We may expect as the sun leaves us on the west some magnetic effect correspondent to that of the approach of a body of cold air from the east. Again, the innumerable circumstances that break up more or less any average arrangement of the air temperatures may be expected to give not merely differences in the regularity, direction, and degree of magnetic variation, but, because of vicinity, differences so large as to be many times greater than the mean difference for a given short period, and they may also cause irregularities in the times of their occurrence. Yet again, the atmosphere diminishes in density upwards, and this diminution will affect the transmission of the electric force.

The result of the *annual variation* that may be expected from the magnetic constitution and condition of the atmosphere seems to me to be of the following kind.

Since the axis of the earth's rotation is inclined 23° 28′ to the plane of the ecliptic, the two hemispheres will become alternately warmer and cooler than each other. The air of the cooled hemisphere will conduct magnetic influence more freely than if in the mean state, and the lines of force passing through it will increase in amount, whilst in the other hemisphere the warmed air will conduct with less readiness than before, and the intensity will diminish. In addition to this effect of temperature, there ought to be another due to the increase of the ponderable portion of the air in the cooled hemisphere, consequent on its contraction and the coincident expansion of the air in the warmer half, both of which circumstances tend to increase the variation in power of the two hemispheres from the normal state. Then, as the earth rolls on its annual journey, that which was at one time the cooler becomes the warmer hemisphere, and in its turn sinks as far below the average magnetic intensity as it before had stood above it, while the other hemisphere changes its magnetic condition from less to more intense.

ELECTRO-CHEMICAL ACTION

The theory of definite electrolytical or electro-chemical action appears to me to touch immediately upon the absolute quantity of electricity belonging to different bodies. As soon as we perceive that chemical powers are definite for each body, and that the electricity which we can loosen from each body has definite chemical action which can be measured, we seem to have found the link which connects the proportion of that we have evolved to the proportion belonging to the particles in their natural state.

Now, it is wonderful to observe how small a quantity of a compound body is decomposed by a certain quantity of electricity. One gram of water, for instance, acidulated to facilitate conduction, will require an electric current to be continued for three minutes and three-quarters to effect its decomposition, and the current must be powerful enough to keep a platina wire 1/104 inch in thickness red hot in the air during the whole time, and to produce a very brilliant and constant star of light if interrupted anywhere by charcoal points. It will not be too much to say that this necessary quantity of electricity is equal to a very powerful flash of lightning; and yet when it has performed its full work of electrolysis, it has separated the elements of only a single grain of water.

On the other hand, the relation between the conduction of the electricity and the decomposition of the water is so close that one cannot take place without the other. If the water be altered only in that degree which consists in its having the solid instead of the fluid state, the conduction is stopped and the decomposition is stopped with it. Whether the conduction be considered as depending upon the decomposition or not, still the relation of the two functions is equally intimate.

Considering this close and twofold relation—namely, that without decomposition transmission of electricity does not occur, and that for a given definite quantity of electricity passed an equally definite and constant quantity of water or other matter is decomposed; considering also that the agent, which is electricity, is simply employed in overcoming electrical powers in the body subjected to its action, it seems a probable and almost a natural consequence that the quantity which passes is the equivalent of that of the particles separated; *i.e.*, that if the electrical power which holds the elements of a grain of water in combination, or which makes a grain of oxygen and hydrogen in the right proportions unite into water when they are made to combine, could be thrown into a current, it would exactly equal the current required for the separation of that grain of water into its elements again; in other words, that the electricity which decomposes and that which is evolved by the decomposition of a certain quantity of matter are alike.

This view of the subject gives an almost overwhelming idea of the extraordinary quantity or degree of electric power which naturally belongs to the particles of matter, and the idea may be illustrated by reference to the voltaic pile.

The source of the electricity in the voltaic instrument is due almost entirely to chemical action. Substances interposed between its metals are all electrolytes, and the current cannot be transmitted without their decomposition. If, now, a voltaic trough have its extremities connected by a body capable of being decomposed, such as water, we shall have a continuous current through the apparatus, and we may regard the part where the acid is acting on the plates and the part where the current is acting upon the water as the reciprocals of each other. In both parts we have the two conditions, *inseparable in such bodies as these*: the passing of a current, and decomposition. In the one case we have decomposition associated with a current; in the other, a current followed by decomposition.

Let us apply this in support of my surmise respecting the enormous electric power of each particle or atom of matter.

Two wires, one of platina, and one of zinc, each one-eighteenth of an inch in diameter, placed five-sixteenths of an inch apart, and immersed to the depth of five-eighths of an inch in acid, consisting of one drop of oil of vitriol and four ounces of distilled water at a temperature of about 60° Fahrenheit, and connected at the other ends by a copper wire eighteen feet long, and one-eighteenth of an inch in thickness, yielded as much electricity in little more than three seconds of time as a Leyden battery charged by thirty turns of a very large and powerful plate electric machine in full action. This quantity, although sufficient if passed at once through the head of a rat or cat to have killed it, as by a flash of lightning, was evolved by the mutual action of so small a portion of the zinc wire and water in contact with it that the loss of weight by either would be inappreciable; and as to the water which could be decomposed by that current, it must have been insensible in quantity, for no trace of hydrogen appeared upon the surface of the platina during these three seconds. It would appear that 800,000 such charges of the Leyden battery would be necessary to decompose a single grain of water; or, if I am right, to equal the quantity of electricity which is naturally associated with the elements of that grain of water, endowing them with their mutual chemical affinity.

This theory of the definite evolution and the equivalent definite action of electricity beautifully harmonizes the associated theories of definite proportions and electro-chemical affinity.

According to it, the equivalent weights of bodies are simply those quantities of them which contain equal quantities of electricity, or have naturally equal electric powers, it being the electricity which *determines* the equivalent number, *because* it determines the combining force. Or if we adopt the atomic theory or phraseology, then the atoms of bodies which are equivalent to each other in their ordinary chemical action have equal quantities of electricity naturally associated with them. I cannot refrain from recalling here the beautiful idea put forth, I believe by Berzelius in his development of his views of the electro-chemical theory of affinity, that the heat and light evolved during cases of powerful combination are the consequence of the electric discharge which is at the moment taking place. The idea is in perfect accordance with the view I have taken of the quantity of electricity associated with the particles of matter.

The definite production of electricity in association with its definite action proves, I think, that the current of electricity in the voltaic pile is sustained by chemical decomposition, or, rather, by chemical action, and not by contact only. But here, as elsewhere, I beg to reserve my opinion as to the real action of contact.

Admitting, however, that chemical action is the source of electricity, what an infinitely small fraction of that which is active do we obtain and employ in our voltaic batteries! Zinc and platina wires one-eighteenth of an inch in diameter and about half an inch long, dipped into dilute sulphuric acid, so weak that it is not sensibly sour to the tongue, or scarcely sensitive to our most delicate test papers, will evolve more electricity in one-twentieth of a minute, than any man would willingly allow to pass through his body at once.

The chemical energy represented by the satisfaction of the chemical affinities of a grain of water and four grains of zinc can evolve electricity equal in quantity to that of a powerful thunderstorm. Nor is it merely true that the quantity is active;

it can be directed—made to perform its full equivalent duty. Is there not, then, great reason to believe that, by a closer investigation of the development and action of this subtile agent, we shall be able to increase the power of our batteries, or to invent new instruments which shall a thousandfold surpass in energy those we at present possess?

THE GYMNOTUS, OR ELECTRIC EEL

Wonderful as are the laws and phenomena of electricity when made evident to us in inorganic or dead matter, then interest can bear scarcely any comparison with that which attaches to the same force when connected with the nervous system and with life.

The existence of animals able to give the same concussion to the living system as the electrical machine, the voltaic battery, and the thunderstorm being made known to us by various naturalists, it became important to identify their electricity with the electricity produced by man from dead matter. In the case of the *Torpedo* (a fish belonging to the family of Electric Rings) this identity has been fully proved, but in the case of the *Gymnotus* the proof has not been quite complete, and I thought it well to obtain a specimen of the latter fish.

A gymnotus being obtained, I conducted a series of experiments. Besides the hands two kinds of collectors of electricity were used—one with a copper disc for contact with the fish, and the other with a plate of copper bent into saddle shape, so that it might enclose a certain extent of the back and sides of the fish. These conductors, being put over the fish, collected power sufficient to produce many electric effects.

Shock. The shock was very powerful when the hands were placed one near the head and the other near the tail, and the nearer the hands were together, within certain limits, the less powerful was the shock. The disc conductors conveyed the shock very well when the hands were wetted.

297

Galvanometer. A galvanometer was readily affected by using the saddle conductors, applied to the anterior and posterior parts of the gymnotus. A powerful discharge of the fish caused a deflection of thirty or forty degrees. The deflection was constantly in a given direction, the electric current being always from the anterior part of the animal through the galvanometer wire to the posterior parts. The former were, therefore, for the time externally positive and the latter negative.

Making a Magnet. When a little helix containing twenty-two feet of silked wire wound on a quill was put into a circuit, and an annealed steel needle placed in the helix, the needle became a magnet and the direction of its polarity in every case indicated a current from the anterior to the posterior parts of the gymnotus.

Chemical Decomposition. Polar decomposition of a solution of iodide of potassium was easily obtained.

Evolution of Heat. Using a Harris' thermo-electrometer, we thought we were able, in one instance, to observe a feeble elevation of temperature.

Spark. By suitable apparatus a spark was obtained four times.

Such were the general electric phenomena obtained from the gymnotus, and on several occasions many of the phenomena were obtained together. Thus, a magnet was made, a galvanometer deflected, and, perhaps, a wire heated by one single discharge of the electric force of the animal. When the shock is strong, it is like that of a large Leyden battery charged to a low degree, or that of a good voltaic battery of, perhaps, one hundred or more pairs of plates, of which the circuit is completed for a moment only.

I endeavored by experiment to form some idea of the quantity of electricity, and came to the conclusion that a single medium discharge of the fish is at least equal to the electricity of a Leyden battery of fifteen jars, containing 3,500 square inches of glass coated on both sides, charged to its highest degree. This conclusion is in perfect accordance with the degree of deflection which the discharge can produce in a galvanometer needle, and also with the amount of chemical decomposition produced in the electrolysing experiments.

298

The gymnotus frequently gives a double and even a triple shock, with scarcely a sensible interval between each discharge.

As at the moment of shock the anterior parts are positive and the posterior negative, it may be concluded that there is a current from the former to the latter through every part of the water which surrounds the animal, to a considerable distance from its body. The shock which is felt, therefore, when the hands are in the most favorable position is the effect of a very small portion only of the electricity which the animal discharges at the moment, by far the largest portion passing through the surrounding water.

This enormous external current must be accompanied by some effect within the fish *equivalent* to a current, the direction of which is from the tail towards the head, and equal to the sum of *all these external* forces. Whether the process of evolving or exciting the electricity within the fish includes the production of the internal current, which is not necessarily so quick and momentary as the external one, we cannot at present say; but at the time ot the shock the animal does not apparently feel the electric sensation which he causes in those around him.

The gymnotus can stun and kill fish which are in very various relations to its own body. The extent of surface which the fish that is about to be struck offers to the water conducting the electricity increases the effect of the shock, and the larger the fish, accordingly, the greater must be the shock to which it will be subjected.

JEAN BAPTISTE JOSEPH FOURIER

(1768–1830)

A French mathematician and physicist who traveled with Napoleon on his Egyptian expedition, Fourier was for a time Governor of Lower Egypt and later a Prefect of France. He is remembered, however, for his researches into the theory of heat, his best-known work being *Théorie Analytique de la Chaleur* (1822), from which the selection here is taken. His work in numerical equations, culminating in the theorem known by his name, was of great importance in the later development of theoretical physics.

ANALYTICAL THEORY OF HEAT

157. The investigation of the laws of movement of heat in solids now consists in the integration of the equations which we have constructed; this is the object of the following chapters. We conclude this chapter with general remarks on the nature of the quantities which enter into our analysis.

In order to measure these quantities and express them numerically, they must be compared with different kinds of units, five in number, namely, the unit of length, the unit of time, that of temperature, that of weight, and finally the unit which serves to measure quantities of heat. For the last unit, we might have chosen the quantity of heat which raises a given volume of a certain substance from the temperature 0 to the temperature 1. The choice of this unit would have been preferable in many respects to that of the quantity of heat required to convert a mass of ice of a given weight, into an equal mass of water at 0, without raising its temperature. We have adopted the last unit only because it had been in a manner fixed beforehand in several works on physics; besides, this supposition would introduce no change into the results of analysis.

158. The specific elements which in every body determine the measurable effects of heat are three in number, namely, the conducibility proper to the body, the conducibility relative to the atmospheric air, and the capacity for heat. The numbers which express these quantities are, like the specific gravity, so many natural characters proper to different substances.

We have already remarked, Art. 36, that the conducibility of the surface would be measured in a more exact manner, if we had sufficient observations on the effects of radiant heat in spaces deprived of air.

It may be seen, that only three specific coefficients, K, h, C,[1] enter into the investigation; they must be determined by observation; and we shall point out in the sequel the experiments adapted to make them known with precision.

159. The number C which enters into the analysis, is always multiplied by the density D, that is to say, by the number of units of weight which are equivalent to the weight of unit volume; thus the product CD may be replaced by the coefficient c. In this case we must understand by the specific capacity for heat, the quantity required to raise from temperature 0 to temperature 1 unit of volume of a given substance, and not unit of weight of that substance.

With the view of not departing from the common definition, we have referred the capacity for heat to the weight and not to the volume; but it would be preferable to employ the coefficient c which we have just defined; magnitudes measured by the unit of weight would not then enter into the analytical expressions: we should have to consider only, 1st, the linear dimension x, the temperature v, and the time t; 2nd, the coefficients c, h, and K. The three first quantities are undetermined, and the three others are, for each substance, constant elements which experiment determines. As to the unit of surface and the unit of volume, they are not absolute, but depend on the unit of length.

160. It must now be remarked that every undetermined magnitude or constant has one *dimension* proper to itself, and that the

[1] These specific coefficients represent conducibility (K), surface conducibility (h), and specific heat (C).

terms of one and the same equation could not be compared, if they had not the same *exponent of dimension*. We have introduced this consideration into the theory of heat, in order to make our definitions more exact, and to serve to verify the analysis, it is derived from primary notions on quantities; for which reason, in geometry and mechanics, it is the equivalent of the fundamental lemmas which the Greeks have left us without proof.

161. In the analytical theory of heat, every equation (E) expresses a necessary relation between the existing magnitudes x, t, v, c, h, K. This relation depends in no respect on the choice of the unit of length, which from its very nature is contingent, that is to say, if we took a different unit to measure the linear dimensions, the equation (E) would still be the same. Suppose then the unit of length to be changed, and its second value to be equal to the first divided by m. Any quantity whatever x which in the equation (E) represents a certain line ab, and which, consequently, denotes a certain number of times the unit of length, becomes mx, corresponding to the same length ab; the value t of the time, and the value v of the temperature will not be changed; the same is not the case with the specific elements h, K, c: the

first, h, becomes $\dfrac{h}{m^2}$; for it expresses the quantity of heat which

escapes, during the unit of time, from the unit of surface at the temperature 1. If we examine attentively the nature of the coefficient K, as we have defined it in previous Articles we perceive that it becomes K/m; for the flow of heat varies directly as the area of the surface, and inversely as the distance between two definite planes. As to the coefficient c which represents the product CD, it also depends on the unit of length and

becomes $\dfrac{c}{m^3}$; hence equation (E) must undergo no change when

we write mx instead of x, and at the same time $\dfrac{k}{m}, \dfrac{h}{m^2}, \dfrac{c}{m^3}$, instead of K, h, c; the number m disappears after these substitutions: thus the dimension of x with respect to the unit of length is 1, that of K is -1, that of h is -2, and that of c is -3. If we attribute to each quantity its own *exponent of dimension*, the equation will be homogeneous, since every term will have the same total exponent. Numbers such as S, which represent surfaces or solids, are of two dimensions in the first case, and of three dimensions in the second. Angles, sines, and other trigonometrical functions, logarithms or exponents of powers, are, according to the principles of analysis, *absolute* numbers which do not change with the unit of length; their dimensions must therefore be taken equal to 0, which is the dimension of all abstract numbers.

If the unit of time, which was at first 1, becomes $1/n$, the number t will become nt, and the numbers x and v will not change. The coefficients K, h, c, will become K/n, h/n, c. Thus the dimensions of x, t, v with respect to the unit of time are 0, 1, 0, and those of K, h, c, are -1, -1, 0.

If the unit of temperature be changed, so that the temperature 1 becomes that which corresponds to an effect other than the boiling of water; and if that effect requires a less temperature, which is to that of boiling water in the ratio of 1 to the number p; v will become vp, x and t will keep their values, and the coefficients K, h, c, will become K/p, h/p, c/p.

162. If we retain the coefficients C and D, whose product has been represented by c, we should have to consider the unit of weight, and we should find that the exponent of dimension, with respect to the unit of length, is -3 for the density D, and 0 for C.

Quantity of Constant	Length	Duration	Temperature
Exponent of dimension of x	1	0	0
Exponent of dimension of t	0	1	0
Exponent of dimension of v	0	0	1
The specific conducibility, K	-1	-1	-1
The surface conducibility, b	-2	-1	-1
The capacity for heat, c	-3	0	-1

On applying the preceding rule to the different equations and their transformations, it will be found that they are homogeneous with respect to each kind of unit, and that the dimension of every angular or exponential quantity is nothing. If this were not the case, some error must have been committed in the analysis, or abridged expressions must have been introduced.

If for example, we take equation (b) of Art. 105,

$$\frac{dv}{dt} = \frac{K}{CD}\frac{d^2v}{dx^2} - \frac{hl}{CDS}\,v,$$

we find that, with respect to the unit of length, the dimension of each of the three terms is 0; it is 1 for the unit of temperature, and -1 for the unit of time.

In the equation $v = Ae^{-x}\sqrt{\dfrac{2h}{Kl}}$ of Art. 76, the linear dimension of each term is 0, and it is evident that the dimension of the exponent $x\sqrt{2h/Kl}$ is always nothing, whatever be the units of length, time, or temperature.

BENJAMIN FRANKLIN

(1706-1790)

Franklin's career as a statesman, diplomat, publisher, printer, signer of the Declaration of Independence and member of the Constitutional Convention are an inseparable part of American history. So, indeed, are his invention of the Franklin stove and his founding of the first American scientific society, the American Philosophical Society (1743). The more original and colorful of his inventions are described here: the kite experiments in electricity; his account of lead poisoning, and the invention of bifocal spectacles. In time, at least, Franklin is the father of American science. He wrote little for publication after giving up his printing business, and the majority of his "works," including the following descriptions of his discoveries, consist almost entirely of private letters.

EXPERIMENTS IN ELECTRICITY

(TO PETER COLLINSON)

SIR,

[Philadelphia], 1749

. . . Chagrined a little that we have been hitherto able to produce nothing in this way of use to mankind and the hot weather coming on, when electrical experiments are not so agreeable, it is proposed to put an end to them for this season, somewhat humorously, in a party of pleasure on the banks of *Skuylkil*. Spirits, at the same time, are to be fired by a spark sent from side to side through the river, without any other conductor than the water; an experiment which we some time since performed, to the amazement of many.

A turkey is to be killed for our dinner by the *electrical shock*,

305

and roasted by the *electrical jack*, before a fire kindled by the *electrified bottle*: when the healths of all the famous electricians in *England, Holland, France*, and *Germany* are to be drank in *electrified bumpers*, under the discharge of guns from the *electrical battery*.

April 29, 1749

(TO PETER COLLINSON)

[Philadelphia] October 19, 1752

SIR,

As frequent mention is made in public papers from *Europe* of the success of the *Philadelphia* experiment for drawing the electric fire from clouds by means of pointed rods of iron erected on high buildings, and, it may be agreeable to the curious to be informed, that the same experiment has succeeded in *Philadelphia* though made in a different and more easy manner, which is as follows:

Make a small cross of two light strips of cedar, the arms so long as to reach to the four corners of a large thin silk handkerchief when extended; tie the corners of the handkerchief to the extremities of the cross, so you have the body of a kite; which being properly accommodated with a tail, loop, and string, will rise in the air, like those made of paper; but this being of silk, is fitter to bear the wet and wind of a thunder-gust without tearing. To the top of the upright stick of the cross is to be fixed a very sharp-pointed wire, rising a foot or more above the wood. To the end of the twine, next the hand, is to be tied a silk ribbon, and where the silk and twine join, a key may be fastened. This kite is to be raised, when a thunder-gust appears to be coming on, and the person who holds the string must stand within a door or window or under some cover, so that the silk ribbon may not be wet; and care must be taken that the twine does not touch the frame of the door or window. As soon as any of the thunder-clouds come over the kite, the pointed wire will draw the electric fire from them, and the kite, with all the twine, will be electrified, and the loose filaments of the twine will stand out every way, and be attracted by an approaching finger. And when the rain has wet the kite and twine, so that it can conduct the electric fire freely, you will find it stream out plentifully from the key on the approach of your knuckle. At this key the phial may be charged; and from electric fire thus obtained, spirits may be kindled, and all the other electric experiments be performed, which are usually done by the help of a rubbed glass globe or tube, and thereby the sameness of the electric matter with that of lightning completely demonstrated.

B. FRANKLIN

LEAD POISONING

(TO BENJAMIN VAUGHAN)

Philada, July 31, 1768

DEAR FRIEND,

I recollect, that, when I had the great pleasure of seeing you at Southampton, now a 12month since, we had some conversation on the bad effects of lead taken inwardly; and that at your request I promis'd to send you in writing a particular account of several facts I then mention'd to you, of which you thought some good use might be made. I now sit down to fulfill that promise.

The first thing I remember of this kind was a general discourse in Boston, when I was a boy, of a complaint from North Carolina against New England rum, that it poisn'd their people, giving them the dry bellyach, with a loss of the use of their limbs. The distilleries being examin'd on the occasion, it was found that several of them used leaden still-heads and worms, and the physicians were of opinion, that the mischief was occasioned by that use of lead. The legislature of Massachusetts thereupon pass'd an Act, prohibiting under severe penalties the use of such still-heads and worms thereafter. Inclos'd I send you a copy of the Act, taken from my printed law-book.

In 1724, being in London, I went to work in the printing-house of Mr. Palmer, Bartholomew Close, as a compositor. I there found a practice, I had never seen before, of drying a case of types (which are wet in distribution) by placing it sloping before the fire. I found this had the additional advantage, when the types were not only dry'd but heated, of being comfortable to the hands working over them in cold weather. I therefore sometimes heated my case when the types did not want drying. But an old workman, observing it, advis'd me not to do so, telling me I might lose the use of my hands by it, as two of our companions had nearly done, one of whom that us'd to earn his guinea a week, could not then make more than ten shillings, and the other, who had the dangles, but seven and sixpence. This, with a kind of obscure pain, that I had sometimes felt, as it were in the bones of my hand when working over the types made very hot, induced me to omit the practice, but talking afterwards with Mr. James, a letter-founder in the same Close, and asking him if his people, who work'd over the little furnaces of melted metal, were not subject to that disorder; he made light of any danger from the effluvia, but ascribed it to particles of the metal swallow'd with their food by slovenly workmen, who went to their meals after handling the metal, without well washing their fingers, so that some of the metalline particles were taken off by their bread and eaten with it. This appeared to have some reason in it. But the pain I had experienc'd made me still afraid of those effluvia.

Being in Derbyshire at some of the furnaces for smelting of lead ore, I was told, that the smoke of those furnaces was pernicious to the neighboring grass and other vegetables; but I do not recollect to have heard any thing of the effect of such vegetables eaten by animals. It may be well to make the enquiry.

In America I have often observ'd, that on the roofs of our shingled houses, where moss is apt to grow in northern exposures, if there be any thing on the roof painted with white lead, such as balusters, or frames of dormant windows, etc., there is constantly a streak on the shingles from such paint down to the eaves, on which no moss will grow, but the wood remains constantly clean and free from it. We seldom drink rain water that falls on our houses; and if we did, perhaps the small quantity of lead, descending from such paint, might not be sufficient to produce any sensible ill effect on our bodies. But I have been told of a case in Europe, I forgot the place, where a whole family was afflicted with what we call the dry bellyach, or *Colica Pictonum*, by drinking rain-water. It was at a country-seat, which, being situated too high to have the advantage of a well, was supply'd with water from a tank, which received the water from the leaded roofs. This had been drunk several years without mischief; but some young trees planted near the house, growing up above the roof, and shedding their leaves upon it, it was suppos'd that an acid in those leaves had corroded the lead they cover'd and furnish'd the water of that year with its baneful particles and qualities.

When I was in Paris with Sir John Pringle in 1767, he visited *La Charité*, a hospital particularly famous for the cure of that malady, and brought from thence a pamphlet containing a list of the names of persons, specifying their professions or trades, who had been cured there. I had the curiosity to examine that list, and found that all the patients were of trades, that, some way or other, use or work in lead; such as plumbers, glaziers, painters, etc., excepting only two kinds, stonecutters and soldiers. These I could not reconcile to my notion, that lead was the cause of that disorder. But on my mentioning this difficulty to a physician of that hospital, he inform'd me that the stonecutters are continually using melted lead to fix the ends of iron balustrades in stone; and that the soldiers had been employ'd by painters, as labourers, in grinding of colours.

This, my dear friend, is all I can at present recollect on the subject. You will see by it, that the opinion of this mischievous effect from lead is at least above sixty years old; and you will observe with concern how long a useful truth may be known and exist, before it is generally receiv'd and practis'd on.

I am, ever, yours most affectionately,

B. FRANKLIN

BIFOCAL SPECTACLES

(TO GEORGE WHATLEY)

Passy, May 23, 1785

. . . By Mr. Dollond's saying, that my double spectacles can only serve particular eyes, I doubt he has not been rightly informed of their construction. I imagine it will be found pretty generally true, that the same convexity of glass, through which a man sees clearest and best at the distance proper for reading, is not the best for greater distances. I therefore had formerly two pair of spectacles, which I shifted occasionally, as in travelling I sometimes read, and often wanted to regard the prospects. Finding this change troublesome, and not always sufficiently ready, I had the glasses cut, and half of each kind associated in the same circle, thus,

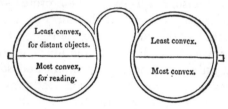

By this means, as I wear my spectacles constantly, I have only to move my eyes up or down, as I want to see distinctly far or near, the proper glasses being always ready. This I find more particularly convenient since my being in France, the glasses that serve me best at table to see what I eat, not being the best to see the faces of those on the other side of the table who speak to me; and when one's ears are not well accustomed to the sounds of a language, a sight of the movements in the features of him that speaks helps to explain; so that I understand French better by the help of my spectacles. . . .

B. FRANKLIN

THE ONE FLUID THEORY OF ELECTRICITY

1. A person standing on wax, and rubbing a tube, and another person on wax drawing the fire; they will both of them, provided they do not stand so as to touch one another, appear to be electrified to a person standing on the floor; that is, he will perceive a spark on approaching each of them with his knuckle.

2. But if the persons on wax touch one another during the exciting of the tube, neither of them will appear to be electrified.

3. If they touch one another after the exciting the tube and drawing the fire as aforesaid, there will be a stronger spark between them than was between either of them and the person on the floor.

4. After such a strong spark neither of them discover any electricity.

These appearances we attempt to account for thus:

We suppose, as aforesaid, that electrical fire is a common element, of which every one of these three persons has his equal share before any operation is begun with the tube. *A*, who stands upon wax, and rubs the tube, collects the electrical fire from himself into the glass; and his communication with the common stock being cut off by the wax, his body is not again immediately supplied. *B*, who stands upon the wax likewise, passing his knuckle along near the tube, receives the fire which was collected by the glass from *A*; and his communication with the common stock being cut off, he retains the additional quantity received. To *C* standing on the floor, both appear to be electrified; for he, having only the middle quantity of electrical fire receives a spark upon approaching *B*, who has an over quantity, but gives one to *A*, who has an under quantity. If *A* and *B* approach to touch each other, the spark is stronger; because the difference between them is greater. After such touch, there is no spark between either of them and *C*, because the electrical fire in all is reduced to the original equality. If they touch while electrising, the equality is never destroyed, the fire only circulating. Hence have arisen some new terms among us. We say, *B*

311

(and bodies alike circumstanced) is electrised positively; *A,* negatively; or rather, *B* is electrised *plus, A, minus.* And we daily in our experiments electrise *plus* or *minus,* as we think proper. To electrise *plus* or *minus,* no more needs be known than this; that the parts of the tube or sphere that are rubbed, do in the instant of the friction attract the electrical fire, and therefore take it from the thing rubbing. The same parts immediately, as the friction upon them ceases, are disposed to give the fire, they have received, to any body that has less. Thus you may circulate it, as *Mr. Watson* has shown; you may also accumulate or subtract it upon or from any body, as you connect that body with the receiver, the communication with the common stock being cut off.

JOSEPH VON FRAUNHOFER

(1787–1826)

This German optician was the maker of the finest lenses and refractors of his time. He gave the name of "Fraunhofer lines" to the dark lines in the solar spectrum, of which he plotted some 576, though he was unable to explain them. He made improvements in telescopes, prisms and other optical instruments, and invented a heliometer, a micrometer and a diffraction grating for the measurement of the wave lengths of light.

PRISMATIC AND DIFFRACTION SPECTRA

In the window-shutter of a darkened room I made a narrow opening—about 15 seconds broad and 36 minutes high—and through this I allowed sunlight to fall on a prism of flint-glass which stood upon the theodolite described before. The theodolite was 24 feet from the window, and the angle of the prism was about 60.° The prism was so placed in front of the objective of the theodolite-telescope that the angle of incidence of the light was equal to the angle at which the beam emerged. I wished to see if in the color-image from sunlight there was a bright band similar to that observed in the color-image of lamplight. But instead of this I saw with the telescope an almost countless number of strong and weak vertical lines, which are, however, darker than the rest of the color-image; some appeared to be almost perfectly black. If the prism was turned so as to increase the angle of incidence, these lines vanished; they disappear also if the angle of incidence is made smaller. For increased angle of incidence, however, these lines become visible again if the telescope is made shorter; while, for a smaller angle of incidence, the eye-piece must be drawn out considerably in order to make the lines reappear.

313

If the eye-piece was so placed that the lines in the red portion of the color-image could be plainly seen, then, in order to see the lines in the violet portion, it must be pushed in slightly. If the opening through which the light entered was made broader, the fine lines ceased to be clearly seen, and vanished entirely if the opening was made 40 seconds wide. If the opening was made 1 minute wide, even the broad lines could not be seen plainly. The distances apart of the lines, and all their relations to each other, remained unchanged, both when the width of the opening in the window-shutter was altered and when the distance of the theodolite from the opening was changed. The prism could be of any kind of refractive material, and its angle might be large or small; yet the lines remained always visible, and only in proportion to the size of the color-image did they become stronger or weaker, and therefore were observed more easily or with more difficulty.

The relations of these lines and streaks among themselves appeared to be the same with every refracting substance; so that, for instance, one particular band is found in every case only in the blue; another is found only in the red; and one can, therefore, at once recognize which line he is observing. These lines can be recognized also in the spectra formed by both the ordinary and the extraordinary rays of Iceland spar. The strongest lines do not in any way mark the limits of the various colors; there is almost always the same color on both sides of a line, and the passage from one color into another cannot be noted.

With reference to these lines the color-image is as shown in the accompanying figure. It is, however, impossible to show on this scale all the lines and their intensities. (The red end of the color-image is in the neighborhood of A; the violet end is near I.) It is, however impossible to set a definite limit at either end, although it is easier at the red than at the violet. Direct sunlight, or sunlight reflected by a mirror, seems to have its limits on the one hand, somewhere between G and H; on the other, at B; yet with sunlight of great intensity the color-image becomes half again as long. In order, however, to see this great spreading-out of the spectrum, the light from the space between C and G must

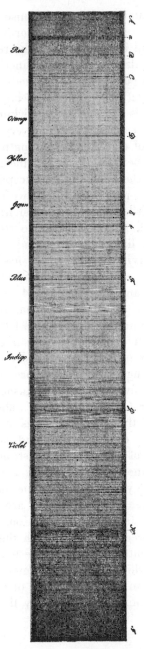

be prevented from entering the eye, because the impression which the light from the extremities of the color-image makes upon the eye is very weak, and is destroyed by the rest of the light. At A there is easily recognized a sharply defined line; yet this is not the limit of the red color, for it proceeds much beyond. At A there are heaped together many lines which form a band; B is sharply defined and is of noticeable thickness. In the space between B and C there can be counted 9 very fine, sharply defined lines. The line C is of considerable strength, and, like B, is very black. In the space between C and D there can be counted 30 very fine lines; but these (with two exceptions), like those between B and C, can be plainly seen only with strong magnification or with prisms which have great dispersion; they are, moreover, very sharply defined. D consists of two strong lines which are separated by a bright line. Between D and E there can be counted some 84 lines of varying intensities. E itself consists of several lines, of which the one in the middle is somewhat stronger than the rest. Between E and b are about 24 lines. At b there are 3 very strong lines, two of which are separated by only a narrow bright line; they are among the strongest lines in the spectrum. In the space between b and F there can be counted about 52 lines; F is fairly strong. Between F and G there are about 185 lines of different strengths. At G there are massed together many lines, among which several are distinguished by their intensity. In the space between G and H there are about 190 lines, whose intensities differ greatly. The two bands at H are most remarkable; they are almost exactly equal, and each consists of many lines; in the middle of each there is a strong line which is very black. From H to I the lines are equally numerous. . . .

I have convinced myself by many experiments and by varying the methods that these lines and bands are due to the nature of sunlight, and do not arise from diffraction, illusion, etc. If light from a lamp is allowed to pass through the same narrow opening in the window-shutter, none of these lines are observed, only the bright line R, which, however, comes exactly in the same place as the line D, so that the indices of refraction of the rays D and R are the same. The reason why the lines fade away, or

316

even entirely vanish, when the opening at the window is made too wide is not difficult to give. The stronger lines have a width of from five to ten seconds; so, if the opening of the window is not so narrow that the light which passes through can be regarded as belonging to one ray, or if the angular width of the opening is much more than that of the line, the image of one and the same line is repeated several times side by side, and consequently becomes indistinct, or vanishes entirely if the opening is made too wide.

GALEN

(*c*. 130–201)

For some thirteen centuries the works of this Greek physician remained the ultimate medical authority in the West. Nearly one hundred of his treatises were preserved, largely in Arabic, through the Dark Ages. A true disciple of Hippocrates, Galen disregarded the fads and superstitions of his contemporaries and acquired his anatomy through the dissection of animals, his clinical medicine from personal experience. Later physician to Marcus Aurelius, Galen began his practice as surgeon to gladiators in Asia Minor. His works remained untranslated into English until the present century.

ON THE DISSECTION OF APES

WHAT TENT poles are to tents, and walls to houses, so to animals is their bony structure; the other parts adapt themselves to this and change with it. Thus, if an animal's cranium is round, its brain must be the same; or, again, if it is oblong, then the animal's brain must also be oblong. If the jaws are small, and the face as a whole roundish, the muscles of these parts will also necessarily be small; and similarly, if the jaws are prominent, the animal's face as a whole will be long, as also the facial muscles. Consequently also the monkey is of all animals the likest to man in its viscera, muscles, arteries, veins, and nerves, because it is also in the form of its bones. From the nature of these it walks on two legs, uses its front limbs as hands, has the flattest breastbone of all quadrupeds, collarbones like those of a man, a round face, and a short neck. And these being similar, the muscles cannot be different; for they are extended on the outside of the bones in such a manner that they resemble them in size and form. To the muscles, again, correspond the arteries,

318

veins, and nerves; so these, being similar, must correspond to the bones. . . .

First of all, then, I would ask you to make yourself acquainted with the human bones, and to look on this as a matter of secondary importance. Nor must you merely read the subject up in one of these books which are called by some "Osteology," by others "the Skeleton," and by others simply "On Bones," as is my own book; which, by the way, I am certain is better than any previously written, both as regards the exactitude of its matter and the brevity and clearness of its explanations. Make it your earnest business, then, not only to learn exactly from the book the appearance of each of the bones, but to become yourself by the use of your eyes an eager firsthand observer of human osteology.

At Alexandria this is very easy, since the physicians in that country accompany the instruction they give to their students with opportunities for personal inspection. Hence you must try to get to Alexandria for this reason alone, if for no other. But if you cannot manage this, still it is not impossible to obtain a view of human bones. Personally I have very often had a chance to do this where tombs or monuments have become broken up. On one occasion a river, having risen to the level of a grave which had been carelessly constructed a few months previously, easily disintegrated this; then by the force of its current it swept right over the dead man's body, of which the flesh had already putrefied, while the bones were still closely attached to one another. This it carried downstream for the distance of a league, till, coming to a lakelike stretch with sloping banks, it here deposited the corpse. And here the latter lay ready for inspection, just as though prepared by a doctor for his pupil's lesson.

Once also I examined the skeleton of a robber, lying on a mountain-side a short distance from the road. This man had been killed by some traveler whom he had attacked, but who had been too quick for him. None of the inhabitants of the district would bury him; but in their detestation of him they were delighted when his body was eaten by birds of prey; the latter, in fact, devoured the flesh in two days and left the skeleton ready, as it

319

were, for any one who cared to enjoy an anatomical demonstration.

As regards yourself, then, even if you do not have the luck to see anything like this, still you can dissect an ape, and learn each of the bones from it, by carefully removing the flesh. For this purpose you must choose the apes which most resemble man. . . .

Thus if you should also later meet with a human skeleton, you would easily recognize and remember everything. . . . When apes are not available, one should be prepared to dissect the bodies of other animals, distinguishing at once in what ways they differ from apes.

THE LADY AND THE DANCER

I was called in to see a woman who was stated to be sleepless at night and to lie tossing about from one position into another. Finding she had no fever, I made a detailed inquiry into everything that had happened to her, especially considering such factors as we know to cause insomnia. But she either answered little or nothing at all, as if to show that it was useless to question her. Finally she turned away, hiding herself completely by throwing the bedclothes over her whole body, and laying her head on another small pillow, as if desiring sleep.

After leaving I came to the conclusion that she was suffering from one of two things; either from a melancholy dependent on black bile, or else trouble about something she was unwilling to confess. I therefore deferred till the next day a closer investigation of this. Further, on first arriving I was told by her attendant maid that she could not at present be seen; and on returning a second time, I was told the same again. So I went yet a third time, but the attendant asked me to go away, as she did not want her mistress disturbed. Having learned, however, that when I left she had washed and taken food in her customary manner, I came back the next day, and in a private conversation with the maid on one subject and another I found out exactly what was worrying the patient. And this I discovered by chance.

320

After I had diagnosed that there was no bodily trouble, and that the woman was suffering from some mental uneasiness, it happened that, at the very time I was examining her, this was confirmed. Somebody came from the theater and said he had seen Pylades dancing. Then both her expression and the color of her face changed. Seeing this, I applied my hand to her wrist and noticed that her pulse had suddenly become extremely irregular (anomalous). This kind of pulse indicates that the mind is disturbed; thus it occurs also in people who are disputing over any subject. So on the next day I said to one of my followers that, when I paid my visit to the woman, he was to come a little later and announce to me, "Morphus is dancing today." When he said this, I found that the pulse was unaffected. Similarly also on the next day, when I had an announcement made about the third member of the troupe, the pulse remained unchanged as before. On the fourth evening I kept very careful watch when it was announced that Pylades was dancing, and I noticed that the pulse was very much disturbed. Thus I found out that the woman was in love with Pylades, and by careful watch on the succeeding days my discovery was confirmed.

Similarly, too, I diagnosed the case of a slave who administered the household of another wealthy man, and who sickened in the same way. He was concerned about having to give an account of his expenses, in which he knew that there was a considerable sum wanting; the thought of this kept him awake, and he grew thin with anxiety. I first told his master that there was nothing physically wrong with the old man, and advised an investigation to be made as to whether he feared his master was about to ask an account of the sums he had entrusted to him, and for this reason was worried, knowing that a considerable amount would be found wanting. The master told me I had made a good suggestion, so in order to make the diagnosis certain, I advised him to do as follows; he was to tell the slave to give him back all the money he had in hand, lest, in the event of his sudden death, it should be lost, owing to the administration passing into the hands of some other servant whom he did not know, for there would be no use asking for an account from such an one. And

321

when the master said this to him, he felt sure he would not be questioned. So he ceased to worry, and by the third day had regained his natural physical condition.

Now what was it that escaped the notice of previous physicians when examining the aforesaid woman and the aforesaid slave? For such discoveries are made by common inductions (*epilogisms*) if one has even the smallest acquaintance with medical science. I suppose it is because they have no clear conception (*diagnosis*) of how the body tends to be affected by mental conditions. Possibly also they do not know that the pulse is altered by quarrels and alarms which suddenly disturb the mind.

THE EMPEROR'S BELLYACHE

What happened in the case of the Emperor [Marcus Aurelius] himself was really wonderful. His own opinion and that of the physicians of his entourage who had gone abroad with him was that some febrile paroxysm had begun. But they all proved wrong both on the second and third day, in the morning and at the third hour. He had on the preceding day taken a draught of bitter aloes at the first hour, and then some theriac, as was his daily custom. Next he took some food about the sixth hour, washed at sunset, and had a small meal. During the whole night there ensued colicky pains with intestinal evacuations. This made him feverish, and when his attendant physicians observed this, they gave orders that he should be kept quiet; then they prescribed slop diet at the ninth hour. After this I was myself also summoned to come and sleep in the palace. Then, when the lamps were newly lit, a messenger came to call me at the Emperor's bidding. Three doctors had been observing him since about daybreak, and two of them feeling his pulse, and they all considered this the beginning of a febrile attack. I stood by, however, without saying anything; so the Emperor, looking at me first, asked why, when the others felt his pulse, I alone did not do so. I said to him, "two of these gentlemen have already done this, and probably when they were abroad with you they already learned by experience the characteristics of your pulse; hence I expect they will be better able to judge its present condition [*diathesis*]." On my saying this he bade me also feel his pulse. It seemed to me that, taking his age and constitution into account, the pulse was far from indicating the beginning of a febrile attack. I declared that this was no onset of fever, but that his stomach was overloaded by the food he had taken, which had turned to phlegm prior to ejection.

My diagnosis seemed praiseworthy to the Emperor, and he repeated three times in succession: "That's it. It is just what you say. I feel I have taken too much cold food." And he asked what was to be done. I answered what I knew, and said to him: "If it were anyone else who was in this state, I should follow my custom and give him wine sprinkled with pepper. But in the case of kings like yourself, physicians are in the habit of giving safer remedies; hence it will be enough to apply over your stomach some wool impregnated with warm spikenard ointment." The Emperor said that in any case when his stomach was out of order he was in the habit of applying warm spikenard ointment enveloped in purple wool. So he gave orders to Pitholaus to do this, and to let me go. When this application had been made, and his feet thoroughly heated by rubbing with the warm hand, he asked for some Sabine wine, sprinkled pepper in it, and drank. He then declared to Pitholous that he had "one physician, and he was a perfect gentleman." Further, as you know, he keeps constantly saying about me that I am "first among the physicians and alone among the philosophers." For he had already had experience of many who were not only mercenary, but also quarrelsome, conceited, selfish, and malicious. . . .

GALILEO GALILEI

(1564–1642)

One of the titans of science, Galileo's triumphs and defeats are probably more generally known than those of most scientists: How from the oscillations of a cathedral lamp at Pisa he deduced the law of the pendulum. How by the dropping of objects from the Leaning Tower he demonstrated that bodies of different weight fall with the same velocity. How he perfected the refracting telescope while professor of mathematics at Padua, and with it pursued investigations which convinced him of the correctness of the Copernican theory. How his *Letters on the Solar Spots* (1616) aroused the denunciation of the Church. How he promised to abstain from future advocacy of the condemned doctrines, but in 1632 published his *Dialogo sopra i due Massimi Sistemi del Mondo*, for which he was incarcerated, tried by the Inquisition, forced to abjure his beliefs, sentenced to imprisonment, but allowed to retire to a villa near Florence. Galileo was the virtual founder of dynamics, anticipating Newton's three laws of motion, and was one of the first "modern" astronomers, discovering that the moon's light is reflected, that the Milky Way is made up of innumerable stars, that there are spots on the sun, and that the moon has monthly and annual librations.

SYSTEM OF THE WORLD

THERE WAS published some years since in Rome a salutiferous Edict, that, for the obviating of the dangerous Scandals of the present Age, imposed a seasonable Silence upon the Pythagorean Opinion of the Mobility of the Earth. There want not such as unadvisedly affirm, that the Decree was not the production of a sober Scrutiny, but of an ill informed Passion; and one may hear some mutter that Consultors altogether ignorant of Astronomical Observations ought not to clip the Wings of Speculative Wits

324

with rash Prohibitions. My zeale cannot keep silence when I hear these inconsiderate complaints. I thought fit, as being thoroughly acquainted with that prudent Determination, to appear openly upon the Theatre of the World as a Witness of the naked Truth. I was at that time in Rome; and had not only the audiences, but applauds of the most Eminent Prelates of that Court; nor was that Decree Published without Previous Notice given me thereof. Therefore, it is my resolution in the present case to give Foreign Nations to see, that this point is as well understood in Italy, and particularly in Rome, as Transalpine Diligence can imagine it to be: and collecting together all the proper speculations that concern the Copernican Systeme, to let them know, that the notice of all preceded the Censure of the Roman Court; and that there proceed from this Climate not only Doctrines for the health of the Soul, but also ingenious Discoveries for the recreating of the Mind.

To this end I have personated the Copernican in this Discourse; proceeding upon an Hypothesis purely Mathematical; striving by all artificial wayes to represent it Superiour, not to that of the Immobility of the Earth absolutely, but according as it is mentioned by some, that retain no more, but the name of Peripateticks, and are content, without going farther, to adore shadows, not philosophizing with requisit caution, but with the sole remembrance of four Principles, but badly understood.

We shall treat of three principall heads. First I will endeavor to show that all Experiments that can be made upon the Earth are insufficient means to conclude its Mobility, but are indifferently applicable to the Earth moveable or immoveable: and I hope that on this occasion we shall discover many observable passages unknown to the Ancients. Secondly, we will examine the Cœlestiall Phœnomena that make for the Copernican Hypothesis, as if it were to prove absolutely victorious; adding by the way certain new observations, which yet serve only for the Astronomical Facility, not for Natural Necessity. In the third place I will propose an ingenuous Fancy. I remember that I have said many years since, that the unknown Probleme of the Tide might receive some light, admitting the Earth's Motion. This Position of mine

325

passing from one to another had found charitable Fathers that adopted it for the issue of their own wit. Now, because no stranger may ever appear that defending himself with our armes, shall charge us with want of caution in so principal an Accident, I have thought good to lay down those probabilities that would render it credible, admitting that the Earth did move. I hope, that by these Considerations the World will come to know, that if other Nations have Navigated more than we, we have not studied less than they; and that our returning to assert the Earth's Stability, and to take the contrary only for a Mathematical Capriccio, proceeds not from inadvertency of what others have thought thereof, but (had we no other inducements) from those Reasons that Piety, Religion, the Knowledge of the Divine Omnipotency, and consciousness of the incapacity of man's Understanding dictate unto us . . .

SALVIATUS. You argue very well; but you know that the principal scope of *Astronomers*, is to render only reason for the appearances in the Cælestial Bodies, and to them, and to the motions of the Stars, to accommodate such structures and compositions of Circles, that the motions following those calculations, answer to the said appearances, little scrupling to admit of some exorbitances, that indeed upon other accounts they would much stick at. And *Copernicus* himself writes, that he had in his first studies restored the Science of *Astronomy* upon the very suppositions of *Ptolomy*, and in such manner corrected the motions of the Planets, that the computations did very exactly agree with the *Phænomena*, and the *Phænomena* with the supputations, in case that he took the Planets severally one by one. But he addeth, that in going about to put together all the structures of the particular Fabricks, there resulted thence a Monster and *Chimæra*, composed of members most disproportionate to one another, and altogether incompatible; so that although it satisfied an *Astronomer* merely *Arithmetical*, yet did not afford satisfaction or content to the *Astronomer Phylosophical*. And because he very well understood, that if one might salve the Cælestial appearances with false assumptions in nature, it might with much more ease be done by true suppositions, he set himself diligently to search

326

whether any amongst the ancient men of fame, had ascribed to the World any other structure, than that commonly received by *Ptolomy*; and finding that some *Pythagoreans* had in particular assigned the Diurnal conversion to the Earth, and others the annual motion also, he began to compare the appearances, and particularities of the Planets motions, with these two new suppositions, all which things jump exactly with his purpose; and seeing the whole correspond, with admirable facility to its parts, he imbraced this new System, and it took up his rest.

SIMPLICIUS. But what great exorbitancies are there in the *Ptolemaick* Systeme, for which there are not greater to be found in this of *Copernicus*?

SALVIATUS. In the *Ptolemaick Hypothesis* there are diseases, and in the *Copernican* their cures. And first will not all the Sects of *Phylosophers*, account it a great inconvenience, that a body naturally moveable in circumgyration, should move irregularly upon its own Centre, and regularly upon another point? And yet there are such deformed motions as these in the *Ptolomaean* Hypothesis, but in the *Copernican* all move evenly about their own Centres. In the *Ptolomaick*, it is necessary to assign to the Cælestial bodies, contrary motions, and to make them all to move, from East to West, and at the same time, from West to East; but in the *Copernican*, all the Cælestial revolutions are towards one onely way, from West to East. But what shall we say of the apparent motion of the Planets, so irregular, that they not only go one while swift, and another while slow, but sometimes wholly ceases to move; and then after a long time return back again? To salve which appearances *Ptolomie* introduceth very great *Epicicles*, accommodating them one by one to each Planet, with some rules of incongruous motions, which are all with one single motion of the Earth taken away. And would not you, *Simplicius*, call it a great absurditie, if in the *Ptolomaick* Hypothesis, in which the particular Planets, have their peculiar Orbs assigned them one above another, one must be frequently forced to say, that *Mars*, constituted above the Sphære of the Sun, doth so descend, that breaking the Solar Orb, it goeth under it, and approacheth nearer to the Earth, than to the Body of the

327

Sun, and by and by immesurably ascendeth above the same? And yet this, and other exorbitancies are remedied by the sole and single annual motion of the Earth.

SAGREDUS. I would gladly be better informed how these stations, and retrograde and direct motions, which did ever seem to me great improbabilities, do accord in this *Copernican* Systeme.

SALVIATUS. You shall see them so to accord, *Sagredus*, that this onely conjecture ought to be sufficient to make one that is not more than pertinacious or stupid, yield, assent to all the rest of this Doctrine. I tell you therefore, that nothing being altered in the motion of *Saturn*, which is 30 years, in that of *Jupiter*, which is 12, in that of *Mars*, which is 2, in that of *Venus*, which is 9 moneths, in that of *Mercury*, which 80 dayes, or thereabouts, the sole annual motion of the Earth between *Mars* and *Venus*, causeth the apparent inequalities in all the five stars before named. And for a facile and full understanding of the whole, I will describe this figure of it. Therefore suppose the Sun to be placed in the centre O, about which we will draw the Orb described by the Earth, with the annual motion BGM, and let the circle described, *v. gr.* by *Jupiter* about the Sun in 12 years, be this BGM, and in the starry sphere let us imagine the Zodiac YVS. Again, in the annual Orb of the Earth let us take certain equal arches, BC, CD, EF, FG, GH, HI, IK, KL, LM, and in the Sphere of *Jupiter* let us make certain other arches, passed in the same times in which the Earth passeth hers, which let be BC, CD, DE, EF, FG, GH, HI, IK, KL, LM, which shall each be proportionally lesse than these marked in the Earths Orb, like as the motion of *Jupiter* under the Zodiac is slower than the annual. Supposing now, that when the Earth is in B, *Jupiter* is in B, it shall appear to us in the Zodiack to be in P, describing the right line BBP. Next suppose the Earth to be moved from B to C, and *Jupiter* from B to C, in the same time; *Jupiter* shall appear to have passed in the Zodiak to Q, and to have moved straight forwards, according to the order of the signes PQ. In the next place, the Earth passing to D, and *Jupiter* to D, it shall be seen in the Zodiack in R, and from E, *Jupiter* being come to E; will appear

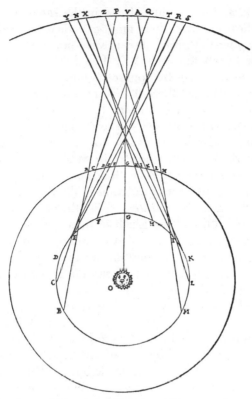

in the Zodiack in S, having all this while moved right forwards. But the Earth afterwards beginning to interpose more directly between *Jupiter* and the Sun, she being come to F, and *Jupiter* to F, he will appear in T, to have already begun to return apparently back again under the Zodiack, and in that time that the Earth shall have passed the arch EF, *Jupiter* shall have entertained himself between the points ST, and shall have appeared to us almost motionlesse and stationary. The Earth being afterwards come to G, and *Jupiter* to G, in opposition to the Sun, it shall be visible in the Zodiack at V, and much returned backwards by all the arch of the Zodiack TV; howbeit that all the way pursuing its even course it hath really gone forwards not onely in its own circle, but in the Zodiack also in respect to the center of **the** said Zodiack, and to the Sun placed in the same. The Earth and *Jupiter* again continuing their motions, when the Earth is come to H, and *Jupiter* to H, it shall seem very much gone backward in the Zodiack by all the arch VX. The Earth being come to I, and *Jupiter* to I, it shall be apparently moved in the Zodiack by the little space XY, and there it will seem stationary. When afterwards the Earth shall be come to K, and *Jupiter* to K; in the Zodiack he shall have passed the arch YN in a direct motion; and the Earth pursuing its course to L, shall see *Jupiter* in L, in the point Z. And lastly *Jupiter* in M shall be seen from the Earth M, to have passed to A, with a motion still right forwards; and its whole apparent retrogradation in the Zodiack shall answer to the arch SY, made by *Jupiter*, whilst that he in his own circle passeth the arch EI, and the Earth in hers the arch EI. And this which hath been said, is intended of *Saturn* and of *Mars* also; and in *Saturn* those retrogradations are somewhat more frequent than in *Jupiter*, by reason that its motion is a little slower than that of *Jupiter*, so that the Earth overtaketh it in a shorter space of time; in *Mars* again they are more rare, for that its motion is more swift than that of *Jupiter*. Whereupon the Earth consumeth more time in recovering it. Next as to *Venus* and *Mercury*, whose Circles are comprehended by that of the Earth, their stations and regressions appear to be occasioned, not by their motions that really are such, but by the annual motion of the said Earth, as *Copernicus* excellently demonstrateth.

ACCELERATION AND LAWS OF FALLING BODIES

SALVIATUS. The present does not seem to be the proper time to investigate the cause of the acceleration of natural motion concerning which various opinions have been expressed by various philosophers, some explaining it by attraction to the center, others to repulsion between the very small parts of the body, while still others attribute it to a certain stress in the surrounding medium which closes in behind the falling body and drives it from one of its positions to another. Now, all these fantasies, and others too, ought to be examined; but it is not really worth while. At present it is the purpose of our Author merely to investigate and to demonstrate some of the properties of accelerated motion (whatever the cause of this acceleration may be)—meaning thereby a motion, such that the momentum of its velocity goes on increasing after departure from rest, in simple proportionality to the time, which is the same as saying that in equal time-intervals the body receives equal increments of velocity; and if we find the properties (of accelerated motion) which will be demonstrated later are realized in freely falling and accelerated bodies, we may conclude that the assumed definition includes such a motion of falling bodies and that their speed goes on increasing as the time and the duration of the motion.

SAGREDUS. So far as I see at present, the definition might have been put a little more clearly perhaps without changing the fundamental idea, namely, uniformly accelerated motion is such that its speed increases in proportion to the space traversed; so that, for example, the speed acquired by a body in falling four cubits would be double that acquired in falling two cubits and this latter speed would be double that acquired in the first cubit. Because there is no doubt but that a heavy body falling from the height of six cubits has, and strikes with, a momentum double that it had at the end of three cubits, triple that which it had at the end of one.

SALVIATUS. It is very comforting to me to have such a companion in error; and moreover let me tell you that your proposition seems so highly probable that our Author himself admitted, when I advanced this opinion to him, that he had for some time shared the same fallacy. But what most surprised me was to see two propositions so inherently probable that they commanded the assent of everyone to whom they were presented, proven in a few simple words to be not only false, but impossible.

SIMPLICIUS. I am one of those who accept the proposition, and believe that a falling body acquires force in its descent, its velocity increasing in proportion to the space, and that the momentum of the falling body is doubled when it falls from a doubled height; these propositions, it appears to me, ought to be conceded without hesitation or controversy.

331

SALVIATUS. And yet they are as false and impossible as that motion should be completed instantaneously; and here is a very clear demonstration of it. If the velocities are in proportion to the spaces traversed, or to be traversed, then these spaces are traversed in equal intervals of time; if, therefore, the velocity with which the falling body traverses a space of eight feet were double that with which it covered the first four feet (just as the one distance is double the other) then the time-intervals required for these passages would be equal. But for one and the same body to fall eight feet and four feet in the same time is possible only in the case of instantaneous (discontinuous) motion; but observation shows us that the motion of a falling body occupies time, and less of it in covering a distance of four feet than of eight feet; therefore it is not true that its velocity increases in proportion to the space.

The falsity of the other proposition may be shown with equal clearness. For if we consider a single striking body the difference of momentum in its blows can depend only upon difference of velocity; for if the striking body falling from a double height were to deliver a blow of double momentum, it would be necessary for this body to strike with a double velocity; but with this doubled speed it would traverse a doubled space in the same time-interval; observation however shows that the time required for fall from the greater height is longer.

SAGREDUS. You present these recondite matters with too much evidence and ease; this great facility makes them less appreciated than they would be had they been presented in a more abstruse manner. For, in my opinion, people esteem more lightly that knowledge which they acquire with so little labor than that acquired through long and obscure discussion.

SALVIATUS. If those who demonstrate with brevity and clearness the fallacy of many popular beliefs were treated with contempt instead of gratitude the injury would be quite bearable; but on the other hand it is very unpleasant and annoying to see men, who claim to be peers of anyone in a certain field of study, take for granted certain conclusions which later are quickly and easily shown by another to be false. I do not describe such a feeling as one of envy, which usually degenerates into hatred and anger against those who discover such fallacies; I would call it a strong desire to maintain old errors, rather than accept newly discovered truths. This desire at times induces them to unite against these truths, although at heart believing in them, merely for the purpose of lowering the esteem in which certain others are held by the unthinking crowd. Indeed, I have heard from our Academician many such fallacies held as true but easily refutable; some of these I have in mind.

SAGREDUS. You must not withhold them from us, but, at the proper time, tell us about them even though an extra session be necessary. But now, continuing the thread of our talk, it would seem that up to the present we have established the definition of uniformly accelerated motion which is expressed as follows:

A motion is said to be equally or uniformly accelerated when, starting from rest, its momentum receives equal increments in equal times.

SALVIATUS. This definition established, the Author makes a single assumption, namely,

The speeds acquired by one and the same body moving down planes of different inclinations are equal when the heights of these planes are equal.

By the height of an inclined plane we mean the perpendicular let fall from the upper end of the plane upon the horizontal line drawn through the lower end of the same plane. Thus, to illustrate, let the line *AB* (Fig. 1) be horizontal, and let the planes *CA* and *CD* be inclined to it; then the Author calls the perpendicular *CB* the "height" of the planes *CA* and *CD*; he sup-

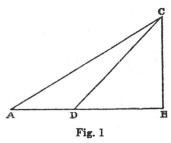

Fig. 1

poses that the speeds acquired by one and the same body, descending along the planes *CA* and *CD* to the terminal points *A* and *D* are equal since the heights of these planes are the same, *CB*; and also it must be understood that this speed is that which would be acquired by the same body falling from *C* to *B*.

SAGREDUS. Your assumption appears to me so reasonable that it ought to be conceded without question, provided of course there are no chance or outside resistances, and that the planes are hard and smooth, and that the figure of the moving body is perfectly round, so that neither plane nor moving body is rough. All resistance and opposition having been removed, my reason tells me at once that a heavy and perfectly round ball descending along the lines *CA*, *CD*, *CB* would reach the terminal points *A, D, B*, with equal momenta.

SALVIATUS. Your words are very plausible; but I hope by experiment to increase the probability to an extent which shall be little short of a rigid demonstration.

Imagine this page to represent a vertical wall, with a nail driven into it; and from the nail let there be suspended a lead bullet of one or two ounces by means of a fine vertical thread, *AB*, (Fig. 2) say from four to six feet long, on this wall draw a horizontal line *DC*, at right angles to the vertical thread *AB*, which hangs about two finger-breadths in front of the wall. Now bring the thread *AB* with the attached ball into the position *AC*

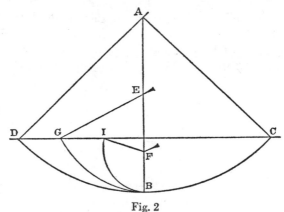

Fig. 2

and set it free; first it will be observed to descend along the arc *CBD*, to pass the point *B*, and to travel along the arc *BD*, till it almost reaches the horizontal *CD*, a slight shortage being caused by the resistance of the air and the string; from this we may rightly infer that the ball in its descent through the arc *CB* acquired a momentum on reaching *B*, which was just sufficient to carry it through a similar arc *BD* to the same height. Having repeated this experiment many times, let us now drive a nail into the wall close to the perpendicular *AB*, say at *E* or *F*, so that it projects out some five of six finger-breadths in order that the thread, again carrying the bullet through the arc *CB*, may strike upon the nail *E* when the bullet reaches *B*, and thus compel it to traverse the arc *BG*, described about *E* as center. From this we can see what can be done by the same momentum which previously starting at the same point *B* carried the same body through the arc *BD* to the horizontal *CD*. Now, gentlemen, you will observe with pleasure that the ball swings to the point *G* in the horizontal, and you would see the same thing happen if the obstacle were placed at some lower point, say at *F*, about which the ball would describe the arc *BI*, the rise of the ball always terminating exactly on the line *CD*. But when the nail is placed so low that the remainder of the thread below it will not reach to the height *CD* (which would happen if the nail were placed nearer *B* than to the intersection of *AB* with the horizontal *CD*) then the thread leaps over the nail and twists itself about it.

This experiment leaves no room for doubt as to the truth of our supposition; for since the two arcs *CB* and *DB* are equal and similarly placed, the momentum acquired by the fall through the arc *CB* is the same as that gained by fall through the arc *DB*; but the momentum acquired at *B*, owing to fall through *CB*, is able to lift the same body through the arc *BD*; therefore, the momentum acquired in the fall *BD* is equal to that which lifts the same body through the same arc from *B* to *D*; so, in general, every momentum acquired by fall through an arc is equal to that which can lift the same body through the same arc. But all these momenta which cause a rise through the arcs *BD*, *BG*, and *BI* are equal, since they are produced by the same momentum, gained by fall through *CB*, as experiment shows. Therefore all the momenta gained by fall through the arcs *DB, GB, IB* are equal.

SAGREDUS. The argument seems to me so conclusive and the experiment so well adapted to establish the hypothesis that we may, indeed, consider it as demonstrated.

SALVIATUS. I do not wish, Sagredo, that we trouble ourselves too much about this matter, since we are going to apply this principle mainly in motions which occur on plane surfaces, and not upon curved, along which acceleration varies in a manner greatly different from that which we have assumed for planes.

So that, although the above experiment shows us that the descent of the moving body through the arc *CB* confers upon it momentum just sufficient to carry it to the same height through any of the arcs *BD, BG, BI*, we are not able, by similar means, to show that the event would be identical in the case of a perfectly round ball descending along planes whose inclinations are respectively the same as the chords of these arcs. It seems likely, on the other hand, that, since these planes form angles at the point *B*, they will present an obstacle to the ball which has descended along the chord *CB*, and starts to rise along the chord *BD, BG, BI*.

In striking these planes some of its momentum will be lost and it will not be able to rise to the height of the line *CD*; but this obstacle, which interferes with the experiment, once removed, it is clear that the momentum (which gains in strength with descent) will be able to carry the body to the same height. Let us then, for the present, take this as a postulate, the absolute truth of which will be established when we find that the inferences from it correspond to and agree perfectly with experiment. The author having assumed this single principle passes next to the propositions which he clearly demonstrates; the first of these is as follows:

Theorem I, Proposition I

The time in which any space is traversed by a body starting from rest and uniformly accelerated is equal to the time in

336

which that same space would be traversed by the same body moving at a uniform speed whose value is the mean of the highest speed and the speed just before acceleration began.

Let us represent by the line AB (Fig. 3) the time in which the space CD is traversed by a body which starts from rest at C and

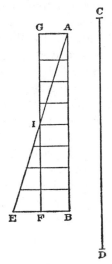

Fig. 3

is uniformly accelerated; let the final and highest value of the speed gained during the interval AB be represented by the line EB drawn at right angles to AB; draw the line AE, then all lines drawn from equidistant points on AB and parallel to BE will represent the increasing values of the speed, beginning with the instant A. Let the point F bisect the line EB; draw FG parallel to BA, and GA parallel to FB, thus forming a parallelogram $AGFB$ which will be equal in area to the triangle AEB, since the side GF bisects the side AE at the point I; for if the parallel lines in the triangle AEB are extended to GI, then the sum of all the parallels contained in the quadrilateral is equal to the sum of those contained in the triangle AEB; for those in the triangle IEF are equal to those contained in the triangle GIA, while those

337

included in the trapezium *AIFB* are common. Since each and every instant of time in the time-interval *AB* has its corresponding point on the line *AB*, from which points parallels drawn in and limited by the triangle *AEB* represent the increasing values of the growing velocity, and since parallels contained within the rectangle represent the values of a speed which is not increasing, but constant, it appears, in like manner, that the momenta assumed by the moving body may also be represented, in the case of the accelerated motion, by the increasing parallels of the triangle *AEB*, and, in the case of the uniform motion, by the parallels of the rectangle *GB*. For, what the momenta may lack in the first part of the accelerated motion (the deficiency of the momenta being represented by the parallels of the triangle *AGI*) is made up by the momenta represented by the parallels of the triangle *IEF*.

Hence it is clear that equal spaces will be traversed in equal times by two bodies, one of which, starting from rest, moves with a uniform acceleration, while the momentum of the other, moving with uniform speed, is one-half its maximum momentum under accelerated motion.

Q. E. D.

Theorem II, Proposition II

The spaces described by a body falling from rest with a uniformly accelerated motion are to each other as the squares of the time-intervals employed in traversing these distances.

Let the time beginning with any instant *A* be represented by the straight line *AB* (Fig. 4) in which are taken any two time-intervals *AD* and *AE*. Let *HI* represent the distance through which the body, starting from rest at *H*, falls with uniform acceleration. If *HL* represents the space traversed during the time-interval *AD*, and *HM* that covered during the interval *AE*, then the space *MH* stands to the space *LH* in a ratio which is the square of the ratio of the time *AE* to the time *AD*; or we may say simply that the distances *HM* and *HL* are related as the squares of *AE* and *AD*.

338

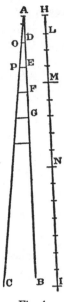

Fig. 4

Draw the line *AC* making any angle whatever with the line *AB*; and from the points *D* and *E*, draw the parallel lines *DO* and *EP*; of these two lines, *DO* represents the greatest velocity attained during the interval *AD*, while *EP* represents the maximum velocity acquired during the interval *AE*. But it has just been proved that so far as distances traversed are concerned it is precisely the same whether a body falls from rest with a uniform acceleration or whether it falls during an equal time-interval with a constant speed which is one-half the maximum speed attained during the accelerated motion. It follows therefore that the distances *HM* and *HL* are the same as would be traversed, during the time-intervals *AE* and *AD*, by uniform velocities equal to one-half those represented by *DO* and *EP* respectively. If, therefore, one can show that the distances *HM* and *HL* are in the same ratio as the squares of the time-intervals *AE* and *AD*, our proposition will be proven.

But in the fourth proposition of the first book it has been

339

shown that the spaces traversed by two particles in uniform motion bear to one another a ratio which is equal to the product of the ratio of the velocities by the ratio of the times. But in this case the ratio of the velocities is the same as the ratio of the time-intervals (for the ratio of AE to AD is the same as that of $\frac{1}{2}EP$ to $\frac{1}{2}DO$ or of EP to DO). Hence the ratio of the spaces traversed is the same as the squared ratio of the time-intervals.

Q.E.D.

Evidently then the ratio of the distances is the square of the ratio of the final velocities, that is, of the lines EP and DO, since these are to each other as AE to AD.

Corollary I

Hence it is clear that if we take any equal intervals of time whatever, counting from the beginning of the motion, such as AD, DE, EF, FG, in which the spaces HL, LM, MN, NI are traversed, these spaces will bear to one another the same ratio as the series of odd numbers, 1, 3, 5, 7; for this is the ratio of the differences of the squares of the lines (which represent time), differences which exceed one another by equal amounts, this excess being equal to the smallest line (viz. the one representing a single time-interval): or we may say (that this is the ratio) of the differences of the squares of the natural numbers beginning with unity.

While, therefore, during equal intervals of time the velocities increase as the natural numbers, the increments in the distances traversed during these equal time-intervals are to one another as the odd numbers beginning with unity. . . .

SIMPLICIUS. In truth, I find more pleasure in this simple and clear argument of Sagredo than in the Author's demonstration which to me appears rather obscure; so that I am convinced that matters are as described, once having accepted the definition of uniformly accelerated motion. But as to whether this acceleration is that which one meets in nature in the case of falling bodies, I am still doubtful; and it seems to me, not only for my own

340

sake but also for all those who think as I do, that this would be the proper moment to introduce one of those experiments—and there are many of them, I understand—which illustrate in several ways the conclusions reached.

SALVIATUS. The request which you, as a man of science, make, is a very reasonable one; for this is the custom—and properly so—in those sciences where mathematical demonstrations are applied to natural phenomena, as is seen in the case of perspective, astronomy, mechanics, music, and others where the principles, once established by well-chosen experiments, become the foundations of the entire superstructure. I hope therefore it will not appear to be a waste of time if we discuss at considerable length this first and most fundamental question upon which hinge numerous consequences of which we have in this book only a small number, placed there by the Author, who has done so much to open a pathway hitherto closed to minds of speculative turn. So far as experiments go they have not been neglected by the Author; and often, in his company, I have attempted in the following manner to assure myself that the acceleration actually experienced by falling bodies is that above described.

A piece of wooden moulding or scantling, about 12 cubits long, half a cubit wide, and three finger-breadths thick, was taken; on its edge was cut a channel a little more than one finger in breadth; having made this groove very straight, smooth, and polished, and having lined it with parchment, also as smooth and polished as possible, we rolled along it a hard, smooth, and very round bronze ball. Having placed this board in a sloping position, by lifting one end some one or two cubits above the other, we rolled the ball, as I was just saying, along the channel, noting, in a manner presently to be described, the time required to make the descent. We repeated this experiment more than once in order to measure the time with an accuracy such that the deviation between two observations never exceeded one-tenth of a pulse-beat. Having performed this operation and having assured ourselves of its reliability, we now rolled the ball only one-quarter the length of the channel; and having measured the time of its descent, we found it precisely one-half of the former. Next we

341

tried other distances, comparing the time for the whole length with that for the half, or with that for two-thirds, or indeed for any fraction; in such experiments, repeated a full hundred times, we always found that the spaces traversed were to each other as the squares of the times, and this was true for all inclinations of the plane, i.e., of the channel, along which we rolled the ball. We also observed that the times of descent, for various inclinations of the plane, bore to one another precisely that ratio which, as we shall see later, the Author had predicted and demonstrated for them.

For the measurement of time, we employed a large vessel of water placed in an elevated position; to the bottom of this vessel was soldered a pipe of small diameter giving a thin jet of water, which we collected in a small glass during the time of each descent, whether for the whole length of the channel or for a part of its length; the water thus collected was weighed, after each descent, on a very accurate balance; the differences and ratios of these weights gave us the difference and ratios of the times, and this with such accuracy that although the operation was repeated many, many times, there was no appreciable discrepancy in the results.

SIMPLICIUS. I would like to have been present at these experiments; but feeling confidence in the care with which you performed them, and in the fidelity with which you relate them, I am satisfied and accept them as true and valid.

SALVIATUS. Then we can proceed without discussion.

Corollary II

Secondly, it follows that, starting from any initial point, if we take any two distances, traversed in any time-interval whatsoever, these time-intervals bear to one another the same ratio as one of the distances to the mean proportional of the two distances. For if we take two distances ST and SY (Fig. 5) measured from the initial point S, the mean proportional of which is SX, the time of fall through ST is to the time of fall through SY as ST is to SX; or one may say the time of fall through SY is to the

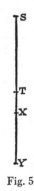

Fig. 5

time of fall through ST as SY is to SX. Now since it has been shown that the spaces traversed are in the same ratio as the squares of the times; and since, moreover, the ratio of the space SY to the space ST is the square of the ratio SY to SX, it follows that the ratio of the times of fall through SY and ST is the ratio of the respective distances SY and SX.

Scholium

The above corollary has been proven for the case of vertical fall; but it holds also for planes inclined in any angle; for it is to be assumed that along these planes the velocity increases in the same ratio, that is, in proportion to the time, or, if you prefer, as the series of natural numbers.

SALVIATUS. Here, Sagredo, I should like, if it be not too tedious to Simplicio, to interrupt for a moment the present discussion in order to make some additions on the basis of what has already been proved and of what mechanical principles we have already learned from our Academician. This addition I make for the better establishment on logical and experimental grounds, of the principle which we have above considered; and what is more important, for the purpose of deriving it geometrically, after first demonstrating a single lemma which is fundamental in the science of motion.

SAGREDUS. If the advance which you propose to make is such

as will confirm and fully establish these sciences of motion, I will gladly devote to it any length of time. Indeed, I shall not only be glad to have you proceed, but I beg of you at once to satisfy the curiosity which you have awakened in me concerning our proposition; and I think that Simplicio is of the same mind.

SIMPLICIUS. Quite right.

SALVIATUS. Since then I have your permission, let us first of all consider this notable fact, that the momenta or speeds of one and the same moving body vary with the inclination of the plane.

The speed reaches a maximum along a vertical direction, and for other directions diminishes as the plane diverges from the vertical. Therefore the impetus, ability, energy, or, one might say, the momentum of descent of the moving body is diminished by the plane upon which it is supported and along which it rolls.

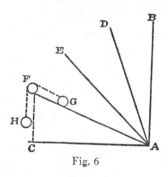

Fig. 6

For the sake of greater clearness erect the line *AB* (Fig. 6) perpendicular to the horizontal *AC*; next draw *AD, AE, AF*, etc., at different inclinations to the horizontal. Then I say that all the momentum of the falling body is along the vertical and is a maximum when it falls in that direction; the momentum is less along *DA* and still less along *EA*, and even less yet along the more inclined plane *FA*. Finally on the horizontal plane the momentum vanishes altogether; the body finds itself in a condition of indifference as to motion or rest; has no inherent tendency to move in any direction, and offers no resistance to being set in motion. For just as a heavy body or system of bodies cannot of itself move upwards, or recede from the common center

344

toward which all heavy things tend, so it is impossible for any body of its own accord to assume any motion other than one which carries it nearer to the aforesaid common center. Hence, along the horizontal, by which we understand a surface, every point of which is equidistant from this same common center, the body will have no momentum whatever.

This change of momentum being clear, it is here necessary for me to explain something which our Academician wrote when in Padua, embodying it in a treatise on mechanics prepared solely for the use of his students, and proving it at length and conclusively when considering the origin and nature of that marvellous machine, the screw. What he proved is the manner in which the momentum varies with the inclination of the plane, as for instance that of the plane FA, one end of which is elevated through a vertical distance FC. This direction FC is that along which the momentum of a heavy body becomes a maximum; let us discover what ratio this momentum bears to that of the same body moving along the inclined plane FA. This ratio, I say, is the inverse of that of the aforesaid lengths. Such is the lemma preceding the theorem which I hope to demonstrate a little later.

It is clear that the impelling force acting on a body in descent is equal to the resistance or least force sufficient to hold it at rest. In order to measure this force and resistance I propose to use the weight of another body. Let us place upon the plane FA a body G connected to the weight H by means of a cord passing over the point F; then the body H will ascend or descend, along the perpendicular, the same distance which the body G ascends or descends along the inclined plane FA; but this distance will not be equal to the rise or fall of G along the vertical in which direction alone G, as other bodies, exerts its force. This is clear. For if we consider the motion of the body G, from A to F, in the triangle AFC to be made up of a horizontal component AC and a vertical component CF, and remember that this body experiences no resistance to motion along the horizontal (because by such a motion the body neither gains nor loses distance from the common center of heavy things) it follows that resistance is met only in consequence of the body rising through the vertical distance

345

CF. Since then the body *G* in moving from *A* to *F* offers resistance only in so far as it rises through the vertical distance *CF*, while the other body *H* must fall vertically through the entire distance *FA*, and since this ratio is maintained whether the motion be large or small, the two bodies being inextensibly connected, we are able to assert positively that, in case of equilibrium (bodies at rest) the momenta, the velocities, or their tendency to motion, i.e., the spaces which would be traversed by them in equal times, must be in the inverse ratio to their weights. This is what has been demonstrated in every case of mechanical motion. So that, in order to hold the weight *G* at rest, one must give *H* a weight smaller in the same ratio as the distance *CF* is smaller than *FA*. If we do this, *FA:FC* = weight *G*:weight *H*; then equilibrium will occur, that is, the weights *H* and *G* will have the same impelling forces, and the two bodies will come to rest.

And since we are agreed that the impetus, energy, momentum or tendency to motion of a moving body is as great as the force or least resistance sufficient to stop it, and since we have found that the weight *H* is capable of preventing motion in the weight *G*, it follows that the less weight *H* whose entire force is along the perpendicular, *FC*, will be an exact measure of the component of force which the larger weight *G* exerts along the plane *FA*. But the measure of the total force on the body *G* is its own weight, since to prevent its fall it is only necessary to balance it with an equal weight, provided this second weight be free to move vertically; therefore the component of the force of *G* along the inclined plane *FA* will bear to the maximum and total force on this same body *G* along the perpendicular *FC* the same ratio as the weight *H* to the weight *G*. This ratio is, by construction, the same which the height, *FC*, of the inclined plane bears to the length *FA*. We have here the lemma which I proposed to demonstrate and which, as you will see, has been assumed by our Author in the second part of the sixth proposition of the present treatise.

SAGREDUS. From what you have shown thus far, it appears to me that one might infer, arguing *ex aequali con la proportione perturbata*, that the tendencies of one and the same body to move along planes differently inclined, but having the same vertical height, as FA and FI, are to each other inversely as the lengths of the planes.

SALVIATUS. Perfectly right. This point established, I pass to the demonstration of the following theorem:

If a body falls freely along smooth planes inclined at any angle whatsoever, but of the same height, the speeds with which it reaches the bottom are the same.

First we must recall the fact that on a plane of any inclination whatever a body starting from rest gains speed or momentum in direct proportion to the time, in agreement with the definition of naturally accelerated motion given by the Author. Hence, as he has shown in the preceding proposition, the distances traversed are proportional to the squares of the times and therefore to the squares of the speeds. The speed relations are here the same as in the motion first studied [i.e., *vertical motion*], since in each case the gain of speed is proportional to the time.

Let AB (Fig. 7) be an inclined plane whose height above the level BC is AC. As we have seen above, the force impelling a body to fall along the vertical AC is to the force which drives the same body along the inclined plane AB as AB is to AC. On the incline AB, lay off AD a third proportional to AB and AC; then the force producing motion along AC is to that along AB (i.e., along AD) as the length AC is to the length AD. And therefore the body will traverse the space AD, along the incline AB, in the same time which it would occupy in falling the vertical distance AC, (since the forces are in the same ratio as these distances); also the speed at C is to the speed at D as the distance AC is to the distance AD. But, according to the definition of accelerated motion, the speed at B is to the speed of the same body at D as the time required to traverse AB is to the time required for AD; and according to the last corollary of the second proposition, the time of passing through the distance AB bears to the time of passing through AD the same ratio as the distance AC (a mean proportional between AB and AD) to AD. Accordingly the two speeds at B and C each bear to the speed at D the same ratio,

347

namely, that of the distances AC and AD; hence they are equal. This is the theorem which I set out to prove.

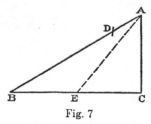

Fig. 7

From the above we are better able to demonstrate the following third proposition of the Author in which he employs the following principle, namely, the time required to traverse an inclined plane is to that required to fall through the vertical height of the plane in the same ratio as the length of the plane to its height.

For, according to the second corollary of the second proposition if BA represents the time required to pass over the distance BA, the time required to pass the distance AD will be a mean proportional between these two distances and will be represented by the line AC; but if AC represents the time needed to traverse AD it will also represent the time required to fall through the distance AC, since the distances AC and AD are traversed in equal times; consequently if AB represent the time required for AB then AC will represent the time required for AC. Hence the times required to traverse AB and AC are to each other as the distances AB and AC.

In like manner it can be shown that the time required to fall through AC is to the time required for any other incline AE as the length AC is to the length AE; therefore, *ex aequali*, the time of fall along the incline AB is to that along AE as the distance AB is to the distance AE, etc.

One might by application of this same theorem, as Sagredo will readily see, immediately demonstrate the sixth proposition of the Author; but let us here end this digression which Sagredo has perhaps found rather tedious, though I consider it quite important for the theory of motion.

SAGREDUS. On the contrary it has given me great satisfaction, and indeed I find it necessary for a complete grasp of this principle.

SALVIATUS. I will now resume the reading of the text.

THE PENDULUM

SALVIATUS. Let us see whether we cannot derive from the pendulum a satisfactory solution of all these difficulties. And first, as to the question whether one and the same pendulum really performs its vibrations, large, medium, and small, all in exactly the same time, I shall rely upon what I have already heard from our Academician. He has clearly shown that the time of descent is the same along all chords, whatever the arcs which subtend them, as well along an arc of 180° (i.c., the whole diameter) as along one of 100°, 60°, 10°, 2°, ½°, or 4'. It is understood, of course that these arcs all terminate at the lowest point of the circle, where it touches the horizontal plane.

If now we consider descent along arcs instead of their chords then, provided these do not exceed 90°, experiment shows that they are all traversed in equal times; but these times are greater for the chord than for the arc, an effect which is all the more remarkable because at first glance one would think just the opposite to be true. For since the terminal points of the two motions are the same and since the straight line included between these two points is the shortest distance between them, it would seem reasonable that motion along this line should be executed in the shortest time; but this is not the case, for the shortest time —and therefore the most rapid motion—is that employed along the arc of which this straight line is the chord.

As to the times of vibration of bodies suspended by threads of different lengths, they bear to each other the same proportion as the square roots of the lengths of the thread; or one might say the lengths are to each other as the squares of the times; so that if one wishes to make the vibration-time of one pendulum twice that of another, he must make its suspension four times as long. In like manner, if one pendulum has a suspension nine times as long as another, this second pendulum will execute three vibrations during each one of the first; from which it follows that the lengths of the suspending cords bear to each other the (inverse) ratio of the squares of the number of vibrations performed in the same time.

SAGREDUS. Then, if I understand you correctly, I can easily measure the length of a string whose upper end is attached at any height whatever even if this end were invisible and I could see only the lower extremity. For if I attach to the lower end of this string a rather heavy weight and give it a to-and-fro motion, and if I ask a friend to count a number of its vibrations, while I during the same time-interval, count the number of vibrations of a pendulum which is exactly one cubit in length, then knowing the number of vibrations which each pendulum makes in the given interval of time one can determine the length of the string. Suppose, for example, that my friend counts 20 vibrations of the long cord during the same time in which I count 240 of my string which is one cubit in length; taking the squares of the two numbers, 20 and 240, namely 400 and 57600, then, I say, the long string contains 57600 units of such length that my pendulum will contain 400 of them; and since the length of my string is one cubit, I shall divide 57600 by 400 and thus obtain 144. Accordingly I shall call the length of the string 144 cubits.

SALVIATUS. Nor will you miss it by as much as a hand's breadth, especially if you observe a large number of vibrations.

SAGREDUS. You give me frequent occasion to admire the wealth and profusion of nature when, from such common and even trivial phenomena, you derive facts which are not only striking and new but which are often far removed from what we would have imagined. Thousands of times I have observed vibrations especially in churches where lamps, suspended by long cords, had been inadvertently set into motion; but the most which I could infer from those observations was that the view of those who think that such vibrations are maintained by the medium is highly improbable: for, in that case, the air must

350

needs have considerable judgment and little else to do but kill time by pushing to and fro a pendent weight with perfect regularity. But I never dreamed of learning that one and the same body, when suspended from a string a hundred cubits long and pulled aside through an arc of 90° or even 1° or ½°, would employ the same time in passing through the least as through the largest of these arcs; and, indeed, it still strikes me as somewhat unlikely. Now I am waiting to hear how these same simple phenomena can furnish solutions for those acoustical problems —solutions which will be at least partly satisfactory.

SALVIATUS. First of all one must observe that each pendulum has its own time of vibration so definite and determinate that it is not possible to make it move with any other period than that which nature has given it. For let any one take in his hand the cord to which the weight is attached and try, as much as he pleases, to increase or diminish the frequency of its vibrations; it will be time wasted. On the other hand, one can confer motion upon even a heavy pendulum which is at rest by simply blowing against it; by repeating these blasts with a frequency which is the same as that of the pendulum one can impart considerable motion. Suppose that by the first puff we have displaced the pendulum from the vertical by, say, half an inch; then if, after the pendulum has returned and is about to begin the second vibration, we add a second puff, we shall impart additional motion; and so on with other blasts provided they are applied at the right instant, and not when the pendulum is coming toward us since in this case the blast would impede rather than aid the motion. Continuing thus with many impulses we impart to the pendulum such momentum that a greater impulse than that of a single blast will be needed to stop it.

SAGREDUS. Even as a boy, I observed that one man alone by giving these impulses at the right instant was able to ring a bell so large that when four, or even six, men seized the rope and tried to stop it they were lifted from the ground, all of them together being unable to counterbalance the momentum which a single man, by properly-timed pulls, had given it.

351

MOTION OF PROJECTILES

Let us imagine an elevated horizontal line or plane ab (Fig. 8) along which a body moves with uniform speed from a to b. Suppose this plane to end abruptly at b; then at this point the body will, on account of its weight, acquire also a natural motion downwards along the perpendicular bn. Draw the line be along the plane ba to represent the flow, or measure, of time; divide this line into a number of segments, bc, cd, de, representing equal intervals of time; from the points b, c, d, e, let fall lines which are parallel to the perpendicular bn. On the first of these lay off any distance ci, on the second a distance four times as long, df; on the third, one nine times as long, eb; and so on, in proportion to the squares of cb, db, eb, or, we may say, in the squared ratio of these same lines. Accordingly we see that while the body moves from b to c with uniform speed, it also falls perpendicularly through the distance ci, and at the end of the time-interval bc finds itself at the point i. In like manner at the end of the time-interval bd, which is the double of bc, the vertical fall will be four times the first distance ci; for it has been shown in a previous discussion that the distance traversed by a freely falling body varies as the square of the time; in like manner the space eh traversed during the time be will be nine times ci; thus it is evident that the distances eh, df, ci will be to one another as the squares of the lines be, bd, bc. Now from the points i, f, h draw the straight lines io, fg, hl parallel to be; these lines hl, fg, io are

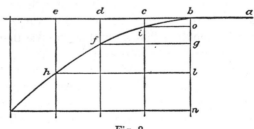

Fig. 8

equal to eb, db, and cb, respectively; so also are the lines bo, bg, bl respectively equal to ci, df, and eh. The square of hl is to that of fg as the line lb is to bg; and the square of fg is to that of io as gb is to bo; therefore the points i, f, b, lie on one and the same parabola. In like manner it may be shown that, if we take equal time-intervals of any size whatever, and if we imagine the particle to be carried by a similar compound motion, the positions of this particle, at the ends of these time-intervals, will lie on one and the same parabola.   Q. E. D.

SALVIATUS. This conclusion follows from the converse of the first of the two propositions given above. For, having drawn a parabola through the points b and h, any other two points, f and i, not falling on the parabola must lie either within or without; consequently the line fg is either longer or shorter than the line which terminates on the parabola. Therefore the square of hl will not bear to the square of fg the same ratio as the line lb to bg, but a greater or smaller; the fact is, however, that the square of hl *does* bear this same ratio to the square of fg. Hence the point f does lie on the parabola, and so do all the others.

SAGREDUS. One cannot deny that the argument is new, subtle and conclusive, resting as it does upon this hypothesis, namely, that the horizontal motion remains uniform, that the vertical motion continues to be accelerated downwards in proportion to the square of the time, and that such motions and velocities as these combine without altering, disturbing, or hindering each other, so that as the motion proceeds the path of the projectile does not change into a different curve: but this, in my opinion, is impossible. For the axis of the parabola along which we imagine the natural motion of a falling body to take place stands perpendicular to a horizontal surface and ends at the center of the earth; and since the parabola deviates more and more from its axis no projectile can ever reach the center of the earth or, if it does, as seems necessary, then the path of the projectile must transform itself into some other curve very different from the parabola.

SIMPLICIUS. To these difficulties, I may add others. One of these is that we suppose the horizontal plane, which slopes neither up nor down, to be represented by a straight line as if each point on this line were equally distant from the center, which is not the case; for as one starts from the middle (of the line) and goes toward either end, he departs farther and farther from the center (of the earth) and is therefore constantly going uphill. Whence it follows that the motion cannot remain uniform through any distance whatever, but must continually diminish. Besides, I do not see how it is possible to avoid the resistance of the medium which must destroy the uniformity of the horizontal motion and change the law of acceleration of falling bodies. These various difficulties render it highly improbable that a result derived from such unreliable hypotheses should hold true in practice.

SALVIATUS. All these difficulties and objections which you urge are so well founded that it is impossible to remove them; and, as for me, I am ready to admit them all, which indeed I think our Author would also do. I grant that these conclusions proved in the abstract will be different when applied in the concrete and will be fallacious to this extent, that neither will the horizontal motion be uniform nor the natural acceleration be in the ratio assumed, nor the path of the projectile a parabola, etc. But, on the other hand, I ask you not to begrudge our Author that which other eminent men have assumed even if not strictly true. The authority of Archimedes alone will satisfy everybody. In his Mechanics and in his first quadrature of the parabola he takes for granted that the beam of a balance or steelyard is a straight line, every point of which is equidistant from the common center of all heavy bodies, and that the cords by which heavy bodies 'are suspended are parallel to each other.

Some consider this assumption permissible because, in practice, our instruments and the distances involved are so small in comparison with the enormous distances from the center of the earth that we may consider a minute of arc on a great circle as a straight line, and may regard the perpendiculars let fall from its two extremities as parallel. For if in actual practice one had to consider such small quantities, it would be necessary first of all to criticize the architects who presume, by use of a plumb-line, to erect high towers with parallel sides. I may add that, in all their discussions, Archimedes and the others considered themselves as located at an infinite distance from the center of the earth, in which case their assumptions were not false, and therefore their conclusions were absolutely correct. When we wish to apply our proven conclusions to distances which, though finite, are very large, it is necessary for us to infer, on the basis of demonstrated truth, what correction is to be made for the fact that our distance from the center of the earth is not really infinite, but merely very great in comparison with the small dimensions of our apparatus. The largest of these will be the range of our projectiles—and even here we need consider only the artillery—which, however great, will never exceed four of those miles of which as many thousand separate us from the center of the earth; and since these paths terminate upon the surface of the earth only very slight changes can take place in their parabolic figure which, it is conceded, would be greatly altered if they terminated at the center of the earth.

As to the perturbation arising from the resistance of the medium this is more considerable and does not, on account of its manifold forms, submit to fixed laws and exact description.

FRANCIS GALTON

(1822–1911),

This many-sided English scientist has several claims to fame, though he is remembered best for his beginnings in the science of eugenics (*Hereditary Genius*, 1869), (*Natural Inheritance*, 1889). His studies of heredity were based on English families of genius (including his own—he was a cousin of Charles Darwin), anthropometric measurements and experiments in mental testing. As a criminologist, he devised a system of fingerprint identification (*Finger Prints, Essays on Eugenics*). As a meteorologist, he created the basis of the modern weather map (*Meteorographica*, 1863). As an explorer, he sought the source of the Nile (*Narrative of an Explorer in Tropical South Africa*, 1855). And to round out his credentials as an acceptable member of a British family of genius, Galton even wrote a novel at the age of eighty.

THE ANCESTRAL LAW OF HEREDITY

As THESE lines are being written, the circumstances under which I first clearly grasped the important generalization that the laws of heredity were solely concerned with deviations expressed in statistical units are vividly recalled to my memory. It was in the grounds of Naworth Castle, where an invitation had been given to ramble freely. A temporary shower drove me to seek refuge in a reddish recess in the rock by the side of the pathway. There the idea flashed across me, and I forgot everything else for a moment in my great delight.

The following question had been much in my mind. How is it possible for a population to remain alike in its features, as a whole, during many successive generations, if the *average* produce of each couple resemble their parents? Their children are not

356

alike, but vary: therefore some would be taller, some shorter than their average height; so among the issue of gigantic couples there would be usually some children more gigantic still. Conversely as to very small couples. But from what I could thus far find, parents had issue less exceptional than themselves. I was very desirous of ascertaining the facts of the case. After much consideration and many inquiries I determined, in 1885, on experimenting with sweet peas, which were suggested to me both by Sir Joseph Hooker and by Mr. Darwin. Their merits are threefold. They have so little tendency to become cross-fertilized that seedsmen do not hesitate to grow differently colored plants in neighboring beds; all the seeds in their pods are of the same size, that is to say, there is no little pea at the end as in the pod of the common pea, and they are very hardy and prolific. I procured a large number of seeds from the same bin and selected seven weights, calling them K (the largest), L, M, N, O, P, and Q (the smallest), forming an arithmetic series. Curiously, their lengths, found by measuring ten of a kind in a row, also formed an arithmetic series, owing, I suppose, to the larger and plumper seeds being more spherical and therefore taking less room for their weight than the others. Ten peas of each of these seven descriptions, seventy in all, formed what I called a "set." . . .

I must stop for a moment to pay tribute to the memory of Mendel, with whom I sentimentally feel myself connected, owing to our having been born in the same year, 1822. His careful and long-continued experiments show how much can be performed by those who, like him and Charles Darwin, never or hardly ever leave their homes, and again how much might be done in a fixed laboratory after a uniform tradition of work had been established. Mendel clearly showed that there were such things as alternative atomic characters of equal potency in descent. How far characters generally may be due to simple, or to molecular characters more or less correlated together, has yet to be discovered.

I had thought of experimenting with mice, as cheap to rear and very prolific, and had taken some steps to that end, when I became aware of the large collections of basset hounds belonging to the late Sir Everard Millais. He offered me every facility. The basset hound records referring to his own and other breeds had been carefully kept, and the studbook he lent me contained accounts of nearly one thousand animals, of which I was able to utilize 817. All were descended from parents of known colors; in 567 of them the colors of all four grandparents were also known. Wherever the printed studbook was deficient, Sir Everard Millais supplied the want in manuscript from the original records. My inquiry was into the heredity of two alternative colors, one containing no black, the other containing it; their technical names were lemon-white and tricolor (black, lemon, white) respectively. I was assured that no difficulty was felt in determining the category to which each individual belonged. These data were fully discussed in a memoir, published (1897) in the "Proceedings of the Royal Society," on what is now termed the "ancestral law," namely, that the *average* contribution of each parent is one fourth, of each grandparent one sixteenth, and so on. Or, in other words, that of the two parents taken together is one half, of the four grandparents together one fourth, and so on. My data were not as numerous as is desirable; still, the results were closely congruous and seem to be a near approximation to the truth. The conclusions have been much discussed and criticized, and they have been modified by Professor Karl Pearson; but they have not been seriously shaken, so far as I know.

LUIGI GALVANI

(1737–1798)

This Italian physician and natural scientist is remembered chiefly for his discovery of "animal electricity" or galvanism. To this he attributed the twitchings of the muscles in frogs' legs in response to an external electrical stimulus. His later researches had little influence on physics, but his fundamental discovery was developed by Volta.

GALVANISM

THE DISCOVERY was made in this way. I had dissected and prepared a frog and while I was attending to something else, I laid it on a table on which stood an electrical machine at some distance from its conductor and separated from it by a considerable space. Now when one of the persons who were present touched accidentally and lightly the inner crural nerves of the frog with the point of a scalpel all the muscles of the legs seemed to contract again and again as if they were affected by powerful cramps. Another one who was there, who was helping us in electrical researches, thought that he had noticed that the action was excited when a spark was discharged from the conductor of the machine. Being astonished by this new phenomenon he called my attention to it, who at that time had something else in mind and was deep in thought. Whereupon I was inflamed with an incredible zeal and eagerness to test the same and to bring to light what was concealed in it. I therefore myself touched one or the other nerve with the point of the knife and at the same time one of those present drew a spark. The phenomenon was always the same. Without fail there occurred lively contractions in every

359

muscle of the leg at the same instant as that in which the spark jumped, as if the prepared animal was affected by tetanus.

With the thought that these motions might arise from the contact with the point of the knife, which perhaps caused the excited condition, rather than by the spark, I touched the same nerves again in the same way in other frogs with the point of the knife, and indeed with greater pressure, yet so that no one during this time drew off a spark. Now no motions could be detected. I therefore came to the conclusion that perhaps to excite the phenomenon there were needed both the contact of a body and the electric spark.

Therefore I again pressed the blade of the knife on the nerve and kept it there at rest while the spark passed and while the machine was not in motion. The phenomenon only occurred while the sparks were passing.

We repeated the experiment, always using the same knife. But it was remarkable that when the spark passed the motions observed sometimes occurred and sometimes not.

Excited by the novelty of the phenomenon, we undertook to investigate the thing in one way and another and to follow it up experimentally, while still using one and the same scalpel, so that if possible we might discover the causes of this unexpected difference. And this new effort was not without results. We discovered that the whole phenomenon was to be ascribed to the different parts of the scalpel by which it was held by the fingers. The scalpel had a bone handle, and if this handle was held in the hand no contractions occurred when the spark passed; but they did occur if the finger rested on the metallic or on the iron rivet by which the blade was held in the handle.

Now since fairly dry bones have an electric nature but the metal blade and the iron rivet have a conducting or so called non-electric nature, we were led to assume that conditions were such that if we held the bone handle in the fingers the electric fluid which in some way or other was active in the frog would be kept from entering, but that it could enter if we touched the blade or the rivet which was connected with it.

Now to put the thing beyond all doubt we used instead of the scalpel sometimes a slender glass rod, which had been wiped clean from dampness and dust, and sometimes an iron rod. With the glass rod we not only touched the nerves of the leg but rubbed them hard while the sparks were passing. But in vain; in spite of all our trouble the phenomenon never appeared, even when a number of powerful sparks were drawn from the conductor of the machine at a small distance from the animal. The phenomenon occurred however if we even lightly touched the same nerve with the iron rod and only little sparks passed. . . .

After we had investigated the forces of atmospheric electricity during thunder storms our hearts burned with desire to investigate also the force of electricity in quiet times during the day.

Therefore, as I had casually noticed that the prepared frogs, which were hung by a brass hook passing through the spinal cord to the iron grating which enclosed a hanging garden of our house, showed the usual contractions not only when there was lightning but also when the sky was clear and fair, I thought that the origin of these contractions might be found in the changes which nevertheless were going on in the atmospheric electricity. Therefore I began, not without hope, carefully to investigate the action of these changes in the muscular motion and to set up experiments in one way and another. Thus I observed at different hours and indeed for days at a time suitably arranged animals, but scarcely ever did a motion of the muscles occur. Finally, tired of this useless waiting, I began to squeeze and press the hooks which were fastened in the spinal cord against the iron grating, in order to see whether such an artifice might excite the contraction of the muscles and whether instead of its depending on the condition of the atmosphere and its electricity any other change and alteration might have an influence. I quite often observed contractions, but none which depended upon the different conditions of the atmosphere and its electricity.

As I had observed these contractions only in the open air and as hitherto no researches had been undertaken in other places, there seemed to be little lacking to my argument and I might have referred such contractions to the atmospheric electricity

361

which enters the animal and accumulates there and suddenly leaves it when the hook is brought in contact with the iron grating. So easy is it to deceive oneself in experimenting, and to think that we have seen and found that which we wish to see and find.

But when I transferred the animal to a closed room, had laid it on an iron plate, and begun to press the hook which was in the spinal cord against the plate, behold, the same contractions, the same motions! I repeated the experiment by using other metals at other places and on other hours and days; with the same result, only that the contractions were different when different metals were used, being more lively for some and more sluggish for the others. At last it occurred to us to use other bodies which conduct electricity only a little or not at all, made of glass, rubber, resin, stone or wood and always dried, and with these nothing similar occurred, no muscular contractions and motions could be seen. Naturally such a result excited in us no slight astonishment and caused us to think that possibly the electricity was present in the animal itself. We were confirmed in this view by the assumption of a very fine nervous fluid which during the occurrence of the phenomenon flows from the nerves to the muscle like the electric current in the Leyden jar. . . .

To make the thing plainer I had with the greatest success laid the frog on a non-conducting plate, as on glass or on resin, and then using a curved rod, sometimes conducting and sometimes either altogether or partly non-conducting, I touched with one end of it the hook which entered the spinal cord and with the other end either the muscles of the leg or the feet. In this experiment, when we used the conducting rod, we saw the contractions occur, but when we used the rod which was non-conducting, there were no contractions. The conducting rod was an iron wire, the hook was a brass wire. After these last discoveries it appeared to us that the contractions which, as has been said, occur in a frog laid on a metallic plate if the hook in the spinal cord is pressed against the plate, must come from a similar circuit in place of which, in a way, the metallic plate acts, and therefore it happens that the contractions will not occur in frogs

362

which are laid on a non-conducting plate even when the same procedure is employed.

This opinion of ours has clearly explained a not unwelcome and accidentally observed phenomenon, if my judgment is correct. If the frog is held up in the fingers by one leg so that the hook that is fastened in the spinal cord touches a silver plate and the other free leg can come in contact with the plate, then if this leg touches the plate the muscles are repeatedly contracted, so that the leg is lifted, but soon, when it becomes quiet and falls down to the plate again, it again comes in contact with it and therefore is lifted again and in short it so proceeds to rise and fall that in a certain sense it seems like an electrical pendulum, to the greatest astonishment and delight of the observer. . . .

Before we end our discussion of the use of the curved rod and its forces we should not neglect to make clear its significance and, if I may so say, its necessity for such muscular contractions. These occur more clearly and more quickly not only with one but with two curved rods, if they are so applied and arranged that the end of one of them touches the muscle and the end of the other the nerves in a similar way, and the two other ends are brought in contact with each other or if necessary are rubbed together. In this connection it is noticeable that the electricity which causes the contractions is not conducted away and dissipated by the contact of the hands with the two rods or by the repeated contacts of the rods with the parts of the animal's body. Furthermore we were fortunate enough to observe this peculiar and remarkable phenomenon, that the use of more than one metallic substance and the differences between them contribute much to the excitation, as also especially to the increase of the muscular contraction, far more indeed than when one and the same metal is used. Thus for example, if the whole rod was iron or the hook was iron and the conducting plate also, the contractions either did not occur or were very small. But if one of them was iron and the other brass, or better if it was silver (silver seems to us the best of all the metals for conducting animal electricity) there occur repeated and much greater and more prolonged contractions. The same thing occurs with one and the same arrangement

363

of the non-conducting plate. If strips of different metals are laid in the same way on two points separate from each other, as for example, if you put a zinc strip at one place and a brass strip at the other, the contractions are usually much greater than when metal strips of the same sort are used, even when both places are brought in contact with silver.

KARL FRIEDRICH GAUSS

(1777–1855)

Gauss is considered the founder of the mathematical theory of electricity, since he made the first measurements of electric quantities in absolute units. (The gauss, a magnetic unit, is named after him.) This German astronomer had what amounted to his own observatory at the University of Göttingen, where he invented the method of least squares, used in his work on orbit theory (*Theoria Motus Corporum Coelestium*, 1809). He also invented a magnetometer to measure the earth's magnetic force. Other works: *Disquisitiones Arithmeticae* (1801), on the theory of numbers, and *Intensitas Vis Magneticae Terrestris* (1833), on magnetism.

THEORY OF THE MOTION OF THE HEAVENLY BODIES

INTRODUCTION

To determine the orbit of a heavenly body, without any hypothetical assumption, from observations not embracing a great period of time, and not allowing a selection with a view to the application of special methods, was almost wholly neglected up to the beginning of the present century; or, at least, not treated by any one in a manner worthy of its importance . . .

Some ideas occurred to me in the month of September of the year 1801, engaged at the time on a very different subject, which seemed to point to the solution of the great problem of which I have spoken. Under such circumstances we not unfrequently, for fear of being too much led away by an attractive investigation, suffer the associations of ideas, which, more attentively considered, might have proved most fruitful in results, to be lost from neglect. And the same fate might have befallen these con-

365

ceptions, had they not happily occurred at the most propitious moment for their preservation and encouragement that could have been selected. For just about this time the report of the new planet, discovered on the first day of January of that year with the telescope at Palermo, was the subject of universal conversation; and soon afterwards the observations made by that distinguished astronomer *Piazzi* from the above date to the eleventh of February were published. Nowhere in the annals of astronomy do we meet with so great an opportunity, and a greater one could hardly be imagined, for showing most strikingly, the value of this problem, than in this crisis and urgent necessity, when all hope of discovering in the heavens this planetary atom, among innumerable small stars after the lapse of nearly a year, rested solely upon a sufficient approximate knowledge of its orbit to be based upon these very few observations. Could I ever have found a more seasonable opportunity to test the practical value of my conceptions, than now in employing them for the determination of the orbit of the planet Ceres, which during these forty-one days had described a geocentric arc of only three degrees, and after the lapse of a year must be looked for in a region of the heavens very remote from that in which it was last seen? The first application of the method was made in the month of October, 1801, and the first clear night, when the planet was sought for as directed by the numbers deduced from it, restored the fugitive to observation. Three other new planets, subsequently discovered, furnished new opportunities for examining and verifying the efficiency and generality of the method.

DETERMINATION OF AN ORBIT FROM THREE COMPLETE OBSERVATIONS

Seven elements are required for the complete determination of the motion of a heavenly body in its orbit, the number of which, however, may be diminished by one, if the mass of the heavenly body is either known or neglected; neglecting the mass can scarcely be avoided in the determination of an orbit wholly unknown, where all the quantities of the order of the perturbations must be omitted, until the masses on which they depend become otherwise known. Wherefore, in the present inquiry, the mass of the body being neglected, we reduce the number of the elements to six, and, therefore, it is evident, that as many quantities depending on the elements, but independent of each other, are required for the determination of the unknown orbit. These quantities are necessarily the places of the heavenly body observed from the earth; since each one of which furnishes two data, that is, the longitude and latitude, or the right ascension and declination, it will certainly be the most simple to adopt *three geocentric places* which will, in general, be sufficient for determining the six unknown elements. This problem is to be regarded as the most important in this work, and, for this reason, will be treated with the greatest care in this section.

But in the special case, in which the plane of the orbit coincides with the ecliptic, and thus both the heliocentric and geocentric latitudes, from their nature, vanish, the three vanishing geocentric latitudes cannot any longer be considered as three data independent of each other: then, therefore, this problem would remain indeterminate, and the three geocentric places might be satisfied by an infinite number of orbits. Accordingly, in such a case, four geocentric longitudes must, necessarily, be given, in order that the four remaining unknown elements (the inclination of the orbit and the longitude of the node being omitted) may be determined. But although, from an indiscernible principle, it is not to be expected that such a case would ever actually present itself in nature, nevertheless, it is easily imagined that the problem, which, in an orbit exactly coinciding with the plane of the ecliptic, is absolutely indeterminate, must, on account of the limited accuracy of the observations, remain nearly indeterminate in orbits very little inclined to the ecliptic, where the very slightest errors of the observations are sufficient altogether to confound the determination of the unknown quantities. Wherefore, in order to examine this case, it will be necessary to select six data; for which purpose we will show in section second, how to determine an unknown orbit from four observations, of which

367

two are complete, but the other two incomplete, the latitudes or declinations being deficient.

Finally, as all our observations, on account of the imperfection of the instruments and of the senses, are only approximations to the truth, an orbit based only on the six absolutely necessary data may be still liable to considerable errors. In order to diminish these as much as possible, and thus to reach the greatest precision attainable, no other method will be given except to accumulate the greatest number of the most perfect observations, and to adjust the elements, not so as to satisfy this or that set of observations with absolute exactness, but so as to agree with all in the best possible manner. For which purpose, we will show in the third section how, according to the principles of the calculus of probabilities, such an agreement may be obtained, as will be, if in no one place perfect, yet in all the places the strictest possible.

The determination of orbits in this manner, therefore, so far as the heavenly bodies move in them according to the laws of *Kepler*, will be carried to the highest degree of perfection that is desired. Then it will be proper to undertake the final correction, in which the perturbations that the other planets cause in the motion, will be taken account of: we will indicate briefly in the fourth section, how these may be taken account of, so far at least, as it shall appear consistent with our plan.

Before the determination of any orbit from geocentric observations, if the greatest accuracy is desired, certain reductions must be applied to the latter on account of nutation, precession, parallax, and aberration: these small quantities may be neglected in the rougher calculation . . .

It would not be difficult, from the connection between the data and unknown quantities of our problem, to reduce its statement to six equations, or even to less, since one or another of the unknown quantities might, conveniently enough, be eliminated: but since this connection is most complicated, these equations would become very intractable; such a separation of the unknown quantities as finally to produce an equation containing only one, can, generally speaking, be regarded as impossible, and, therefore, still less will it be possible to obtain a complete solution of the problem by direct processes alone.

But our problem may at least be reduced, and that too in various ways, to the solution of *two* equations $X = 0$, $Y = 0$, in which only two unknown quantities x, y, remain. It is by no means necessary that x, y, should be two of the elements: they may be quantities connected with the elements in any manner whatever, if, only, the elements can be conveniently deduced from them when found. Moreover, it is evidently not requisite that X, Y, be expressed in explicit functions of x, y: it is sufficient if they are connected with them by a system of equations in such manner that we can proceed from given values of x, y, to the corresponding values of X, Y ...

The ten methods explained on previous occasions, rest upon the assumption that approximate values of the distances of the heavenly body from the earth, or of the position of the plane of the orbit, are already known. When the problem is, to correct, by means of observations more remote from each other, the dimensions of an orbit, the approximate values of which are already, by some means, known, as, for instance, by a previous calculation based on other observations, this assumption will evidently be liable to no difficulty. But it does not as yet appear from this, how the first calculation is to be entered upon when all the dimensions of the orbit are still wholly unknown: this case of our problem is by far the most important and the most difficult, as may be imagined from the analogous problem in the theory of comets, which, as is well known, has perplexed geometers for a long time, and has given rise to many fruitless attempts. In order that our problem may be considered as correctly solved, that is, if the solution be given in accordance with what has been explained in the 119th and subsequent articles, it is evidently requisite to satisfy the following conditions:—*First*, the quantities x, y, are to be chosen in such a manner, that we can find approximate values of them from the very nature of the problem, at all events, as long as the heliocentric motion of the heavenly body between the observations is not too great. *Secondly*, it is necessary that, for small changes in the quantities x, y, there be not too great corresponding changes in the quantities to be derived from them, lest the errors accidentally introduced in the assumed values of the former, prevent the latter from being considered as approximate. *Thirdly* and lastly, we require that the processes by which we pass from the quantities x, y, to X, Y, successively, be not too complicated.

These conditions will furnish the criterion by which to judge of the excellence of any method: this will show itself more plainly by frequent applications. The method which we are now prepared to explain, and which, in a measure, is to be regarded as the most important part of this work, satisfies these conditions so that it seems to leave nothing further to be desired . . .

The method which we have fully explained is principally suited to the first determination of a wholly unknown orbit: still it is employed with equally great success, where the object is the correction of an orbit already approximately known by means of three observations however distant from each other . . .

DETERMINATION OF AN ORBIT FROM ANY NUMBER OF OBSERVATIONS

From these general discussions we return to our special subject for the sake of which they were undertaken. Before the most accurate determination of the orbit from more observations than are absolutely requisite can be commenced, there should be an approximate determination which will nearly satisfy all the given observations. The corrections to be applied to these approximate elements, in order to obtain the most exact agreement, will be regarded as the objects of the problem. And when it can be assumed that these are so small that their squares and products may be neglected, the corresponding changes, produced in the computed geocentric places of a heavenly body, can be obtained by means of the differential formulas given in the Second Section of the First Book. The computed places, therefore, which we obtain from the corrected elements, will be expressed by linear functions of the corrections of the elements, and their comparison with the observed places according to the principles before explained, will lead to the determination of the most probable values. These processes are so simple that they require no further illustration, and it appears at once that any number of observations, however remote from each other, can be employed. The same method may also be used in the correction of the *parabolic* orbits of comets, should we have a long series of observations and the best agreement be required.

THE METHOD OF LEAST SQUARES

The investigation of an orbit having, strictly speaking, the *maximum* probability, will depend upon a knowledge of the law according to which the probability of errors decreases as the errors increase in magnitude: but that depends upon so many vague and doubtful considerations—physiological included—which cannot be subjected to calculation, that it is scarcely, and indeed less than scarcely, possible to assign properly a law of this kind in any case of practical astronomy. Nevertheless, an investigation of the connection between this law and the most probable orbit, which we will undertake in its utmost generality, is not to be regarded as by any means a barren speculation.

To this end let us leave our special problem, and enter upon a very general discussion and one of the most fruitful in every application of the calculus to natural philosophy. Let V, V', V'', etc. be functions of the unkown quantities p, q, r, s, etc., μ the number of those functions, v the number of the unknown quantities; and let us suppose that the values of the functions found by direct observation are $V = M$, $V' = M'$, $V'' = M''$, etc. Generally speaking, the determination of the unknown quantities will constitute a problem, indeterminate, determinate, or more than determinate, according as $\mu < v$, $\mu = v$, or $\mu > v$. We shall confine ourselves here to the last case, in which, evidently, an

371

exact representation of all the observations would only be possible when they were all absolutely free from error. And since this cannot, in the nature of things, happen, every system of values of the unknown quantities p, q, r, s, etc., must be regarded as possible, which gives the values of the functions $V - M$, $V' - M'$, $V'' - M''$, etc., within the limits of the possible errors of observation; this, however, is not to be understood to imply that each one of these systems would possess an equal degree of probability.

Let us suppose, in the first place, the state of things in all the observations to have been such, that there is no reason why we should suspect one to be less exact than another, or that we are bound to regard errors of the same magnitude as equally probable in all. Accordingly, the probability to be assigned to each error $\triangle$ will be expressed by a function of $\triangle$ which we shall denote by $\phi\triangle$. Now although we cannot precisely assign the form of this function, we can at least affirm its value should be a maximum for $\triangle = 0$, equal, generally, for equal opposite values of $\triangle$, and should vanish, if, for $\triangle$ is taken the greatest error, or a value greater than the greatest error: $\phi\triangle$, therefore, would appropriately be referred to the class of discontinuous functions, and if we undertake to substitute any analytical function in the place of it for practical purposes, this must be of such a form that it may converge to zero on both sides, asymptotically, as it were, from $\triangle = 0$, so that beyond this limit it can be regarded as actually vanishing. Moreover, the probability that an error lies between the limits $\triangle$ and $\triangle + d\triangle$ differing from each other by the infinitely small difference $d\triangle$, will be expressed by $\phi\triangle d\triangle$; hence the probability generally, that the error lies between D and D′, will be given by the integral $\int\phi\triangle.d\triangle$ extended from $\triangle = D$ to $\triangle = D'$. This integral taken from the greatest negative value of $\triangle$ to the greatest positive value, or more generally from $\triangle = -\infty$ to $\triangle = +\infty$ must necessarily be equal to unity. Supposing, therefore, any determinate system of the values of the quantities p, q, r, s, etc., the probability that observation would give for V the value M, will be expressed by $\phi(M-V)$, substituting in V for p,

q, r, s, etc., their values; in the same manner $\varphi(M'-V')$, $\varphi(M''-V'')$, etc. will express the probabilities that observation would give the values M', M'', etc., of the functions V', V'', etc. Wherefore, since we are authorized to regard all the observations as events independent of each other, the product

$$\varphi(M-V)\varphi(M'-V')\varphi(M''-V'') \text{ etc.,} = \Omega$$

will express the expectation or probability that all those values will result together from observation.

Now in the same manner as, when any determinate values whatever of the unknown quantities being taken, a determinate probability corresponds, previous to observation, to any system of values of the functions V, V', V''', etc.; so, inversely, after determinate values of the functions have resulted from observation, a determinate probability will belong to every system of values of the unknown quantities, from which the values of the functions could possibly have resulted: for, evidently, those systems will be regarded as the more probable in which the greater expectation had existed of the event which actually occurred. The estimation of this probability rests upon the following theorem:—

If, any hypothesis H *being made, the probability of any determinate event* E *is* h, *and if, another hypothesis* H' *being made excluding the former and equally probable in itself, the probability of the same event is* h': *then I say, when the event* E *has actually occurred, that the probability that* H *was the true hypothesis, is to the probability that* H' *was the true hypothesis, as* h *to* h'.

For demonstrating which let us suppose that, by a classification of all the circumstances on which it depends whether, with H or H' or some other hypothesis, the event E or some other event, should occur, a system of the different cases is formed, each one of which cases is to be considered as equally probable in itself (that is, as long as it is uncertain whether the event E, or some other, will occur), and that these cases be so distributed,

373

that among them may be found	in which should be assumed the hypothesis	in such a mode as would give occasion to the event
m	H	E
n	H	different from E
m'	H'	E
n'	H'	different from E
m''	different from H and H'	E
n''	different from H and H'	different from E

Then we shall have

$$b = \frac{m}{m+n}, \; b' = \frac{m'}{m'+n'};$$

moreover, before the event was known the probability of the hypothesis H was

$$\frac{m+n}{m+n+m'+n'+m''+n''},$$

but after the event is known, when the cases n, n', n'' disappear from the number of the possible cases, the probability of the same hypothesis will be

$$\frac{m}{m+m'+m''};$$

in the same way the probability of the hypothesis H' before and after the event, respectively, will be expressed by

$$\frac{m'+n'}{m+n+m'+n'+m''+n''} \text{ and } \frac{m'}{m+m'+m''}$$

since, therefore, the same probability is assumed for the hypotheses H and H' before the event is known, we shall have

374

$$m + n = m' + n',$$

whence the truth of the theorem is readily inferred.

Now, so far as we suppose that no other data exist for the determination of the unknown quantities besides the observations $V = M$, $V' = M'$, $V'' = M''$, etc., and, therefore, that all systems of values of these unknown quantities were equally probable previous to the observations, the probability, evidently, of any determinate system subsequent to the observations will be proportional to Ω. This is to be understood to mean that the probability that the values of the unknown quantities lie between the infinitely near limits p and $p + dp$, q and $q + dq$, r and $r + dr$, s and $s + ds$, etc. respectively, is expressed by

$$\lambda\Omega dp dq dr ds \ldots, \text{etc.,}$$

where the quantity λ will be a constant quantity independent of p, q, r, s, etc.: and, indeed, $\dfrac{1}{\lambda}$ will, evidently, be the value of the integral of the order v,

$$\int v \Omega dp dq dr ds \ldots, \text{etc.,}$$

for each of the variables p, q, r, s, etc., extended from the value $-\infty$ to the value $+\infty$.

Now it readily follows from this, that the most probable system of values of the quantities p, q, r, s, etc. is that in which Ω acquires the maximum value, and, therefore, is to be derived from the v equations

$$\frac{d\Omega}{dp} = 0, \frac{d\Omega}{dq} = 0, \frac{d\Omega}{dr} = 0, \frac{d\Omega}{ds} = 0, \text{etc.}$$

These equations, by putting

$V - M = v, V' - M' = v', V'' - M'' = v''$, etc., and $\dfrac{d\varphi\triangle}{\varphi\triangle d\triangle}$

$= \varphi'\triangle$, assume the following form:—

$$\frac{dv}{dp}\,\varphi'v + \frac{dv'}{dp}\,\varphi'v' + \frac{dv''}{dp}\,\varphi'\,v'' + \text{etc.} = 0$$

$$\frac{dv}{dq}\,\varphi'v + \frac{dv'}{dq}\,\varphi'v' + \frac{dv''}{dq}\,\varphi'\,v'' + \text{etc.} = 0,$$

$$\frac{dv}{dr}\,\varphi'v + \frac{dv'}{dr}\,\varphi'v' + \frac{dv''}{dr}\,\varphi'\,v'' + \text{etc.} = 0$$

$$\frac{dv}{ds}\,\varphi'v + \frac{dv'}{ds}\,\varphi'v' + \frac{dv''}{ds}\,\varphi'\,v'' + \text{etc.} = 0.$$

Hence, accordingly, a completely determinate solution of the problem can be obtained by elimination, as soon as the nature of the function φ' is known. Since this cannot be defined a priori, we will, approaching the subject from another point of view, inquire upon what function, tacitly, as it were, assumed as a base, the common principle, the excellence of which is generally acknowledged, depends. It has been customary certainly to regard as an axiom the hypothesis that if any quantity has been determined by several direct observations, made under the same circumstances and with equal care, the arithmetical mean of the observed values affords the most probable value, if not rigorously, yet very nearly at least, so that it is always most safe to adhere to it. By putting, therefore,

$$V = V' = V''' \text{ etc.} = p,$$

we ought to have in general,

$$\varphi'\,(M\!-\!p) + \varphi'(M'\!-\!p) + \varphi'\,(M''\!-\!p) + \text{etc.} = 0$$

if instead of p is substituted the value

$$\frac{1}{\mu}(M + M' + M'' + \text{etc.}),$$

whatever positive integer μ expresses. By supposing, therefore,

$$M' = M'' = \text{etc.} = M - \mu N,$$

we shall have in general, that is, for any positive integral value of μ,

$$\varphi'(\mu\!-\!1)N = (1\!-\!\mu)\varphi'(-N),$$

whence it is readily inferred that $\dfrac{\varphi'\triangle}{\triangle}$ must be a constant quan-

tity, which we will denote by k. Hence we have

$$\log \varphi\triangle = \tfrac{1}{2}\,k\triangle\triangle + \text{Constant},$$
$$\varphi\triangle = \kappa e^{\frac{1}{2}k\triangle\triangle}$$

denoting the base of the hyperbolic logarithms by e and assuming

$$\text{Constant} = \log \kappa.$$

Moreover, it is readily perceived that k must be negative, in order that Ω may really become a maximum, for which reason we shall put

$$\tfrac{1}{2}k --- hh;$$

and since, by the elegant theorem first discovered by Laplace, the integral

$$\int e^{-hh\triangle\triangle}d\triangle$$

from $\triangle = -\infty$ to $\triangle = +\infty$ is $\dfrac{\sqrt{\pi}}{h}$, (denoting by π the

semicircumference of the circle the radius of which is unity), our function becomes

$$\varphi\triangle = \frac{h}{\sqrt{\pi}}e^{-hh\triangle\triangle}$$

The function just found cannot, it is true, express rigorously the probabilities of the errors: for since the possible errors are in all cases confined within certain limits, the probability of errors exceeding those limits ought always to be zero, while our formula always gives some value. However, this defect, which every analytical function must, from its nature, labor under, is of no importance in practice, because the value of our function decreases so rapidly, when $h\triangle$ has acquired a considerable magnitude, that it can safely be considered as vanishing. Besides, the nature of the subject never admits of assigning with absolute rigor the limits of error.

Finally, the constant h can be considered as the measure of precision of the observations. For if the probability of the error $\triangle$ is supposed to be expressed in any one system of observations by

$$\frac{h}{\sqrt{\pi}}e^{-hh\triangle\triangle},$$

and in another system of observations more or less exact by

$$\frac{h'}{\sqrt{\pi}}e^{-h'h'\triangle\triangle},$$

the expectation, that the error of any observation in the former

378

system is contained between the limits $-\delta$ and $+\delta$ will be expressed by the integral

$$\int \frac{h}{\sqrt{\pi}} e^{-hh\Delta\Delta} d\Delta$$

taken from $\Delta = -\delta$ to $\Delta = +\delta$; and in the same manner the expectation, that the error of any observation in the latter system does not exceed the limits $-\delta'$ and $+\delta'$ will be expressed by the integral

$$\int \frac{h'}{\sqrt{\pi}} e^{-h'h'\Delta\Delta} d\Delta$$

extended from $\Delta = -\delta'$ to $\Delta = +\delta'$: but both integrals manifestly become equal when we have $h\delta = h'\delta'$. Now, therefore, if for example $h' = 2h$, a double error can be committed in the former system with the same facility as a single error in the latter, in which case, according to the common way of speaking, a double degree of precision is attributed to the latter observations.

We will now develop the conclusions which follow from this law. It is evident, in order that the product

$$\Omega = h\mu\pi^{-\frac{1}{2}\mu} e^{-hh(vv+v'v'+v''v''+\ldots)}$$

may become a maximum, that the sum

$$vv + v'v' + v''v'' + \text{etc.,}$$

must become a minimum. *Therefore, that will be the most probable system of values of the unknown quantities* p, q, r, s, *etc., in which the sum of the squares of the differences between the observed and computed values of the functions* V, V', V'', *etc. is a minimum,* if the same degree of accuracy is to be presumed

379

in all the observations. This principle, which promises to be of most frequent use in all applications of the mathematics to natural philosophy, must, everywhere, be considered an axiom with the same propriety as the arithmetical mean of several observed values of the same quantity is adopted as the most probable value.

This principle can be extended without difficulty to observations of *unequal* accuracy. If, for example, the measures of precision of the observations by means of which $V = M$, $V' = M'$, $V'' = M''$, etc. have been found, are expressed, respectively, by h, h', h'', etc., that is, if it is assumed that errors reciprocally proportional to these quantities might have been made with equal facility in those observations, this, evidently, will be the same as if, by means of observations of equal precision (the measure of which is equal to unity), the values of the functions hV, $h'V'$, $h''V''$, etc., had been directly found to be hM, $h'M'$, $h''M''$, etc.: wherefore, the most probable system of values of the quantities p, q, r, s, etc., will be that in which the sum of $hhvv + h'h'v'v' + h''h''v''v'' +$ etc., that is, *in which the sum of the squares of the differences between the actually observed and computed values multiplied by numbers that measure the degree of precision, is a minimum*. In this way it is not necessary that the functions V, V', V'', etc. relate to homogeneous quantities, but they may represent heterogeneous quantities also (for example, seconds of arc and time), provided only that the ratio of the errors, which might have been committed with equal facility in each, can be estimated.

WILLIAM GILBERT

(1540–1603)

Sometimes called the father of electricity, because of his experiments with magnetism and invention of the terms "electric force," "electric attraction" and "magnetic pole," Gilbert was personal physician to Queen Elizabeth. His treatise, *De Magnete, Magneticisque Corporibus* (1600), is generally considered the first great scientific work published in England. In it he asserted the magnetic nature of the earth, and described the true nature of the lodestone or magnetic needle. The gilbert, a unit of magnetomotive force, is named after him.

ON MAGNETISM AND MAGNETIC BODIES

THE LOADSTONE POSSESSES PARTS DIFFERING IN THEIR NATURAL POWERS, AND HAS POLES CONSPICUOUS FOR THEIR PROPERTIES

THE MANY QUALITIES exhibited by the loadstone itself, qualities hitherto recognized yet not well investigated, are to be pointed out in the first place, to the end the student may understand the powers of the loadstone and of iron, and not be confused through want of knowledge at the threshold of the arguments and demonstrations. In the heavens astronomers give to each moving sphere two poles; thus do we find two natural poles of excelling importance even in our terrestrial globe, constant points related to the movement of its daily revolution, to wit, one pole pointing to Arctos (Ursa) and the north; the other looking toward the opposite part of the heavens. In like manner the loadstone has from nature its two poles, a northern and a southern; fixed, definite points in the stone, which are the primary termini of the movements and effects, and the limits and regulators of the

381

several actions and properties. It is to be understood, however, that not from a mathematical point does the force of the stone emanate, but from the parts themselves; and all these parts in the whole—while they belong to the whole—the nearer they are to the poles of the stone the stronger virtues do they acquire and pour out on other bodies. These poles look toward the poles of the earth, and move toward them, and are subject to them.

The magnetic poles may be found in every loadstone, whether strong and powerful (male, as the term was in antiquity) or faint, weak, and female; whether its shape is due to design or to chance, and whether it be long, or flat, or foursquare, or three-cornered, or polished; whether it be rough, broken off, or unpolished: the loadstone ever has and ever shows its poles. . . .

ONE LOADSTONE APPEARS TO ATTRACT ANOTHER IN THE NATURAL POSITION; BUT IN THE OPPOSITE POSITION REPELS IT AND BRINGS IT TO RIGHTS

First we have to describe in popular language the potent and familiar properties of the stone; afterward, very many subtle properties, as yet recondite and unknown, being involved in obscurities, are to be unfolded; and the causes of all these (nature's secrets being unlocked) are in their place to be demonstrated in fitting words and with the aid of apparatus. The fact is trite and familiar that the loadstone attracts iron; in the same way, too, one loadstone attracts another. Take the stone on which you have designated the poles, N. and S., and put it in its vessel so that it may float; let the poles lie just in the plane of the horizon, or at least in a plane not very oblique to it; take in your hand another stone the poles of which are also known, and hold it so that its south pole shall lie toward the north pole of the floating stone, and near it alongside; the floating loadstone will straightway follow the other (provided it be within the range and dominion of its powers), nor does it cease to move nor does it quit the other till it clings to it, unless by moving your hand away you manage skillfully to prevent the conjunction.

382

In like manner, if you oppose the north pole of the stone in your hand to the south pole of the floating one, they come together and follow each other. For opposite poles attract opposite poles. But now, if in the same way you present N. to N. or S. to S., one stone repels the other; and as though a helmsman were bearing on the rudder it is off like a vessel making all sail, nor stands nor stays as long as the other stone pursues. One stone also will range the other, turn the other around, bring it to right about and make it come to agreement with itself. But when the two come together and are conjoined in nature's order, they cohere firmly.

For example, if you present the north pole of the stone in your hand to the Tropic of Capricorn (for so we may distinguish with mathematical circles the round stone or terrella, just as we do the globe itself) or to any point between the Equator and the South Pole: immediately the floating stone turns round and so places itself that its south pole touches the north pole of the other and is most closely joined to it. In the same way you will get like effect at the other side of the Equator by presenting pole to pole; and thus by art and contrivance we exhibit attraction and repulsion, and motion in a circle toward the concordant position, and the same movements to avoid hostile meetings. Furthermore, in one same stone we are thus able to demonstrate all this: but also we are able to show how the selfsame part of one stone may by division become either north or south. Take the oblong stone *ad* (Fig. 1) in which *a* is the north pole and *d* the south. Cut the stone in two equal parts, and put part *a* in a vessel and let it float in water.

You will find that *a*, the north point, will turn to the south as before; and in like manner the point *d* will move to the north, in the divided stone, as before division. But *b* and *c*, before connected, now separated from each other, are not what they were before. *B* is now south while *c* is north. *B* attracts *c*, longing for union and for restoration of the original continuity. They are two stones made out of one, and on that account, the *c* of one turning toward the *b* of the other, they are mutually attracted, and, being freed from all impediments and from their own

383

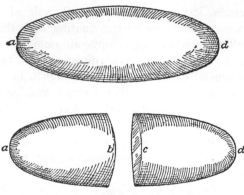

Fig. 1

weight, borne as they are on the surface of the water, they come together and into conjunction.

But if you bring the part or point *a* up to *c* of the other, they repel one another and turn away; for by such a position of the parts nature is crossed and the form of the stone is perverted: but nature observes strictly the laws it has imposed upon bodies: hence the flight of one part from the undue position of the other, and hence the discord unless everything is arranged exactly according to nature. And nature will not suffer an unjust and inequitable peace, or agreement, but makes war and employs force to make bodies acquiesce fairly and justly. Hence, when rightly arranged, the parts attract each other, i.e., both stones, the weaker and the stronger, come together and with all their might tend to union: a fact manifest in all loadstones, and not, as Pliny supposed, only in those from Ethiopia.

The Ethiopic stones, if strong, and those brought from China, which are all powerful stones, show the effect most quickly and most plainly, attract with most force in the parts nighest the pole, and keep turning till pole looks straight on pole. The pole of a stone has strongest attraction for that part of another stone which answers to it (the *adverse*, as it is called); e.g., the north pole of one has strongest attraction for, has the most vigorous pull on, the south part of another; so, too, it attracts iron more powerfully, and iron clings to it more firmly, whether previously magnetized or not. Thus it has been settled by nature, not without reason, that the parts nigher the pole shall have the greatest attractive force; and that in the pole itself shall be the seat, the throne, as it were, of a high and splendid power; and that magnetic bodies brought near thereto shall be attracted most powerfully and relinquished with most reluctance. So, too, the poles are readiest to spurn and drive away what is presented to them amiss, and what is inconformable and foreign.

THOMAS GRAHAM

(1805–1869)

Another founder of physical chemistry is the Scottish chemist, Thomas Graham. His study of the three forms of phosphoric acid that led to the concept of polybasic acids was called *Researches on the Arseniates, Phosphates, and Modifications of Phosphoric Acid* (1833), and is quoted in part below. His work on the diffusion of gases, published in *A Short Account of Experimental Researches on the Diffusion of Gases Through Each Other, and Their Separation by Mechanical Means* (1829), contains the essentials of what came to be known as Graham's law: that the diffusion rate of gases is inversely as the square root of their density. He also discovered the properties of colloids, and conducted important researches on the solubility of salts and dialysis.

RESEARCHES ON THE ARSENIATES, PHOSPHATES, AND MODIFICATIONS OF PHOSPHORIC ACID

THE DISTINCTIVE character of phosphoric acid which exists in common phosphate of soda, as compared with the other modifications, is a disposition to form salts which contain three atoms of base to the double atom of acid. Of these salts the most remarkable is the yellow subphosphate of silver, which the soluble phosphates precipitate when added to nitrate of silver. This acid does not affect albumen; and the other modifications pass directly into the condition of this acid on keeping their aqueous solutions for some days, and more rapidly on boiling these solutions; or upon fusing the other modifications or their salts with at least three proportions of fixed base.

Pyrophosphoric acid, or the acid which exists in the fused

phosphate of soda, is remarkably disposed to form salts having two atoms base, which is the constitution of the white pyrophosphate of silver, formed on testing the pyrophosphate of soda with a salt of silver. Such salts of the preceding acid as contain no more than two atoms of fixed base, pass into pyrophosphates when heated to redness. The acid under consideration, when free, does not disturb albumen, nor produce a precipitate in muriate of barytes.

The metaphosphoric acid is disposed to form salts which contain one atom of base to the double atom of acid. The other modifications pass into metaphosphoric acid when heated to redness per se, or when heated to redness in contact with no more than one atomic proportion of certain fixed bases, such as soda. This acid, when free, occasions precipitates in solutions of the salts of barytes and of most of the other earths and metallic oxides, and forms an insoluble compound with albumen. The glacial or metaphosphoric acid appears to be capable of dissolving in general only about four fifths of the quantity of carbonate of soda which it can decompose when converted into phosphoric acid. But a large quantity of the meta-acid passes into phosphoric acid on uniting with alkali, and the solution deposits phosphate of soda in tufts composed of fine crystalline plates of a silky lustre. The salt presented itself of this appearance, it will be remembered, in the case of a solution of phosphate of soda which had been boiled for a long time in a glass vessel. The liquid about the crystals, in the present case, still contained metaphosphoric acid.

Now it is a matter of certainty that if we take one combining proportion of any modification of phosphoric acid, and fuse it with soda or its carbonate, we shall form a metaphosphate, a pyrophosphate, or a phosphate, according as we employ one, two, or three proportions of base. The acid when separated from the base will possess, and retain for some time, the characters of its peculiar modification. It would appear, therefore, that the acid is impressed with a disposition to form different classes of salts by the proportion of base to which it has been united, and that it retains this disposition even when liberated from the original compound. But I suspect that the modifications of phosphoric acid, when in what we would call a free state, are still in combination with their usual proportion of base, and that that base is water. Thus the three modifications of phosphoric acid may be composed as follows:

Phosphoric acid	H^3P
Pyrophosphoric acid	H^2P
Metaphosphoric acid	$HP;*$

or they are respectively a terphosphate, a biphosphate, and phosphate of water. Now, when one of these compounds is treated with a strong base, the whole or a part of the water is supplanted, *but the amount of base in combination with the acid remains unaltered.* There are thus three sets of phosphates, in which the oxygen in the acid being five, the oxygen in the base is three, two, and one. The constitution of the acids and of the salts of soda which they form, is exhibited in the following Table.

	Oxygen in		
	Soda.	Water.	Acid.
First Class			
Phosphoric acid	0	3	5
Biphosphate of soda	1	2	5
Phosphate of soda	2	1	5
Subphosphate of soda	3	0	5
Second Class			
Pyrophosphoric acid	0	2	5
Bipyrophosphate of soda	1	1	5
Pyrophosphate of soda	2	0	5
Third Class			
Metaphosphoric acid	0	1	5
Metaphosphate of soda	1	0	5

* [*I.e.*, $3H_2O.P_2O_5$, $2H_2O.P_2O_5$, $H_2O.P_2O_5$.]

The hypothetic composition of the acid hydrates may also be stated as follows:

	Acid.	Water.
Phosphoric acid	100	37.81 = 3 atoms
Pyrophosphoric acid	100	25.21 = 2 atoms
Metaphosphoric acid	100	12.61 = 1 atom

By a heat of 300° a dilute solution of phosphoric acid in a platinum crucible concentrates readily till the water is reduced to the proportion of three atoms, at which stage the acid assumes a dark color, and is of the consistence of treacle when cold, but much more fluid when hot. In this condition the acid gives an unmixed yellow precipitate with silver, and is entirely phosphoric acid. By exposure for seven days over sulphuric acid in the vacuum of an air-pump, the water was reduced to 43.5 parts, and almost the whole of the acid had crystallized in thin plates, which were deliquescent in the extreme, and which there is every reason to believe were the terhydrate. By a protracted exposure to 300° or 320°, the acid continues to lose water, but much more slowly. At 460° the water was quickly reduced to 34.4 parts, or little more than 2⅔ atoms, in an experiment conducted in an open crucible, and the acid now precipitated silver white with a trace of yellow; but when neutralized by carbonate of soda, it afforded crystalline plates of phosphate of soda, among which no crystals of pyrophosphate existed. But it may be deemed possible from this result that a hydrate of phosphoric acid exists, containing 2⅔ atoms of water to 1 atom acid, which is 8 atoms base to 3 atoms acid, the proportion of base to acid in the salt termed by Berzelius, the phosphate of lime of bones. In another case in which the evaporation was conducted much more slowly in a platinum flask, the above compound was certainly not formed; but the evaporation at 415°, after advancing for several days, seemed to cease entirely when the water was reduced to 29.9 parts, which is very nearly 2⅓ atoms of water. Acid at this degree of concentration, neutralized as usual by ammonia, gave, with silver, a chalky white precipitate without a shade of yellow, which suggests the idea that an acid hydrate of 2⅓ water may exist, having a corresponding silver salt. Acid, so far concentrated, when neutralized by carbonate of soda, afforded a mixture of crystals of phosphate and pyrophosphate of soda, in which the latter predominated. For the production of metaphosphoric acid, the concentration of a much higher temperature was requisite; but this acid was observed to appear before the proportion of water had fallen under 2 atoms, namely, when it amounted to 28.05 per cent in one experiment. By the greatest heat of the sand-bath, which was considerably above the melting point of lead, the proportion of water was reduced a little under 2 atoms, namely, to 22.99 parts; and the acid then contained abundance of metaphosphoric acid, as evinced by its power to coagulate albumen. In the glacial phosphoric acid, Dulong found 100 acid united with 20.6 water, and Rose 100 acid with only 10.42 water. The latter determination falls short of 1 atom water, and would indicate that phosphoric acid may be rendered partially anhydrous by heat. I do not enter upon the details of my experiments on the hydrates of phosphoric acid, as the subject is difficult, and requires a much more minute investigation than I have as yet had it in my power to give it.

Although of opinion that there is only one phosphoric acid, and that the modifications are entirely due to the quantity of water combined with the acid, I have still retained the names which have come into use, and even proposed a third, *meta*phosphoric acid, implying merely that the acid to which this name is applied is phosphoric acid with something else, namely, with an atom of water. As the classes of salts which the acid hydrates form are quite distinct, these trivial names are practically convenient, and may be adopted provisionally till chemists are prepared, by an extended knowledge of the salts, to innovate upon their nomenclature with more advantage than can be done at present. . . .

JAMES HALL

(1761–1832)

Still another Scottish chemist, Sir James Hall, became the founder
of experimental geology through his simulation of geological formations in the laboratory. The purpose of these experiments was to
confirm the theories of his friend and teacher, James Hutton.

ACCOUNT OF A SERIES OF EXPERIMENTS

OF ALL mineral substances, the *Carbonate of Lime* is unquestionably the most important in a general view. As limestone or marble, it constitutes a very considerable part of the solid mass of
many countries; and, in the form of veins and nodules of spar,
pervades every species of stone. Its history is thus interwoven in
such a manner with that of the mineral kingdom at large, that
the fate of any geological theory must very much depend upon
its successful application to the various conditions of this substance. But, till Dr. Black, by his discovery of Carbonic Acid,
explained the chemical nature of the carbonate, no rational
theory could be formed, of the chemical revolutions which it has
undoubtedly undergone.

This discovery was, in the first instance, hostile to the supposed
action of fire; for the decomposition of limestone by fire in every
common kiln being thus proved, it seemed absurd to ascribe to
that same agent the formation of limestone, or of any mass containing it.

The contemplation of this difficulty led Dr. Hutton to view the
action of fire in a manner peculiar to himself, and thus to form
a geological theory, by which, in my opinion, he has furnished
the world with the true solution of one of the most interesting
problems that has ever engaged the attention of men of science.

391

He supposed,

1. That Heat has acted, at some remote period, on all rocks.
2. That during the action of heat, all these rocks (even such as now appear at the surface) lay covered by a superincumbent mass, of great weight and strength.
3. That in consequence of the combined action of Heat and Pressure, effects were produced different from those of heat on common occasions; in particular, that the carbonate of lime was reduced to a state of fusion, more or less complete, without any calcination.

The essential and characteristic principle of this theory is thus comprised in the word *Compression*; and by one bold hypothesis, founded on this principle, he undertook to meet all the objections to the action of fire, and to account for those circumstances in which minerals are found to differ from the usual products of our furnaces. . . .

After three years of almost daily warfare with Dr. Hutton, on the subject of his theory, I began to view his fundamental principles with less and less repugnance.

. . . If we take a hollow tube or barrel closed at one end, and open at the other, of one foot or more in length; it is evident, that by introducing one end into a furnace, we can supply to it as great heat as art can produce, while the other end is kept cool, or, if necessary, exposed to extreme cold. If, then, the substance which we mean to subject to the combined action of heat and pressure, be introduced into the breech or closed end of the barrel, and if the middle part be filled with some refractory substance, leaving a small empty space at the muzzle, we can apply heat to the muzzle, while the breech containing the subject of experiment, is kept cool, and thus close the barrel by any of the numerous modes which heat affords, from the welding of iron to the melting of sealing wax. Things being then reversed, and the breech put into the furnace a heat of any required intensity may be applied to the subject of experiment, now in a state of constraint.

My first application of this scheme was carried on with a common gun-barrel, cut off at the touch-hole, and welded very strongly at the breech by means of a plug of iron. Into it I introduced the carbonate, previously rammed into a cartridge of paper or pasteboard, in order to protect it from the iron, by which, in some former trials, the subject of experiment had been contaminated throughout during the action of heat. I then rammed the rest of the barrel full of pounded clay, previously baked in a strong heat, and I had the muzzle closed like the breech, by a plug of iron welded upon it in a common forge; the rest of the barrel being kept cold during this operation, by means of wet cloths. The breech of the barrel was then introduced horizontally into a common muffle heated to about 25° of Wedgwood. To the muzzle a rope was fixed, in such a manner, that the barrel could be withdrawn without dangers from an explosion. I likewise, about this time, closed the muzzle of the barrel, by means of a plug, fixed by solder only; which method has this peculiar advantage, that I could shut and open the barrel, without having recourse to a workman. In these trials, though many barrels yielded to the expansive force, others resisted it, and afforded some results that were in the highest degree encouraging, and even satisfactory, could they have been obtained with certainty on repetition of the process. In many of them, chalk, or common limestone previously pulverized, was agglutinated into a stony mass, which required a smart blow of a hammer to break it, and felt under the knife like a common limestone; at the same time, the substance, when thrown into nitric acid, dissolved entirely with violent effervescence.

On the third of March of the same year (1801), I made a similar experiment, in which a pyrometer-piece was placed within the barrel, and another in the muffle; they agreed in indicating 23 degrees. The inner tube which was of Reaumur's porcelain, contained 80 grains of pounded chalk. The carbonate was found, after the experiment, to have lost 3½ grains. A thin rim, less than the 20th of an inch in thickness, of whitish matter, appeared on the outside of the mass. In other respects, the carbonate was in a very perfect state; it was of a yellowish color, and had a decided semitransparency and saline fracture. But what renders this result of the greatest value, is, that on breaking the mass, a space of more than the tenth of an inch square, was found to be completely crystallized, having acquired the rhomboidal fracture of calcareous spar. It was white and opaque, and presented to the view three sets of parallel plates which are seen under three different angles.

I have likewise made some experiments with coal, treated in the same manner as the carbonate of lime: but I have found it much less tractable; for the bitumen, when heat is applied to it, tends to escape by its simple elasticity, whereas the carbonic acid in marble, is in part retained by the chemical force of quicklime. I succeeded, however, in constraining the bituminous matter of the coal, to a certain degree, in red heats, so as to bring the substance into a complete fusion, and to retain its faculty of burning with flame. But, I could not accomplish this in heats capable of agglutinating the carbonate; for I have found, where I rammed them successively into the same tube, and where the vessel has withstood the expansive force, that the carbonate has been agglutinated into a good limestone, but that the coal has lost about half its weight, together with its power of giving flame when burnt, remaining in a very compact state, with a shining fracture. Although this experiment has not afforded the desired result, it answers another purpose admirably well. It is known, that where a bed of coal is crossed by a dike of whinstone, the coal is found in a peculiar state in the immediate neighborhood of the whin: the substance in such places being incapable of giving flame, it is distinguished by the name of *blind coal*.

I found that the organization of animal substance was entirely obliterated by a slight action of heat, but that a stronger heat was required to perform the entire fusion of vegetable matter. This, however, was accomplished; and in several experiments, pieces of wood were changed to a jet-black and inflammable substance, generally very porous, in which no trace could be discovered of the original organization. In others, the vegetable fibres were still visible, and are forced asunder by large and shining air-bubbles.

JAMES HALL

EXPERIMENTS ON WHINSTONE AND LAVA

THE experiments described in this paper were suggested to me many years ago, when employed in studying the *Geological System* of the late Dr. Hutton, by the following plausible objection, to which it seems liable.

Granite, porphyry, and basaltes, are supposed by Dr. Hutton to have flowed in a state of perfect fusion into their present position; but their internal structure, being universally rough and stony, appears to contradict this hypothesis; for the result of the fusion of earthy substances, hitherto observed in our experiments, either is glass, or possesses, in some degree, the vitreous character.

This objection, however, loses much of its force, when we attend to the peculiar circumstances under which, according to this theory, the action of heat was exerted. These substances, when in fusion, and long after their congelation, are supposed to have occupied a subterraneous position far below what was then the surface of the earth; and Dr. Hutton has ascribed to the modification of heat, occasioned by the pressure of the superincumbent mass, many important phenomena of the mineral kingdom, which he has thus reconciled to his system.

One necessary consequence of the position of these bodies, seems, however, to have been overlooked by Dr. Hutton himself; I mean, that, after their fusion, they must have cooled very slowly; and it appeared to me probable, on that account, that, during their congelation, a crystallization had taken place, with more or less regularity, producing the stony and crystallized structure, common to all unstratified substances, from the large grained granite, to the fine grained and almost homogeneous basalt. This conjecture derived additional probability from an accident similar to those formerly observed by Mr. Keir, which had just happened at Leith: a large glass-house pot, filled with green bottle glass in fusion, having cooled slowly, its contents had lost every character of glass, and had completely assumed the stony structure. . . .

Encouraged by this reasoning, I began my projected series of

395

experiments in the course of the same year (1790), with very promising appearances of success. I found that I could command the result which had occurred accidentally at the glass-house; for, by means of slow cooling, I converted bottle glass, after fusion, into a stony substance, which again, by the application of strong heat, and subsequent rapid cooling, I restored to the state of perfect glass. This operation I performed repeatedly with the same specimen, so as to ascertain that the character of the result was stony or vitreous, according to the mode of its cooling.

Some peculiar circumstances interrupted the prosecution of these experiments till last winter, when I determined to resume them. Deliberating on the substance most proper to submit to experiment on this occasion, I was decided by the advice of Dr. Hope, well known by his discovery of the Earth of Strontites, to give the preference to whinstone.

The term whinstone, as used in most parts of Scotland, denotes a numerous class of stones, distinguished in other countries by the names of basaltes, trap, wacken, grünstein and porphyry. As they are, in my opinion, mere varieties of the same class, I conceive that they ought to be connected by some common name, and have made use of this, already familiar to us, and which seems liable to no objection, since it is not confined to any particular species. . . .

The whinstone first employed was taken from a quarry near the Dean, on the Water of Leith, in the neighborhood of Edinburgh. This stone is an aggregate of black and greenish-black hornblend, intimately mixed with a pale reddish-brown matter, which has some resemblance to feldspar, but is far more fusible. Both substances are imperfectly and confusedly crystallized in minute grains. The hornblend is in the greatest proportion; and its fracture appears to be striated, though in some parts foliated; that of the reddish-brown matter is foliated. The fracture of the stone *en masse* is uneven, and it abounds in small facettes, which have some degree of lustre. It may be scratched, though with difficulty, by a knife, and gives an earthy smell when breathed on. It frequently contains small specks of pyrites.

On the 17th of January 1798, I introduced a black lead

[graphite] crucible, filled with fragments of this stone, into the great reverberating furnace at Mr. Barker's iron foundery. In about a quarter of an hour, I found that the substance had entered into fusion, and was agitated by a strong ebullition. I removed the crucible, and allowed it to cool rapidly. The result was a black glass, with a tolerably clean fracture, interrupted however by some specks. . . .

At last, on the 27th of January, I succeeded completely in the object I had in view. A crucible, containing a quantity of whinstone, melted in the manner above described, being removed from the reverberatory, and conveyed rapidly to a large open fire, was immediately surrounded with burning coals, and the fire, after being maintained several hours, was allowed to go out. The crucible, when cold, was broken, and was found to contain a substance, differing in all respects from glass, and in texture completely resembling whinstone. Its fracture was rough, stony and crystalline; and a number of shining facettes were interspersed through the whole mass. The crystallization was still more apparent in cavities produced by air bubbles, the internal surface of which was lined with distinct crystals.

LAVA OF SANTA VENERE

This current has flowed in the neighborhood of a little chapel, called Santa Venere, above the village of Piedimonte, on the north side of Mount Aetna. Owing to the strong resemblance which it bears to stones supposed not volcanic, we took care that our specimens should be broken from the actual current; and to one of them, though mostly compact, is attached a scorified mass, which had made part of the external surface. The solid part is of a black, or rather dark blue, color, very fine grained and homogeneous, having a multitude of minute and shining facettes visible in the sun; in this, and in other circumstances, it greatly resembles the rock of Edinburgh Castle. This lava is the second in M. Dolomieu's *Catalogue,* and is well described.

The pure black glass formed from this lava yielded, in the

regulated heat, the most highly crystallized mass we have obtained from any lava or whin.

These experiments seem to establish, in a direct manner what I had deduced, analogically, from the properties of whinstone, namely, that the stony character of a lava is fully accounted for by slow cooling after the most perfect fusion; and, consequently, that no argument against the intensity of volcanic fire can be founded upon that character. We are therefore justified in believing, as numberless facts indicate, that volcanic heat has often been of excessive intensity.

EDMUND HALLEY

(1656–1742)

Famous for the comet which bears his name, and whose return in 1758 he accurately predicted in 1682, Halley was the first astronomer to perform such a feat. A friend of Sir Isaac Newton, he encouraged the latter to write his *Principia* and subsidized its publication. He also published the first map of the winds on the earth's surface, and suggested that sea salt came from the deposits of rivers. He conducted many researches on the orbits of comets and is credited with initiating the science of life statistics with his *Breslau Table of Mortality*. He also surveyed the coast of the English Channel and made a chart of its tides, and compiled a catalogue of the stars in the Southern Hemisphere.

A SYNOPSIS OF THE ASTRONOMY OF COMETS

HITHERTO I have consider'd the Orbits of Comets as exactly Parabolic; upon which supposition it wou'd follow, that Comets being impell'd towards the Sun by a Centripetal Force, would descend as from spaces infinitely distant, and by their so falling acquire such a Velocity, as that they may again fly off into the remotest parts of the Universe, moving upwards with a perpetual tendency, so as never to return again to the Sun. But since they appear frequently enough, and since some of them can be found to move with a Hyperbolic Motion, or a Motion swifter than what a Comet might acquire by its Gravity to the Sun, 'tis highly probable they rather move in very Excentric Elliptic Orbits, and make their returns after long periods of Time: For so their number will be determinate, and, perhaps, not so very great. Besides, the space between the Sun and the Fix'd Stars is so immense, that there is room enough for a Comet to revolve,

399

tho' the Period of its revolution be vastly long. Now, the *Latus Rectum* of an Ellipsis, is to the *Latus Rectum* of a Parabola, which has the same Distance in its Perihelium; as the Distance in the Aphelium in the Ellipsis, is to the whole Axis of the Ellipsis. And the Velocities are in a Sub-duplicate ratio of the same: Wherefore in very Excentric Orbits the ratio comes very near to a ratio of Equality; and the very small difference which happens on account of the greater Velocity in the Parabola, is easily compensated in determining the situation of the Orbit. The principal use therefore, of this Table of the Elements of their Motions, and that which indeed induced me to construct it, is, that whenever a new Comet shall appear, we may be able to know, by comparing together the Elements, whether it be any of those which has appear'd before, and consequently to determine its Period, and the Axis of its Orbit, and to foretell its Return. And, indeed there are many things which make me believe that the Comet which *Apian* observ'd in the Year 1531, was the same with that which *Kepler* and *Longomontanus* more accurately describ'd in the Year 1607; and which I myself have seen return, and observ'd in the Year 1682. All the Elements agree, and nothing seems to contradict this my opinion, besides the Inequality of the Periodic revolutions. Which Inequality is not so great neither, as that it may not be owing to Physical Causes. For the Motion of Saturn is so disturbed by the rest of the Planets, especially Jupiter, that the Periodic time of that Planet is uncertain for some whole days together. How much more therefore will a Comet be subject to such like errors, which rises almost four times higher than Saturn, and whose Velocity, tho' increased but a very little, would be sufficient to change its Orbit, from an Elliptical to a Parabolical one. And I am the more confirmed in my opinion of its being the same; for that in the Year 1456, in the Summer time, a Comet was seen passing Retrograde between the Earth and the Sun, much after the same manner: Which tho' nobody made observations upon it, yet from its Period and the manner of its Transit, I cannot think different from those I have just now mention'd. And since looking over the Histories of Comets I find, at an equal interval

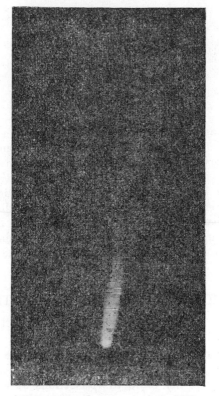

Halley's Comet at the return in 1910

of Time, a Comet to have been seen about Easter in the Year 1305, which is another double Period of 151 Years before the former. Hence I think I may venture to foretel, that it will return again in the Year 1758. And, if it should then so return, we shall have no reason to doubt but the rest may return also: Therefore, Astronomers have a large field wherein to exercise themselves for many ages, before they will be able to know the number of these many and great Bodies revolving about the common Center of the Sun, and to reduce their Motions to certain Rules.

WILLIAM HARVEY

(1578–1657)

Sir William Harvey was physician to both James I and Charles I, following the latter even into battle. He is more famous, of course, for his discovery of the true circulation of the blood, published in 1628 in his *Essay on the Motion of the Heart and the Blood in Animals*. Medicine had been aware of arterial circulation, but had not previously understood the return of the blood to the heart. Harvey distinguished between pulmonary circulation—from the right side of the heart through the lungs—and systemic circulation—from the left to the right of the heart and through the body.

ON THE MOTION OF THE HEART AND THE BLOOD IN ANIMALS

MOTIONS OF THE HEART IN LIVING ANIMALS

WHEN first I gave my mind to vivisections as a means of discovering the motions and uses of the heart, I found the task so truly arduous that I was almost tempted to think, with Fracastorius, that the motion of the heart was only to be comprehended by God. For I could neither rightly perceive at first when the systole and when the diastole took place, nor when and where dilation and contraction occurred, by reason of the rapidity of the motion, which, in many animals, is accomplished in the twinkling of an eye, coming and going like a flash of lightning. At length it appeared that these things happen together or at the same instant: the tension of the heart, the pulse of its apex, which is felt externally by its striking against the chest, the thickening of its walls, and the forcible expulsion of the blood it contains by the constriction of its ventricles.

Hence the very opposite of the opinions commonly received appears to be true; inasmuch as it is generally believed that when the heart strikes the breast and the pulse is felt without, the heart is dilated in its ventricles and is filled with blood. But the contrary of this is the fact; that is to say, the heart is in the act of contracting and being emptied. Whence the motion, which is generally regarded as the diastole of the heart, is in truth its systole. And in like manner the intrinsic motion of the heart is not the diastole but the systole; neither is it in the diastole that the heart grows firm and tense, but in the systole; for then alone when tense is it moved and made vigorous. When it acts and becomes tense the blood is expelled; when it relaxes and sinks together it receives the blood in the manner and wise which will by and by be explained.

From divers facts it is also manifest, in opposition to commonly received opinions, that the diastole of the arteries corresponds with the time of the heart's systole; and that the arteries are filled and distended by the blood forced into them by the contraction of the ventricles. It is in virtue of one and the same cause, therefore, that all the arteries of the body pulsate, *viz.*, the contraction of the left ventricle in the same way as the pulmonary artery pulsates by the contraction of the right ventricle.

I am persuaded it will be found that the motion of the heart is as follows. First of all, the auricle contracts and throws the blood into the ventricle, which, being filled, the heart raises itself straightway, makes all its fibres tense, contracts the ventricles and performs a beat, by which beat it immediately sends the blood supplied to it by the auricle into the arteries; the right ventricle sending its charge into the lungs by the vessel called *vena arteriosa*, but which, in structure and function, and all things else, is an artery; the left ventricle sending its charge into the aorta, and through this by the arteries to the body at large.

The grand cause of hesitation and error in this subject appears to me to have been the intimate connection between the heart and the lungs. When men saw both the pulmonary artery and the pulmonary veins losing themselves in the lungs, of course it became a puzzle to them to know how the right ventricle should distribute the blood to the body, or the left draw it from the *venæ cavæ*. Or they have hesitated because they did not perceive the route by which the blood is transferred from the veins to the arteries, in consequence of the intimate connection between the heart and lungs. And that this difficulty puzzled anatomists not a little when in their dissections they found the pulmonary artery and left ventricle full of black and clotted blood, plainly appears when they felt themselves compelled to affirm that the blood made its way from the right to the left ventricle by sweating through the septum of the heart.

Had anatomists only been as conversant with the dissection of the lower animals as they are with that of the human body, the matters that have hitherto kept them in perplexity of doubt would, in my opinion, have met them freed from every kind of difficulty. And first in fishes, in which the heart consists of but a single ventricle, they having no lungs, the thing is sufficiently manifest. Here the sac, which is situated at the base of the heart, and is the part analogous to the auricle in man, plainly throws the blood into the heart, and the heart in its turn conspicuously transmits it by a pipe or artery, or vessel analogous to an artery; these are facts which are confirmed by simple ocular experiment. I have seen, further, that the same thing obtained most obviously.

And since we find that in the greater number of animals, in all indeed at a certain period of their existence, the channels for the transmission of the blood through the heart are so conspicuous, we have still to inquire wherefore in some creatures—those, namely, that have warm blood and that have attained to the adult age, man among the number—we should not conclude that the same thing is accomplished through the substance of the lungs, which, in the embryo, and at a time when the functions of these organs is in abeyance, Nature effects by direct passages, and which indeed she seems compelled to adopt through want of a passage by the lungs; or wherefore it should be better (for Nature always does that which is best) that she should close up the various open routes which she had formerly made use of in the embryo, and still uses in all other animals; not only opening up no new apparent channels for the passage of the blood therefore, but even entirely shutting up those which formerly existed in the embryos of those animals that have lungs. For while the lungs are yet in a state of inaction, Nature uses the two ventricles of the heart as if they formed but one for the transmission of the blood. The condition of the embryos of those animals which have lungs is the same as that of those animals which have no lungs.

Thus, by studying the structure of the animals who are nearer to and further from ourselves in their modes of life and in the construction of their bodies, we can prepare ourselves to understand the nature of the pulmonary circulation in ourselves, and of the systemic circulation also.

SYSTEMIC CIRCULATION

What remains to be said is of so novel and unheard of a character that I not only fear injury to myself from the envy of a few, but I tremble lest I have mankind at large for my enemies, so much do wont and custom that become as another nature, and doctrine once sown that hath struck deep root, and respect for antiquity, influence all men.

And, sooth to say, when I surveyed my mass of evidence, whether derived from vivisections and my previous reflections on them, or from the ventricles of the heart and the vessels that enter into and issue from them, the symmetry and size of these conduits—for Nature, doing nothing in vain, would never have given them so large a relative size without a purpose; or from the arrangement and intimate structure of the valves in particular and of the many other parts of the heart in general, with many things besides; and frequently and seriously bethought me and long revolved in my mind what might be the quantity of

405

blood which was transmitted, in how short a time its passage might be effected and the like; and not finding it possible that this could be supplied by the juices of the ingested aliment without the veins on the one hand becoming drained, and the arteries on the other getting ruptured through the excessive charge of blood, unless the blood should somehow find its way from the arteries into the veins, and so return to the right side of the heart; when I say, I surveyed all this evidence, I began to think whether there might not be a *motion as it were in a circle.*

Now this I afterwards found to be true; and I finally saw that the blood, forced by the action of the left ventricle into the arteries, was distributed to the body at large, and its several parts, in the same manner as it is sent through the lungs, impelled by the right ventricle into the pulmonary artery; and that it then passed through the veins and along the *vena cava,* and so round to the left ventricle in the manner already indicated; which motion we may be allowed to call circular, in the same way as Aristotle says that the air and the rain emulate the circular motion of the superior bodies. For the moist earth, warmed by the sun, evaporates; the vapors drawn upwards are condensed, and descending in the form of rain moisten the earth again. And by this arrangement are generations of living things produced; and in like manner, too, are tempests and meteors engendered by the circular motion of the sun.

And so in all likelihood does it come to pass in the body through the motion of the blood. The various parts are nourished, cherished, quickened by the warmer, more perfect, vaporous, spirituous, and, as I may say, alimentive blood; which, on the contrary, in contact with these parts becomes cooled, coagulated, and, so to speak, effete; whence it returns to its sovereign, the heart, as if to its source, or to the inmost home of the body, there to recover its state of excellence or perfection. Here it resumes its due fluidity, and receives an infusion of natural heat —powerful, fervid, a kind of treasury of life—and is impregnated with spirits and, it might be said, with balsam; and thence it is again dispersed. And all this depends upon the motion and action of the heart.

CONFIRMATIONS OF THE THEORY

Three points present themselves for confirmation, which, being established, I conceive that the truth I contend for will follow necessarily and appear as a thing obvious to all. The first point is this. The blood is incessantly transmitted by the action of the heart from the *vena cava* to the arteries in such quantity that it cannot be supplied from the ingesta, and in such wise that the whole mass must very quickly pass through the organ.

Let us assume the quantity of blood which the left ventricle of the heart will contain when distended to be, say, two ounces (in the dead body I have found it to contain upwards of two ounces); and let us suppose, as approaching the truth, that the fourth part of its charge is thrown into the artery at each contraction. Now, in the course of half an hour the heart will have made more than one thousand beats. Multiplying the number of drachms propelled by the number of pulses, we shall have one thousand half-ounces sent from this organ into the artery; a larger quantity than is contained in the whole body. This truth, indeed, presents itself obviously before us when we consider what happens in the dissection of living animals. The great artery need not be divided, but a very small branch only (as Galen even proves in regard to man), to have the whole of the blood in the body, as well that of the veins as of the arteries, drained away in the course of no long time—some half hour or less.

The second point is this. The blood, under the influence of the arterial pulse, enters, and is impelled in a continuous, equable, and incessant stream through every part and member of the body in much larger quantity than were sufficient for nutrition, or than the whole mass of fluids could supply.

I have here to cite certain experiments. Ligatures are either very tight or of middling tightness. A ligature I designate as tight, or perfect, when it is drawn so close about an extremity that no vessel can be felt pulsating beyond it. Such ligatures are employed in the removal of tumors; and in these cases, all afflux

407

of nutriment and heat being prevented by the ligature, we see the tumors dwindle and die, and finally drop off. Now let anyone make an experiment upon the arm of a man, either using such a fillet as is employed in bloodletting, or grasping the limb tightly with his hand; let a ligature be thrown about the extremity and drawn as tightly as can be borne. It will first be perceived that beyond the ligature the arteries do not pulsate, while above it the artery begins to rise higher at each diastole and to swell with a kind of tide as if it strove to break through and overcome the obstacle to its current.

Then let the ligature be brought to that state of middling tightness which is used in bleeding, and it will be seen that the hand and arm will instantly become deeply suffused and extended, and the veins show themselves tumid and knotted. Which is as much as to say that when the arteries pulsate the blood is flowing through them, but where they do not pulsate they cease from transmitting anything. The veins again being compressed, nothing can flow through them; the certain indication of which is that below the ligature they are much more tumid than above it.

Whence is this blood? It must needs arrive by the arteries. For that it cannot flow in by the veins appears from the fact that the blood cannot be forced towards the heart unless the ligature be removed. Further, when we see the veins below the ligature instantly swell up and become gorged when from extreme tightness it is somewhat relaxed, the arteries meanwhile continuing unaffected, this is an obvious indication that the blood passes from the arteries into the veins, and not from the veins into the arteries, and that there is either an anastomosis of the two orders of vessels, or pores in the flesh and solid parts generally that are permeable to the blood.

And now we understand wherefore in phlebotomy we apply our fillet above the part that is punctured, not below it. Did the flow come from above, not from below, the bandage in this case would not only be of no service, but would prove a positive hindrance. And further, if we calculate how many ounces flow through one arm or how many pass in twenty or thirty pulsations under the medium ligature, we shall perceive that a circulation is absolutely necessary, seeing that the quantity cannot be supplied immediately from the ingesta, and is vastly more than can be requisite for the mere nutrition of the parts.

And the third point to be confirmed is this. That the veins return this blood to the heart incessantly from all parts and members of the body.

This position will be made sufficiently clear from the valves which are found in the cavities of the veins themselves, from the uses of these, and from experiments cognizable by the senses. The celebrated Hieronymus Fabricius, of Aquapendente, first gave representations of the valves in the veins, which consist of raised or loose portions of the inner membranes of these vessels of extreme delicacy and a sigmoid, or semi-lunar shape. Their office is by no means explained when we are told that it is to hinder the blood, by its weight, from flowing into inferior parts; for the edges of the valves in the jugular veins hang downwards, and are so contrived that they prevent the blood from rising upwards.

The valves, in a word, do not invariably look upwards, but always towards the trunks of the veins—towards the seat of the heart. They are solely made and instituted lest, instead of advancing from the extreme to the central parts of the body, the blood should rather proceed along the veins from the center to the extremities; but the delicate valves, while they readily open in the right direction, entirely prevent all such contrary motion, being so situated and arranged that if anything escapes, or is less perfectly obstructed by the flaps of the one above, the fluid passing, as it were, by the chinks between the flaps, it is immediately received on the convexity of the one beneath, which is placed transversely with reference to the former, and so is effectually hindered from getting any farther. And this I have frequently experienced in my dissections of veins. If I attempted to pass a probe from the trunk of the veins into one of the smaller branches, whatever care I took I found it impossible to introduce it far any way by reason of the valves; whilst, on the contrary, it was most easy to push it along in the opposite direction, from without inwards, or from the branches towards the trunks and roots.

And now I may be allowed to give in brief my view of the circulation of the blood, and to propose it for general adoption.

THE CONCLUSION

Since all things, both argument and ocular demonstration, show that the blood passes through the lungs and heart by the action of the ventricles; and is sent for distribution to all parts of the body, where it makes its way into the veins and pores of the flesh; and then flows by the veins from the circumference on every side to the center, from the lesser to the greater veins; and is by them finally discharged into the *vena cava* and right auricle of the heart, and this in such a quantity or in such a flux and reflux, thither by the arteries, hither by the veins, as cannot possibly be supplied by the ingesta, and is much greater than can be required for mere purposes of nutrition; therefore, it is absolutely necessary to conclude that the blood in the animal body is impelled in a circle and is in a state of ceaseless motion; and that this is the act, or function, which the heart performs by means of its pulse, and that it is the sole and only end of the motion and contraction of the heart. For it would be very difficult to explain in any other way to what purpose all is constructed and arranged as we have seen it to be.

WERNER KARL HEISENBERG

(1901——)

One of the major nuclear physicists of our day, Heisenberg received his training at Munich and Göttingen, and while still in his twenties had already completed important work on the quantum theory and atomic structure, and evolved the principle of indeterminacy. In 1932, two years after the publication of his *Principien der Quantentheorie*, he was awarded the Nobel prize for physics. He was director of the Planck Institute, Berlin, during the war, and subsequently director of the Planck Institute, Göttingen.

THE TOOLS OF NUCLEAR PHYSICS

I. THE METHODS OF DETECTION AND OBSERVATION

THE following sections of this book will deal with the tools and methods available to the nuclear physicist both for generating and observing the phenomena discussed in the preceding lectures. These procedures call for immense quantities of energy, and the most powerful instruments known to technical science must be used to supply them. Yet, the material results achieved even with these vast stores of energy are extremely small. Consequently, for these studies it is indispensable to have extraordinarily sensitive instruments, for the phenomena which are to be studied take place in one individual atom or, at best, in a very few atoms—in structures which are inconceivably small according to ordinary conceptions.

We shall begin with the instruments of detection and study. The oldest method is the *scintillation method*. When a very fast particle—an alpha particle for instance—impinges on a zinc sulphide screen, a reaction occurs there which produces a weak

411

flash of lightning, a *scintillation*. It is therefore possible to observe the impact of each individual particle of sub-atomic order of magnitude, as the impact of bullets on a plastered wall can be observed, and we can also count the particles this way. It is, however, a poor policy to depend on the unaided eye, which is bound to grow tired little by little during the process of counting. This method is scarcely ever employed these days. It has been taken up recently by recording the weak flashes not with the eye but by electric amplification.

The *ionization chamber* supplies the fundamental principle on which most of the modern methods of observation are based. Let us attempt to describe this apparatus in a very rudimentary form: A gold-leaf electroscope consists of an earthed metal box containing an insulated metal rod with two gold leaves which spread apart when an electric charge reaches the rod. (Figure 1). An inverted metal hood, charged by a battery to about 100 volts relatively to the earth, is placed above the electroscope and insulated from the latter. When a charged particle—an alpha or beta particle, or even a gamma-ray photon—enters the space between the electroscope and the hood, it tears electrons off the air molecules. These electrons attach themselves to other molecules and form negative ions, while the molecules thus deprived of electrons remain behind as positive ions. As shown in Figure 1, such ions are created all along the track of the particle. If

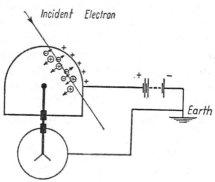

Fig. 1
The principle of the ionization chamber

the hood is positively charged, the positive ions stream to the rod of the electroscope, and the negative ions to the hood. Thus the electroscope becomes charged, and its leaves spread apart. Of course, the apparatus in this rudimentary form is not sensitive enough to detect individual particles. Indeed a far more delicate apparatus, such as a string electrometer, while able to detect a rather weak radiation, cannot register individual particles. The method of detecting small charges has been improved considerably in various ways and respects, according to the particular nuclear-physical purpose in view.

The first apparatus of general applicability (for the detection of individual particles) was *Geiger's point counter* (Figure 2). Fundamentally it is simply a vastly improved ionization chamber. In this apparatus, a metal rod is drawn to a fine point, and the chamber is given a fairly high voltage, with the result that a strong electric field is created in the vicinity of the point. When a charged particle or a gamma-ray photon flies past and liberates electrons there, these liberated electrons are so strongly accelerated by the intense field that they, in turn, are able to tear electrons off air molecules. These electrons, in turn, are able to do the same thing, and thus the number of electrons liberated

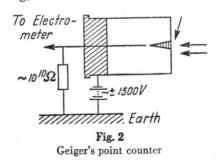

Fig. 2
Geiger's point counter

increases like an avalanche, and their number ceases to increase only where the field is weaker. But during this process, such enormous numbers of them are produced even by the effect of one single particle or photon that they can be detected by the means available to us.

Under certain conditions, when the voltage is not too high,

413

the multiplication of the number of electrons always increases by the same factor. Therefore we speak of a *proportional region* of the counter and also of a *proportional count.* The factor just mentioned may be of the order of magnitude of 1,000 or even higher. But if the voltage on the counter is increased beyond a certain limit, we pass beyond the proportional region. In that case, the electrons liberated by the particle start a genuine glow discharge, so that the result is a ten-millionfold or even a hundred-millionfold increase. In that case the discharge must be stopped, so that the counter may once again be ready for a new particle. In this *resolving region,* the amplification is independent of the number of the primarily liberated electrons. The amplification continues always until the very moment when a glow discharge begins to take place.

About fifteen years ago, this point counter was considerably improved by Geiger and Müller, and has become the counter which is still by far the most important observing apparatus

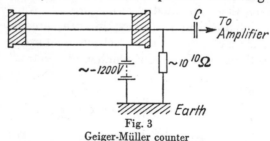

Fig. 3
Geiger-Müller counter

of the nuclear physicist. In principle it is very similar to the original Geiger point counter, except that instead of a point, a thin wire is placed in its center. (Figure 3.) Usually, it is filled not with air, but with a mixture of argon, under a pressure of 60 to 80 mm. of mercury, and alcohol vapor under a pressure of about 10 mm. of mercury. But there are also several variants. The wire is earthed through a very big resistance, and the outer cover has a potential difference of 1,000—1,200 volts relative to the earth.

The situation here is similar to that in the point counter. At a lesser voltage, a proportional amplification, by the factor

414

1,000, takes place. When the voltage is higher, a glow discharge begins; the device is now operating in the resolving region. From the moment of the inception of the glow discharge, the wire, which may be connected to a condenser, becomes strongly charged, as does also the condenser, since owing to the very high resistance, an appreciable time must elapse before the charge flows to the earth. Therefore, during this period, both the wire and the condenser, C, connected with the wire, are at a certain voltage which can be amplified by methods commonly employed in broadcasting technique. As is customarily done in most of these measurements, a counting device, similar to a telephone counter, can be attached, or the voltage can be transferred to a loudspeaker, and thus one can count and register every particle that passes through the counting tube.

The number of the ions produced by beta and gamma radiation is small. Therefore, big amplification is required, and it is customary to work in the resolving region. Furthermore, since the beta particles are not very penetrating, thin-walled tubes are used for counting beta particles; on the other hand, for gamma-ray photons thick-walled tubes are used, so as to keep other types of radiation out as much as possible. When dealing with alpha rays, which produce far more electrons, big amplification can be dispensed with, and it is possible to work in the proportional region. The advantage of this method is that, if the counting device is properly connected, it does not react to other types of radiation. The latter produce weak potential impulses only. A special amplifier, called the *thyratron,* which transmits impulses above a certain wavelength only, permits the weaker impulses to be eliminated, so that only those produced by alpha radiation are counted. This is important mainly because, in addition to the radiation under investigation, all other conceivable types of penetrating radiation are roaming through space. In the first place, electrons are liberated everywhere, even in the counter itself, by cosmic radiation which cannot be screened sufficiently by any known means. Secondly, no existing substance is entirely free from radioactive impurities, so that even the material of which the counter is made tends to release impulses occasionally. Such limited effects are simply just inevitable with these measuring devices. When counting alpha particles, the counting tube must be equipped with a thin window of mica, to enable the particles to enter, since they would not be able to pass through anything thicker.

Another very important instrument of the nuclear physicist is Wilson's *cloud chamber,* the operation of which was explained in our second lecture. The advantage of this device consists principally in the fact that it permits us to obtain a visual record of nuclear processes, thus showing simultaneously a great many of the details of the process.

Figure 4 shows a simple sketch of the cloud chamber. The upper section contains air, saturated with water vapor. It is

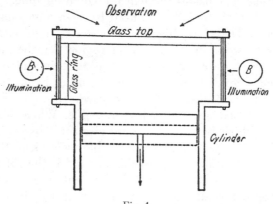

Fig. 4
Simplified sketch of Wilson's cloud chamber

covered with a glass plate at the top to permit observation; below there is a movable piston, covered by a damp layer of gelatine, so that the air above it is kept saturated with water vapor. The light necessary for observing the cloud tracks is admitted through an aperture in the side. The piston is suddenly moved downward, so that the air expands adiabatically and cools. The result is that the water vapor becomes supersaturated and the ionization produced by a particle entering the chamber causes condensation along its path—the well-known cloud tracks.

Many phenomena which one would like to observe in the cloud chamber, in particular the phenomena of cosmic radiation, are extremely rare, and the observer may have to wait for several hours before they eventually take place. The chances of encountering just such a reaction when observing an expansion, are very small indeed. Therefore, if we had to rely on chance alone for the eventual observation of such rare occurrences, studies of this kind would require a very great deal of time. However, this handicap is eliminated by skilfully connecting the cloud chamber with a counter which acts, so to speak, as a sentry at the gate of the cloud chamber. The counter is adjusted so that it will react to the specific phenomenon which it is desired to observe in the cloud chamber. If such a phenomenon actually takes place, the counter immediately effects the expansion through an amplifier. This takes place so fast that the ions formed in the chamber have not yet diffused away from the paths of the particles, and they are therefore visible as cloud tracks. This is the method which has yielded the most important data known concerning the nature of cosmic radiation, during the past decade.

Finally, the photographic plate, too, can be used as a detector of charged particles.

These methods enable us to count or detect every radiation with which an electric charge is associated (alpha and beta radiation, as well as all other types of nuclear debris which carry an electric charge), and also gamma-ray photons, so that the question of the detection of neutrons remains the only one still to be explained. Since neutrons carry no electric charge, they do not themselves produce ionization, and therefore we must rely on the observation of a secondary effect in order to detect their presence. The simplest device for this purpose is a boron counter. The inside of the wall of this counter is lined with boron or some boron compound, and the tube is used in the proportional region, so that it will count alpha particles only. As the neutrons strike the boron layer, they produce there the following nuclear reaction:

$$_5B^{10} + _0n^1 \rightarrow _3Li^7 + _2He^4$$

417

This reaction produces fast helium nuclei, i.e., artificial alpha particles—one alpha particle per neutron. Every neutron evoking a nuclear reaction causes the counter to react with an impulse, in which the lithium nucleus will also participate. Not every neutron, by any means, striking the counter causes a nuclear reaction; many of them traverse the tube without any effect whatsoever. Nevertheless, the counter registers a number of neutrons proportional to the actual total number of neutrons. The constant factor of proportionality being as yet unknown.

Another frequently employed method consists in placing a *tracer* at the point where neutrons are suspected to be present. A tracer is a substance—for example, a piece of silver foil—made artificially radioactive by a neutron-induced nuclear reaction. The following two reactions will then take place in the silver, in this order:

$$(1) \quad {}_{47}Ag^{107} + {}_{0}n^{1} \rightarrow {}_{47}Ag^{108}$$
$$(2) \quad {}_{47}Ag^{108} \rightarrow {}_{48}Cd^{108} + {}_{1}e^{0}$$

In other words, the silver isotope of mass number 107 first changes into another silver isotope, which has the mass number 108. The latter is unstable, has a half-life of 22 seconds, and emits an electron and thus changes into a nuclear isobar, the cadmium atom ${}_{48}Cd^{108}$. The ${}_{47}Ag^{108}$ atom must be unstable, because its nucleus has 61 neutrons and 47 protons, in other words, it is a 'doubly odd' nucleus.

Since, as we have already seen, slow neutrons are usually more prone to capture by a nucleus than are fast neutrons, a boron counter will register a greater number of slow neutrons than fast ones. If a counter of this type is brought into the vicinity of a source of fast neutrons, a loudspeaker can be used, which is capable of making the individual impulses audible at a certain average rate, say, one per second. As we already know, neutrons can be slowed down by being made to pass through a hydrogen-containing substance, such as paraffin. If the counter is surrounded by paraffin, the impulses will multiply very considerably and a crackling sound will be audible. Thus, contrary to the naïve assumption that the application of paraffin is bound to reduce the effect, a quite considerable intensification of the latter is the result. This method for the increase of the output in nuclear transmutations by means of slowing down neutrons, is employed very frequently in nuclear physics.

II. THE PROCEDURES FOR PRODUCING NUCLEAR TRANSMUTATION

As a general rule, particles very rich in energy are required to produce a nuclear transmutation. It is only when the transmutation is induced by neutrons that the energy content of the bombarding particle is frequently reduced deliberately as much as possible. But neutrons, to start with, must be produced by a nuclear reaction induced by fast particles, such, for instance, as the bombardment of beryllium by alpha particles.

Nature itself provides us with the most convenient source of energy-rich particles: The natural alpha emitters. To be sure, the radiation of even the most powerful radioactive preparations is always relatively weak, and sufficient for the transmutation of only a small number of atoms. On the other hand, in addition to the alpha particles, still other types of particles, namely, fast protons and deuterons, are needed in order to produce all possible sorts of nuclear transformation.

The most logical method of producing particles of high energy consists in a very strong acceleration of charged particles by a very high voltage, possibly 1,000,000 volts or more. Of course, direct-current voltage must be used. It is of course much more difficult to produce such a high direct-current voltage than it would be to generate an alternating-current voltage of the same magnitude.

The system known as the *Greinacher circuit* (Fig., 5) is one very frequently employed today in high-voltage generators. Two columns, with condensers, *C,* are connected by a system of valves, *V,* each of which permits a beam of electrons to pass through in one direction only, for instance, in the direction indicated by arrows in our diagram. The entire system is designed so that the point *d,* for instance, can be charged posi-

419

tively (but not negatively) relative to the earthed point a, without being discharged. Similarly, c can be charged positively relative to d, likewise f relative to c, e relative to f etc. Now, if an alternating-current voltage (usually between 200 and 300 kv or so) is applied, by means of a transformer, T, between the two columns, the points d, c, f, etc., become positively charged through the valves until the alternating-current voltage of, for instance, the point d never falls, throughout an entire period, below that of a, which may be taken as equal to 0; for otherwise a current would still flow through the valve V_1. Thus, if the peak voltage of the transformer is $+E$, the potential of the point d, in a stationary state, fluctuates between 0 and $2E$, and the point c has the constant potential $2E$. No current flows then through the valves. Similarly, we find that in a stationary state the points e, g, i have the constant potentials $4E$, $6E$ and $8E$,

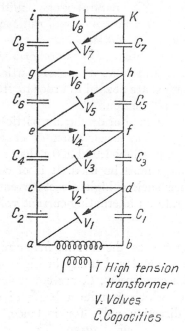

T High tension
transformer
V: Valves
C. Capacities

Fig. 5
Greinacher's form

while the potential of the points f, h, k fluctuates between $2E$ and $4E$, between $4E$ and $6E$, and between $6E$ and $8E$, respectively. When, for instance, a current enters at the point i, the potential there decreases slightly, and the valves let through a beam of electrons in the direction of the arrow; these electrons carry the charge along, so that the potential at the point i cannot drop very far below $8E$. Thus, proceeding by n steps, we obtain a $2n$-fold of the peak voltage of the transformer—for instance, when the initial voltage E is 200 kv and three steps are used, the direct-current voltage ultimately obtained is 1,200,-000 volts.

Figure 6 shows an exterior view of the high-voltage generator of the *Kaiser Wilhelm Institut für Physik* in Berlin-Dahlem. The slanting parts are the valves, and the globes correspond to the points c, e, f in Figure 5.

The high voltage thus produced must now be used to accelerate charged particles. These latter originate as canal rays in an ordinary discharge tube. They then enter the highly evacuated accelerator tube, with the high voltage drop between its ter-

Fig. 6
High-tension generator of the Kaiser Wilhelm Institute in Berlin-Dahlem

421

minals. At the end of the accelerator tube they hit the substance which is meant to be transmuted.

The disadvantage of this apparatus is that it is extremely expensive. Therefore efforts have been made to achieve the same results by simpler means. In this connection the *Van de Graaff high-voltage generator* deserves attention. It is based on the old, and now hardly ever used principle of the influence machine. This generator consists of a large hollow metal sphere (Figure 7), or cylinder, serving as conductor, with a pulley within it and another pulley underneath it. A wide closed belt of some insulating material, for instance, silk, travels on these two pulleys. Outside of the conductor, electric charge is sprayed on the belt by means of a rectifier and a corona comb, and the belt, carrying this charge, enters the conductor, in which the charge is removed by a second corona comb and is transferred to the conductor. The conductor can thus be charged up to any desired voltage. Certain limitations are imposed by the dimensions of the space in which the generator is installed, since when a certain voltage is reached (the magnitude of which depends on the dimensions of this space and of the conductor itself) a spark jumps across to the walls and discharges the conductor. In 1939,

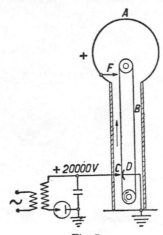

Fig. 7
Van de Graaff's high-tension generator

there existed as yet no operating generator capable of attaining more than 2,000,000 volts. Figure 8 shows the largest installation of this nature, which was under construction in the United States several years ago. It is designed to produce 5,000,000 volts, and therefore built in a very large space, an old airship hangar. It has two conductors, supposed to be charged with opposite charges, in order to produce the double voltage for the discharge tube.

By far the most efficient apparatus for the production of fast particles is the *cyclotron*, invented by the American Lawrence. It is based on a very interesting principle, that of very frequently repeated acceleration by the same, not very high, voltage; thus it has, among other advantages, the good feature that it dispenses with the high voltages which are so difficult both to obtain and to control. The essential part of the cyclotron is a

Fig. 8
Van de Graaff's high-tension apparatus

423

very large electromagnet which creates a powerful, very homogeneous and wide magnetic field of 10,000—15,000 oersteds between its pole pieces. The pole pieces are placed quite near to each other and the space between them is well evacuated. When a moving particle enters such a field, it describes a circular path, the radius of which is proportional to the velocity of the particle (Figure 9). Therefore, the velocity of the particles is proportional also to the circumference of the circle, and as a result, particles of the same kind, even though having different velocities, require exactly the same time to complete a full revolution. The space between the pole pieces houses two semicylindrical boxes, called *dees,* insulated from each other; between these dees, a potential difference of 30—100 kv is produced by a high-frequency generator. The result is a high-frequency alternating field in the small space between the dees. The frequency of this alternating field is regulated so as to correspond exactly to the period of the revolution of the particles in the magnetic field. The charged particles are made to enter the

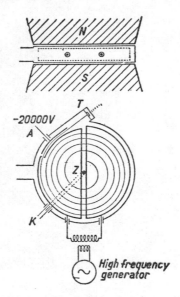

Fig. 9. Cyclotron

space between the pole pieces, near the centre (Z). There they come under the influence of the electric field; they attain a certain velocity and move in a semicircle in the space inside a dee where there is a magnetic field only. Proceeding in this manner, they reach the channel between the dees at the exact moment when the electric potential drop there is exactly equal, but opposite in direction, to what it was at the moment of their initial acceleration. They are now of course moving from one dee to the other in the opposite sense, which is that of the electric field, and in consequence are further accelerated. So the same process is repeated over and over again, and the velocity of the particles continues to mount. They move in an approximately spiral orbit, composed of semicircles, always further and further outward, until they are hurled through a window (T), designed so as to be penetrable by them, to perform their appointed task, the production of nuclear reactions.

The adjustment of such an apparatus calls for a great deal of technical skill. Moreover, the cyclotron is a machine of such dimensions as are seldom encountered in any other appliance used in physical research. Let us illustrate this by mentioning a few figures. The pole pieces of a cyclotron in use in the United States for some time are 95 cm. in diameter. The magnet of this cyclotron produces a magnetic field of 14,000 oersteds, and 60 tons of iron and 10 tons of copper went into its construction. The production of the magnetic field of 14,000 oersteds requires an input of 30 kilowatts. If this cyclotron is used to accelerate deuterons, these will emerge from it with an energy of 9 Mev.—in other words, as if they had passed through a potential drop of 9,000,000 volts. A current of only $0 \cdot 1$ milliampere flowing through this drop of potential would represent a power of nearly 1 kilowatt (900 watts to be precise). As each particle carries an elementary quantum of electricity, $1 \cdot 6 \times 10^{-19}$ coulombs, it is easy to compute that this current is the equivalent of roughly 6×10^{14} particles per second.

Figure 10 shows an exterior view of such a cyclotron. The windings of the magnet are visible; between the pole pieces of the magnet are the dees, in which the particles begin their

425

Fig. 10. Cyclotron

acceleration. The beam emerging from the cyclotron is also visible in the photograph.

Numerous cyclotrons are already in use in the United States. Several have been built in Europe, too. Germany has had one

Fig. 11. Magnet of the giant cyclotron

since 1944, in the *Kaiser Wilhelm Institut* in Heidelberg, destined primarily for medical use. The universal recognition of the importance of the cyclotron is demonstrated by the amount of money spent on it in the United States, where the rough structure of a giant cyclotron was completed in 1940; its size makes it look more like a battleship than a scientific instrument. Its pole pieces are $4 \cdot 7$ metres in diameter, and its magnet is $17 \cdot 8$ metres in length (Figure 11). Its foundation contains 1,200 tons of concrete; the magnet contains 3,700 tons of iron and 300 tons of copper, wound in a strip of $10 \cdot 2$ cm. in width and 6mm. in thickness. The frame of the magnet is made of 36 steel plates, each $5 \cdot 5$ mm. in thickness. The magnetic field intensity is 10,000 oersteds, and the frequency of the alternating electric field corresponds to a wavelength of 39 metres. Lawrence completed this cyclotron after the war, and it has enabled him to accelerate deuterons up to 100 Mev. and alpha particles up to 200 Mev.

In other words, the cyclotron is an extremely costly and also extremely complex apparatus. However, it is still by far the most useful nuclear-physical research instrument designed for the same purpose. In the United States it has made it possible to accomplish many nuclear reactions which would not have been feasible by any other means.

HERMANN LUDWIG FERDINAND VON HELMHOLTZ

(1821–1894)

Physicist, mathematician, anatomist and physiologist, Helmholtz was equally distinguished in numerous fields, and made a prodigious number of contributions to science, beginning with his statement of the principle of the conservation of energy (*Uber die Erhaltung der Kraft*, 1847). His researches in optics led to the invention of the ophthalmometer, the phakoscope and the ophthalmoscope, and a theory of color vision. In physiological acoustics he proposed a resonance theory of hearing that is still largely accepted, including an explanation of the perception of tone. He also measured the speed of nerve impulses. In physics he studied the vortex motion of fluids, advanced the theory of electricity, and was interested in epistemology, geometry, etc. Among his other works: *Sensations of Tone, Physiological Optics.*

ON THE CONSERVATION OF ENERGY

INTRODUCTION

THE PRINCIPAL contents of the present memoir show it to be addressed to physicists chiefly, and I have therefore thought it judicious to lay down its fundamental principles purely in the form of a physical premise, and independent of metaphysical considerations,—to develop the consequences of these principles, and to submit them to a comparison with what experience has established in the various branches of physics. The deduction of the propositions contained in the memoir may be based on either of two maxims; either on the maxim that it is not possible by any combination whatever of natural bodies to derive an unlimited amount of mechanical force, or on the assumption that all actions in nature can be ultimately referred to attractive or repulsive forces, the intensity of which depends solely upon the distances between the points by which the forces are exerted. That both these propositions are identical is shown at the commencement of the memoir itself. Meanwhile the important bearing which they have upon the final aim of the physical sciences may with propriety be made the subject of a special introduction.

The problem of the sciences just alluded to is, in the first place, to seek the laws by which the particular processes of nature may be referred to, and deduced from, general rules. These rules,— for example, the law of the reflexion and refraction of light, the law of Mariotte and Gay-Lussac regarding the volumes of gases, —are evidently nothing more than general ideas by which the various phaenomena which belong to them are connected together. The finding out of these is the office of the experimental portion of our science. The theoretic portion seeks, on the contrary, to evolve the unknown causes of the processes from the visible actions which they present; it seeks to comprehend these processes according to the laws of causality. We are justified, and indeed impelled in this proceeding, by the conviction that every change in nature *must* have a sufficient cause. The proximate causes to which we refer phaenomena may, in themselves, be either variable or invariable; in the former case the above conviction impels us to seek for causes to account for the change, and thus we proceed until we at length arrive at final causes which are unchangeable, and which therefore must, in all cases where the exterior conditions are the same, produce the same invariable effects. The final aim of the theoretic natural sciences is therefore to discover the ultimate and unchangeable causes of natural phaenomena. Whether all the processes of nature be actually referrible to such,—whether changes occur which are not subject to the laws of necessary causation, but spring from spontaneity or freedom, this is not the place to decide; it is at all events clear that the science whose object it is to comprehend nature must proceed from the assumption that it is comprehensible, and in accordance with this assumption investigate and

429

conclude until perhaps, she is at length admonished by irrefragable facts that there are limits beyond which she cannot proceed.

Science regards the phaenomena of the exterior world according to two processes of abstraction: in the first place it looks upon them as simple existences, without regard to their action upon our organs of sense or upon each other; in this aspect they are named *matter*. The existence of matter in itself is to us something tranquil and devoid of action: in it we distinguish merely the relations of space and of quantity (mass), which is assumed to be eternally unchangeable. To matter, thus regarded, we must not ascribe qualitative differences, for when we speak of different kinds of matter we refer to differences of action, that is, to differences in the forces of matter. Matter in itself can therefore partake of one change only,—a change which has reference to space, that is, motion. Natural objects are not, however, thus passive; in fact we come to a knowledge of their existence solely from their actions upon our organs of sense, and infer from these actions a something which acts. When, therefore, we wish to make actual application of our idea of matter, we can only do it by means of a second abstraction, and ascribe to it properties which in the first case were excluded from our idea, namely the capability of producing effects, or, in other words, of exerting force. It is evident that in the application of the ideas of matter and force to nature the two former should never be separated: a mass of pure matter would, as far as we and nature are concerned, be a nullity, inasmuch as no action could be wrought by it either upon our organs of sense or upon the remaining portion of nature. A pure force would be something which must have a basis, and yet which has no basis, for the basis we name matter. It would be just as erroneous to define matter as something which has an actual existence, and force as an idea which has no corresponding reality. Both, on the contrary, are abstractions from the actual formed in precisely similar ways. Matter is only discernible by its forces, and not by itself.

We have seen above that the problem before us is to refer back the phaenomena of nature to unchangeable final causes. This requirement may now be expressed by saying that for final

causes unchangeable forces must be found. Bodies with unchangeable forces have been named in science (chemistry) elements. Let us suppose the universe decomposed into elements
possessing unchangeable qualities, the only alteration possible
to such a system is an alteration of position, that is, motion;
hence, the forces can be only moving forces dependent in their
action upon conditions of space.

To speak more particularly: the phaenomena of nature are to
be referred back to motions of material particles possessing unchangeable moving forces, which are dependent upon conditions
of space alone.

Motion is the alteration of the conditions of space. Motion, as
a matter of experience, can only appear as a change in the
relative position of at least two material bodies. Force, which
originates motion, can only be conceived of as referring to the
relation of at least two material bodies towards each other; it is
therefore to be defined as the endeavour of two masses to alter
their relative position. But the force which two masses exert
upon each other must be resolved into those exerted by all their
particles upon each other; hence in mechanics we go back to
forces exerted by material points. The relation of one point to
another, as regards space, has reference solely to their distance
apart: a moving force, therefore, exerted by each upon the other,
can only act so as to cause an alteration of their distance, that
is, it must be either attractive or repulsive.

Finally, herefore, we discover the problem of physical natural
science to be, to refer natural phaenomena back to unchangeable
attractive and repulsive forces, whose intensity depends solely
upon distance. The solvability of this problem is the condition
of the complete comprehensibility of nature. In mechanical calculations this limitation of the idea of moving force has not yet
been assumed: a great number, however, of general principles
referring to the motion of compound systems of bodies are only
valid for the case that these bodies operate upon each other by
unchangeable attractive or repulsive forces; for example, the
principle of virtual velocities; the conservation of the motion
of the centre of gravity; the conservation of the principal plane

431

of rotation; of the moment of rotation of free systems, and the conservation of *vis viva*. In terrestrial matters application is made chiefly of the first and last of these principles, inasmuch as the others refer to systems which are supposed to be completely free; we shall however show that the first is only a special case of the last, which therefore must be regarded as the most general and important consequence of the deduction which we have made.

Theoretical natural science therefore, if she does not rest contented with half views of things, must bring her notions into harmony with the expressed requirements as to the nature of simple forces, and with the consequences which flow from them. Her vocation will be ended as soon as the reduction of natural phaenomena to simple forces is complete, and the proof given that this is the only reduction of which the phaenomena are capable.

I. THE PRINCIPLE OF THE CONSERVATION OF VIS VIVA

We will set out with the assumption that it is impossible, by any combination whatever of natural bodies, to produce force continually from nothing. By this proposition Carnot and Clapeyron have deduced theoretically a series of laws, part of which are proved by experiment and part not yet submitted to this test, regarding the latent and specific heats of various natural bodies. The object of the present memoir is to carry the same principle, in the same manner, through all branches of physics; partly for the purpose of showing its applicability in all those cases where the laws of the phaenomena have been sufficiently investigated, partly, supported by the manifold analogies of the known cases, to draw further conclusions regarding laws which are as yet but imperfectly known, and thus to indicate the course which the experimenter must pursue.

The principle mentioned can be represented in the following manner:—Let us imagine a system of natural bodies occupying certain relative positions towards each other, operated upon by forces mutually exerted among themselves, and caused to move until another definite position is attained; we can regard the velocities thus acquired as a certain mechanical work and translate them into such. If now we wish the same forces to act a second time, so as to produce again the same quantity of work, we must, in some way, by means of other forces placed at our disposal, bring the bodies back to their original position, and in effecting this a certain quantity of the latter forces will be consumed. In this case our principle requires that the quantity of work gained by the passage of the system from the first position to the second, and the quantity lost by the passage of the system from the second position back again to the first, are always equal, it matters not in what way or at what velocity the change has been effected. For were the quantity of work greater in one way than another, we might use the former for the production of work and the latter to carry the bodies back to their primitive positions, and in this way procure an indefinite amount of mechanical force. We should thus have built a *perpetuum mobile* which could not only impart motion to itself, but also to exterior bodies.

If we inquire after the mathematical expression of this principle, we shall find it in the known law of the conservation of *vis viva*. The quantity of work which is produced and consumed may, as is known, be expressed by a weight m, which is raised to a certain height h; it is then mgh, where g represents the force of gravity. To rise perpendicularly to the height h, the body m requires the velocity $v = \sqrt{2gh}$, and attains the same by falling through the same height. Hence we have $\frac{1}{2}mv^2 = mgh$; and hence we can set the half of the product mv^2, which is known in mechanics under the name of the *vis viva* of the body m, in the place of the quantity of work. For the sake of better agreement with the customary manner of measuring the intensity of force, I propose calling the quantity $\frac{1}{2}mv^2$ the quantity of *vis viva*, by which it is rendered identical with the quantity of work. For the applications of the doctrine of *vis viva* which have been hitherto made this alteration is of no importance, but we shall derive much advantage from it in the following. The principle

433

of the conservation of *vis viva,* as is known, declares that when any number whatever of material points are set in motion, solely by such forces as they exert upon each other, or as are directed against fixed centres, the total sum of the *vires vivae,* at all times when the points occupy the same relative position, is the same, whatever may have been their paths or their velocities during the intervening times. Let us suppose the *vires vivae* applied to raise the parts of the system or their equivalent masses to a certain height, it follows from what has just been shown, that the quantities of work, which are represented in a similar manner, must also be equal under the conditions mentioned. This principle however is not applicable to all possible kinds of forces; in mechanics it is generally derived from the principle of virtual velocities, and the latter can only be proved in the case of material points which act in the direction of the lines which unite them, and the intensity of which depends only upon the distance. In mechanics such forces are generally named central forces. Hence, conversely, it follows that in all actions of natural bodies upon each other, where the above principle is capable of general application, even to the ultimate particles of these bodies, such central forces must be regarded as the simplest fundamental ones. . . .

CONCLUSIONS

1. Whenever natural bodies act upon each other by attractive or repulsive forces, which are independent of time and velocity, the sum of their *vires vivae* and tensions must be constant; the maximum quantity of work which can be obtained is therefore a limited quantity.

2. If, on the contrary, natural bodies are possessed of forces which depend upon time and velocity, or which act in other directions than the lines which unite each two separate material points, for example, rotatory forces, then combinations of such bodies would be possible in which force might be either lost or gained *ad infinitum.*

3. In the case of the equilibrium of a system of bodies under

the operation of central forces, the exterior and the interior forces must, each system for itself, be in equilibrium, if we suppose that the bodies of the system cannot be displaced, the whole system only being moveable in regard to bodies which lie without it. A rigid system of such bodies can therefore never be set in motion by the action of its interior forces, but only by the operation of exterior forces. If, however, other than central forces had an existence, rigid combinations of natural bodies might be formed which could move of themselves without needing any relation whatever to other bodies. . . .

THERMO-ELECTRIC CURRENTS

In these currents we must seek the origin of force in the actions discovered by Peltier at the place of contact, by which a current opposed to the given one is developed. Let us suppose the case of a constant hydro-electric current into the conducting wire of which a piece of another metal is soldered, the temperatures of the places of union being $t_,$ and $t_{,,,}$ the electric current will then during the element of time dt, generate in the entire conduction the heat $I^2 R dt$; besides this, at one of the points where the metals are soldered together, the quantity $q_, dt$ will be developed, and at the other the quantity $q_{,,} dt$ absorbed. Let the electromotive force of the entire circuit be A, hence $A I dt$ the heat to be generated chemically, it then follows from the law of the conservation of force.

$$AL = I^2 R + q_, - q_{,,} \ldots \ldots \ldots \ldots (1)$$

Let the electromotive force of the thermo-circuit be B_t when one of the soldered junctions possesses the temperature t, and the other any constant temperature whatever, for example $0°$; then, for the entire circuit, we have

$$I = \frac{A - B_{t,} + B_{t_{,,}}}{R} \ldots \ldots \ldots \ldots (2)$$

435

When $t_, = t_{,,}$, we have

$$I = \frac{A}{R},$$

This set in equation (1) gives

$$q_, = q_{,,},$$

that is, when the temperatures of the places of soldering are both the same and the intensity of the current constant, the heat developed and that absorbed must be equal, independently of the cross section. If we assumed that the process is the same in every point of the cross section, it would follow that the heat developed in equal spaces of different cross sections is proportional to the density of the current, and from this again, that the quantities generated by different currents in the whole of the transverse sections are directly proportional to the intensity of the current.

When the solderings are of different temperatures, it follows from equations (1) and (2), that

$$(B_{t_,} - B_{t_{,,}}) \, I = q_, - q_{,,},$$

that is to say, with the same intensity of current both the force which generates and which absorbs the heat increases with the temperature, in the same proportion as the electromotive force.

I am thus far unacquainted with any quantitative experiments with which either of the inferences might be compared.

THE FORCE-EQUIVALENT OF ELECTRO-MAGNETISM

When a magnet moves under the influence of a current, the *vis viva* gained thereby must be furnished by the tensions consumed in the current. During the portion of time dt, according to the notation before made use of, these are, $A I dt$ in units of heat, or $a A I dt$ in mechanical units, where a is the mechanical equivalent of the unit of heat. The *vis viva* generated in the path of the current is $a I^2 R dt$, that gained by the magnet $I \frac{dV}{dt} dt$, where V represents its potential towards the conductor through which the unit of current passes. Hence

$$aAIdt = aI^2Rdt + I\frac{dV}{dt}dt$$

consequently

$$I = \frac{A\frac{1}{a}\cdot\frac{dV}{dt}}{R}.$$

We can distinguish the quantity $\frac{1}{a}\frac{dV}{dt}$ as a new electromotive force, that of the induced current. It always acts against that which moves the magnet in the direction which it follows, or which would increase its velocity. As this force is independent of the intensity of the current, it must remain the same, when before the motion of the magnet no current existed.

If the intensity be changeable, the whole induced current during a certain time is

$$\int Idt = -\frac{1}{aR}\int\frac{dV}{dt}dt = \frac{I}{a}\frac{V_,-V_{,,}}{R},$$

where $V_,$ denotes the potential at the beginning, and $V_{,,}$ at the end of the motion. If the magnet comes from a very great distance, we have

$$\int Idt = -\frac{\frac{1}{a}-V_{,,}}{R}$$

independent of the route or the velocity of the magnet.

We can express the law thus:—The entire electromotive force of the induced current, generated by a change of position of a

437

magnet relative to a closed conductor, is equal to the change which thereby takes place in the potential of the magnet towards the conductor, when the latter is traversed by the current —1/a. The unit of the electromotive force is here regarded as that by which the arbitrary unit of current is generated in the unit of resistance, the latter being that in which the above unit of current develops the unit of heat in the unit of time.

THE SPEED OF THE NERVE IMPULSE

The duration of the twitch of an animal muscle is ordinarily only a small fraction of a second, except for a longer lasting, weak after-effect. Since our senses are not capable of immediate perception of single time elements of such short duration, we must use more artificial methods to observe and measure them. Two of these especially are to be considered here. In the first, the events whose time intervals one wishes to find out are recorded by a suitable mechanism on a surface which moves with even speed. The time intervals appear on it as proportional space differences and can be measured by the latter. Ludwig has already used this method for physiological purposes in order to show the fluctuations of blood pressure in the arteries and of atmospheric pressure in the pleural cavity. The other, essentially different, method of measuring time is the one proposed by Pouillet. The duration is here measured by the effect which a force of known intensity has produced during this interval. Pouillet has a galvanic current act on a resting magnet. The beginning and end of the current correspond exactly to the beginning and end of the interval to be measured; the magnitude of arc of the excursions which the magnet performs is, then, proportional to the duration to be measured. . . .

The foundation of Pouillet's method for measuring small time intervals is as follows: the time during which a galvanic current of known intensity from a coil has affected a magnet can be calculated exactly from its changed movement. Up to the present, one cannot anticipate a lower limit of time divisions measurable in this way, since one can increase at will the intensity of the acting current and the magnitude of its effect on the magnet by increasing the electromotor cells and the windings on the coil. But a limitation is imposed in the application of this procedure; namely, one must know how to cause the beginning and end of the supposed current, which from now on we shall call the time-measuring one, to coincide exactly with the beginning and end of the mechanical process the duration of which is to be measured. In the experiments to be described here the time-measuring current started at the moment when an instantaneous electric shock passed through the muscle or its nerve, and stopped when the circuit within which it circulated was interrupted by the contraction of the muscle. At the same time one could determine exactly the tension which the muscle had to develop in order to be able to separate the conductive metals from each other. The duration of the time-measuring current to be calculated is therefore identical with the time which elapses between the stimulation of the muscle, or of its nerve, and the moment at which its tension reaches a certain magnitude. . . .

In making measurements of the time which elapses between the stimulation of the nerve and the lifting of the overweight by the muscle, one finds that the time depends upon the point on the nerve at which one applies the electrical shock; the time is the longer, the longer the portion of the nerve between the stimulated point and the muscle. The experiment . . . can be repeated any number of times, by placing two of the four conducting wires, about two to three lines apart, on the nerve close to where it enters the muscle, and the two others, just as far apart, on the pelvic part of the nerve. I found it to be of advantage to move this second place not quite to the transected end of the sciatic plexus, but approximately to the place where the strands of this plexus combine to form the trunk of the sciatic nerve, because the extreme cut ends become inefficient relatively fast. Depending on whether one connects the first or the second pair of the leads with the induction coil, either the nerve point closer to the muscle, or the more distant one, will be affected by the current. Comparative measurements, which incidentally are carried out like those previously discussed, prove that the deflec-

439

tions of the magnet by the time-measuring current are on the average from 5—7 dial parts larger when the more distant point of the nerve is stimulated than the one closer to the muscle.

Apparently this difference cannot be caused by any of the formerly discussed sources of error, which are based on the mechanical and electrical occurrences in our measuring procedure, because all of these affect the experiments involving stimulation of the distant or near nerve point equally. Rather occurrences inside of the nerve itself must be the cause. . . .

We must . . . make sure that the intensity of stimulation is the same at both places. If this is so, then experiments show that whatever places on the nerve are stimulated, corresponding energy stages will follow each other at like time intervals, but the time between each of these energy stages (and the stimulation) is larger by a definite amount, as the stimulated spot is further away from the muscle. Therefore, if we express by curves the rise and fall of energy for two different nerve points, then the curve corresponding to the stimulation of the more distant point is congruent with the other, but between its starting point and the point corresponding to the moment of stimulation, here lies a larger part of the abscissa. From the nature of the time lapse which the muscle exhibits following stimulation we can draw conclusions concerning the course of the corresponding processes in the nerve which are mostly still unknown. . . . Now, since duration and strength of the stimulating electric current are exactly the same in both stimulated places the retardation of the effect must be due to the fact that a certain time elapses until it has spread from the more distant spot to the muscle. These experiments, therefore, enable us to find out the rate of propagation of the impulse in the motor nerves of the frog, provided that we understand by impulse those processes in the nerve, which develop in it as a result of an external *stimulus*.

As long as the physiologists thought that nerve action could be ascribed to the propagation of an imponderable or psychic principle, it would have appeared incredible that the speed of this current should be measurable within the short distances of the animal body. At present we know from the investigations on the electromotor properties of nerves by Du Bois-Reymond, that the activity by which the conduction of an impulse is mediated is at least closely associated with, perhaps even essentially caused by, a changed arrangement of their material molecules. Accordingly, the conduction in the nerve would belong to the group of propagated molecular effects of ponderable bodies, to which, *e.g.*, belongs sound conduction in air and in elastic substances or the discharge of a tube filled with an explosive mixture. Under these circumstances, it is no longer surprising to see that the rate of conduction is not only measurable but as we shall see, even very moderate. Incidentally, the impossibility of observing time intervals of this kind in the daily perceptions of our own body, or in physiological experiments on muscle twitches must not surprise us, since the intervals which we may be sure that we observe between sensations involving the nerve fibers of our different sense organs are not much smaller than a second. One will recall that the most experienced astronomers differ by a full second in the comparative observation of visual and acoustic perceptions. . . .

From the greater number of my experimental series, all of which gave the same result, with more or less exactness, I shall present herewith those which seem to be the most reliable on account of their extent or the correspondence of their single observations. For stimulation, we have invariably used currents which brought about maximum excitation. This was controlled by simultaneously observed elevations expressed in millimeters.

The series are arranged according to different plans. In some of them, all observations are made with the same or only two different overweights, in order to get as extensive figures as possible for the calculation of the essential time interval. For these I have calculated the means of the time-lapse between stimulation and muscle reaction for both points on the nerve, the difference between these means which corresponds to the rate of conduction in the nerve, and finally, in order to evaluate their exactness, the probable errors of all these values according to the rules of probability.

In other experimental series, the overweights have been ex-

441

changed as often as possible in order to prove that the delay is the same, for different degrees of muscle energy, provided one stimulates from the more distant point on the nerve, but the form of the energy increase is not alerted. Obviously, the few experiments made with each overweight cannot furnish such exact values for differences due to nerve conduction as would longer series; therefore the individual means for these differences often vary considerably. However, the larger and smaller values are distributed entirely irregularly, and those for different over-weights do not differ more from each other than those for the same overweight in successive observations. It follows that the magnitude of the difference does not depend noticeably on the amount of overweight, as is so definitely the case when the deflections of the magnet increase by decrease of the stimulation.

Finally, the rate of propagation of the nerve impulse was calculated after each experimental series. To do this, one must know the length of the traversed nerve piece, that is, the distance between the terminals at the two stimulated nerve places closest to the muscle. Unfortunately this length is very uncertain on account of the great extensibility of the nerve. If the nerve is not stretched, its fibers are bent in an undulating fashion; in order to measure its length I have always stretched it to such an extent that the transverse satin-like striations of its surface disappeared, on the assumption that the fibers would then run approximately straight. But a few millimeters are then always left to one's own discretion. Incidentally, it would not yet pay to devise an improved measuring technique since the inaccuracies of the time measurements are relatively much greater than those of the length measurements. Therefore it is not surprising that the established values of the rate of conduction still differ considerably from each other. . . .

EXPERIMENTAL SERIES X

Done on December 29 with the muscles of a frog kept for four months. Through the more distant point on the nerve is sent a stronger current, generated with the coils touching each other, and through the nearer point a weaker current with a distance between the coils of 2½ cm. After each two observations the muscle is reset.

A. Right muscle—nerve length 40 mm., deflection before 116.09, after 112.45, mean 114.27.

MEASUREMENTS OF THE TIME-LAPSE OF THE TWITCH OF ANIMAL* MUSCLES AND OF THE RATE OF PROPAGATION OF THE NERVE IMPULSE

| Number | Overweight | Lift | Difference of deflection on stimulation of | |
			further nervepoint	nearer
1	20 gr.	1.19	100.09	
2		1.22	96.15	
3		1.22		93.92
4		1.15		97.19
5		1.10	97.70	
6		1.10	104.33	
7		1.17		93.87
8		1.12		92.27
9		1.15	106.43	
10		1.15	101.74	
11		1.12		98.00
12		1.17		98.60
13		1.12	96.81	
14		1.10	103.99	

Mean	100.98	95.64
Probable error of the mean	±0.86	±0.66
The same of the single observation	±2.42	±1.61
Duration of the time in sec. from stimulation to lifting	0.02437	0.02307
Probable error of the same	±0.00020	±0.00016
Time difference due to propagation	0.00130 ± 0.00027	
Rate of propagation	30.8 ± 6.4†	

* *I.e.*, skeletal.
† *I.e.*, meters/sec.

The values found for the rate of propagation between 11 and 21° C. are therefore:

a) from series IX, X, and XI.

$$24.6 \pm 2.0$$
$$30.8 \pm 6.4$$
$$32.0 \pm 9.7$$
$$31.4 \pm 7.1$$
$$38.4 \pm 10.6$$

From these one finds by the method of least squares as most probable mean: 26.4 [meters/sec.].

b) from series XII, XIII, and XIV.

$$29.1$$
$$25.1$$
$$26.9$$
$$\overline{}$$

Mean 27.0

Finally, I summarize the results of the present investigations: I) If animal (skeletal) muscle, or its nerve, is stimulated by a momentary electric shock, a short time passes during which its elastic tension does not change noticeably; then it gradually rises to a maximum, and just as gradually falls again. The contraction of animal muscle differs from that which occurs in organic (visceral), nonrhythmically reaction muscle, after a relatively short stimulation, only in that its single phases pass much more rapidly.

If two different points of a motor nerve are stimulated by a momentary stimulus and if the magnitude of the stimulations is the same for both, then the time-lapse of the subsequent muscle twitch, is also the same; however, if the more distant point on the nerve has been stimulated, all of the muscle twitch stages occur later by an equal amount. From this, we conclude that the conduction of the nerve impulse to the muscle requires a measurable time. . . .

HERMANN LUDWIG FERDINAND VON HELMHOLTZ

In the first series of my investigations on the time relations of muscle and nerve activity I have proved by the electromagnetic method of measuring time, that the mechanical reactions of the muscle, following a nerve stimulation, set in later if the excitation has to pass a longer portion of the nerve before getting to the muscle. The method mentioned offers, in fact, the best guarantee where safe execution of exact measurements is desired, but it has the great disadvantage of yielding the said result only after extensive and tedious series of experiments, which on account of their long duration require an especially favorable condition of the frog preparation. The other graphic method of measuring time, the application of which has been mentioned before, is essentially one in which the muscle during twitching records the magnitudes of its contractions on a moving surface; this promised a much simpler and easier demonstration of the rate of propagation in the nerves, and, since this seemed to me sufficiently important, I undertook to follow up the matter in this way, and I was perfectly successful.

The procedure of the experiments, I have already briefly indicated in the previous paper. A pen which is raised by the twitching muscle draws a curve on a surface moving with uniform speed, the vertical coordinates of the curve are proportionate to the contradictions of the muscle, the horizontal ones proportionate to the time. As a starting point of this curve we shall fix that point which corresponds to the moment of stimulation of the muscle or its nerve. Now, if we arrange for two curves to be drawn in succession, and if we take care that at the moment of stimulation the pen occupies always exactly the same point on the surface, then both curves will have the same starting point, and from the congruence or noncongruence of their individual parts one can observe whether or not the different stages of the mechanical muscle response have occurred, in both instances, at the same or a later time after stimulation. . . .

If the animal parts are rather vigorous and fresh, then the shapes of the double curve are all alike, at whatever nerve spot one may start the stimulation. Then, each drawing consists of two curves of congruent shape which are shifted in a horizontal

445

direction with respect to each other by a certain amount as in Fig. 1, such that the curve which has been drawn upon stimulation of the nearer nerve spot, is also nearer to the starting point of stimulation. The curve *adefg* corresponds to the stimulation of the nearer nerve point, *aδεφg* to the one of the more distant nerve point . . .

When we look at the double curve Fig. 1 it is evident that both of the muscle twitches recorded have been entirely identical as to strength, duration, and course of the different stages of contraction except that the one has started later after stimula-

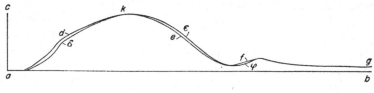

Fig. 1

tion than the other one. Now, since the arrangement of the apparatus and the mechanical forces of the muscle have been exactly the same, the delay of the reaction in one instance can only have been derived from the longer time of propagation in the nerve. . . .

It is the great advantage of the described method that one can recognize immediately in each single drawing from the shape of the two curves whether the muscle has worked uniformly in both instances, whereas this fact could be deduced by the electromagnetic method of time measurement only from a long series of single experiments. As to the absolute value of the rate of propagation, the horizontal distances of the two curves cannot be measured with great accuracy; nevertheless, the values of that rate are about the same as in the former method. For instance, the horizontal distance in Fig. 1 is about 1 mm, the circumference of the cylinder corresponding to 1/6 sec, is 85.7 mm, therefore the length of the abscissae is 514.2 mm per second. One mm corresponds therefore to 1/514.2 sec. The length of

446

the nerve involved in propagation was 53 mm, from which follows a rate of propagation of 27.25 m per sec. The most probable value from previous experiments was 26.4 m.

SENSATIONS OF TONE

Physicists, then, having in their mind such curvilinear forms, representing the law of motion of sounding bodies, speak briefly of the *form of vibration* of a sounding body, and assert that *the quality of tone depends on the form of vibration*. This assertion, which has hitherto been simply on the fact of our knowing that the quality of the tone could not possibly depend on the periodic time of a vibration, or on its amplitude, will be strictly examined hereafter. It will be shewn to be in so far correct that every different quality of tone requires a different form of vibration, but on the other hand it will also appear that different forms of vibration may correspond to the same quality of tone.

On exactly and carefully examining the effect produced on the ear by different forms of vibration we meet with a strange and unexpected phenomenon, long known indeed to individual musicians and physicists, but commonly regarded as a mere curiosity, its generality and its great significance for all matters relating to musical tones not having been recognized. The ear when its attention has been properly directed to the effect of the vibrations which strike it, does not hear merely that one musical tone whose pitch is determined by the period of vibrations in the manner already explained, but in addition to this it becomes aware of a whole series of higher musical tones, which we will call the *harmonic upper partial tones*, and sometimes simply the *upper partials* of the whole musical tone or note, in contradistinction to the *fundamental* or *prime partial tone* or simply the *prime*, as it may be called, which is the lowest and generally the loudest of all the partial tones, and by the pitch of which we judge of the pitch of the whole *compound musical tone* itself. The series of these upper partial tones is precisely

447

the same for all compound musical tones which correspond to a uniformly periodical motion of the air. It is as follows:—

The first upper partial tone (or second partial tone) is the upper Octave of the prime tone, and makes double the number of vibrations in the same time. If we call the prime *C*, this upper Octave will be *c*.

The second upper partial tone (or third partial tone) is the Fifth of this Octave, or *g*, making three times as many vibrations in the same time as the prime.

The third upper partial tone (or fourth partial tone) is the second higher Octave, or *c'*, making four times as many vibrations as the prime in the same time.

The fourth upper partial tone (or fifth partial tone) is the major third of this second higher Octave, or *e'*, with five times as many vibrations as the prime in the same time.

The fifth upper partial tone (or sixth partial tone) is the Fifth of the second higher Octave, or *g'*, making six times as many vibrations as the prime in the same time.

And thus they go on, becoming continually fainter, to tones making 7, 8, 9, etc., times as many vibrations in the same time, as the prime tone. . . .

The whole sensation excited in the ear by a periodic vibration of the air we have called a *musical tone*. We now find that this is *compound*, containing a series of different tones, which we distinguish as the *constituents* or *partial tones* of the *compound*. The first of these constituents is the *prime partial tone* of the compound, and the rest its *harmonic upper partial tones*. The *number* which shews the *order* of any partial tone in the series shews how many times its vibrational number exceeds that of the prime tone. Thus, the second partial tone makes twice as many, the third, three times as many vibrations in the same time as the prime tone, and so on.

JOHN FREDERICK WILLIAM HERSCHEL

(1792–1871)

Son of Sir William Herschel, discoverer of the planet Uranus, Sir John Herschel carried on his father's work in astronomy, discovering some 525 nebulae and clusters. He led a four-year expedition to Cape Town for the purpose of charting the southern heavens, added to our knowledge of the Milky Way, and made researches in light, sound and celestial physics. As a chemist he invented sensitized paper for use in photography, was a pioneer in celestial photography and the first to use the terms "negative" and "positive" for photographic images. Works: *Outlines of Astronomy* (1849) and many contributions to the Encyclopaedia Britannica.

OUTLINES OF ASTRONOMY

THE WONDERS OF THE MILKY WAY

THERE IS no science which draws more largely than does astronomy on that intellectual liberality which is ready to adopt whatever is demonstrated or concede whatever is rendered highly probable, however new and uncommon the points of view may be in which objects the most familiar may thereby become placed. Almost all its conclusions stand in open and striking contradiction with those of superficial and vulgar observation, and with what appears to everyone the most positive evidence of his senses.

There is hardly anything which sets in a stronger light the inherent power of truth over the mind of man, when opposed by no motives of interest or passion, than the perfect readiness with which all its conclusions are assented to as soon as their evidence is clearly apprehended, and the tenacious hold they acquire over our belief when once admitted.

449

If the comparison of the apparent magnitude of the stars with their number leads to no immediately obvious conclusion, it is otherwise when we view them in connection with their local distribution over the heavens. If indeed we confine ourselves to the three or four brightest classes we shall find them distributed with a considerable approach to impartiality over the sphere; a marked preference, however, being observable, especially in the southern hemisphere, to a zone or belt passing through *epsilon* Orionis and *alpha* Crucis. But if we take in the whole amount visible to the naked eye we shall perceive a great increase of numbers as we approach the borders of the Milky Way. And when we come to telescopic magnitudes we find them crowded beyond imagination along the extent of that circle and of the branches which it sends off from it; so that, in fact, its whole light is composed of nothing but stars of every magnitude from such as are visible to the naked eye down to the smallest points of light perceptible with the best telescopes.

These phenomena agree with the supposition that the stars of our firmament, instead of being scattered indifferently in all directions through space, form a stratum of which the thickness is small in comparison with its length and breadth; and in which the earth occupies a place somewhere about the middle of its thickness and near the point where it subdivides into two principal laminæ inclined at a small angle to each other. For it is certain that to an eye so situated the apparent density of the stars, supposing them pretty equally scattered through the space they occupy, would be least in the direction of the visual ray perpendicular to the lamina, and greatest in that of its breadth; increasing rapidly in passing from one to the other direction, just as we see a slight haze in the atmosphere thickening into a decided fog-bank near the horizon by the rapid increase of the mere length of the visual ray.

Such is the view of the construction of the starry firmament taken by Sir William Herschel, whose powerful telescopes first effected a complete analysis of this wonderful zone, and demonstrated the fact of its entirely consisting of stars.

So crowded are they in some parts of it that by counting the stars in a single field of his telescope he was led to conclude that 50,000 had passed under his review in a zone two degrees in breadth during a single hour's observation. The immense distances at which the remoter regions must be situated will sufficiently account for the vast predominance of small magnitudes which are observed in it.

The process of gauging the heavens was devised by Sir William Herschel for this purpose. It consisted simply in counting the stars of all magnitudes which occur in single fields of view, of fifteen minutes in diameter, visible through a reflecting telescope of 18 inches aperture, and 20 feet focal length, with a magnifying power of 180 degrees, the points of observation being very numerous and taken indiscriminately in every part of the surface of the sphere visible in our latitudes.

On a comparison of many hundred such "gauges," or local enumerations, it appears that the density of starlight (or the number of stars existing on an everage of several such enumerations in any one immediate neighborhood) is least in the pole of the Galactic circle [*i.e.*, the great circle to which the course of the Milky Way most nearly conforms: *gala*=milk], and increases on all sides down to the Milky Way itself, where it attains its maximum. The progressive rate of increase in proceeding from the pole is at first slow, but becomes more and more rapid as we approach the plane of that circle, according to a law from which it appears that the mean density of the stars in the galactic circle exceeds, in a ratio of very nearly 30 to 1, that in its pole, and in a proportion of more than 4 to 1 that in a direction 15 degrees inclined to its plane.

As we ascend from the galactic plane we perceive that the density decreases with great rapidity. So far we can perceive no flaw in this reasoning if only it be granted (1) that the level planes are continuous and of equal density throughout; and (2) that an absolute and definite limit is set to telescopic vision, beyond which, if stars exist, they elude our sight, and are to us as if they existed not. It would appear that, with an almost exactly similar law of apparent density in the two hemispheres, the southern were somewhat richer in stars than the northern, which may arise from our situation not being precisely in the middle of its thickness, but somewhat nearer to its northern surface.

PENETRATING INFINITE SPACE

When examined with powerful telescopes, the constitution of this wonderful zone is found to be no less various than its aspect to the naked eye is irregular. In some regions the stars of which it is composed are scattered with remarkable uniformity over immense tracts, while in others the irregularity of their distribution is quite as striking, exhibiting a rapid succession of closely clustering rich patches separated by comparatively poor intervals, and indeed in some instances absolutely dark and *completely* void of any star even of the smallest telescopic magnitude. In some places not more than 40 or 50 stars on an average occur in a "gauge" field of 15 minutes, while in others a similar average gives a result of 400 or 500.

Nor is less variety observable in the character of its different regions in respect of the magnitude of the stars they exhibit, and the proportional numbers of the larger and smaller magnitudes associated together, than in respect of their aggregate numbers. In some, for instance, extremely minute stars, though never altogether wanting, occur in numbers so moderate as to lead us irresistibly to the conclusion that in these regions we are *fairly through* the starry stratum, since it is impossible otherwise (supposing their light not intercepted) that the numbers of the smaller magnitudes should not go on increasing *ad infinitum*. In

In such cases, moreover, the ground of the heavens, as seen between the stars, is for the most part perfectly dark, which again would not be the case if innumerable multitudes of stars, too minute to be individually discernible, existed beyond. In other regions we are presented with the phenomenon of an almost uniform degree of brightness of the individual stars, accompanied with a very even distribution of them over the ground of the heavens, both the larger and smaller magnitudes

452

w is limited by this sort of cosmical veil, which extin-
 the smaller magnitudes, cuts off the nebulous light of
 masses, and closes our view in impenetrable darkness;
 at another we are compelled, by the clearest evidence
pes can afford, to believe that star-strewn vistas *lie open*,
ting their powers and stretching out beyond their utmost
as is proved by that very phenomenon which the existence
 a veil would render impossible—*viz*, infinite increase of
 and diminution of magnitude, terminating in complete
ble nebulosity.

s, in effect, the spectacle afforded by a very large por-
e Milky Way in that interesting region near its point
tion in Scorpio, where, through the hollows and deep
 its complicated structure, we behold what has all the
 of a wide and indefinitely prolonged area strewed
iscontinuous masses and clouds of stars, which the
 last refuses to analyse. Whatever other conclusions
, this must anyhow be regarded as the direction of
inear extension of the ground-plan of the galaxy.
 appear to follow also that in those regions where
early resolved into stars well separated and *seen*
 black ground, and where, by consequence, it i
foregoing views be correct, that we look out h
 space, the smallest visible stars appear as s
 excessive distance, but of inferiority of si

BLE, TEMPORARY AND BINARY STARS

 trace the law of periodicity w
 idea of rotatory or orbital
 which, though in no wa
 pparent change of place,
 n telescopes, yet unde
 rease and diminutio
 complete extinction

being strikingly deficient. In such cases
not to perceive that we are looking t
nearly of a size and of no great thic
distance which separates them from
should be driven to suppose the more
the larger, so as to compensate by
their greater distance, a suppositio

In others again, and that not
with a double phenomenon of th
it were, of large stars spread o
the intermediate magnitudes b
here seems equally evident th
two sidereal sheets separated

Throughout by far the
Milky Way in both hemis
ground of the heavens on
absence of that innumer
of the smallest visible m
aggregate light of mul
which the contrary sup
we think, be conside
sions, in *directions*
not infinite, but t
scopes suffices fai

It is but right
sion has been c
to be put aside
s to a defect
rtue of wh
re than i
s origin
e incr
space
nce

g
dis
while
telesc
exhaus
reach,
of such
number
irresolva

Such
tion of th
of bifurca
recesses of
appearance
over with
telescope at
we may dra
the greatest
And it would
that zone is c
projected on a
certain, if the
yond them into
not by reason o
brightness.

VARIA

Wherever we ca
impressed with the
the stars are severa
from others by any
ence of appearance
regular periodical in
in one or two cases a

454

called periodic stars. The longest known, and one of the most remarkable, is the star *Omicron* in the constellation Cetus (sometimes called Mira Ceti), which was first noticed as variable by Fabricius in 1596. It appears about twelve times in eleven years, remains at its greatest brightness about a fortnight, being then on some occasions equal to a large star of the second magnitude, decreases during about three months, till it becomes completely invisible to the naked eye, in which state it remains about five months, and continues increasing during the remainder of its period. Such is the general course of its phases. But the mean period above assigned would appear to be subject to a cyclical fluctuation embracing eighty-eight such periods, and having the effect of gradually lengthening and shortening alternately those intervals to the extent of twenty-five days one way and the other. The irregularities in the degree of brightness attained at the maximum are also periodical.

Such irregularities prepare us for other phenomena of stellar variation which have hitherto been reduced to no law of periodicity—the phenomena of temporary stars which have appeared from time to time in different parts of the heavens blazing forth with extraordinary lustre, and after remaining awhile, apparently immovable, have died away and left no trace. In the years 945, 1264, and 1572 brilliant stars appeared in the region of the heavens between Cepheus and Cassiopeia; and we may suspect them, with Goodricke, to be one and the same star with a period of 312, or perhaps 156 years. The appearance of the star of 1572 was so sudden that Tycho Brahe, a celebrated Dutch astronomer, returning one evening from his laboratory to his dwellinghouse, was surprised to find a group of country people gazing at a star which he was sure did not exist half an hour before. This was the star in question. It was then as bright as Sirius, and continued to increase till it surpassed Jupiter when brightest, and was visible at midday. It began to diminish in December of the same year, and in March 1574 had entirely disappeared.

In 1803 it was announced by Sir William Herschel that there exist sidereal systems composed of two stars revolving about each other in regular orbits, and constituting which may be called, to distinguish them from double stars, which are only optically double, binary stars. That which since then has been most assiduously watched, and has offered phenomena of the greatest interest, is *gamma Virginis*. It is a star of the vulgar third magnitude, and its component individuals are very nearly equal, and, as it would seem, in some slight degree variable. It has been known to consist of two stars since the beginning of the eighteenth century, the distance being then between six and seven seconds, so that any tolerably good telescope would resolve it. When observed by Herschel in 1780 it was 5.66 seconds, and continued to decrease gradually and regularly, till at length, in 1836, the two stars had approached so closely as to appear perfectly round and single under the highest magnifying power which could be applied to most excellent instruments—the great refractor of Pulkowa alone, with a magnifying power of a thousand, continuing to indicate, by the wedge-shaped form of the disc of the star, its composite nature.

By estimating the ratio of its length to its breadth, and measuring the former, M. Struve concludes that at this epoch the distance of the two stars, center from center, might be stated at .22 seconds. From that time the star again opened, and is now again a perfectly easily separable star. This very remarkable diminution, and subsequent increase, of distance has been accompanied by a corresponding and equally remarkable increase and subsequent diminution of relative angular motion. Thus in 1783 the apparent angular motion hardly amounted to half a degree per annum; while in 1830 it had decreased to 5 degrees, in 1834 to 20 degrees, in 1835 to 40 degrees, and about the middle of 1836 to upwards of 70 degrees per annum, or at the rate of a degree in five days.

This is in entire conformity with the principles of dynamics, which establish a necessary connection between the angular velocity and the distance, as well in the apparent as in the real orbit of one body revolving about another under the influence of mutual attraction; the former varying inversely as the square of the latter, in both orbits, whatever be the curve described and whatever the law of the attractive force.

JOHN FREDERICK WILLIAM HERSCHEL

It is not with the revolutions of bodies of a planetary or cometary nature round a solar center that we are concerned; it is that of sun round sun—each perhaps, at least in some binary systems, where the individuals are very remote and their period of revolution very long, accompanied by its train of planets and their satellites, closely shrouded from our view by the splendor of their respective suns, and crowded into a space bearing hardly a greater proportion to the enormous interval which separates them than the distances of the satellites of our planets from their primaries bear to their distances from the sun itself.

A less distinctly characterized subordination would be incompatible with the stability of their systems and with the planetary nature of their orbits. Unless close under the protecting wing of their immediate superior, the sweep of their other sun, in its perihelion passage round their own, might carry them off or whirl them into orbits utterly incompatible with conditions necessary for the existence of their inhabitants.

THE NEBULAE

It is to Sir William Herschel that we owe the most complete analysis of the great variety of those objects which are generally classed as nebulæ. The great power of his telescopes disclosed the existence of an immense number of these objects before unknown, and showed them to be distributed over the heavens not by any means uniformly, but with a marked preference to a certain district extending over the northern pole of the galactic circle. In this region, occupying about one-eighth of the surface of the sphere, one-third of the entire nebulous contents of the heavens are situated.

The resolvable nebulæ can, of course, only be considered as clusters either too remote, or consisting of stars intrinsically too faint, to affect us by their individual light, unless where two or three happen to be close enough to make a joint impression and give the idea of a point brighter than the rest. They are almost universally round or oval, their loose appendages and irregulari-

457

ties of form being, as it were, extinguished by the distance, and only the general figure of the condensed parts being discernible. It is under the appearance of objects of this character that all the greater globular clusters exhibit themselves in telescopes of insufficient optical power to show them well.

The first impression which Halley and other early discoverers of nebulous objects received from their peculiar aspect was that of a phosphorescent vapor (like the matter of a comet's tail), or a gaseous and, so to speak, elementary form of luminous sidereal matter. Admitting the existence of such a medium, Sir W. Herschel was led to speculate on its gradual subsidence and condensation, by the effect of its own gravity, into more or less regular spherical or spheroidal forms, denser (as they must in that case be) towards the center.

Assuming that in the progress of this subsidence local centers of condensation subordinate to the general tendency would not be wanting, he conceived that in this way solid nuclei might arise whose local gravitation still further condensing, and so absorbing the nebulous matter each in its immediate neighborhood, might ultimately become stars, and the whole nebula finally take on the state of a cluster of stars.

Among the multitude of nebulæ revealed by his telescope every stage of this process might be considered as displayed to our eyes, and in every modification of form to which the general principle might be conceived to apply. The more or less advanced state of a nebula towards its segregation into discrete stars, and of these stars themselves towards a denser state of aggregation round a central nucleus, would thus be in some sort an indication of age.

HEINRICH RUDOLPH HERTZ

(1857–1894)

An assistant of Helmholtz, Hertz is responsible for the developments which led to the invention of wireless telegraphy and radio. Following Maxwell's predictions, he demonstrated the existence of electric or electromagnetic waves in the ether (once called Hertzian waves, now popularly known as radio waves), measured their wave length and velocity, and showed that they could be reflected, refracted and polarized as light is. Today the behavior he described is known to apply not only to light and radio waves, but to heat, infrared, ultraviolet and cosmic rays.

ON THE RELATIONS BETWEEN LIGHT
AND ELECTRICITY

WHEN ONE speaks of the relations between light and electricity, the lay mind at once thinks of the electric light. With this the present lecture is not concerned. To the mind of the physicist there occur a series of delicate mutual reactions between the two agents, such as the rotation of the plane of polarization by the current or the alteration of the resistance of a conductor by the action of light. In these, however, light and electricity do not directly meet; between the two there comes an intermediate agent—ponderable matter. With this group of phenomena again we shall not concern ourselves. Between the two agents there are yet other relations—relations in a closer and stricter sense than those already mentioned. I am here to support the assertion that light of every kind is itself an electrical phenomenon—the light of the sun, the light of a candle, the light of a glowworm.

Take away from the world electricity, and light disappears; remove from the world the luminiferous ether, and electric and

459

magnetic actions can no longer traverse space. This is our assertion. It does not date from today or yesterday; already it has behind it a long history. In this history its foundations lie. Such researches as I have made upon this subject form but a link in a long chain. And it is of the chain, and not only of the single link, that I would speak to you. I must confess that it is not easy to speak of these matters in a way at once intelligible and accurate. It is in empty space, in the free ether, that the processes which we have to describe take place. They cannot be felt with the hand, heard by the ear, or seen by the eye. They appeal to our intuition and conception, scarcely to our senses. Hence we shall try to make use, as far as possible, of the intuitions and conceptions which we already possess. Let us, therefore, stop to inquire what we do with certainty know about light and electricity before we proceed to connect the one with the other.

What, then, is light? Since the time of Young and Fresnel we know that it is a wave motion. We know the velocity of the waves, we know their length, we know that they are transversal waves; in short, we know completely the geometrical relations of the motion. To the physicist it is inconceivable that this view should be refuted; we can no longer entertain any doubt about the matter. It is morally certain that the wave theory of light is true, and the conclusions that necessarily follow from it are equally certain. It is therefore certain that all space known to us is not empty but is filled with a substance, the ether, which can be thrown into vibration. But whereas our knowledge of the geometrical relations of the processes in this substance is clear and definite, our conceptions of the physical nature of these processes is vague, and the assumptions made as to the properties of the substance itself are not altogether consistent.

At first, following the analogy of sound, waves of light were freely regarded as elastic waves and treated as such. But elastic waves in fluids are only known in the form of longitudinal waves. Transversal elastic waves in fluids are unknown. They are not even possible; they contradict the nature of the fluid state. Hence men were forced to assert that the ether which fills space behaves like a solid body. But when they considered and tried being strikingly deficient. In such cases it is equally impossible not to perceive that we are looking through a sheet of stars nearly of a size and of no great thickness compared with the distance which separates them from us. Were it otherwise we should be driven to suppose the more distant stars were uniformly the larger, so as to compensate by their intrinsic brightness for their greater distance, a supposition contrary to all probability.

In others again, and that not infrequently, we are presented with a double phenomenon of the same kind—*viz.*, a tissue, as it were, of large stars spread over another of very small ones, the intermediate magnitudes being wanting, and the conclusion here seems equally evident that in such cases we look through two sidereal sheets separated by a starless interval.

Throughout by far the larger portion of the extent of the Milky Way in both hemispheres the general blackness of the ground of the heavens on which its stars are projected, and the absence of that innumerable multitude and excessive crowding of the smallest visible magnitudes, and of glare produced by the aggregate light of multitudes too small to affect the eye singly, which the contrary supposition would appear to necessitate, must, we think, be considered unequivocal indications that its dimensions, in *directions where those conditions obtain,* are not only not infinite, but that the space-penetrating power of our telescopes suffices fairly to pierce through and beyond it.

It is but right, however, to warn our readers that this conclusion has been controverted, and that by an authority not lightly to be put aside, on the ground of certain views taken by Olbers as to a defect of perfect transparency in the celestial spaces, in virtue of which the light of the more distant stars is enfeebled more than in proportion to their distance. The extinction of light thus originating proceeding in geometrical ratio, while the distance increases in arithmetical, a limit, it is argued, is placed to the space-penetrating power of telescopes far within that which distance alone, apart from such obscuration, would assign.

It must suffice here to observe that the objection alluded to, if applicable to any, is equally so to every part of the galaxy. We are not at liberty to argue that at one part of its circumference

453

our view is limited by this sort of cosmical veil, which extinguishes the smaller magnitudes, cuts off the nebulous light of distant masses, and closes our view in impenetrable darkness; while at another we are compelled, by the clearest evidence telescopes can afford, to believe that star-strewn vistas *lie open*, exhausting their powers and stretching out beyond their utmost reach, as is proved by that very phenomenon which the existence of such a veil would render impossible—*viz*, infinite increase of number and diminution of magnitude, terminating in complete irresolvable nebulosity.

Such is, in effect, the spectacle afforded by a very large portion of the Milky Way in that interesting region near its point of bifurcation in Scorpio, where, through the hollows and deep recesses of its complicated structure, we behold what has all the appearance of a wide and indefinitely prolonged area strewed over with discontinuous masses and clouds of stars, which the telescope at last refuses to analyse. Whatever other conclusions we may draw, this must anyhow be regarded as the direction of the greatest linear extension of the ground-plan of the galaxy. And it would appear to follow also that in those regions where that zone is clearly resolved into stars well separated and *seen projected on a black ground*, and where, by consequence, it is certain, if the foregoing views be correct, that we look out beyond them into space, the smallest visible stars appear as such not by reason of excessive distance, but of inferiority of size or brightness.

VARIABLE, TEMPORARY AND BINARY STARS

Wherever we can trace the law of periodicity we are strongly impressed with the idea of rotatory or orbital motion. Among the stars are several which, though in no way distinguishable from others by any apparent change of place, nor by any difference of appearance in telescopes, yet undergo a more or less regular periodical increase and diminution of lustre, involving in one or two cases a complete extinction and revival. These are called periodic stars. The longest known, and one of the most remarkable, is the star *Omicron* in the constellation Cetus (sometimes called Mira Ceti), which was first noticed as variable by Fabricius in 1596. It appears about twelve times in eleven years, remains at its greatest brightness about a fortnight, being then on some occasions equal to a large star of the second magnitude, decreases during about three months, till it becomes completely invisible to the naked eye, in which state it remains about five months, and continues increasing during the remainder of its period. Such is the general course of its phases. But the mean period above assigned would appear to be subject to a cyclical fluctuation embracing eighty-eight such periods, and having the effect of gradually lengthening and shortening alternately those intervals to the extent of twenty-five days one way and the other. The irregularities in the degree of brightness attained at the maximum are also periodical.

Such irregularities prepare us for other phenomena of stellar variation which have hitherto been reduced to no law of periodicity—the phenomena of temporary stars which have appeared from time to time in different parts of the heavens blazing forth with extraordinary lustre, and after remaining awhile, apparently immovable, have died away and left no trace. In the years 945, 1264, and 1572 brilliant stars appeared in the region of the heavens between Cepheus and Cassiopeia; and we may suspect them, with Goodricke, to be one and the same star with a period of 312, or perhaps 156 years. The appearance of the star of 1572 was so sudden that Tycho Brahe, a celebrated Dutch astronomer, returning one evening from his laboratory to his dwellinghouse, was surprised to find a group of country people gazing at a star which he was sure did not exist half an hour before. This was the star in question. It was then as bright as Sirius, and continued to increase till it surpassed Jupiter when brightest, and was visible at midday. It began to diminish in December of the same year, and in March 1574 had entirely disappeared.

In 1803 it was announced by Sir William Herschel that there exist sidereal systems composed of two stars revolving about each other in regular orbits, and constituting which may be called, to distinguish them from double stars, which are only optically double, binary stars. That which since then has been most assiduously watched, and has offered phenomena of the greatest interest, is *gamma Virginis*. It is a star of the vulgar third magnitude, and its component individuals are very nearly equal, and, as it would seem, in some slight degree variable. It has been known to consist of two stars since the beginning of the eighteenth century, the distance being then between six and seven seconds, so that any tolerably good telescope would resolve it. When observed by Herschel in 1780 it was 5.66 seconds, and continued to decrease gradually and regularly, till at length, in 1836, the two stars had approached so closely as to appear perfectly round and single under the highest magnifying power which could be applied to most excellent instruments—the great refractor of Pulkowa alone, with a magnifying power of a thousand, continuing to indicate, by the wedge-shaped form of the disc of the star, its composite nature.

By estimating the ratio of its length to its breadth, and measuring the former, M. Struve concludes that at this epoch the distance of the two stars, center from center, might be stated at .22 seconds. From that time the star again opened, and is now again a perfectly easily separable star. This very remarkable diminution, and subsequent increase, of distance has been accompanied by a corresponding and equally remarkable increase and subsequent diminution of relative angular motion. Thus in 1783 the apparent angular motion hardly amounted to half a degree per annum; while in 1830 it had decreased to 5 degrees, in 1834 to 20 degrees, in 1835 to 40 degrees, and about the middle of 1836 to upwards of 70 degrees per annum, or at the rate of a degree in five days.

This is in entire conformity with the principles of dynamics, which establish a necessary connection between the angular velocity and the distance, as well in the apparent as in the real orbit of one body revolving about another under the influence of mutual attraction; the former varying inversely as the square of the latter, in both orbits, whatever be the curve described and whatever the law of the attractive force.

It is not with the revolutions of bodies of a planetary or cometary nature round a solar center that we are concerned; it is that of sun round sun—each perhaps, at least in some binary systems, where the individuals are very remote and their period of revolution very long, accompanied by its train of planets and their satellites, closely shrouded from our view by the splendor of their respective suns, and crowded into a space bearing hardly a greater proportion to the enormous interval which separates them than the distances of the satellites of our planets from their primaries bear to their distances from the sun itself.

A less distinctly characterized subordination would be incompatible with the stability of their systems and with the planetary nature of their orbits. Unless close under the protecting wing of their immediate superior, the sweep of their other sun, in its perihelion passage round their own, might carry them off or whirl them into orbits utterly incompatible with conditions necessary for the existence of their inhabitants.

THE NEBULAE

It is to Sir William Herschel that we owe the most complete analysis of the great variety of those objects which are generally classed as nebulæ. The great power of his telescopes disclosed the existence of an immense number of these objects before unknown, and showed them to be distributed over the heavens not by any means uniformly, but with a marked preference to a certain district extending over the northern pole of the galactic circle. In this region, occupying about one-eighth of the surface of the sphere, one-third of the entire nebulous contents of the heavens are situated.

The resolvable nebulæ can, of course, only be considered as clusters either too remote, or consisting of stars intrinsically too faint, to affect us by their individual light, unless where two or three happen to be close enough to make a joint impression and give the idea of a point brighter than the rest. They are almost universally round or oval, their loose appendages and irregulari-

457

ties of form being, as it were, extinguished by the distance, and only the general figure of the condensed parts being discernible. It is under the appearance of objects of this character that all the greater globular clusters exhibit themselves in telescopes of insufficient optical power to show them well.

The first impression which Halley and other early discoverers of nebulous objects received from their peculiar aspect was that of a phosphorescent vapor (like the matter of a comet's tail), or a gaseous and, so to speak, elementary form of luminous sidereal matter. Admitting the existence of such a medium, Sir W. Herschel was led to speculate on its gradual subsidence and condensation, by the effect of its own gravity, into more or less regular spherical or spheroidal forms, denser (as they must in that case be) towards the center.

Assuming that in the progress of this subsidence local centers of condensation subordinate to the general tendency would not be wanting, he conceived that in this way solid nuclei might arise whose local gravitation still further condensing, and so absorbing the nebulous matter each in its immediate neighborhood, might ultimately become stars, and the whole nebula finally take on the state of a cluster of stars.

Among the multitude of nebulæ revealed by his telescope every stage of this process might be considered as displayed to our eyes, and in every modification of form to which the general principle might be conceived to apply. The more or less advanced state of a nebula towards its segregation into discrete stars, and of these stars themselves towards a denser state of aggregation round a central nucleus, would thus be in some sort an indication of age.

HEINRICH RUDOLPH HERTZ

(1857–1894)

An assistant of Helmholtz, Hertz is responsible for the developments which led to the invention of wireless telegraphy and radio. Following Maxwell's predictions, he demonstrated the existence of electric or electromagnetic waves in the ether (once called Hertzian waves, now popularly known as radio waves), measured their wave length and velocity, and showed that they could be reflected, refracted and polarized as light is. Today the behavior he described is known to apply not only to light and radio waves, but to heat, infrared, ultraviolet and cosmic rays.

ON THE RELATIONS BETWEEN LIGHT
AND ELECTRICITY

WHEN ONE speaks of the relations between light and electricity, the lay mind at once thinks of the electric light. With this the present lecture is not concerned. To the mind of the physicist there occur a series of delicate mutual reactions between the two agents, such as the rotation of the plane of polarization by the current or the alteration of the resistance of a conductor by the action of light. In these, however, light and electricity do not directly meet; between the two there comes an intermediate agent—ponderable matter. With this group of phenomena again we shall not concern ourselves. Between the two agents there are yet other relations—relations in a closer and stricter sense than those already mentioned. I am here to support the assertion that light of every kind is itself an electrical phenomenon—the light of the sun, the light of a candle, the light of a glowworm.

Take away from the world electricity, and light disappears; remove from the world the luminiferous ether, and electric and

459

magnetic actions can no longer traverse space. This is our assertion. It does not date from today or yesterday; already it has behind it a long history. In this history its foundations lie. Such researches as I have made upon this subject form but a link in a long chain. And it is of the chain, and not only of the single link, that I would speak to you. I must confess that it is not easy to speak of these matters in a way at once intelligible and accurate. It is in empty space, in the free ether, that the processes which we have to describe take place. They cannot be felt with the hand, heard by the ear, or seen by the eye. They appeal to our intuition and conception, scarcely to our senses. Hence we shall try to make use, as far as possible, of the intuitions and conceptions which we already possess. Let us, therefore, stop to inquire what we do with certainty know about light and electricity before we proceed to connect the one with the other.

What, then, is light? Since the time of Young and Fresnel we know that it is a wave motion. We know the velocity of the waves, we know their length, we know that they are transversal waves; in short, we know completely the geometrical relations of the motion. To the physicist it is inconceivable that this view should be refuted; we can no longer entertain any doubt about the matter. It is morally certain that the wave theory of light is true, and the conclusions that necessarily follow from it are equally certain. It is therefore certain that all space known to us is not empty but is filled with a substance, the ether, which can be thrown into vibration. But whereas our knowledge of the geometrical relations of the processes in this substance is clear and definite, our conceptions of the physical nature of these processes is vague, and the assumptions made as to the properties of the substance itself are not altogether consistent.

At first, following the analogy of sound, waves of light were freely regarded as elastic waves and treated as such. But elastic waves in fluids are only known in the form of longitudinal waves. Transversal elastic waves in fluids are unknown. They are not even possible; they contradict the nature of the fluid state. Hence men were forced to assert that the ether which fills space behaves like a solid body. But when they considered and tried to explain the unhindered course of the stars in the heavens, they found themselves forced to admit that the ether behaves like a perfect fluid. These two statements together land us in a painful and unintelligible contradiction which disfigures the otherwise beautiful development of optics. Instead of trying to conceal this defect let us turn to electricity; in investigating it we may perhaps make some progress toward removing the difficulty.

What, then, is electricity? This is at once an important and a difficult question. It interests the lay as well as the scientific mind. Most people who ask it never doubt the existence of electricity. They expect a description of it—an enumeration of the peculiarities and powers of this wonderful thing. To the scientific mind the question rather presents itself in the form: Is there such a thing as electricity? Cannot electrical phenomena be traced back, like all others, to the properties of the ether and of ponderable matter? We are far from being able to answer this question definitely in the affirmative. In our conceptions the thing conceived of as electricity plays a large part. The traditional conceptions of electricities which attract and repel each other, and which are endowed with actions at a distance as with spiritual properties—we are all familiar with these, and in a way fond of them; they hold undisputed sway as common modes of expression at the present time. The period at which these conceptions were formed was the period in which Newton's law of gravitation won its most glorious successes, and in which the idea of direct action at a distance was familiar. Electric and magnetic attractions followed the same law as gravitational attraction; no wonder men thought the simple assumption of action at a distance sufficient to explain these phenomena, and to trace them back to their ultimate intelligible cause.

The aspect of matters changed in the present century, when the reactions between electric currents and magnets became known; for these have an infinite manifoldness, and in them motion and time play an important part. It became necessary to increase the number of actions at a distance and to improve their form. Thus the conception gradually lost its simplicity and physical probability. Men tried to regain this by seeking for more comprehensive and simple laws—so-called elementary laws. Of these the celebrated Weber's law is the most important example. Whatever we may think of its correctness, it is an attempt which altogether formed a comprehensive system full of scientific charm; those who were once attracted into its magic circle remained prisoners there. And if the path indicated was a false one, warning could only come from an intellect of great freshness —from a man who looked at phenomena with an open mind and without preconceived opinions, who started from what he saw, not from what he had heard, learned, or read. Such a man was Faraday.

Faraday, doubtless, heard it said that when a body was electrified something was introduced into it; but he saw that the changes which took place only made themselves felt outside and not inside. Faraday was taught that forces simply acted across space; but he saw that an important part was played by the particular kind of matter filling the space across which the forces were supposed to act. Faraday read that electricities certainly existed, whereas there was much contention as to the forces exercised by them; but he saw that the effects of these forces were clearly displayed, whereas he could perceive nothing of the electricities themselves. And so he formed a quite different, an opposite conception of the matter. To him the electric and magnetic forces became the actually present, tangible realities; to him electricity and magnetism were the things whose existence might be disputable.

The lines of force, as he called the forces independently considered, stood before his intellectual eye in space as conditions of space, as tensions, whirls, currents, whatever they might be —that he was himself unable to state—but there they were, acting upon each other, pushing and pulling bodies about, spreading themselves about and carrying the action from point to point. To the objection that complete rest is the only condition possible in empty space he could answer, Is space really empty? Do not the phenomena of light compel us to regard it as being filled with something? Might not the ether which transmits the waves of light also be capable of transmitting the changes which we call electric and magnetic force? Might there not conceivably be some connection between these changes and the light waves? Might not the latter be due to something like a quivering of the lines of force?

Faraday had advanced as far as this in his ideas and conjectures. He could not prove them, although he eagerly sought for proof. He delighted in investigating the connection between light, electricity, and magnetism. The beautiful connection which he did discover was not the one which he sought. So he tried again and again, and his search only ended with his life. Among the questions which he raised there was one which continually presented itself to him: Do electric and magnetic forces require time for their propagation? When we suddenly excite an electromagnet by a current, is the effect perceived simultaneously at all distances? Or does it first affect magnets close at hand, then more distant ones, and lastly, those which are quite far away? When we electrify and discharge a body in rapid succession, does the force vary at all distances simultaneously? Or do the oscillations arrive later, the further we go from the body? In the latter case the oscillation would propagate itself as a wave through space. Are there such waves? To these questions Faraday could get no answer.

And yet the answer is most closely connected with his own fundamental conceptions. If such waves of electric force exist, traveling freely from their origin through space, they exhibit plainly to us the independent existence of the forces which produce them. There can be no better way of proving that these forces do not act across space, but are propagated from point to point, than by actually following their progress from instant to instant. The questions asked are not unanswerable; indeed they can be attacked by very simple methods. If Faraday had had the good fortune to hit upon these methods, his views would forthwith have secured recognition. The connection between light and electricity would at once have become so clear that it could not have escaped notice even by eyes less sharpsighted than his own.

But a path so short and straight as this was not vouchsafed to science. For a while experiments did not point to any solution, nor did the current theory tend in the direction of Faraday's conceptions. The assertion that electric forces could exist independently of their electricities was in direct opposition to the accepted electrical theories. Similarly the prevailing theory of optics refused to accept the idea that waves of light could be other than elastic waves. Any attempt at a thorough discussion of the one or the other of these assertions seemed almost to be idle speculation. All the more must we admire the happy genius of the man who could connect together these apparently remote conjectures in such a way that they mutually supported each other and formed a theory of which everyone was at once bound to admit that it was at least plausible. This was an Englishman —Maxwell.

You know the paper which he published in 1865 upon the electromagnetic theory of light. It is impossible to study this wonderful theory without feeling as if the mathematical equations had an independent life and an intelligence of their own, as if they were wiser than ourselves, indeed wiser than their discoverer, as if they gave forth more than he had put into them. And this is not altogether impossible: it may happen when the equations prove to be more correct than their discoverer could with certainty have known. It is true that such comprehensive and accurate equations only reveal themselves to those who with keen insight pick out every indication of the truth which is faintly visible in nature. The clue which Maxwell followed is well known to the initiated. It had attracted the attention of other investigators: it had suggested to Reimann and Lorentz speculations of a similar nature, although not so fruitful in results. Electricity in motion produces magnetic force, and magnetism in motion produces electric force; but both of these effects are only perceptible at high velocities. Thus velocities appear in the mutual relations between electricity and magnetism, and the constant which governs these relations and continually recurs in them is itself a velocity of exceeding magnitude. This constant was determined in various ways, first by Kohlrausch and Weber, by purely electrical experiments, and proved to be identical, allowing for the experimental errors incident to such a difficult measurement, with another important velocity—the velocity of light.

This might be an accident, but a pupil of Faraday's could scarcely regard it as such. To him it appeared as an indication that the same ether must be the medium for the transmission of both electric force and light. The two velocities which were found to be nearly equal must really be identical. But in that case the most important optical constants must occur in the electrical equations. This was the bond which Maxwell set himself to strengthen. He developed the electrical equations to such an extent that they embraced all the known phenomena, and in addition to these a class of phenomena hitherto unknown— electric waves. These waves would be transversal waves, which might have any wave length but would always be propagated in the ether with the same velocity—that of light. And now Maxwell was able to point out that waves having just these geometrical properties do actually occur in nature, although we are accustomed to denote them not as electrical phenomena but by the special name of light. If Maxwell's electrical theory was regarded as false, there was no reason for accepting his views as to the nature of light. And if light waves were held to be purely elastic waves, his electrical theory lost its whole significance. But if one approached the structure without any prejudices arising from the views commonly held, one saw that its parts supported each other like the stones of an arch stretching across an abyss of the unknown and connecting two tracts of the known.

On account of the difficulty of the theory the number of its disciples at first was necessarily small. But everyone who studied it thoroughly became an adherent and forthwith sought diligently to test its original assumptions and its ultimate conclusions. Naturally the test of experiment could for a long time be applied only to separate statements, to the outworks of the theory.

I have just compared Maxwell's theory to an arch stretching across an abyss of unknown things. If I may carry on the analogy

465

further, I would say that for a long time the only additional support that was given to this arch was by way of strengthening its two abutments. The arch was thus enabled to carry its own weight safely; but still its span was so great that we could not venture to build up further upon it as upon a secure foundation. For this purpose it was necessary to have special pillars built up from the solid ground, and serving to support the center of the arch. One such pillar would consist in proving that electrical or magnetic effects can be directly produced by light. This pillar would support the optical side of the structure directly and the electrical side indirectly. Another pillar would consist in proving the existence of waves of electric or magnetic force capable of being propagated after the manner of light waves. This pillar again would directly support the electrical side, and indirectly the optical side.

In order to complete the structure symmetrically, both pillars would have to be built; but it would suffice to begin with one of them. With the former we have not as yet been able to make a start; but fortunately, after a protracted search, a safe point of support for the latter has been found. A sufficiently extensive foundation has been laid down; a part of the pillar has already been built up; with the help of many willing hands it will soon reach the height of the arch and so enable this to bear the weight of the further structure which is to be erected upon it. At this stage I was so fortunate as to be able to take part in the work. To this I owe the honor of speaking to you today; and you will therefore pardon me if I now try to direct your attention solely to this part of the structure. Lack of time compels me, against my will, to pass by the researches made by many other investigators; so that I am not able to show you in how many ways the path was prepared for my experiments, and how near several investigators came to performing these experiments themselves.

Was it then so difficult to prove that electric and magnetic forces need time for their propagation? Would it not have been easy to charge a Leyden jar and to observe directly whether the corresponding disturbance in a distant electroscope took place somewhat later? Would it not have sufficed to watch the behavior of a magnetic needle while someone at a distance suddenly excited an electromagnet?

As a matter of fact these and similar experiments had already been performed without indicating that any interval of time elapsed between the cause and the effect. To an adherent of Maxwell's theory this is simply a necessary result of the enormous velocity of propagation. We can only perceive the effect of charging a Leyden jar or exciting a magnet at moderate distances, say up to ten meters. To traverse such a distance, light, and therefore according to the theory electric force likewise, takes only the thirty millionth part of a second. Such a small fraction of time we cannot directly measure or even perceive. It is still more unfortunate that there are no adequate means at our disposal for indicating with sufficient sharpness the beginning and end of such a short interval. If we wish to measure a length correctly to the tenth part of a millimeter it would be absurd to indicate the beginning of it with a broad chalk line. If we wish to measure a time correctly to the thousandth part of a second it would be absurd to denote its beginning by the stroke of a big clock.

Now the time of discharge of a Leyden jar is, according to our ordinary ideas, inconceivably short. It would certainly be that if it took about the thirty thousandth part of a second. And yet for our present purpose even that would be a thousand times too long. Fortunately nature here provides us with a more delicate method. It has long been known that the discharge of a Leyden jar is not a continuous process, but that, like the striking of a clock, it consists of a large number of oscillations, of discharges in opposite senses which follow each other at exactly equal intervals. Electricity is able to simulate the phenomena of elasticity. The period of a single oscillation is much shorter than the total duration of the discharge, and this suggests that we might use a single oscillation as an indicator. But, unfortunately, the shortest oscillation yet observed takes fully a millionth of a second. While such an oscillation is actually in progress its effects spread out over a distance of three hundred meters; within the modest dimensions of a room they would be perceived almost at the instant the oscillation commenced. Thus no progress could be made with the known methods; some fresh knowledge was required.

This came in the form of the discovery that not only the discharge of Leyden jars but, under suitable conditions, the discharge of every kind of conductor gives rise to oscillations. These oscillations may be much shorter than those of the jars. When you discharge the conductor of an electrical machine you excite oscillations whose period lies between a hundred millionth and a thousand millionth of a second. It is true that these oscillations do not follow each other in a long continuous series; they are few in number and rapidly die out. It would suit our experiments much better if this were not the case. But there is still the possibility of success if we can only get two or three such sharply defined indications. So in the realm of acoustics, if we were denied the continuous tones of pipes and strings, we could get a poor kind of music by striking strips of wood.

We now have indicators for which the thirty thousandth part of a second is not too short. But these would be of little use to us if we were not in a position to actually perceive their action up to the distance under consideration, viz., about ten meters. This can be done by very simple means. Just at the spot where we wish to detect the force we place a conductor, say a straight wire, which is interrupted in the middle by a small spark gap. The rapidly alternating force sets the electricity of the conductor in motion and gives rise to a spark at the gap. The method had to be found by experience, for no amount of thought could well have enabled one to predict that it would work satisfactorily. For the sparks are microscopically short, scarcely a hundredth of a millimeter long; they only last about a millionth of a second. It almost seems absurd and impossible that they should be visible; but in a perfectly dark room they *are* visible to an eye which has been well rested in the dark. Upon this thin thread hangs the success of our undertaking.

In beginning it we are met by a number of questions. Under what conditions can we get the most powerful oscillations? These conditions we must carefully investigate and make the best use

468

of. What is the best form we can give to the receiver? We may choose straight wires or circular wires, or conductors of other forms; in each case the choice will have some effect upon the phenomena. When we have settled the form, what size shall we select? We soon find that this is a matter of some importance, that a given conductor is not suitable for the investigation of all kinds of oscillations, that there are relations between the two which remind us of the phenomena of resonance in acoustics. And lastly, are there not an endless number of positions in which we can expose a given conductor to the oscillations? In some of these the sparks are strong, in others weaker, and in others they entirely disappear.

I might perhaps interest you in the peculiar phenomena which here arise, but I dare not take up your time with these, for they are details—details when we are surveying the general results of an investigation, but by no means unimportant details to the investigator when he is engaged upon work of this kind. They are the peculiarities of the instruments with which he has to work; and the success of a workman depends upon whether he properly understands his tools. The thorough study of the implements, of the questions above referred to, formed a very important part of the task to be accomplished. After this was done, the method of attacking the main problem became obvious.

If you give a physicist a number of tuning forks and resonators and ask him to demonstrate to you the propagation in time of sound waves, he will find no difficulty in doing so even within the narrow limits of a room. He places a tuning fork anywhere in the room, listens with the resonator at various points around and observes the intensity of the sound. He shows how at certain points this is very small, and how this arises from the fact that at these points every oscillation is annulled by another one which started subsequently but traveled to the point along a shorter path. When a shorter path requires less time than a longer one, the propagation is a propagation in time. Thus the problem is solved. But the physicist now further shows us that the positions of silence follow each other at regular and equal distance: from this he determines the wave length, and, if he

469

knows the time of vibration of the fork, he can deduce the velocity of the wave.

In exactly the same way we proceed with our electric waves. In place of the tuning fork we use an oscillating conductor. In place of the resonator we use our interrupted wire, which may also be called an electric resonator. We observe that in certain places there are sparks at the gap, in others none; we see that the dead points follow each other periodically in ordered succession. Thus the propagation in time is proved and the wave length can be measured. Next comes the question whether the waves thus demonstrated are longitudinal or transverse. At a given place we hold our wire in two different positions with reference to the wave: in one position it answers, in the other not. This is enough—the question is settled: our waves are transversal. Their velocity has now to be found. We multiply the measured wave length by the calculated period of oscillation and find a velocity which is about that of light. If doubts are raised as to whether the calculation is trustworthy, there is still another method open to us. In wires, as well as in air, the velocity of electric waves is enormously great, so that we can make a direct comparison between the two.

Now the velocity of electric waves in wires has long since been directly measured. This was an easier problem to solve, because such waves can be followed for several kilometers. Thus we obtain another measurement, purely experimental, of our velocity, and if the result is only an approximate one it at any rate does not contradict the first.

All these experiments in themselves are very simple, but they lead to conclusions of the highest importance. They are fatal to any and every theory which assumes that electric force acts across space independently of time. They mark a brilliant victory for Maxwell's theory.

ELECTRIC RADIATION

As SOON as I had succeeded in proving that the action of an electric oscillation spreads out as a wave into space, I planned experiments with the object of concentrating this action and making it perceptible at greater distances by putting the primary conductor in the focal line of a large concave parabolic mirror. These experiments did not lead to the desired result, and I felt certain that the want of success was a necessary consequence of the disproportion between the length (4-5 meters) of the waves used and the dimensions which I was able, under the most favorable circumstances, to give to the mirror. Recently I have observed that the experiments which I have described can be carried out quite well with oscillations of more than ten times the frequency, and with waves less than one-tenth the length of those which were first discovered. I have, therefore, returned to the use of concave mirrors, and have obtained better results than I had ventured to hope for. I have succeeded in producing distinct rays of electric force, and in carrying out with them the elementary experiments which are commonly performed with light and radiant heat. The following is an account of these experiments:—

THE APPARATUS

The short waves were excited by the same method which we used for producing the longer waves. The primary conductor used may be most simply described as follows:—Imagine a cylindrical brass body, 3 cm. in diameter and 26 cm. long, interrupted midway along its length by a spark-gap whose poles on either side are formed by spheres of 2 cm. radius. The length of the conductor is approximately equal to the half wave-length of the corresponding oscillation in straight wires; from this we are at once able to estimate approximately the period of oscillation. It is essential that the pole-surfaces of the spark-gap should be frequently repolished, and also that during the experiments they should be carefully protected from illumination by simultaneous side-discharges; otherwise the oscillations are not excited. Whether the spark-gap is in a satisfactory state can always be recognized by the appearance and sound of the sparks. The discharge is led to the two halves of the conductor by means of

471

two gutta-percha-covered wires which are connected near the spark-gap on either side. I no longer made use of the large Ruhmkorff, but found it better to use a small induction-coil by Keiser and Schmidt; the longest sparks, between points, given by this were 4.5 cm. long. It was supplied with current from three accumulators, and gave sparks 1-2 cm. long between the spherical knobs of the primary conductor. For the purpose of the experiments the spark-gap was reduced to 3 mm.

Here, again, the small sparks induced in a secondary conductor were the means used for detecting the electric forces in space. As before, I used partly a circle which could be rotated within itself and which had about the same period of oscillation as the primary conductor. It was made of copper wire 1 mm. thick, and had in the present instance a diameter of only 7.5 cm. One end of the wire carried a polished brass sphere a few millimeters in diameter; the other end was pointed and could be brought up, by means of a fine screw insulated from the wire, to within an exceedingly short distance from the brass sphere. As will be readily understood, we have here to deal only with minute sparks of a few hundredths of a millimeter in length; and after a little practice one judges more according to the brilliancy than the length of the sparks.

The circular conductor gives only a differential effect, and is not adapted for use in the focal line of a concave mirror. Most of the work was therefore done with another conductor arranged as follows:—Two straight pieces of wire, each 50 cm. long and 5 mm. in diameter, were adjusted in a straight line so that their near ends were 5 cm. apart. From these ends two wires, 15 cm. long and 1 mm. in diameter, were carried parallel to one another and perpendicular to the wires first mentioned to a spark-gap arranged just as in the circular conductor. In this conductor the resonance-action was given up, and indeed it only comes slightly into play in this case. It would have been simpler to put the spark-gap directly in the middle of the straight wire; but the observer could not then have handled and observed the spark-gap in the focus of the mirror without obstructing the aperture. For this reason the arrangement above described was chosen in preference to the other which would in itself have been more advantageous.

THE PRODUCTION OF THE RAY

If the primary oscillator is now set up in a fairly large free space, one can, with the aid of the circular conductor, detect in its neighborhood on a smaller scale all those phenomena which I have already observed and described as occurring in the neighborhood of a larger oscillation. The greatest distance at which sparks could be perceived in the secondary conductor was 1.5 meter, or, when the primary spark-gap was in very good order, as much as 2 meters. When a plane reflecting plate is set up at a suitable distance on one side of the primary oscillator, and parallel to it, the action on the opposite side is strengthened. To be more precise:—If the distance chosen is either very small, or somewhat greater than 30 cm., the plate weakens the effect; it strengthens the effect greatly at distances of 8-15 cm., slightly at a distance of 45 cm., and exerts no influence at greater distances. We have drawn attention to this phenomenon in an earlier paper, and we conclude from it that the wave in air corresponding to the primary oscillation has a half wave-length of about 30 cm. We may expect to find a still further reinforcement if we replace the plane surface by a concave mirror having the form of a parabolic cylinder, in the focal line of which the axis of the primary oscillation lies. The focal length of the mirror should be chosen as small as possible, if it is properly to concentrate the action. But if the direct wave is not to annul immediately the action of the reflected wave, the focal length must not be much smaller than a quarter wave-length. I therefore fixed on 12½ cm. as the focal length, and constructed the mirror by bending a zinc sheet 2 meters long, 2 meters broad, and ½ mm. thick into the desired shape over a wooden frame of the exact curvature. The height of the mirror was thus 2 meters, the breadth of its aperture 1.2 meter, and its depth 0.7 meter. The primary oscillator was fixed in the middle of the focal line. The wires which conducted the discharge were led

473

through the mirror; the induction-coil and the cells were accordingly placed behind the mirror so as to be out of the way. If we now investigate the neighborhood of the oscillator with our conductors, we find that there is no action behind the mirror or at either side of it; but in the direction of the optical axis of the mirror the sparks can be perceived up to a distance of 5-6 meters. When a plane conducting surface was set up so as to oppose the advancing waves at right angles, the sparks could be detected in its neighborhood at even greater distances—up to about 9-10 meters. The waves reflected from the conducting surface reinforce the advancing waves at certain points. At other points again the two sets of waves weaken one another. In front of the plane wall one can recognize with the rectilinear conductor very distinct maxima and minima, and with the circular conductor the characteristic interference-phenomena of stationary waves which I have described in an earlier paper. I was able to distinguish four nodal points, which were situated at the wall and at 33, 65, and 98 cm. distance from it. We thus get 33 cm. as a closer approximation to the half wave-length of the waves used, and 1.1 thousand-millionth of a second as their period of oscillation, assuming that they travel with the velocity of light. In wires the oscillation gave a wave-length of 29 cm. Hence it appears that these short waves also have a somewhat lower velocity in wires than in air; but the ratio of the two velocities comes very near to the theoretical value—unity—and does not differ from it so much as appeared to be probable from our experiments on longer waves. This remarkable phenomenon still needs elucidation. Inasmuch as the phenomena are only exhibited in the neighborhood of the optic axis of the mirror, we may speak of the result produced as an electric ray proceeding from the concave mirror.

I now constructed a second mirror, exactly similar to the first, and attached the rectilinear secondary conductor to it in such a way that the two wires of 50 cm. length lay in the focal line, and the two wires connected to the spark-gap passed directly through the walls of the mirror without touching it. The spark-gap was thus situated directly behind the mirror, and the observer could adjust and examine it without obstructing the course of the waves. I expected to find that, on intercepting the ray with this apparatus, I should be able to observe it at even greater distances; and the event proved that I was not mistaken. In the rooms at my disposal I could now perceive the sparks from one end to the other. The greatest distance to which I was able, by availing myself of a doorway, to follow the ray was 16 meters; but according to the results of the reflection-experiments (to be presently described), there can be no doubt that sparks could be obtained at any rate up to 20 meters in open spaces. For the remaining experiments such great distances are not necessary, and it is convenient that the sparking in the secondary conductor should not be too feeble; for most of the experiments a distance of 6-10 meters is most suitable. We shall now describe the simple phenomena which can be exhibited with the ray without difficulty. When the contrary is not expressly stated, it is to be assumed that the focal lines of both mirrors are vertical.

RECTILINEAR PROPAGATION

If a screen of sheet zinc 2 meters high and 1 meter broad is placed on the straight line joining both mirrors, and at right angles to the direction of the ray, the secondary sparks disappear completely. An equally complete shadow is thrown by a screen of tinfoil or gold-paper. If an assistant walks across the path of the ray, the secondary spark-gap becomes dark as soon as he intercepts the ray, and again lights up when he leaves the path clear. Insulators do not stop the ray—it passes right through a wooden partition or door; and it is not without astonishment that one sees the sparks appear inside a closed room. If two conducting screens, 2 meters high and 1 meter broad, are set up symmetrically on the right and left of the ray, and perpendicular to it, they do not interfere at all with the secondary spark so long as the width of the opening between them is not less than the aperture of the mirrors, viz., 1.2 meter. If the opening is made narrower the sparks become weaker, and disappear when the width of the opening is reduced below 0.5 meter. The sparks also disappear if the opening is left with a breadth of 1.2 meter, but is shifted to one side of the straight line joining the mirrors. If the optical axis of the mirror containing the oscillator is rotated to the right or left about 10° out of the proper position, the secondary sparks become weak, and a rotation through 15° causes them to disappear.

There is no sharp geometrical limit to either the ray or the shadows; it is easy to produce phenomena corresponding to diffraction. As yet, however, I have not succeeded in observing maxima and minima at the edge of the shadows.

POLARIZATION

From the mode in which our ray was produced we can have no doubt whatever that it consists of transverse vibrations and is plane-polarized in the optical sense. We can also prove by experiment that this is the case. If the receiving mirror be rotated about the ray as axis until its focal line, and therefore the secondary conductor also, lies in a horizontal plane, the secondary sparks become more and more feeble, and when the two focal lines are at right angles, no sparks whatever are obtained even if the mirrors are moved close up to one another. The two mirrors behave like the polarizer and analyzer of a polarization apparatus.

I next had made an octagonal frame, 2 meters high and 2 meters broad; across this were stretched copper wires 1 mm. thick, the wires being parallel to each other and 3 cm. apart. If the two mirrors were now set up with their focal lines parallel, and the wire screen was interposed perpendicularly to the ray and so that the direction of the wires was perpendicular to the direction of the focal lines, the screen practically did not interfere at all with the secondary sparks. But if the screen was set up in such a way that its wires were parallel to the focal lines, it stopped the ray completely. With regard then, to transmitted energy the screen behaves towards our ray just as a tourmaline plate behaves towards a plane-polarized ray of light. The receiving mirror was now placed once more so that its focal line was horizontal; under these circumstances, as already mentioned, no sparks appeared. Nor were any sparks produced when the screen was interposed in the path of the ray, so long as the wires in the screen were either horizontal or vertical. But if the frame was set up in such a position that the wires were inclined at 45° to the horizontal on either side, then the interposition of the screen immediately produced sparks in the secondary spark-gap. Clearly the screen resolves the advancing oscillation into two components and transmits only that component which is perpendicular to the direction of its wires. This component is inclined at 45° to the focal line of the second mirror, and may thus, after being again resolved by the mirror, act upon the secondary conductor. The phenomenon is exactly analogous to the brightening of the dark field of two crossed Nicols by the interposition of a crystalline plate in a suitable position.

With regard to the polarization it may be further observed that, with the means employed in the present investigation, we are only able to recognize the electric force. When the primary oscillator is in a vertical position the oscillations of this force undoubtedly take place in the vertical plane through the ray, and are absent in the horizontal plane. But the results of experiments with slowly alternating currents leave no room for doubt that the electric oscillations are accompanied by oscillations of magnetic force which take place in the horizontal plane through the ray and are zero in the vertical plane. Hence the polarization of the ray does not so much consist in the occurrence of oscillations in the vertical plane, but rather in the fact that the oscillations in the vertical plane are of an electrical nature, while those in the horizontal plane are of a magnetic nature. Obviously, then, the question, in which of the two planes the oscillation in our ray occurs, cannot be answered unless one specifies whether the question relates to the electric or the magnetic oscillation. It was Herr Kolacek who first pointed out clearly that this consideration is the reason why an old optical dispute has never been decided.

REFLECTION

We have already proved the reflection of the waves from conducting surfaces by the interference between the reflected and the advancing waves, and have also made use of the reflection in the construction of our concave mirrors. But now we are able to go further and to separate the two systems of waves from one another. I first placed both mirrors in a large room side by side, with their apertures facing in the same direction, and their axes converging to a point about 3 meters off. The spark-gap of the receiving mirror naturally remained dark. I next set up a plane vertical wall made of thin sheet zinc, 2 meters high and 2 meters broad, at the point of intersection of the axes, and adjusted it so that it was equally inclined to both. I obtained a vigorous stream of sparks arising from the reflection of the ray by the wall. The sparking ceased as soon as the wall was rotated around a vertical axis through about 15° on either side of the correct position; from this it follows that the reflection is regular, not diffuse. When the wall was moved away from the mirrors, the axes of the latter being still kept converging towards the wall, the sparking diminished very slowly. I could still recognize sparks when the wall was 10 meters away from the mirrors, i.e. when the waves had to traverse a distance of 20 meters. This arrangement might be adopted with advantage for the purpose of comparing the rate of propagation, e.g. through cables.

In order to produce reflection of the ray at angles of incidence greater than zero, I allowed the ray to pass parallel to the wall of the room in which there was a doorway. In the neighboring room to which this door led I set up the receiving mirror so that its optic axis passed centrally through the door and intersected the direction of the ray at right angles. If the plane conducting surface was now set up vertically at the point of intersection, and adjusted so as to make angles of 45° with the ray and also with the axis of the receiving mirror, there appeared in the secondary conductor a stream of sparks which was not interrupted by closing the door. When I turned the reflecting surface about 10° out of the correct position the sparks disappeared.

Thus the reflection is regular, and the angles of incidence and reflection are equal. That the action proceeded from the source of disturbance to the plane mirror, and hence to the secondary conductor, could also be shown by placing shadow-giving screens at different points of this path. The secondary sparks then always ceased immediately; whereas no effect was produced when the screen was placed anywhere else in the room. With the aid of the circular secondary conductor it is possible to determine the position of the wave-front in the ray; this was found to be at right angles to the ray before and after reflection, so that in the reflection it was turned through 90°.

Hitherto the focal lines of the concave mirrors were vertical, and the plane of oscillation was therefore perpendicular to the plane of incidence. In order to produce reflection with the oscillations in the plane of incidence, I placed both mirrors with their focal lines horizontal. I observed the same phenomena as in the previous position; and, moreover, I was not able to recognize any difference in the intensity of the reflected ray in the two cases. On the other hand, if the focal line of the one mirror is vertical, and of the other horizontal, no secondary sparks can be observed. The inclination of the plane of oscillation to the plane of incidence is therefore not altered by reflection provided this inclination has one of the two special values referred to; but in general this statement cannot hold good. It is even questionable whether the ray after reflection continues to be plane-polarized. The interferences which are produced in front of the mirror by the intersecting wave-systems, and which, as I have remarked, give rise to characteristic phenomena in the circular conductor, are most likely to throw light upon all problems relating to the change of phase and amplitude produced by reflection.

One further experiment on reflection from an electrically eolotropic surface may be mentioned. The two concave mirrors were again placed side by side, as in the reflection-experiment first described; but now there was placed opposite to them, as a reflecting surface, the screen of parallel copper wires which has already been referred to. It was found that the secondary spark-gap remained dark when the wires intersected the direction of the oscillations at right angles, but that sparking began as soon as the wires coincided with the direction of the oscillations. Hence the analogy between the tourmaline plate and our surface which conducts in one direction is confined to the trans-mitted part of the ray. The tourmaline plate absorbs the part which is not transmitted; our surface reflects it. If in the experiment last described the two mirrors are placed with their focal lines at right angles, no sparks can be excited in the secondary conductor by reflection from an isotropic screen; but I proved to my satisfaction that sparks are produced when the reflection takes place from the eolotropic wire grating, provided this is adjusted so that the wires are inclined at 45° to the focal lines. The explanation of this follows naturally from what has been already stated.

REFRACTION

In order to find out whether any refraction of the ray takes place in passing from air into another insulating medium, I had a large prism made of so-called hard pitch, a material like asphalt. The base was an isosceles triangle 1.2 meters in the side, and with a refracting angle of nearly 30°. The refracting edge was placed vertical, and the height of the whole prism was 1.5 meters. But since the prism weighed about 12 cwt., and would have been too heavy to move as a whole, it was built up of three pieces, each 0.5 meter high, placed one above the other. The material was cast in wooden boxes which were left around it, as they did not appear to interfere with its use. The prism was mounted on a support of such height that the middle of its refracting edge was at the same height as the primary and secondary spark-gaps. When I was satisfied that refraction did take place, and had obtained some idea of its amount, I arranged the experiment in the following manner:—The producing mirror was set up at a distance of 2.6 meters from the prism and facing one of the refracting surfaces, so that the axis of the beam was directed as nearly as possible towards the center of mass of the prism, and met the refracting surface at an angle of incidence of 25° (on the side of the normal towards the base). Near the refracting edge and also at the opposite side of the prism were placed two conducting screens which prevented the ray from passing by any other path than that through the prism. On the side of the emerging ray there was marked upon the floor a circle of 2.5 meters radius, having as its center the center of mass of the lower end of the prism. Along this the receiving mirror was now moved about, its aperture being always directed towards the center of the circle. No sparks were obtained when the mirror was placed in the direction of the incident ray produced; in this direction the prism threw a complete shadow. But sparks appeared when the mirror was moved towards the base of the prism, beginning when the angular deviation from the first position was about 11°. The sparking increased in intensity until the deviation amounted to about 22°, and then again decreased. The last sparks were observed with a deviation of about 34°. When the mirror was placed in a position of maximum effect, and then moved away from the prism along the radius of the circle, the sparks could be traced up to a distance of 5-6 meters. When an assistant stood either in front of the prism or behind it the sparking invariably ceased, which shows that the action reaches the secondary conductor through the prism and not in any other way. The experiments were repeated after placing both mirrors with their focal lines horizontal, but without altering the position of the prism. This made no difference in the phenomena observed. A refracting angle of 30° and a deviation of 22° in the neighborhood of the minimum deviation corresponds to a refractive index of 1.69. The refractive index of pitchlike materials for light is given as being between 1.5 and 1.6. We must not attribute any importance to the magnitude or even the sense of this difference, seeing that our method was not an accurate one, and that the material used was impure.

We have applied the term rays of electric force to the phenomena which we have investigated. We may perhaps further designate them as rays of light of very great wave-length. The experiments described appear to me, at any rate, eminently

481

adapted to remove any doubt as to the identity of light, radiant heat, and electro-magnetic wave-motion. I believe that from now on we shall have greater confidence in making use of the advantages which this identity enables us to derive both in the study of optics and of electricity. . . .

Explanation of the Figures. In order to facilitate the repetition and extension of these experiments, I append in the accompanying Figures, illustrations of the apparatus which I used, although these were constructed simply for the purpose of experimenting at the time and without any regard to durability. Fig. 1 shows

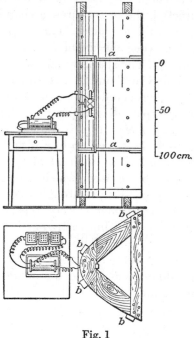

Fig. 1

in plan and elevation (section) the producing mirror. It will be seen that the framework of it consists of two horizontal frames (*a*, *a*) of parabolic form, and four vertical supports (*b*, *b*) which are screwed to each of the frames so as to support and connect them. The sheet metal reflector is clamped between the frames and the supports project above and below beyond the sheet metal so that they can be used as handles in handling the mirror. Fig. 2, *a* represents the primary conductor on a somewhat larger scale. The two metal parts slide with friction in two sleeves of strong paper which are held together by indiarubber bands. The sleeves themselves are fastened by four rods of sealing-wax to a board which again is tied by indiarubber bands to a strip of wood forming part of the frame which can be seen in Fig. 1. The two leading wires (covered with guttapercha) terminate in

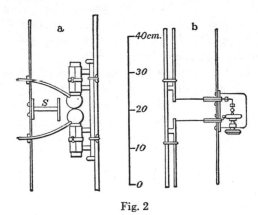

Fig. 2

two holes bored in the knobs of the primary conductor. This arrangement allows of all necessary motion and adjustment of the various parts of the conductor; it can be taken to pieces and put together again in a few minutes, and this is essential in order that the knobs may be frequently repolished. Just at the points where the leading wires pass through the mirror, they are surrounded during the discharge by a bluish light. The smooth wooden screen is introduced for the purpose of shielding the spark-gap from this light, which otherwise would interfere seriously with the production of the oscillations. Lastly, Fig. 2, *b* represents the secondary spark-gap. Both parts of the secondary conductor are again attached by sealing-wax rods and the india-rubber bands to a slip forming part of the wooden framework. From the inner ends of these parts the leading wires, surrounded

483

by glass tubes, can be seen proceeding through the mirror and bending towards one another. The upper wire carries at its pole a small brass knob. To the lower wire is soldered a piece of watch-spring which carries the second pole, consisting of a fine copper point. The point is intentionally chosen of softer metal than the knob; unless this precaution is taken the point easily penetrates into the knob, and the minute sparks disappear from sight in the small hole thus produced. The figure shows how the point is adjusted by a screw which presses against the spring that is insulated from it by a glass plate. The spring is bent in a particular way in order to secure finer motion of the point than would be possible if the screw alone were used.

No doubt the apparatus here described can be considerably modified without interfering with the success of the experiments. Acting upon friendly advice, I have tried to replace the spark-gap in the secondary conductor by a frog's leg prepared for detecting currents; but this arrangement which is so delicate under other conditions does not seem to be adapted for these purposes.

HIPPOCRATES

(460?–377 B.C.)

This Greek physician is called the father of medicine since his works (and others wrongly attributed to him) were long regarded as the ultimate authority in medical practice. Physicians still take the Hippocratic Oath, the pledge of ethical responsibility, which is a reflection of the Greek doctor's high principles. Little is known of his life except that he practiced among the temples of Aesculapius on the island of Cos. His great contribution to science was the concept that disease is not inflicted by supernatural agencies, but is the consequence of natural causes. He left many instructive case histories, and is the author of such familiar aphorisms as "Desperate diseases need desperate remedies" and "One man's meat is another man's poison."

THE HIPPOCRATIC OATH

I SWEAR by Apollo Physician and Aesculapius and Hygeia and Panacea and all the gods and goddesses, making them my witnesses, that I will fulfill according to my ability and judgment this oath and this covenant:

To hold him who has taught me this art as equal to my parents and to live my life in partnership with him, and if he is in need of money to give him a share of mine, and to regard his offspring as equal to my brothers in male lineage and to teach them this art—if they desire to learn it—without fee and covenant; to give a share of precepts and oral instruction and all the other learning to my sons and to the sons of him who has instructed me and to pupils who have signed the covenant and have taken an oath according to the medical law, but to no one else.

I will apply dietetic measures for the benefit of the sick according to my ability and judgment; I will keep them from harm and injustice.

485

I will neither give a deadly drug to anybody if asked for it, nor will I make a suggestion to this effect. Similarly I will not give to a woman an abortive remedy. In purity and holiness I will guard my life and my art.

I will not use the knife, not even on sufferers from stone, but will withdraw in favor of such men as are engaged in this work.

Whatever houses I may visit, I will come for the benefit of the sick, remaining free of all intentional injustice, of all mischief and in particular of sexual relations with both female and male persons, be they free or slaves.

What I may see or hear in the course of the treatment or even outside of the treatment in regard to the life of men, which on no account one must spread abroad, I will keep to myself, holding such things shameful to be spoken about.

If I fulfill this oath and do not violate it, may it be granted to me to enjoy life and art, being honored with fame among all men for all time to come; if I transgress it and swear falsely, may the opposite of all this be my lot.

THE APHORISMS OF HIPPOCRATES

LIFE IS SHORT, and the Art long; the occasion fleeting; experience fallacious, and judgment difficult. The physician must not only be prepared to do what is right himself, but also to make the patient, the attendants, and externals co-operate.

A slender and restricted diet is always dangerous in chronic diseases, and also in acute diseases, where it is not requisite. And again, a diet brought to the extreme point of attenuation is dangerous; and repletion, when in the extreme, is also dangerous.

Old persons endure fasting most easily; next, adults; young persons not nearly so well; and most especially infants, and of them such as are of a particularly lively spirit.

In whatever disease sleep is laborious, it is a deadly symptom; but if sleep does good, it is not deadly.

Both sleep and insomnolency, when immoderate, are bad.

It is better that a fever succeed to a convulsion, than a convulsion to a fever.

Persons who are naturally very fat are apt to die earlier than those who are slender.

In every movement of the body, whenever one begins to endure pain, it will be relieved by rest.

Phthisis [tuberculosis] most commonly occurs between the ages of eighteen and thirty-five years.

In persons who cough up frothy blood, the discharge of it comes from the lungs.

Sneezing coming on, in the case of a person afflicted with hiccup, removes the hiccup.

In acute diseases, complicated with fever, a moaning respiration is bad.

Persons are most subject to apoplexy between the ages of forty and sixty.

In acute diseases, coldness of the extremities is bad.

A chill supervening on a sweat is not good.

Those diseases which medicines do not cure, iron [surgery?] cures; those which iron cannot cure, fire cures; and those which fire cannot cure are to be reckoned wholly incurable.

PROGNOSIS: THE FACE THAT TOKENS DEATH
(THE HIPPOCRATIC FACIES)

I

IT APPEARS to me a most excellent thing for the physician to cultivate prognosis; for by foreseeing and foretelling, in the presence of the sick, the present, the past, and the future, and explaining the omissions which patients have been guilty of, he will be the more readily believed to be acquainted with the circumstances of the sick; so that men will have confidence to intrust themselves to such a physician. And he will manage the cure best who has foreseen what is to happen from the present state of matters. For it is impossible to make all the sick well;

487

this, indeed, would have been better than to be able to foretell what is going to happen; but since men die, some even before calling the physician, from the violence of the disease, and some die immediately after calling him, having lived, perhaps, only one day or a little longer, and before the physician could bring his art to counteract the disease, it therefore becomes necessary to know the nature of such affections, how far they are above the powers of the constitution; and, moreover, if there be anything divine in the diseases, and to learn a foreknowledge of this also. Thus a man will be the more esteemed to be a good physician, for he will be the better able to treat those aright who can be saved, from having long anticipated everything; and by seeing and announcing beforehand those who will live and those who will die, he will thus escape censure.

II

He should observe thus in acute diseases; first, the countenance of the patient, if it be like itself, for this is the best of all; whereas the most opposite to it is the worst, such as the following: a sharp nose, hollow eyes, collapsed temples; the ears cold, contracted, and their lobes turned out; the skin about the forehead being rough, distended, and parched; the color of the whole face being green, black, livid, or lead-colored.[1] If the countenance be such at the commencement of the disease, and if this cannot be accounted for from the other symptoms, inquiry must be made whether the patient has long wanted sleep; whether his bowels have been very loose; and whether he has suffered from want of food; and if any of these causes be confessed to, the danger is to be reckoned so far less; and it becomes obvious, in the course of a day and a night, whether or not the appearance of the countenance proceed from these causes. But if none of these be said to exist, and if the symptoms do not subside in the aforesaid time, it is to be known for certain that death is at hand. And, also, if the disease be in a more advanced stage either on the third or fourth day, and the countenance be

[1] The Hippocratic facies.

such, the same inquiries as formerly directed are to be made, and the other symptoms are to be noted, those in the whole countenance, those on the body, and those in the eyes; for if they shun the light, or weep involuntarily, or squint, or if the one be less than the other, or if the white of them be red, livid, or has black veins in it; if there be a gum upon the eyes, if they are restless, protruding, or are become very hollow; and if the countenance be squalid and dark, or the color of the whole face be changed—all these are to be reckoned bad and fatal symptoms. The physician should also observe the appearance of the eyes from below the eyelids in sleep; for when a portion of the white appears owing to the eyelids not being closed together, and when this is connected with diarrhea or purgation from medicine, or when the patient does not sleep thus from habit, it is to be reckoned an unfavorable and very deadly symptom; but if the eyelid be contracted, livid, or pale, or also the lip, or nose, along with some of the other symptoms, one may know for certain that death is close at hand. It is a mortal symptom also, when the lips are relaxed, pendent, cold, and blanched.

A CASE OF CHILDBIRTH FEVER

THE WIFE of Epicrates, who was lodged at the house of Archigetes, being near the term of delivery, was seized with a violent rigor, and, as was said, she did not become heated; next day the same. On the third, she was delivered of a daughter, and everything went on properly. On the day following her delivery she was seized with acute fever, pain in the cardiac region of the stomach, and in the genital parts. Having had a suppository, was in so far relieved; pain in the head, neck, loins; no sleep; alvine discharges scanty, bilious, thin, and unmixed; urine thin and blackish. Toward the night of the sixth day from the time she was seized with the fever, became delirious. On the seventh, all the symptoms exacerbated; insomnolency, delirium, thirst; stools bilious and highcolored. On the eighth, had a rigor; slept more. On the ninth, the same. On the tenth, her limbs painfully

489

affected; pain again of the cardiac region of the stomach; heaviness of the head; no delirium; slept more; bowels constipated. On the eleventh, passed urine of a better color and, having an abundant sediment, felt lighter. On the fourteenth, had a rigor; acute fever. On the fifteenth, had a copious vomiting of bilious and yellow matters; sweated; fever gone; at night acute fever; urine thick, sediment white. On the seventeenth, an exacerbation; night uncomfortable; no sleep; delirium. On the eighteenth, thirsty; tongue parched; no sleep; much delirium; legs painfully affected. About the twentieth, in the morning, had a slight rigor; was comatose; slept tranquilly; had slight vomiting of bilious and black matters; towards night deafness. About the twenty-first, weight generally in the left side, with pain; slight cough; urine thick, muddy, and reddish; when allowed to stand, had no sediment; in other respects felt lighter; fever not gone; fauces painful from the commencement, and red; uvula retracted; defluxion remained acrid, pungent, and saltish throughout. About the twenty-seventh, free of fever; sediment in the urine; pain in the side. About the thirty-first was attacked with fever, bilious diarrhea; slight bilious vomiting on the fortieth. Had a complete crisis, and was freed from the fever on the eightieth day.

ROBERT HOOKE

(1635–1703)

One-time assistant of Robert Boyle, professor of geometry at Oxford, and surveyor of London after the great fire of 1666, this somewhat erratic physicist was involved in many inventions later associated with the names of other scientists. Both he and Huygens claimed to be the inventor of the hair spring, or balance spring, used in watches. Hooke anticipated Newton in the formulation of the law of gravitation, and anticipated the invention of the steam engine, correctly describing the processes of combustion in *Micrographia* (1665). He calculated the earth's center of gravity, invented a Gregorian telescope, was one of the first to use a microscope to examine minute objects, and formulated the law named after him: the extension of a spring is proportional to the force applied.

HOOKE'S LAW

THE THEORY of springs, though attempted by divers eminent mathematicians of this age has hitherto not been published by any. It is now about eighteen years since I first found it out, but designing to apply it to some particular use, I omitted the publishing thereof.

About three years since His Majesty was pleased to see the experiment that made out this theory tried at *White-Hall*, as also my spring watch.

About two years since I printed this theory in an anagram at the end of my book of the descriptions of helioscopes, *viz.* *c e i i i n o s s s t t u u, id est, ut tensio sic vis;* that is, the power of any spring is in the same proportion with the tension thereof: that is, if one power stretch or bend it one space, two will bend it two, and three will bend it three, and so forward. Now as the theory is very short, so the way of trying it is very easie.

491

Take then a quantity of even-drawn wire, either steel, iron, or brass, and coyl it on an even cylinder into a helix of what length or number of turns you please, then turn the ends of the wire into loops, by one of which suspend this coyl upon a nail, and the other sustain the weight that you would have to extend it, and hanging on several weights observe exactly to what length each of the weights do extend it beyond the length that its own weight doth stretch it to, and you shall find that if one ounce, or one pound, or one certain weight doth lengthen it one line, or one inch, or one certain length, then two ounces, two pounds, or two weights will extend it two lines, two inches, or two lengths; and three ounces, pounds, or weights, three lines, inches, or lengths; and so forwards. And this is the rule or law of nature, upon which all manner of restituent or springing motion doth proceed, whether it be of rarefaction, or extension, or condensation and compression.

Or take a watch spring, and coyl it into a spiral, so as no part thereof may touch another, then provide a very light wheel of brass, or the like, and fix it on an arbor that hath two small pivots of steel, upon which pivot turn the edge of the said wheel very even and smooth, so that a small silk may be coyled upon it, then put this wheel into a frame, so that the wheel may move very freely on its pivots; fasten the central end of the aforesaid spring, close to the pivot hole or center of the frame in which the arbor of the wheel doth move, and the other end thereof to the rim of the wheel, then coyling a fine limber thread of silk upon the edge of the wheel hang a small light scale at the end thereof fit to receive the weight that shall be put thereinto; then suffering the wheel to stand in its own position by a little index fastened to the frame, and pointing to the rim of the wheel, make a mark with ink, or the like, on that part of the rim that the index pointeth at; then put in a drachm weight into the scale, and suffer the wheel to settle, and make another mark on the rim where the index doth point; then add a drachm more, and let the wheel settle again, and note with ink, as before, the place of the rim pointed at by the index; then add a third drachm, and do as before, and so a fourth, fifth, sixth, seventh, eighth, etc., suffering the wheel to settle, and marking the several places pointed at by the index, then examine the distances of all those marks, and comparing them together you shall find that they will all be equal the one to the other, so that if a drachm doth move the wheel ten degrees, two drachms will move it twenty, and three thirty, and four forty, and five fifty, and so forwards.

Or take a wire string of twenty, or thirty, or forty foot long, and fasten the upper part thereof to a nail, and to the other end fasten a scale to receive the weights: then with a pair of compasses take the distance of the bottom of the scale from the ground or floor underneath, and set down the said distance, then put in weights into the said scale in the same manner as in the former trials, and measure the several stretchings of the said string, and set them down. Then compare the several stretchings of the said string, and you will find that they will always bear the same proportions one to the other that the weights do that made them.

The same will be found, if trial be made, with a piece of dry wood that will bend and return, if one end thereof be fixed in a horizontal posture, and to the other end be hanged weights to make it bend downwards.

The manner of trying the same thing upon a body of air, whether it be for the rarefaction or for the compression thereof I did about fourteen years since publish in my *Micrographia*, and therefore I shall not need to add any further description thereof.

EARTHQUAKES

THAT EARTHQUAKES CHANGE THE LEVEL OF STRATA

To proceed then to the Effects of Earthquakes, we find in Histories Four Sorts or *Genius's* to have been performed by them.

The first is the raising of the superficial Parts of the Earth above their former Level: and under this Head there are Four

Species. The 1st is the raising of a considerable Part of a Country, which before lay level with the Sea, and making it lye many Feet, nay, sometimes many Fathoms above its former height. A 2d is the raising of a considerable part of the bottom of the Sea, and making it lye above the Surface of the Water, by which means divers Islands have been generated and produced. A 3d Species is the raising of very considerable Mountains out of a plain and level Country. And a 4th Species is the raising of the Parts of the Earth by the throwing on of a great Access of new Earth, and for burying the former Surface under a covering of new Earth many Fathoms thick.

A second sort of Effects perform'd by Earthquakes, is the depression or sinking of the Parts of the Earth's Surface below the former Level. Under this Head are also comprized Four distinct Species, which are directly contrary to the four last named.

The *First*, is a sinking of some Part of the Surface of the Earth, lying a good way within the Land, and converting it into a Lake of an almost unmeasurable depth.

The *Second*, is the sinking of a considerable Part of the plain Land, near the Sea, below its former Level, and so suffering the Sea to come in and overflow it, being laid lower than the Surface of the next adjoining Sea.

A *Third*, is the sinking of the Parts of the bottom of the Sea much lower, and creating therein vast *Vorages* and *Abysses*.

A *Fourth*, is the making bare, or uncovering of divers Parts of the Earth, which were before a good way below the Surface; and this either by suddenly throwing away these upper Parts by some subterraneous Motion, or else by washing them away by some kind of Eruption of Waters from unusual Places, vomited out by some Earthquake.

A Third sort of Effects produced by Earthquakes, are the Subversions, Conversions, and Transpositions of the Parts of the Earth.

A Fourth sort of Effects, are *Liquefaction, Baking, Calcining, Petrifaction, Transformation, Sublimation, Distillation,* etc.

THAT WATER COUNTERACTS THESE EFFECTS

Another Cause there is which has been also a very great Instrument in the promoting the alterations on the Surface of the Earth, and that is the motion of the Water; whether caus'd 1st. By its Descent from some higher place, such as Rivers and Streams, caus'd by the immediate falls of Rain, or Snow, or by the melting of Snow from the sides of Hills. Or, 2dly. By the natural Motions of the Sea, such as are the Tides and Currents. Or, 3dly. By the accidental motions of it caus'd by Winds and Storms. Of each of these we have very many Instances in Natural Historians, and were they silent, the constant Effects, would daily speak as much. The former Principle seems to be that which generates Hills, and Holes, Cliffs, and Caverns, and all manner of Asperity and irregularity in the Surface of the Earth; and this is that which indeavours to reduce them back again to their pristine Regularity, by washing down the tops of Hills, and filling up the bottoms of Pits, which is indeed consonant to all the other methods of Nature, in working with contrary Principles of Heat and Cold, Driness, and Moisture, Light and Darkness, etc. by which there is, as it were, a continual circulation. Water is rais'd in Vapours into the Air by one Quality and precipitated down in drops by an other, the Rivers run into the Sea, and the Sea again supplies them. In the circular Motion of all the Planets, there is a direct Motion which makes them indeavour to recede from the Sun or Center, and a magnetick or attractive Power that keeps them from receding. Generation creates and Death destroys; Winter reduces what Summer produces: The Night refreshes what the Day has scorcht, and the Day cherishes what the Night benumb'd. The Air impregnates the Ground in one place, and is impregnated by it in another. All things almost circulate and have their Vicissitudes. We have multitudes of instances of the wasting of the tops of Hills, and of the filling or increasing of the Plains or lower Grounds, of Rivers continually carrying along with them great quantities of Sand, Mud, or other Substances from higher to lower places. Of the Seas washing Cliffs away and wasting the Shores: Of Land Floods carrying away with them all things that stand in their way, and covering those Lands with Mud which they overflow, levelling Ridges and filling Ditches. Tides and Currents in the Sea act in all probability what Floods and Rivers do at Land; and Storms effect that on the Sea Coasts, that great Land Floods do on the Banks of Rivers. *Egypt* as lying very low and yearly overflow'd, is inlarg'd by the sediment of the *Nile*; especially towards that part where the *Nile* falls into the *Mediterranean*. The Gulph of *Venice* is almost choak'd with the Sand of the *Po*. The Mouth of the *Thames* is grown very shallow by the continual supply of Sand brought down with the Stream. Most part of the Cliffs that Wall in this Island do Yearly founder and tumble into the Sea. By these means many parts are covered and rais'd by Mud and Sand that lye almost level with the Water, and others are discover'd and laid open that for many Ages have been hid. . . .

THE MOVEMENT OF CONTINENTS

But to proceed to the last Argument to confirm the 6th Proposition I at first undertook to prove, namely, that very many parts of the Surface of the Earth (not now to take notice of others) have been transform'd transpos'd and many ways alter'd since the first Creation of it. And that which to me seems the strongest and most cogent Argument of all is this, That at the tops of some of the highest Hills, and in the bottom of some of the deepest Mines, in the midst of Mountains and Quarries of Stone, etc. divers Bodies have been and daily are found, that if we thoroughly examine we shall find to be real shells of Fishes, which for these following Reasons we conclude to have been at first generated by the Plastick faculty of the Soul or Life-principle of some animal, and not from the imaginary influence of the Stars, or from any Plastick faculty inherent in the Earth itself so form'd; the stress of which Argument lies in these Particulars.

First, That the Bodies there found have exactly the Form and Matter, that is, are of the same kind of Substance for all its sensible Properties, and that the same External and Internal Figure or Shape with the Shells of Animals.

Next, That it is contrary to all the other acts of Nature, that does nothing in vain, but always aims at an end, to make two Bodies exactly of the same Substance and Figure, and one of them to be wholly useless, or at least without any design that we can with any plausibility imagine. . . .

Next therefore, Wherever Nature does work by peculiar Forms and Substances, we find that she always joins the Body so fram'd with some other peculiar Substance. Thus the Shells of Animals, whilst they are forming are join'd with the Flesh of the Animal to which they belong. . . .

Fourthly, Wherever else Nature works by peculiar Forms, we find her always to compleat that form, and not break off abruptly. . . .

Further, if these be the apish Tricks of Nature, Why does it not imitate several other of its own Works? Why do we not dig out of Mines everlasting Vegetables, as Grass for instance, or Roses of the same Substance, Figure, Colour, Smell? etc.

The Seventh Proposition that I undertook to make probable, was, That 'tis very probable that divers of these Transpositions and Metamorphoses have been wrought even here in *England*: Many of its Hills have probably been heretofore under the Sea, and divers other parts that were heretofore high Land and Hills, have since been covered with the Sea. Of the latter of these I have given many Instances already, and that which makes the first probable, is the great quantities of Shells that are found in the most Inland Parts of this Island; in the Hills, in the Plains, in the bottoms of Mines and in the middle of Mountains and Quarries of Stones. . . .

Now 'tis not probable that other Mens Hands, or the general Deluge which lasted but a little while, should bring them there; nor can I imagine any more likely and sufficient way than an Earthquake, which might theretofore raise all these Islands of Great *Britain* and *Ireland* out of the Sea, as it did heretofore, of which I have already mention'd the Histories; or as it lately did that Island in the *Canarys* and *Azores,* in the sight of divers who are yet alive to testifie the Truth and Manner of it: And possibly *England* and *Ireland* might be rais'd by the same Earthquake, by which the *Atlantis,* if we will believe *Plato,* was sunk. . . .

But as to those vast tracts of Ground that lye very far from the Sea, it may perhaps to some seem not impossible, that the Center of Gravity or Method of the attraction of the Globe of the Earth may change and shift places, and if so, then certainly all the fluid parts of the Earth will conform thereto, and then 'twill follow that one part will be cover'd and overflow'd by the Sea that was before dry, and another part be discover'd and laid dry that was before overwhelm'd. . . .

From all which Propositions, if at least they are true, will follow many others mere Corollaries which may be deduced from them.

First, That there may have been in preceding Ages, whole Countries either swallowed up into the Earth, or sunk so low as to be drown'd by the coming in of the Sea, or divers other ways quite destroyed; as *Plato's Atlantis,* etc.

Secondly, That there, may have been as many Countries new made and produced by being raised from under the Water, or from the inward or hidden parts of the Body of the Earth, as *England.*

Thirdly, That there may have been divers Species of things wholly destroyed and annihilated, and divers others changed and varied, for since we find that there are some kinds of Animals and Vegetables peculiar to certain places, and not to be found elsewhere. . . .

Fourthly, That there may have been divers new varieties generated of the same Species, and that by the change of the Soil on which it was produced; for since we find that the alteration of the Climate, Soil and Nourishment doth often produce a very great alteration in those Bodies that suffer it; 'tis not to be doubted but that alterations also of this Nature may cause a very great change in the shape, and other accidents of an animated Body. . . .

ALEXANDER VON HUMBOLDT

(1769–1859)

German traveler, naturalist and statesman, Humboldt is generally regarded as the founder of natural geography and was the first to draw isothermals on a map. His first great journey was a five-year exploration of South America, Mexico and Cuba (1799–1804), where he studied, among other things, the origin of tropical storms, plant zones, volcanoes and the earth's magnetism. His masterwork, *Kosmos* (1845-64), called a magnificent failure, was an attempt to draw a comprehensive picture of the entire physical universe. He also introduced into Europe Peruvian guano, a highly valuable manure.

ESSAY ON NEW SPAIN

LARGE *hill thrown up by a volcano in 1759.* The grand catastrophe in which this volcanic mountain [Jorullo] issued from the earth, and by which the face of a considerable extent of ground was totally altered, was perhaps one of the most extensive physical changes, that the history of our globe exhibits. Geology points out spots in the ocean, where, within the last two thousand years, volcanic islets have arisen above the surface of the sea, as near the Azores, in the Archipelago, and on the south of Iceland: but it records no instance of a mountain of scoriae and ashes, 517 meters (563 yards) above the old level of the neighboring plains, suddenly formed in the center of a thousand small burning cones, thirty-six leagues from the seashore, and forty-two leagues from any other volcano. This phenomenon remained unknown to the mineralogists and natural philosophers of Europe, though it took place but fifty years ago, and within six days journey of the capital of Mexico.

Country described. Descending from the central flat toward

499

the coasts of the Pacific ocean, a vast plain extends from the hills of Aguasarco to the villages of Toipa, and Patatlan, equally celebrated for their fine cotton plantations. Between the picachos del Mortero and the cerras de las Cuevas and de Cuiche, this plain is only from 750 to 800 met. (820 to 880 yards) above the level of the sea. Basaltic hills rise in the midst of a country, in which porphyry with a base of greenstone predominates. Their summits are crowned with oaks always in verdure, and the foliage of laurels and olives intermingled with dwarf fan palms. This beautiful vegetation forms a singular contrast with the arid plain, which has been laid waste by volcanic fire.

A fertile plain shaken by an earthquake, and a hill raised on it. To the middle of the eighteenth century fields of sugarcanes and indigo extended between two rivulets, called Cuitimba and San Pedro. They were skirted by basaltic mountains, the structure of which seems to indicate, that all the country, in remote periods, has several times experienced the violent action of volcanoes. Those fields, irrigated by art, belonged to the estate of San Pedro de Jorullo (Xorullo, or Juvriso), one of the largest and most valuable in the country. In the month of June, 1759, fearful rumbling noises were accompanied with frequent shocks of an earthquake, which succeeded each other at intervals for fifty or sixty days, and threw the inhabitants of the estate into the greatest consternation. From the beginning of the month of September, every thing seemed perfectly quiet, when in the night of the 28th of that month a terrible subterranean noise was heard anew. The frightened Indians fled to the mountains of Aguasarco. A space of three or four square miles, known by the name of Malpays, rose in the shape of a bladder. The boundaries of this rising are still distinguishable in the ruptured strata. The Malpays toward the edge is only 12 met. (13 yards) above the former level of the plain, called las playas de Jorullo; but the convexity of the ground increases progressively toward the center, till it reaches the height of 160 met. (175 yards).

The event described. They who witnessed this grand catastrophe from the top of Aguasarco assert, that they saw flames issue out of the ground for the space of more than half a league square; that fragments of red hot rocks were thrown to a prodigious height; and that through a thick cloud of ashes, illumined by the volcanic fire, and resembling a stormy sea, the softened crust of the earth was seen to swell up. The rivers of Cuitimba and San Pedro then precipitated themselves into the burning crevices. The decomposition of the water contributed to reanimate the flames, which were perceptible at the city of Pascuoro, though standing on a very wide plain 1400 met. (1530 yards) above the level of the playas de Jorullo. Eruptions of mud, particularly of the strata of clay including decomposed nodules of basaltes with concentric layers, seem to prove, that subterranean waters had no small part in this extraordinary revolution. Thousands of small cones, only two or three yards high, which the Indians call ovens, issued from the raised dome of the Malpays. Though the heat of these volcanic ovens has diminished greatly within these fifteen years, according to the testimony of the Indians, I found the thermometer rise to 95° (if centig. 203°F.) in the crevices that emitted an aqueous vapour. Each little cone is a chimney [*fumarole*, in the original], from which a thick smoke rises to the height of ten or fifteen met. (11 or 16 yards). In several a subterranean noise is heard like that of some fluid boiling at no great depth.

Six large hills in one line. Amid these ovens, in a fissure, the direction of which is from N.N.E. to S.S.E., six large hummocks rise 400 or 500 met. (440 or 550 yards) above the old level of the plain. This is the phenomenon of Monte Novo at Naples repeated several times in a row of volcanic hills. The loftiest of these huge hummocks, which reminded me of the country of Auvergne, is the large volcano of Jorullo. It is constantly burning, and has thrown out on the north side an immense quantity of scorified and basaltic lava, including fragments of primitive rocks. These grand eruptions of the central volcano continued till February, 1760. In the succeeding years they became gradually less frequent. The Indians, alarmed by the horrible noise of the new volcano, at first deserted the villages for seven or eight leagues round the plain of Jorullo. In a few months they became familiar with the alarming sight, returned to their huts, and

501

went down to the mountains of Aguasarco and Santa Ines, to admire the sheaves of fire thrown out by an infinite number of large and small volcanic openings. The ashes then covered the houses of Queretoro, more than 48 leagues (120 miles) in a right line from the place of the explosion. Though the subterranean fire appears to be in no great activity[1] at present, and the Malpays and the great volcano begin to be covered with vegetables, we found the air so heated by the little ovens, that in the shade, and at a considerable distance from the ground, the thermometer rose to 43° (109.4°F.). This fact evinces, that there is no exaggeration in the report of some of the old Indians, who say, that the plains of Jorullo were uninhabitable for several years, and even to a considerable distance from the ground raised up, on account of the excessive heat.

Line of volcanoes in Mexico crossing the chain of hills. The situation of the new volcano of Jorullo leads to a very curious geological observation. It has already been observed in the 3d chapter, that there is in New Spain a line of great heights, or a narrow zone included between the latitudes of 18°59′ and 19°12′, in which are all the summits of Anahuac that rise above the region of perpetual snow. These summits are either volcanoes still actually burning; or mountains, the form of which, as well as the nature of their rocks, renders it extremely probable, that they formerly contained subterranean fire. Setting out from the coast of the Gulf of Mexico, and proceeding westward, we find the peak of Oribaza, the two volcanoes of la Puebla, the Nevado de Toluca, the peak of Tancitaro, and the volcano of Colima. These great heights, instead of forming the ridge of the cordillera of Anahuac, and following its direction, which is from S.E.

---

[1] In the bottom of the crater we found the heat of the air 47° (116.6°F.), and in some places 58° and 60° (136.4° and 140°). We had to pass over cracks exhaling sulphurous vapours, in which the thermometer rose to 85° (185°). From these cracks, and the heaps of scoriae that cover considerable hollows, the descent into the craters is not without danger.

to N.W., are on the contrary in a line perpendicular to the axis of the great chain of mountains. It is certainly worthy of remark, that in the year 1759 the new volcano of Jorullo was formed in the continuation of this line, and on the same parallel as the ancient Mexican volcanoes.

Indicate a long interior fissure in the earth. A view of my plan of the environs of Jorullo will show, that the six large hummocks have risen out of the earth on a vein, that crosses the plain from the cerro of Las Cuevas to the picacho del Montero. The new mouths of Vesuvius too are found ranged along a fissure. Do not these analogies give us reason to suppose, that there exists in this part of Mexico, at a great depth within the Earth, a fissure stretching from east to west through a space of 137 leagues (343 miles), and through which the volcanic fire has made its way at different times, bursting the outer crust of porphyritic rocks, from the coasts of the Gulf of Mexico to the South Sea? Is this fissure prolonged to that little groupe of islands, called by Colluet the Archipelago of Regigedo, and round which, in the same parallel with the Mexican volcanoes, pumice stone has been seen floating?

ACCOUNT OF AN EARTHQUAKE WHICH DESTROYED THE TOWN OF CARACCAS

THERE ARE few events in the physical world which are calculated to excite so deep and permanent an interest as the earthquake which destroyed the town of Caraccas, and by which more than 20,000 persons perished, almost at the same instant, in the province of Venezuela. . . .

The 26th of March was a remarkably hot day. The air was calm, and the sky unclouded. It was Holy Thursday, and a great part of the population was assembled in the churches. Nothing seemed to presage the calamities of the day. At seven minutes after four in the afternoon the first shock was felt; it was sufficiently powerful, to make the bells of the churches toll; it lasted five or six seconds, during which time, the ground was in a continual undulating movement, and seemed to heave up like a boiling liquid. The danger was thought to be past, when a tremendous subterraneous noise was heard, resembling the rolling of thunder, but louder, and of longer continuance, than that heard within the tropics in time of storms. This noise preceded a perpendicular motion of three or four seconds, followed by an undulatory movement somewhat longer. The shocks were in opposite directions, from north to south, and from east to west. Nothing could resist the movement from beneath upward, and undulations crossing each other. The town of Caraccas was entirely overthrown. Between nine and ten thousand of the inhabitants were buried under the ruins of the houses and churches. . . . Nine-tenths of the fine town of Caraccas were entirely destroyed. The walls of the houses that were not thrown down, as those of the street San Juan, near the Capuchin Hospital, were cracked in such a manner, that it was impossible to run the risk of inhabiting them.

Shocks as violent as those which, in the space of one minute,[2] overthrew the city of Caraccas, could not be confined to a small portion of the continent. Their fatal effects extended as far as the provinces of Venezuela, Varinas, and Maracaybo, along the coast; and still more to the inland mountains. La Guayra, Mayquetia, Antimano, Baruta, La Vega, San Felipe, and Merida, were almost entirely destroyed. The number of the dead exceeded four or five thousand at La Guayra, and at the town of San Felipe, near the copper-mines of Aroa. It appears that it was on a line running east north-east, and west south-west, from La Guayra and Caraccas to the lofty mountains of Niquitao and Merida, that the violence of the earthquake was principally directed. It was felt in the kingdom of New Granada from the branches of the high Sierra de Santa Marta as far as Santa Fé

---

[2] The duration of the earthquake, that is to say the whole of the movements of undulation and rising which occasioned the horrible catastrophe of the 26th of March 1812, was estimated by some at 50″, by others at 1′12″.

de Bogota and Honda, on the banks of the Magdalena, 180 leagues from Caraccas. It was every where more violent in the Cordilleras of gneiss and micaslate, or immediately at their foot, than in the plains: and this difference was particularly striking in the savannahs of Varinas and Casanara. In the valleys of Aragua, situate between Caraccas and the town of San Felipe, the commotions were very weak: and La Victoria, Maracay, and Valentia, scarcely suffered at all, notwithstanding their proximity to the capital. At Valecillo, a few leagues from Valencia, the earth, opening, threw out such an immense quantity of water, that it formed a new torrent. The same phenomenon took place near Porto-Cabello. On the other hand, the lake of Maracaybo diminished sensibly. At Coro no commotion was felt, though the town is situated upon the coast, between other towns which suffered from the earthquake.

Fifteen or eighteen hours after the great catastrophe, the ground remained tranquil . . . the commotions did not recommence till after the 27th. They were then attended with a very loud and long continued subterranean noise. The inhabitants of Caraooas wandered into the country; but the villages and farms having suffered as much as the town, they could find no shelter till they were beyond the mountains of Los Teques, in the valleys of Aragua, and in the Llanos or Savannahs. No less than fifteen oscillations were often felt in one day. On the 5th of April there was almost as violent an earthquake, as that which overthrew the capital. During several hours the ground was in a state of perpetual undulation. Large masses of earth fell in the mountains; and enormous rocks were detached from the Silla of Caraccas. It was even asserted and believed that the two domes of the Silla sunk fifty or sixty toises; but this assertion is founded on no measurement whatever.

While violent commotions were felt at the same time in the valley of the Mississippi, in the island of St. Vincent, and in the province of Venezuela, the inhabitants of Caraccas, of Calabozo, situated in the midst of the steppes, and on the borders of the Rio Apura, in a space of 4000 square leagues, were terrified on the 30th of April 1812, by a subterraneous noise, which resembled frequent discharges of the largest cannon. This noise began at two in the morning. It was accompanied by no shock; and, what is very remarkable, it was as loud on the coast as at eighty leagues distance inland. It was every where believed to be transmitted through the air; and was so far from being thought a subterraneous noise, that at Caraccas, as well as at Calabozo, preparations were made to put the place into a state of defense against an enemy, who seemed to be advancing with heavy artillery. Mr. Palacio, crossing the Rio Apura near the junction of the Rio Nula, was told by the inhabitants that the *"firing of cannon"* had been heard as distinctly at the western extremity of the province of Varinas, as at the port of La Guayra to the north of the chain of the coast.

The day on which the inhabitants of Terra Firma were alarmed by a subterraneous noise, was that on which happened the eruption of the volcano in the island of St. Vincent. This mountain, near five hundred toises high, had not thrown out any lava since the year 1718. Scarcely was any smoke perceived to issue from its top, when, in the month of May 1811, frequent shocks announced, that the volcanic fire was either rekindled, or directed anew toward that part of the West Indies. The first eruption did not take place till the 27th of April 1812, at noon. It was only an ejection of ashes, but attended with a tremendous noise. On the 30th, the lava passed the brink of the crater, and, after a course of four hours, reached the sea. The noise of the explosion "resembled that of alternate discharges of very large cannon and of musketry; and, what is well worthy of remark, it seemed much louder at sea, at a great distance from the island, than in sight of land, and near the burning volcano."

The distance in a straight line from the volcano of St. Vincent to the Rio Apura, near the mouth of the Nula, is 210 nautical leagues. The explosions were consequently heard at a distance equal to that between Vesuvius and Paris. This phenomenon, connected with a great number of facts observed in the Cordilleras of the Andes, shows how much more extensive the subterranean sphere of activity of a volcano is, than we are disposed to admit from the small changes effected at the surface of the globe. The detonations heard during whole days together in the New World, 80, 100, or even 200 leagues distant from a crater, do not reach us by the propagation of sound through the air; they are transmitted to us by the ground. The little town of Honda, on the banks of the Magdalena, is not less than 145 leagues from Cotopaxi; and yet in the great explosions of this volcano, in 1744, a subterraneous noise was heard at Honda, and supposed to be discharges of heavy artillery. The monks of St. Francis spread the news, that the town of Carthagena was bombarded by the English; and the intelligence was believed. Now the volcano of Cotopaxi is a cone, more than 1800 toises above the basin of Honda, and rises from a table-land, the elevation of which is more than 1500 toises above the valley of the Magdalena. In all the colossal mountains of Quito, of the provinces of Los Pastos, and of Popayan, crevices and valleys without number are interposed. It cannot be admitted, under these circumstances, that the noise could be transmitted through the air, or by the superior surface of the globe, and that it came from that point, where the cone and crater of Cotopaxi are placed. It appears probable, that the higher part of the kingdom of Quito and the neighboring Cordilleras, far from being a group of distinct volcanoes, constitute a single swollen mass, an enormous volcanic wall, stretching from south to north, and the crest of which exhibits a surface of more than six hundred square leagues. Cotopaxi, Tunguragua, Antisana, and Pichincha, are placed on this same vault, on this raised ground. The fire issues sometimes from one, sometimes from another of these summits. The obstructed craters appear to be extinguished volcanoes; but we may presume, that, while Cotopaxi or Tunguragua have only one or two eruptions in the course of a century, the fire is not less continually active under the town of Quito, under Pichincha and Imbaburu.

Advancing toward the north, we find, between the volcano of Cotopaxi and the town of Honda, two other *systems of volcanic mountains*, those of Los Pastos and of Popayan. The connection of these systems was manifested in the Andes in an incontestible manner by a phenomenon, which I have already had occasion to

507

notice. Since the month of November 1796, a thick column of smoke had issued from the volcano of Pasto, west of the town of that name, and near the valley of Rio Guaytara. The mouths of the volcano are lateral, and placed on its western declivity, yet during three successive months the column rose so much higher than the ridge of the mountain, that it was constantly visible to the inhabitants of the town of Pasto. They related to us their astonishment, when, on the 4th of February 1797, they observed the smoke disappear in an instant, without feeling any shock whatever. At that very moment, sixty-five leagues to the south, between Chimborazo, Tunguragua, and the Altar (Capac Urcu), the town of Riobamba was overthrown by the most dreadful earthquake of which tradition has transmitted the history. Is it possible to doubt from this coincidence of phenomena, that the vapors issuing from the small apertures or *ventanillas* of the volcano of Pasto, had an influence on the pressure of those elastic fluids, which shook the ground of the kingdom of Quito, and destroyed in a few minutes thirty or forty thousand inhabitants?

In order to explain these great effects of *volcanic reactions,* and to prove, that the group or system of the volcanoes of the West India Islands may sometimes shake the continent, it was necessary to cite the Cordillera of the Andes. Geological reasoning can be supported only on the analogy of facts that are recent, and consequently well authenticated: and in what other region of the globe could we find greater, and at the same time more varied volcanic phenomena, than in that double chain of mountains heaved up by fire? in that land, where Nature has covered every summit and every valley with her wonders? If we consider a burning crater only as an insulated phenomenon, if we satisfy ourselves with examining the mass of stony substances which it has thrown up, the volcanic action at the surface of the globe will appear neither very powerful nor very extensive. But the image of this action swells in the mind, when we study the relations that link together volcanoes of the same group; for instance, those of Naples and Sicily, of the Canary Islands, of the Azores, of the Caribbee Islands, of Mexico, of Guatimala, and of the table-land of Quito; when we examine either the reactions of these different systems of volcanoes on one another, or the distance to which, by subterranean communications, they at the same moment shake the Earth.

SHOOTING STARS

COMMENCING from the *geometrical* relations of the periodic (not sporadic) falling stars, we direct our attention especially to what recent observations as to the *divergence* or *point of departure* of the meteors, and their *entirely planetary velocity*, have made known. Both these circumstances, divergence and velocity, characterize them with a high degree of probability as luminous bodies which present themselves independently of the Earth's rotation, and penetrate into our atmosphere *from without*, from space. The North American observations of the *November period* on the occasion of the falls of stars in 1833, 1834, and 1837, indicated as the point of departure the star γ Leonis; the observations of the August phenomenon, in the year 1839, Algol in Perseus, or a point between Perseus and Taurus. These centers of divergence were about the constellations toward which the Earth moved at the same epoch. Saigey, who has submitted the American observations of 1833 to a very accurate investigation, remarks that the fixed radiation from the constellation Leo is only observed properly after midnight, in the last three or four hours before daybreak; that of eighteen observers between the town of Mexico and Lake Huron, only ten perceived the same general point of departure of the meteors, which Denison Olmstead, Professor of Mathematics in New Haven (Connecticut), indicated.

The excellent work of Edward Heis, of Aix-la-Chapelle, which presents in a condensed form the very accurate observations of falling stars made by himself during ten years, contains results as to the *phenomena of divergence*, which are so much the more important as the observer has discussed them with mathematical strictness. According to him, ". . . the falling stars of the

509

November period present the peculiarity that their paths are more dispersed than those of the *August period*. In each of the two periods there were simultaneously several points of departure by no means always proceeding *from the same constellation*, as there was too great a tendency to assume since the year 1833." Besides the *principal point of departure of Algol in Perseus*, Heis finds in the *August* periods of the years 1839, 1841, 1842, 1843, 1844, 1847, and 1848, two others in Draco and the *North Pole*. "In order to deduce accurate results as to the points of departure of the paths of the falling stars in the *November periods* for the years 1839, 1841, 1846, and 1847, for the four points (Perseus, Leo, Cassiopeia, and the Dragon's Head), the mean path belonging to each was drawn upon a thirty-inch celestial globe, and in every case the position of the point ascertained from which the greatest number of paths proceeded. The investigation showed that of 407 of the falling stars indicated *according to their paths*, 171 came from Perseus, near the star η in Medusa's Head, 83 from Leo, 35 from Cassiopeia, near the changeable star α, 10 from the Dragon's Head but full 78 from undetermined points. The number of falling stars issuing from Perseus consequently amounted to nearly double those from Leo."

The divergence from Perseus has consequently shown itself *in both* periods as a very remarkable result. An acute observer, Julius Schmidt, attached to the Observatory at Bonn, who has been occupied with meteoric phenomena for eight or ten years, expresses himself upon this subject with great decision in a letter to me (July, 1851): "If I deduct from the abundant falls of shooting stars in November, 1833, and 1834, as well as from subsequent ones, that kind in which the point in Leo sent out whole swarms of meteors, I am at present inclined to consider the *Perseus point* as that point of divergence which presents not only in August, but throughout the *whole year*, the most meteors. This point is situated, according to the result deduced from 478 observations by Heis, in Rt. Asc. 50.3° and Decl. 51.5° (holding good for 1844-1846). In November, 1849 (from the 7th to the 14th), I saw some hundreds more shooting stars than I have ever remarked since 1841. Of these only a few, upon the whole, came from Leo; by far the greater number belonged to the constellation of Perseus. It follows from this, as it appears to me, that the *great* November phenomenon of 1799 and 1833 did not appear at that time (1841). Olbers also believes that the maximum November appearance has a period of thirty-four years. If the directions of the meteor paths are considered in their full complication and periodical recurrence, it is found that there are certain *points of divergence* which are always represented, others which appear only sporadically and changeably."

Whether, moreover, the different points of divergence alter with the years—which, if *closed rings* are assumed, would indicate an alteration in the situation of the ring in which the meteors move—can not at present be determined with certainty from the observations. A beautiful series of such observations by Houzeau (during the years 1839 and 1842) appears to offer evidence against a progressive alteration. Edward Heis has very correctly remarked that, in Grecian and Roman antiquity, attention had already been directed to a certain temporary uniformity in the *direction* of shooting stars darting across the sky. That direction was then considered as the result of a wind already blowing in the higher regions of the atmosphere, and predicted to the sailors an approaching current of air descending thence into the lower regions.

If the *periodic* streams of shooting stars are distinguished from the *sporadic* by the frequent parallelism of their paths, proceeding from one or more points of divergence, a second criterion of them is the numerical—the number of individual meteors referred to a definite measure of time. We come here to the much-disputed question of the distinction of an extraordinary from an ordinary fall of shooting stars. Two excellent observers, Olbers and Quetelet, have given as the mean number of meteors which can be reckoned hourly in the range of vision of one person upon not extraordinary days, the former five to six, the latter eight meteors. For the discussion of this question, which is as important as the determination of the laws of motion

511

of shooting stars, in reference to their direction, a great number of observations are required. I have therefore referred with confidence to the already mentioned observer, Herr Julius Schmidt at Bonn, who, long accustomed to astronomical accuracy, takes up with his peculiar energy the whole phenomena of meteors—of which the formation of aërolites and their fall to the Earth appear to him merely a special phase, the rarest, and, therefore, not the most important. The following are the principal results of the communications which I requested from him.

"The mean number of *sporadic* shooting stars appearing there has been found, from many years of observation (between 3 and 8 years), *a fall of from four to five in the hour.* This is the ordinary condition when nothing periodic occurs. The mean numbers of *sporadic* meteors in the individual months give for the hour, January, 3.4; February,—; March 4.9; April, 2.4; May, 3.9; June, 5.3; July, 4.5; August, 5.3; September, 4.7; October, 4.5; November, 5.3; December, 4.0.

"Of the *periodic* meteors there may be *expected,* on the average, in each hour, *above* 13 *or* 15. For a single period, that of August, the stream of Laurentius[1] presented the following gradual increases from sporadic to periodic, upon an average of from three to eight years of observation.

Time	Number of meteors in one hour	Number of years
6th of August	6	1
7th of August	11	3
8th of August	15	4
9th of August	29	8
10th of August	31	6
11th of August	19	5
12th of August	7	3

[1] The Perseids, occurring about the tenth of August, the festival of St. Lawrence.

. . . All these numbers refer to the circle of vision of one observer. Since the year 1838, the November falls have been less brilliant. (On the 12th of November, 1839, Heis still counted hourly 22 to 35 meteors; likewise, on the 13th of November, 1846, upon the average, 27 to 33.) So variable is the abundance of the periodic streams in individual years; but the number of the falling meteors always remains considerably greater than in ordinary nights, which show in one hour only four or five sporadic falls. The meteors appear to be the most seldom in January (calculating from the 4th), February, and March . . .

"The *upper* limits of the *height* of shooting stars can not be ascertained with accuracy, and Olbers considers all heights above 120 miles as being less certainly determined. The *lower* boundaries which were formerly generally estimated at 16 miles (over 97,388 feet), must be greatly contracted. Some, according to measurement, descend very nearly to the level of the summit of Chimborazo and Aconcagua, to the distance of four geographical miles above the level of the sea. Heis remarked, on the contrary, a falling star seen simultaneously at Berlin and Breslau on the 10th of July, 1037, [which] had, according to accurate calculation, a height of 248 miles when its light first became visible, and a height of 168 on its disappearance; others disappeared during the same night at a height of 56 miles. From the older labors of Brandes (1823), it follows that of 100 well defined shooting stars seen from two points of observation, 4 had an elevation of only 4 to 12 miles; 15 between 12 and 24 m.; 22 from 24 to 40 m.; 35 (nearly one third) from 40 to 60 m.; 13 from 40 to 80 m.; and only 11 (scarcely one tenth) above 80 m.; their heights being between 180 and 240 miles. From 4000 observations collected during nine years, it has been inferred, with regard to the *color* of the shooting stars, that two thirds are white, one seventh yellow, one seventeenth yellowish red, and only one thirty-seventh green."

Olbers reports, that during the fall of meteors in the night of the 12th and 13th of November, in the year 1838, a beautiful northern light was visible at Bremen, which colored large parts of the sky with an intense blood-red light. The shooting stars darting across this region maintained their white color unaltered, whence it may be inferred that the northern light was further removed from the surface of the Earth than the shooting stars were at that point where they became visible. The relative velocity of shooting stars has hitherto been estimated at from 18 to 36 geographical miles a second, while the Earth has only a translatory velocity of 16.4 miles. Corresponding observations of Julius Schmidt at Bonn, and Heis at Aix-la-Chapelle (1849), gave as the actual minimum for a shooting star, which stood 48 miles vertically above St. Goar, and shot over the Lake of Laach, only 14 miles. According to other comparisons of the same observer, and of Houzeau in Mons, the velocity of four shooting stars was found to be between 46 and 95 miles in the second, consequently two to five times as great as the planetary velocity of the Earth. The cosmical origin is indeed most strongly proved by this result, together with the constancy of the simple or multiple points of divergence, i.e., together with the circumstance that periodic shooting stars, independently of the rotation of the Earth, proceed during several hours from the same star, even when this star is not that toward which the Earth is moving at the same time. According to the existing measurements, fireballs appear to move slower than shooting stars; but it nevertheless remains striking, that when the former meteors fall, they sink such a little way into the ground. The mass at Ensisheim, in Alsace, weighing 276 pounds (November 7th, 1492), penetrated only 3 feet, and the aërolite of Braunau (July 14th, 1847) to the same depth. I know of only two meteoric stones which have plowed up the loose earth for 6 and 18 feet: these are the aërolites of Castrovillari, in the Abruzzi (February 9th, 1583), and that of Hradschina, in the Agram district (May 6th, 1751).

THOMAS HENRY HUXLEY

(1825–1895)

Foremost exponent of the Darwinian theory of evolution, Huxley was trained as a doctor and biologist, and became one of the great teachers of the nineteenth century. As an anatomist his word carried weight in scientific circles, while as a writer he had a unique faculty for giving scientific notions popular appeal. He is responsible for the word "agnostic" to explain the philosophic attitude of many scientists of his time. Among his works: *Zoological Evidences as to Man's Place in Nature* (1863), *On the Causes of the Phenomena of Organic Nature* (1863), *Science and Culture* (1881), and *Evolution and Ethics* (1893).

THE GEOLOGICAL HISTORY OF THE HORSE

IN THE highest group of Vertebrates, the Mammalia, the perfection of animal structure is attained. It will hardly be necessary, indeed it will be impossible in the time at our disposal, to give the general characters of the group, but our purpose will be answered as well by devoting a short time to considering the peculiarities of a single well-known animal, the evidence as to the origin of which approaches precision.

The horse is one of the most specialized and peculiar of animals, its whole structure being so modified as to make it the most perfect living locomotive engine which it is possible to imagine. The chief points in which its structure is modified to bring about this specialization, and in which, therefore, it differs most markedly from other mammals, we must now consider.

In the skull the orbit is completely closed behind by bone, a character found only in the most modified mammals. The teeth have a very peculiar character. There are, first of all, in the front part of each jaw, six long curved incisors or cutting teeth,

515

which present a singular dark mark on their biting surfaces, caused by the filling in of a deep groove on the crown of each tooth, by the substances on which the animal feeds. After the incisors, comes on both sides of each jaw a considerable tooth-less interval, or *diastema,* and then six large grinding teeth, or molars and premolars. In the young horse a small extra premolar is found to exist at the hinder end of the diastema, so that there are, in reality, seven grinders on each side above and below; furthermore, the male horse has a tusk-like tooth, or canine, in the front part of the diastema immediately following the last incisor. Thus the horse has, on each side of each jaw, three incisors, one canine, and seven grinders, making a total of forty-four teeth.

It is, however, in the limbs that the most striking deviation from the typical mammalian structure is seen, the most singular modifications having taken place to produce a set of long, jointed levers, combining great strength with the utmost possible spring and lightness.

The humerus is a comparatively short bone inclined back-wards: the radius is stout and strong, but the ulna seems to be reduced to its upper end—the olecranon or elbow; as a matter of fact, however, its distal end is left, fused to the radius, but the middle part has entirely disappeared: the carpus or wrist—the so-called "knee" of the horse—is followed by a long "cannon-bone," attached to the sides of which are two small "splint-bones"; the three together evidently represent the metacarpus, and it can be readily shown that the great cannon-bone is the metacarpal of the third finger, the splint-bones those of the second and fourth. The splint-bones taper away at their lower ends and have no phalanges attached to them, but the cannon-bone is followed by the usual three phalanges, the last of which, the "coffin-bone," is ensheathed by the great nail or hoof.

The femur, like the humerus, is a short bone, but is directed forwards; the tibia turns backwards, and has the upper end of the rudimentary fibula attached to its outer angle. The latter bone, like the ulna, has disappeared altogether as to its middle portion, and its distal end is firmly united to the tibia. The foot has the same structure as the corresponding part in the fore-limb —a great cannon-bone, the third metatarsal; two splints, the second and fourth; and the three phalanges of the third digit, the last of which bears a hoof.

Thus, in both fore and hind limb one toe is selected, becomes greatly modified and enlarged at the expense of the others, and forms a great lever, which, in combination with the levers constituted by the upper and middle divisions of the limb, forms a sort of double C-spring arrangement, and thus gives to the horse its wonderful galloping power.

In the river-beds of the Quaternary age—a time when England formed part of the Continent of Europe—abundant remains of horses are found, which horses resembled altogether our own species, or perhaps are still more nearly allied to the wild ass. The same is the case in America, where the species was very abundant in the Quaternary epoch—a curious fact, as, when first discovered by Europeans, there was not a horse from one end of the vast continent to the other.

In the Pliocene and older Miocene, both of Europe and America, are found a number of horse-like animals, resembling the existing horse in the pattern and number of the teeth, but differing in other particulars, especially the structure of the limbs. They belong to the genera *Protohippus, Hipparion,* &c., and are the immediate predecessors of the Quaternary horses.

In these animals the bones of the fore-arm are essentially like those of the horse, but the ulna is stouter and larger, can be traced from one end to the other, and, although firmly united to the radius, was not ankylosed with it. The same is true, though to a less marked extent, of the fibula.

But the most curious change is to be found in the toes. The third toe though still by far the largest, is proportionally smaller than in the horse, and each of the splint bones bears its own proper number of phalanges; a pair of "dew-claws," like those of the reindeer, being thus formed, one on either side of the great central toe. These accessory toes, however, by no means reached the ground, and could have been of no possible use, except in progression through marshes.

517

The teeth are quite like those of the existing horse, as to pattern, number, presence of cement, &c.; the orbit also is complete, but there is a curious depression on the face-bones, just beneath the orbit, a rudiment of which is, however, found in some of the older horses.

On passing to the older Miocene, we find an animal, known as *Anchitherium*, which bears, in many respects, a close resemblance to Hipparion, but is shorter-legged, stouter-bodied, and altogether more awkward in appearance. Its skull exhibits the depression mentioned as existing in Hipparion, but the orbit is incomplete behind, thus deviating from the specialized structure found in the horse, and approaching nearer to an ordinary typical mammal. The same is the case with the teeth, which are short and formed roots at an early period; their pattern also is simplified, although all the essential features are still retained. The valleys between the various ridges are not filled up with cement, and the little anterior premolar of the horse has become as large as the other grinders, so that the whole forty-four teeth of the typical mammalian dentition are well developed. The diastema is still present between the canines and the anterior grinding teeth—a curious fact in relation to the theory that the corresponding space in the horse was specially constructed for the insertion of the bit; for, if the Miocene men were in the habit of riding the Anchitherium, they were probably able to hold on so well with their hind legs as to be in no need of a bit.

The fibula is a complete bone, though still ankylosed below to the tibia; the ulna also is far stouter and more distinct than in Hipparion. In both fore and hind foot the middle toe is smaller, in relation to the size of the animal, than in either the horse or the Hipparion, and the second and fourth toes, though still smaller than the third, are so large that they must have reached the ground in walking. Thus, it is only necessary for the second and fourth toes, and the ulna and fibula to get smaller and smaller for the limb of Anchitherium to be converted into that of Hipparion, and this again into that of the horse.

Up to the year 1870 this was all the evidence we had about the matter, except for the fact that a species of Palaeotherium from the older Eocene was, in many respects, so horse-like, having, however, well-developed ulna and fibula, and the second and fourth toes larger even than in Anchitherium, that it had every appearance of being the original stock of the horse. But within the last six years some remarkable discoveries in central and western North America, have brought to light forms which are, probably, nearer the direct line of descent than any we have hitherto known.

In the Eocene rocks of these localities, a horse-like animal has been found, with three toes, like those of Anchitherium, but having, in addition, a little style of bone on the outer side of the fore foot, evidently representing the fifth digit. This is the little Orohippus, the lowest member of the Equine series.

It may well be asked why such clear evidence should be obtainable as to the origin of mammals, while in the case of many other groups—fish, for instance—all the evidence seems to point the other way. This question cannot be satisfactorily answered at present, but the fact is probably connected with the great uniformity of conditions to which the lower animals are exposed, for it is invariably the case that the higher the position of any given animal in the scale of being, the more complex are the conditions acting on it.

. . . The accurate information obtained in this department of science has put the *fact* of evolution beyond a doubt; formerly, the great reproach to the theory was, that no support was lent to it by the geological history of living things; now, whatever happens, the fact remains that the hypothesis is founded on the firm basis of palaeontological evidence.

CHRISTIAN HUYGENS

(1629-1693)

Huygens was a gifted Dutch mathematician who, like Newton and Galileo, worked in the related fields of optics, astronomy and mechanics. Following Galileo's suggestion, he investigated the compound pendulum and applied it as the regulator of a clock (1656). His *Horologium Oscillatorium* (1673), a mathematical analysis of this achievement, is a landmark in science. His *Traité de la Lumière* (1678), quoted here, expounded his famous wave theory of light. As an astronomer Huygens constructed powerful telescopes, discovered a satellite of Saturn, proved that Saturn's ring entirely surrounds the planet (*Systema Saturnium*, 1659), and was the first to make a drawing of Mars.

TREATISE ON LIGHT

I DO NOT find that anyone has yet given a probable explanation of the first and most notable phenomena of light, namely, why it is not propagated except in straight lines, and how visible rays, coming from an infinitude of diverse places, cross one another without hindering one another in any way. . . .

It is inconceivable to doubt that light consists in the motion of some sort of matter. For whether one considers its production, one sees that here upon the earth it is chiefly engendered by fire and flame which contain without doubt bodies that are in rapid motion, since they dissolve and melt many other bodies, even the most solid; or whether one considers its effects, one sees that when light is collected, as by concave mirrors, it has the property of burning as a fire does, that is to say, it disunites the particles of bodies. This is assuredly the mark of motion, at least in the true philosophy, in which one conceives the causes of all natural effects in terms of mechanical motions. This, in my opinion, we must necessarily do, or else renounce all hopes of ever comprehending anything in physics.

And as, according to this philosophy, one holds as certain that the sensation of sight is excited only by the impression of some movement of a kind of matter which acts on the nerves at the back of our eyes, there is here yet one reason more for believing that light consists in a movement of the matter which exists between us and the luminous body.

Further, when one considers the extreme speed with which light spreads on every side, and how, when it comes from different regions, even from those directly opposite, the rays traverse one another without hindrance, one may well understand that when we see a luminous object it cannot be by any transport of matter coming to us from this object, in the way in which a shot or an arrow traverses the air; for assuredly that would too greatly impugn these two properties of light, especially the second of them. It is then in some other way that light spreads; and that which which can lead us to comprehend it is the knowledge which we have of the spreading of sound in the air.

We know that by means of the air, which is an invisible and impalpable body, sound spreads around the spot where it has been produced, by a movement which is passed on successively from one part of the air to another; and that the spreading of this movement, taking place equally rapidly on all sides, ought to form spherical surfaces ever enlarging and which strike our ears. Now there is no doubt at all that light also comes from the luminous body to our eyes by some movement impressed on the matter which is between the two; since, as we have already seen, it cannot be by the transport of a body which passes from one to the other. If, in addition, light takes time for its passage —which we are now going to examine—it will follow that this movement, impressed on the intervening matter, is successive; and consequently it spreads, as sound does, by spherical surfaces and waves: for I call them waves from their resemblance to

521

those which are seen to be formed in water when a stone is thrown into it, and which present a successive spreading as circles though these arise from another cause, and are only in a flat surface.

To see then whether the spreading of light takes time, let us consider first whether there are any facts of experience which can convince us to the contrary. As to those which can be made here on the earth, by striking lights at great distances, although they prove that light takes no sensible time to pass over these distances, one may say with good reason that they are too small, and that the only conclusion to be drawn from them is that the passage of light is extremely rapid . . . a hundred thousand times greater than that of sound.

But that which I employed only as a hypothesis has recently received great seemingness as an established truth by the ingenious proof of Mr. Römer which I am going here to relate, expecting him himself to give all that is needed for its confirmation. It is founded . . . upon celestial observations and proves not only that light takes time for its passage, but also demonstrates how much time it takes, and that its velocity is even at least six times greater than that which I have just stated.

For this he makes use of the eclipses suffered by the little planets which revolve around Jupiter, and which often enter his shadow.

The velocity of light is more than six hundred thousand times greater than that of sound. This, however, is quite another thing from being instantaneous, since there is all the difference between a finite thing and an infinite. Now the successive movement of light being confirmed in this way, it follows, as I have said, that it spreads by spherical waves, like the movement of sound. . . .

Now if one examines what this matter may be in which the movement coming from the luminous body is propagated, which I call ethereal matter, one will see that it is not the same that serves for the propagation of sound. For one finds that the latter is really that which we feel and which we breathe, and which, being removed from any place, still leaves there the other kind of matter that serves to convey light. This may be proved by shutting up a sounding body in a glass vessel from which the air is withdrawn by the machine which Mr. Boyle has given us, and with which he has performed so many beautiful experiments. But in doing this of which I speak care must be taken to place the sounding body on cotton or on feathers, in such a way that it cannot communicate its tremors either to the glass vessel which encloses it or to the machine; a precaution which has hitherto been neglected. For then, after having exhausted all the air, one hears no sound from the metal, though it is struck.

One sees here not only that our air, which does not penetrate through glass, is the matter by which sound spreads; but also that it is not the same air but another kind of matter in which light spreads; since if the air is removed from the vessel the light does not cease to traverse it as before.

And this last point is demonstrated even more clearly by the celebrated experiment of Torricelli, in which the tube of glass from which the quicksilver has withdrawn itself, remaining void of air, transmits light just the same as when air is in it. For this proves that a matter different from air exists in this tube, and that this matter must have penetrated the glass or the quicksilver, either one or the other, though they are both impenetrable to the air. And when, in the same experiment, one makes the vacuum after putting a little water above the quicksilver, one concludes equally that the said matter passes through glass or water, or through both. . . .

But the extreme velocity of light, and other properties which it has, cannot admit of such a propagation of motion, and I am about to show here the way in which I conceive it must occur. For this, it is needful to explain the property which hard bodies must possess to transmit movement from one to another.

When one takes a number of spheres of equal size, made of some very hard substance, and arranges them in a straight line, so that they touch one another, one finds, on striking with a similar sphere against the first of these spheres, that the motion

523

passes as in an instant to the last of them, which separates itself from the row, without one's being able to perceive that the others have been stirred. And even that one which was used to strike remains motionless with them. Whence one sees that the movement passes with an extreme velocity which is the greater, the greater the hardness of the substance of the spheres.

EDWARD JENNER

(1749–1823)

The invention of vaccination, to produce artificial immunization to a disease, is attributed to Edward Jenner, an English physician. In his country practice Jenner noticed that milkmaids who contracted cowpox became immune to smallpox. He inoculated an eight-year-old boy with a primitive cowpox vaccine and found the boy had been immunized to smallpox. He announced his discovery in the *Inquiry into the Cause and Effects of the Variolae Vaccinae* (1798), and after the customary bitter opposition from the conservative members of his profession, the discovery was universally adopted.

AN INQUIRY INTO THE CAUSES AND EFFECTS OF THE VARIOLAE VACCINAE, OR COW-POX

THE deviation of man from the stage in which he was originally placed by nature seems to have proved to him a prolific source of diseases. From the love of splendor, from the indulgences of luxury, and from his fondness for amusement he has familiarized himself with a great number of animals, which may not originally have been intended for his associates.

The wolf, disarmed of ferocity, is now pillowed in the lady's lap. The cat, the little tiger of our island, whose natural home is the forest, is equally domesticated and caressed. The cow, the hog, the sheep, and the horse, are all, for a variety of purposes, brought under his care and dominion.

There is a disease to which the horse, from his state of domestication, is frequently subject. The farriers have called it the grease. It is an inflammation and swelling in the heel, from which issues matter possessing properties of a very peculiar kind, which seems capable of generating a disease in the human body (after it has undergone the modification which I shall presently speak of), which bears so strong a resemblance to the smallpox that I think it highly probable it may be the source of the disease.

In this dairy country a great number of cows are kept, and the office of milking is performed indiscriminately by men and maid servants. One of the former having been appointed to apply dressings to the heels of a horse affected with the grease, and not paying due attention to cleanliness, incautiously bears his part in milking the cows, with some particles of the infectious matter adhering to his fingers. When this is the case, it commonly happens that a disease is communicated to the cows, and from the cows to the dairymaids, which spreads through the farm until the most of the cattle and domestics feel its unpleasant consequences. This disease has obtained the name of the cow-pox. . . .

Thus the disease makes its progress from the horse to the nipple of the cow, and from the cow to the human subject.

Morbid matter of various kinds, when absorbed into the system, may produce effects in some degree similar; but what renders the cow-pox virus so extremely singular is that the person who has been thus affected is forever after secure from the infection of the smallpox; neither exposure to the variolous effluvia, nor the insertion of the matter into the skin, producing this distemper.

In support of so extraordinary a fact, I shall lay before my reader a great number of instances. . . .

Case II. Sarah Portlock, of this place, was infected with the cow-pox when a servant at a farmer's in the neighborhood, twenty-seven years ago.

In the year 1792, conceiving herself, from this circumstance, secure from the infection of the smallpox, she nursed one of her own children who had accidentally caught the disease, but no indisposition ensued. During the time she remained in the infected room, variolous matter was inserted into both her arms, but without any further effect than in the preceding case. . . .

526

Case XVII [Entire]. The more accurately to observe the progress of the infection I selected a healthy boy, about eight years old, for the purpose of inoculation for the cow-pox. The matter was taken from a sore on the hand of a dairymaid, who was infected by her master's cows, and it was inserted, on the 14th of May, 1796, into the arm of the boy by means of two superficial incisions, barely penetrating the cutis, each about half an inch long.

On the seventh day he complained of uneasiness in the axilla, and on the ninth he became a little chilly, lost his appetite, and had a slight headache. During the whole of this day he was perceptibly indisposed, and spent the night with some degree of restlessness, but on the day following he was perfectly well.

The appearance of the incisions in their progress to a state of maturation were much the same as when produced in a similar manner by variolous matter. The only difference which I perceived was in the state of the limpid fluid arising from the action of the virus, which assumed rather a darker hue, and in that of the efflorescence spreading round the incisions, which had more of an erysipelatous look than we commonly perceive when variolous matter has been made use of in the same manner; but the whole dies away (leaving on the inoculated parts scabs and subsequent eschars) without giving me or my patient the least trouble.

In order to ascertain whether the boy, after feeling so slight an affection of the system from the cow-pox virus, was secure from the contagion of the smallpox, he was inoculated the 1st of July following with variolous matter, immediately taken from a pustule. Several slight punctures and incisions were made on both his arms, and the matter was carefully inserted, but no disease followed. The same appearances were observable on the arms as we commonly see when a patient has had variolous matter applied, after having either the cow-pox or smallpox. Several months afterwards he was again inoculated with variolous matter, but no sensible effect was produced on the constitution.

Here my researches were interrupted till the spring of the

year 1798, when, from the wetness of the early part of the season, many of the farmers' horses in this neighborhood were affected with sore heels, in consequence of which the cow-pox broke out among several of our dairies, which afforded me an opportunity of making further observations upon this curious disease.

A mare, the property of a person who keeps a dairy in a neighboring parish, began to have sore heels the latter end of the month of February, 1798, which were occasionally washed by the servant men of the farm, Thomas Virgoe, William Wherret, and William Haynes, who in consequence became affected with sores in their hands, followed by inflamed lymphatic glands in the arms and axillae, shiverings succeeded by heat, lassitude, and general pains in the limbs. A single paroxysm terminated the disease; for within twenty-four hours they were free from general indisposition, nothing remaining but the sores on their hands. Haynes and Virgoe, who had gone through the smallpox from inoculation, described their feelings as very similar to those which affected them on sickening with that malady. Wherret never had had the smallpox. Haynes was daily employed as one of the milkers at the farm, and the disease began to shew itself among the cows about ten days after he first assisted in washing the mare's heels. Their nipples became sore in the usual way, with bluish pustules; but as remedies were early applied, they did not ulcerate to any extent. . . .

It is singular to observe that the cow-pox virus, although it renders the constitution unsusceptible of the variolous, should nevertheless, leave it unchanged with respect to its own action. . . .

It is curious also to observe that the virus, which with respect to its effects is undetermined and uncertain previously to its passing from the horse through the medium of the cow, should then not only become more active, but should invariably and completely possess those specific properties which induce in the human constitution symptoms similar to those of the variolous fever, and effect in it that peculiar change which for ever renders it unsusceptible of the variolous contagion. . . .

In some of the preceding cases I have noticed the attention that was paid to the state of the variolous matter previous to the experiment of inserting it into the arms of those who had gone through the cow-pox. This I conceived to be of great importance in conducting these experiments, and, were it always properly attended to by those who inoculate for the smallpox, it might prevent much subsequent mischief and confusion. . . .

Should it be asked whether this investigation is a matter of mere curiosity, or whether it tends to any beneficial purpose, I should answer that, notwithstanding the happy effects of inoculation, with all the improvements which the practice has received since its first introduction into this country, it not very unfrequently produces deformity of the skin, and sometimes, under the best management, proves fatal.

These circumstances must naturally create in every instance some degree of painful solicitude for its consequences. But as I have never known fatal effects arise from the cow-pox, even when impressed in the most unfavorable manner, producing extensive inflammations and suppurations on the hands; and as it clearly appears that this disease leaves the constitution in a state of perfect security from the infection of the smallpox, may we not infer that a mode of inoculation may be introduced preferable to that at present adopted, especially among those families which, from previous circumstances, we may judge to be predisposed to have the disease unfavourably? It is an excess in the number of pustules which we chiefly dread in the smallpox; but in the cow-pox no pustules appear, nor does it seem possible for the contagious matter to produce the disease from effluvia, or by any other means than contact, and that probably not simply between the virus and the cuticle; so that a single individual in a family might at any time receive it without the risk of infecting the rest or of spreading a distemper that fills a country with terror.

JAMES PRESCOTT JOULE

(1818-1889)

Joule is known for his studies in the mechanical equivalence of heat,
and the law named after him: the heat in an electric conductor is
proportional to the resistance times the square of the current (*On the
Production of Heat by Voltaic Electricity,* 1840). A student of John
Dalton, this English physicist is unusual in that he never held an
academic post, and although his findings were presented to the
Royal Society, they were at first ignored. He also made the first calculation of the velocity of a gas molecule, and is one of the founders
of the principle of the conservation of energy. The joule, a unit of
energy, is named after him.

ON THE CHANGES OF TEMPERATURE PRODUCED
BY THE RAREFACTION AND CONDENSATION OF AIR

I PROVIDED another copper receiver (*E*) (Fig. 1) which had a
capacity of 134 cubic inches. Like the former receiver, to which
it could be connected by a coupling nut, it had a piece *D* attached, in the center of which there was a bore ⅛ of an inch
diameter, which could be closed perfectly by means of a proper
stopcock.

Having filled the receiver *R* with about 22 atmospheres of dry
air, and having exhausted the receiver *E* by means of an air-

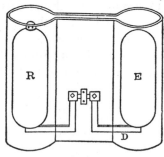

Fig. 1

pump, I screwed them together, and then put them into a tin can containing 16½ lb. of water. The water was first thoroughly stirred, and its temperature taken by the same delicate thermometer which was made use of in the former experiments. The stopcocks were then opened by means of a proper key, and the air allowed to pass from the full into the empty receiver until equilibrium was established between the two. Lastly, the water was again stirred and its temperature carefully noted. . . .

The difference between the means of the expansions and alternations being exactly such as was found to be due to the increased effect of the temperature of the room in the latter case, we arrive at the conclusion that *no change of temperature occurs when air is allowed to expand in such a manner as not to develop mechanical power.*

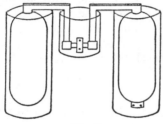

Fig. 2

In order to analyze the above experiments, I inverted the receivers, as shown in Fig. 2, and immersed them, as well as the connecting piece, into separate cans of water. One of the receivers had 2828 cubic inches of dry air condensed into it, while the other was vacuous. After equilibrium was restored by opening the cocks, I found that 2°.36 of cold per lb. of water had been produced in the receiver from which the air had expanded, while 2°.38 of heat had been produced in the other receiver, and 0°.31 of heat also in the can in which the connecting piece was immersed, the sum of the whole amounting nearly to zero. The slight redundance of heat was owing to the loss of cold during the passage of the air from the charged receiver to the stopcocks, through a part of the pipe which could not be immersed in water.

531

IMMANUEL KANT

(1724–1804)

Though primarily a theoretical philosopher—the most imposing of modern times—Kant was a profound student of science and evolved his own original hypotheses regarding the physical universe. Many of these were later restated or demonstrated, including the origin of the planetary system (later known as the Laplacian theory), the slowing down of the earth's rotation through tidal friction, the displacement of the sun to the north of the Milky Way, and the island universe interpretation of the spiral nebulae. Most of these are contained in his *General History of Nature and Theory of the Heavens* (1755), which antedates his major philosophical works, *Critique of Pure Reason* (1781), *Principles of the Metaphysics of Ethics* (1785), *Critique of Judgment* (1790), and *Metaphysics of Morals* (1797).

THEORY OF THE HEAVENS

I ASSUME that all the material of which the globes belonging to our solar system—all the planets and comets—consist, at the beginning of all things was decomposed into its primary elements, and filled the whole space of the universe in which the bodies formed out of it now revolve. This state of nature, when viewed in and by itself without any reference to a system, seems to be the very simplest that can follow upon nothing. At that time nothing had yet been formed. The construction of heavenly bodies at a distance from each other, their distances regulated by their attractions, their form arising out of the equilibrium of their collected matter, exhibit a later state. The state of nature which immediately bordered on the creation was as crude, as unformed, as possible. But even in the essential properties of the elements that constituted this chaos, there could be traced

532

the mark of that perfection which they have derived from their origin, their essential character being a consequence of the eternal idea of the Divine Intelligence. The simplest and most general properties which seem to be struck out without design, the matter which appears to be merely passive and wanting form and arrangement, has in its simplest state a tendency to fashion itself by a natural evolution into a more perfect constitution. But the variety in the kinds of elements, is what chiefly contributes to the stirring of nature and to the formative modification of chaos, as it is by it that the repose which would prevail in a universal equality among the scattered elements is done away, so that the chaos begins to take form at the points where the more strongly attracting particles are. The kinds of this elementary matter are undoubtedly infinitely different, in accordance with the immensity which nature shows on all sides. Those elements, which are of greater specific density and force of attraction, and which of themselves occupy less room and are also rarer, would therefore be more scattered than the lighter kinds when the material of the world was equally diffused in space. Elements of a thousand times greater specific gravity, would, therefore, be thousands or even millions of times more scattered than those that are lighter in that proportion. And as these gradations must be thought to be as infinite as possible, there may be material particles of a kind which exceed those of another in density in the same proportion as a globe described with the radius of the planetary system does another which has only the thousandth part of a line in diameter; and thus these kinds of scattered elements would be separated from each other by a distance as great as those globes themselves.

In a region of space filled in this manner, a universal repose could last only a moment. The elements have essential forces with which to put each other in motion, and thus are themselves a source of life. Matter immediately begins to strive to fashion itself. The scattered elements of a denser kind, by means of their attraction, gather from a sphere around them all the matter of less specific gravity; again, these elements themselves, together with the material which they have united with them, collect in

533

those points where the particles of a still denser kind are found; these in like manner join still denser particles, and so on. If we follow in imagination this process by which nature fashions itself into form through the whole extent of chaos, we easily perceive that all the results of the process would consist in the formation of diverse masses which, when their formation was complete, would by the equality of their attraction be at rest and be for ever unmoved.

But nature has other forces in store, which are especially exerted when matter is decomposed into fine particles. They are those forces by which these particles repel each other, and which, by their conflict with attraction, bring forth that movement which is, as it were, the lasting life of nature. This force of repulsion is manifested in the elasticity of vapors, the effluences of strong smelling bodies, and the diffusion of all spirituous matters. This force is an incontestable phenomenon of matter. It is by it that the elements, which may be falling to the point attracting them, are turned sideways promiscuously from their movement in a straight line; and their perpendicular fall thereby issues in circular movements, which encompass the center towards which they were falling. In order to make the formation of the world more distinctly conceivable, we will limit our view by withdrawing it from the infinite universe of nature and directing it to a particular system, as the one which belongs to our sun. Having considered the generation of this system, we shall be able to advance to a similar consideration of the origin of the greater world-systems, and thus to embrace the infinitude of the whole creation in one conception.

From what has been said, it will appear that if a point is situated in a very large space where the attraction of the elements there situated acts more strongly than elsewhere, then the matter of the elementary particles scattered throughout the whole region will fall to that point. The first effect of this general fall is the formation of a body at this center of attraction which, so to speak, grows from an infinitely small nucleus by rapid strides; and in the proportion in which this mass increases, it also draws with greater force the surrounding particles to unite with it.

When the mass of this central body has grown so great that the velocity with which it draws the particles to itself from great distances, is bent sideways by the feeble degrees of repulsion with which they impede each other, and when it issues in lateral movements which are capable by means of the centrifugal force of encompassing the central body in an orbit, then there are produced whirls or vortices of particles, each of which by itself describes a curved line by the composition of the attracting force and the force of revolution that has been bent sideways. These kinds of orbits all intersect each other, for which their great dispersion in this space gives place. Yet these movements are in many ways in conflict with each other, and they naturally tend to bring one another to a uniformity, that is, into a state in which one movement is as little obstructive to the other as possible. This happens in two ways: first, by the particles limiting each other's movement till they all advance in one direction, and secondly, in this way, that the particles limit their vertical movements in virtue of which they are approaching the center of attraction, till all are moving horizontally, *i.e.* in parallel circles round the sun as their center, no longer intersect each other, and by the centrifugal force becoming equal with the falling force they keep themselves constantly in free circular orbits at the distance at which they move. The result, finally, is that only those particles continue to move in this region of space which have acquired by their fall a velocity, and through the resistance of the other particles a direction, by which they can continue to maintain a *free circular movement*. In this state, when all the particles are moving in one direction and in parallel circles, *i.e.* in free circular movements carried on by the acquired propulsive forces around the central body, the conflict and the concourse of the elements is annulled, and everything is then in the state of the least reciprocal action. This state is the natural consequence which always ensues in the case of matter involved in conflicting movements. It is therefore clear that a great number of the scattered multitude of particles must attain to such exact determinate conditions through the resistance by which they seek to bring each other to this state; although a much greater multitude of them do not reach it and only serve to increase the mass of the central body into which they fall, as they cannot maintain themselves freely at the distance at which they are moving, but cross the circles of the nearer particles, and, finally, by their resistance lose all motion. This body in the center of attraction which, in consequence of all this, has become the chief part of the planetary system by the mass of its collected matter, is the sun, although it has not yet that glow of flame which bursts out on its surface after its formation has become entirely complete.

It is further to be observed, that all the elements of nature, when fashioning itself, thus move, as has been shown, in a direction round the center of the sun; and hence in these revolutions, which are directed to a single region and which are performed as it were upon a common axis, the rotation of the fine matter cannot proceed in this way. Because, according to the laws of centrifugal motion, all the revolutions must intersect the center of attraction with the plane of their orbits; but of all these orbits round a common axis that move in one direction, there is only one which cuts through the center of the sun. Hence all the matter on both sides of this imaginary axis hurries to that circle which passes through the rotation of the axis in the center of the common attraction, which circle is the plane of the reference of all the revolving elements: around which plane they accumulate as much as possible, and contrariwise leave the regions at a distance from this plane empty. For those elements which cannot come so near this plane to which they are all pressing, will not be able to continue to maintain themselves in the places where they are moving, but, impinging on the elements floating around them, this will cause them finally to fall into the sun.

If we, therefore, consider this revolving elementary matter of the world in that state into which it puts itself by attraction and by the mechanical consequence of the general laws of resistance, we see a region of space extending from the center of the sun to unknown distances, contained between two planes not far distant from each other, in the middle of which the general plane of reference is situated. And this elementary matter is diffused in this space within which all the contained particles—each according to the proportion of its distance and of the attraction which prevails there—perform regulated circular movements in free revolutions. And hence, as in this arrangement they obstruct each other as little as possible, they would continue always in this relation, if the attraction of the elementary matters for each other did not then begin to produce its effect, and thereby give occasion to new formations which are the seed of the planets that are about to rise. For the elements which move round the sun in parallel circles and not at too great a difference of distance from the sun, are by the equality of their parallel motion almost at rest respectively towards each other; and thus the attraction of those elements there which are of higher specific attraction immediately produces an important effect, namely, the collecting of the nearest particles for the formation of a body which according to the proportion of the growth of its mass, extends its attraction farther and draws elements from a wide region to unite with it in its further formation.

The view of the formation of the planets in this system has the advantage over every other possible theory in holding that the origin of the masses gives the origin of the movements, and the position of the orbits as arising at the same point of time; nay more, in showing that even the deviations from the greatest possible exactness in these determinations, as well as the accordances themselves, become clear at a glance. The planets are formed out of particles which at the distance at which they move, have exact movements in circular orbits; *and therefore the masses composed out of them will continue the same movements at the same rate and in the same direction.* This suffices to show why the motion of the planets is almost circular, and why their orbits are in one plane. They would be exact circles if the range out of which they collected the elements for their formation was very small, and then the difference of their movements would be very slight. But as a wide range of space is required in order that the dense mass of a planet may be formed out of the fine stuff which is so widely diffused in the celestial space, the difference of the distances which these elements have from the sun, and consequently also the difference of their velocities, is no longer insignificant. In consequence, it would be necessary, in order to maintain in the planet the equilibrium of the centripetal forces and the circular velocity with this difference of movements, that the particles which come together upon it from different distances with different movements should exactly compensate for the defects of each other. And although this really takes place with tolerable exactness, nevertheless, as it falls somewhat short of a perfect compensation, the result is divergence from the circular movement and eccentricity. It is as easily seen that, although the orbits of all the planets ought properly to be in one plane, yet even in this respect a small deviation is presented, because, as already mentioned, the elementary particles while situated as near as possible to the general plane of their movements, yet occupy some space on both sides of it. Now it would be a very happy chance if all the planets were to begin to form themselves exactly in the middle between these two sides in their relative plane, which already would bring about some inclination of their orbits to each other, although the tendency of the particles to limit this divergence on both sides, permits it only within very narrow limits. It is, therefore, not astonishing that the greatest exactness of determination is not to be found here any more than in any of the other products of nature, because the multiplicity of the circumstances which enter into every fact of nature does not admit of absolute regularity.

WILLIAM THOMSON, LORD KELVIN

(1824–1907)

Kelvin became world-famous for his part in making possible the first transatlantic telegraph cable (1857-66), and was regarded by the Victorians at the leading scientist of their age. He held the chair of natural philosophy at Glasgow University for fifty-three years, while he devoted much of his time to research in pure science. He estimated the earth as not over 100 million years old, developed Joule's theories of thermodynamics, and proposed an absolute, or Kelvin, scale of temperature. He advanced research in such fields as the electrodynamic properties of metals and the mathematical theory of magnetism, and invented many instruments (including an improved mariner's compass) still in use.

THE AGE OF THE EARTH AS AN ABODE
FITTED FOR LIFE

THE AGE of the earth as an abode fitted for life is certainly a subject which largely interests mankind in general. For geology it is of vital and fundamental importance—as important as the date of the battle of Hastings is for English history—yet it was very little thought of by geologists of thirty or forty years ago; how little is illustrated by a statement, which I will now read, given originally from the presidential chair of the Geological Society by Professor Huxley in 1869, when for a second time, after a seven years' interval, he was president of the society. "I do not suppose that at the present day any geologist would be found . . . to deny that the rapidity of the rotation of the earth *may* be diminishing, that the sun *may* be waxing dim, or that the earth itself *may* be cooling. Most of us, I suspect, are Gallios, 'who care for none of these things,' being of opinion that, true or fictitious, they have made no practical difference to the earth, during the period of which a record is preserved in stratified deposits."

I believe the explanation of how it was possible for Professor Huxley to say that he and other geologists did not care for things on which the age of life on the earth essentially depends is because he did not know that there was valid foundation for any estimates worth considering as to absolute magnitudes. If science did not allow us to give any estimate whatever as to whether 10 million or 10 billion years is the age of this earth as an abode fitted for life, then I think Professor Huxley would have been perfectly right in saying that geologists should not trouble themselves about it, and biologists should go on in their own way, not inquiring into things utterly beyond the power of human understanding and scientific investigation. This would have left geology much in the same position as that in which English history would be if it were impossible to ascertain whether the battle of Hastings took place 800 years ago, or 800 thousand years ago, or 800 million years ago. If it were absolutely impossible to find out which of these periods is more probable than the other, then I agree we might be Gallios as to the date of the Norman Conquest. But a change took place just about the time to which I refer, and from then till now geologists have not considered the question of absolute dates in their science as outside the scope of their investigations . . .

The rate at which heat is at the present time lost from the earth by conduction outward through the upper crust, as proved by observation of underground temperature in different parts of the world and by measurement of the thermal conductivity of surface rocks and strata, sufficed to refute utterly the doctrine of uniformity as taught by Hutton, Lyell, and their followers.

In an earlier communication to the Royal Society of Edinburgh I had considered the cooling of the earth due to this loss of heat, and by tracing backward the process of cooling had formed a definite estimate of the greatest and least number of million years which can possibly have passed since the surface of the earth was everywhere red-hot. I expressed my conclusion in the following statement: "We are very ignorant as to the effects of high temperatures in altering the conductivities and specific heats and melting temperatures of rocks, and as to their latent heat of fusion. We must, therefore, allow very wide limits in such an estimate, as I have attempted to make; but I think we may with much probability say that the consolidation can not have taken place less than 20 million years ago, or we should now have more underground heat than we actually have; nor more than 400 million years ago, or we should now have less underground heat than we actually have. That is to say, I conclude that Leibnitz's epoch of emergence of the *consistentior status* (the consolidation of the earth from red-hot or white-hot molten matter) was probably between those dates."

During the thirty-five years which have passed since I gave this wide-ranged estimate, experimental investigation has supplied much of the knowledge then wanting regarding the thermal properties of rocks to form a closer estimate of the time which has passed since the consolidation of the earth, and we have now good reason for judging that it was more than 20 and less than 40 million years ago, and probably much nearer 20 than 40 . . .

When the surface of the earth was still white-hot liquid all round, at a temperature fallen to about 1200° C., there must have been hot gases and vapor of water above it in all parts, and possibly vapors of some of the more volatile of the present known terrestrial solids and liquids, such as zinc, mercury, sulphur, phosphorus. The very rapid cooling which followed instantly on the solidification at the surface must have caused a rapid downpour of all the vapors other than water, if any there were; and a little later, rain of water out of the air, as the temperature of the surface cooled from red heat to such moderate temperatures as 40° and 20° and 10° C. above the average due to sun heat and radiation into the ether around the earth. What that primitive atmosphere was, and how much rain of water fell on the earth in the course of the first century after consolidation, we can not tell for certain; but natural history and natural philosophy give us some foundation for endeavors to discover much toward answering the great questions: Whence came our present atmosphere of nitrogen, oxygen, and carbonic

541

acid? Whence came our present oceans and lakes of salt and fresh water? How near an approximation to present conditions was realized in the first hundred centuries after consolidation of the surface?

We may consider it as quite certain that nitrogen gas, carbonic acid gas, and steam escaped abundantly in bubbles from the molten liquor of granite before the primitive consolidation of the surface, and from the mother liquid squeezed up from below in subsequent eruptions of basaltic rock; because all, or nearly all, specimens of granite and basaltic rock which have been tested by chemists in respect to this question have been found to contain, condensed in minute cavities within them, large quantities of nitrogen, carbonic acid, and water. It seems that in no specimen of granite or basalt tested has chemically free oxygen been discovered, while in many chemically free hydrogen has been found, and either native iron or magnetic oxide of iron in those which do not contain hydrogen. From this it might seem probable that there was no free oxygen in the primitive atmosphere, and that if there was free hydrogen it was due to the decomposition of steam by iron or magnetic oxide of iron. Going back to still earlier conditions we might judge that, probably, among the dissolved gases of the hot nebula which became the earth the oxygen all fell into combination with hydrogen and other metallic vapors in the cooling of the nebula, and that although it is known to be the most abundant material of all the chemical elements constituting the earth none of it was left out of combination with other elements to give free oxygen in our primitive atmosphere.

It is, however, possible, although it might seem not probable, that there was free oxygen in the primitive atmosphere. With or without free oxygen, however, *but with sunlight,* we may regard the earth as fitted for vegetable life as now known in some species, wherever water moistened the newly solidified rocky crust cooled down below the temperature of 80° or 70° of our present Centigrade thermometric scale, a year or two after solidification of the primitive lava had come up to the surface. The thick, tough velvety coating of living vegetable matter covering the rocky slopes under hot water flowing direct out of the earth at Banff (Canada) lives without help from any ingredients of the atmosphere above it, and takes from the water and from carbonic acid or carbonates, dissolved in it, the hydrogen and carbon needed for its own growth by the dynamical power of sunlight; thus leaving free oxygen in the water to pass ultimately into the air. Similar vegetation is found abundantly on the terraces of the Mammoth Hot Springs and on the beds of the hot water streams flowing from the geysers in the Yellowstone National Park of the United States. This vegetation, consisting of confervæ, all grows under flowing water at various temperatures, some said to be as high as 74° C. We can not doubt but that some such confervæ, if sown or planted in a rivulet or pool of warm water in the early years of the first century of the solid earth's history and if favored with sunlight would have lived, and grown, and multiplied, and would have made a beginning of oxygen in the air if there had been none of it before their contributions. Before the end of the century if sun heat, and sunlight, and rainfall were suitable the whole earth not under water must have been fitted for all kinds of land plants which do not require much or any oxygen in the air, and which can find or make place and soil for their roots on the rocks on which they grow, and the lakes or oceans formed by that time must have been quite fitted for the life of many or all of the species of water plants living on the earth at the present time. The moderate warming, both of land and water, by underground heat, toward the end of the century, would probably be favorable rather than adverse to vegetation, and there can be no doubt but that if abundance of seeds of all species of the present day had been scattered over the earth at that time an important proportion of them would have lived and multiplied by natural selection of the places where they could best thrive.

But if there was no free oxygen in the primitive atmosphere or primitive water several thousands, possibly hundreds of thousands, of years must pass before oxygen enough for supporting animal life, as we now know it, was produced. Even if the average activity of vegetable growth on land and in water over the whole earth was, in those early times, as great in respect to evolution of oxygen as that of a Hessian forest, as estimated by Liebig fifty years ago, or of a cultivated English hayfield of the present day, a very improbable supposition, and if there were no decay (eremacausis, or gradual recombination with oxygen) of the plants or of portions such as leaves falling from plants, the rate of evolution of oxygen, reckoned as three times the weight of the wood or dry hay produced, would be only about 6 tons per English acre per annum, or 1½ tons per square meter per thousand years. At this rate it would take only 1533 years, and, therefore, in reality a much longer time would almost certainly be required, to produce the 2.3 tons of oxygen which we have at present resting on every square meter of the earth's surface, land and sea. But, probably, quite a moderate number of hundred thousand years may have sufficed. It is interesting, at all events, to remark that at any time the total amount of combustible material on the earth, in the form of living plants or their remains left dead, must have been just so much that to burn it all would take either the whole oxygen of the atmosphere or the excess of oxygen in the atmosphere at the time, above that, if any, which there was in the beginning. This we can safely say, because we almost certainly neglect nothing considerable in comparison with what we assert when we say that the free oxygen of the earth's atmosphere is augmented only by vegetation liberating it from carbonic acid and water, in virtue of the power of sunlight, and is diminished only by virtual burning[1] of the vegetable matter thus produced. But it seems improbable that the average of the whole earth—dry land and sea bottom—contains at present coal, or wood, or oil, or fuel of 0.767 of a ton per square meter of surface, which is the amount of the rate of 1 ton of fuel to 3 tons of oxygen per square meter

---

[1] This "virtual burning" includes eremacausis of decay of vegetable matter, if there is any eremacausis of decay without the intervention of microbes or other animals. It also includes the combination of a portion of the food with inhaled oxygen in the regular animal economy for provision for heat and power.

of surface which our present atmosphere contains. Hence it seems probable that the earth's primitive atmosphere must have contained free oxygen.

Whatever may have been the true history of our atmosphere, it seems certain that if sunlight was ready, the earth was ready, both for vegetable and animal life, if not within a century, at all events within a few hundred centuries after the rocky consolidation of its surface. But was the sun ready? The well-founded dynamical theory of the sun's heat, carefully worked out and discussed by Helmholtz, Newcomb, and myself, says NO if the consolidation of the earth took place as long ago as fifty million years; the solid earth must in that case have waited twenty or thirty million years for the sun to be anything nearly as warm as he is at present. If the consolidation of the earth was finished **twenty or twenty-five** million years ago the sun was probably ready—though probably not then quite so warm as at present, yet warm enough to support some kind of vegetable and animal life on the earth.

My task has been rigorously confined to what, humanly speaking, we may call the fortuitous concourse of atoms in the preparation of the earth as an abode fitted for life, except in so far as I have referred to vegetation, as possibly having been concerned in the preparation of an atmosphere suitable for animal life as we now have it. Mathematics and dynamics fail us when we contemplate the earth, fitted for life but lifeless, and try to imagine the commencement of life upon it. This certainly did not take take place by any action of chemistry, or electricity, or crystalline grouping of molecules under the influence of force, or by any possible kind of fortuitous concourse of atoms. We must pause, face to face with the mystery and miracle of the creation of living creatures.

IF NATURE COULD RUN BACKWARD

IF, THEN, the motion of every particle of matter in the universe were precisely reversed at any instant, the course of nature would be simply reversed forever after. The bursting bubble of

545

foam at the foot of a waterfall would reunite and descend into the water; the thermal motions would reconcentrate their energy and throw the mass up the fall in drops re-forming into a close column of ascending water. Heat which had been generated by the friction of solids and dissipated by conduction, and radiation with absorption, would come again to the place of contact and throw the moving body back against the force to which it had previously yielded. Boulders would recover from the mud the materials required to rebuild them into their previous jagged forms, and would become reunited to the mountain peak from which they had formerly broken away. And if, also, the materialistic hypothesis of life were true, living creatures would grow backward, with conscious knowledge of the future but with no memory of the past, and would become again unborn.

But the real phenomena of life infinitely transcend human science, and speculation regarding consequences of their imagined reversal is utterly unprofitable. Far otherwise, however, is it in respect to the reversal of the motions of matter uninfluenced by life, a very elementary consideration of which leads to the full explanation of the theory of dissipation of energy.

JOHANNES KEPLER

(1571–1630)

Kepler's three laws of planetary motion formed the basis of Newton's later discoveries, and are considered the starting point of modern astronomy. An adherent of Copernican principles, friend and co-worker of Tycho Brahe, Kepler spent most of his life as a teacher and court "astrologer" and mathematician to various Teutonic princes. His first two laws, which wiped out the last vestiges of Greek astronomy, were published in his *Astronomia Nova de Motibus Stellae Mortis ex Observationibus Tychonis Brahe* (1609), the third in his *Harmonice Mundi* (1619). Kepler also did pioneer work in optics and in mathematics leading to the invention of calculus.

INTRODUCTION UPON MARS

It MUST be confessed, that there are very many who are devoted to Holiness, that dissent from the Judgment of *Copernicus*, fearing to give the Lye to the Holy Ghost speaking in the Scriptures, if they should say, that the Earth moveth, and the Sun stands still. But let us consider, that since we judge of very many, and those the most principal things by the Sense of Seeing, it is impossible that we should alienate our Speech from this Sense of our Eyes. Therefore, many things daily occur, of which we speak according to the Sense of Sight, when as we certainly know that the things themselves are otherwise. An example whereof we have in that Verse of *Virgil*;

Provehimur portu, Terraeque urbesque recedunt...

And I do also beseech my Reader, not forgetting the Divine Goodnesse conferred on Mankind; the consideration of which

547

the Psalmist doth chiefly urge, that when he returneth from the Temple, and enters into the School of *Astronomy*, he would with me praise and admire the Wisdome and Greatnesse of the Creator, which I discover to him by a more narrow explication of the World's Form, the Disquisition of Causes, and Detection of the Errours of Sight: And so he will not onely extoll the Bounty of God in the preservation of Living Creatures of all kindes, and establishment of the Earth; but even in its Motion also, which is so strange, so admirable, he will acknowledge the Wisdome of the Creator. But he who is so stupid as not to comprehend the Science of *Astronomy*, or so weak and scrupulous as to think it an offence of Piety to adhere to *Copernicus*, him I advise, that leaving the Study of *Astronomy*, and censuring the opinions of Philosophers at pleasure, he betake himself to his own concerns, and that desisting from further pursuit of these intricate Studies, he keep at home and manure his own Ground; and with those Eyes wherewith alone he seeth, being elevated towards this to be admired Heaven, let him pour forth his whole heart in thanks and praises to God the Creator; and assure himself that he shall therein perform as much Worship to God, as the *Astronomer*, on whom God hath bestowed this Gift, that though he seeth more clearly with the Eye of his Understanding; yet whatever he hath attained to, he is both able and willing to extoll his God above it.

And thus much concerning the Authority of Sacred Scripture. Now as touching, the opinions of the Saints about these Natural Points. I answer in one word, That in Theology the weight of Authority, but in Philosophy the weight of Reason is to be considered. Therefore Sacred was *Lactantius*, who denied the Earth's rotundity; Sacred was *Augustine*, who granted the Earth to be round, but denied the *Antipodes*; Sacred is the Liturgy (Officium) of our Moderns, who admit the smallnesse of the Earth, but deny its Motion: But to me more sacred than all these is Truth, who with respect to the Doctors of the Church, do demonstrate from Philosophy that the Earth is both round, circumhabited by *Antipodes*, of a most contemptible smallnesse and in a word, that it is ranked amongst the Planets.

548

JOHANNES KEPLER

CHIEF POINTS OF ASTRONOMICAL LEARNING, NECESSARY FOR THE CONTEMPLATION OF THE CELESTIAL HARMONIES

IN THE beginning let my readers understand this: that the old astronomical hypotheses of Ptolemy, as they are set forth in the *Theoriae* of Purbach and the writings of the other epitomizers, are to be kept far from the present enquiry and banished wholly from the mind; for they fail to give a true account either of the arrangement of the heavenly bodies or of the laws governing their motions.

In their place I cannot do otherwise than substitute simply Copernicus's theory of the universe, and (were it possible) convince all men of its truth; but, since among the mass of students the idea is still unfamiliar, and the theory that the Earth is one of the planets and moves among the stars about the Sun, which is stationary, sounds to the most of them quite absurd, let those who are offended by the strangeness of this doctrine know that these harmonic speculations hold a place even among the hypotheses of Tycho Brahe. While that author agrees with Copernicus in regard to everything else which concerns the arrangement of the heavenly bodies and the laws governing their motions, the annual motion of the Earth alone, as held by Copernicus, he transfers to the whole system of the planetary orbits and to the Sun, which, according to both authors, is the center of the system. For from this transference, motion results just the same, so that, if not in that utterly vast and immense space of the sphere of the fixed stars, at least in the system of the planetary world, the Earth holds at any one time the same place according to Brahe as is given to it by Copernicus. Furthermore, just as he who draws a circle on paper moves the writing foot of the compass around, while he who fastens the paper or a board to a revolving wheel keeps the foot of the compass or the style stationary and draws the same circle on the moving board, so also in the present case; for Copernicus, the Earth measures out its orbit, between the outer circle of Mars and the inner circle of Venus, by the real motion of its own body,

549

while for Tycho Brahe the whole planetary system (in which among the other orbits are also those of Mars and Venus) turns around like the board on the wheel and brings to the stationary Earth, as to the style of the turner, the space between the orbits of Mars and Venus; and from this motion of the system it results that the Earth, itself remaining stationary, marks on space the same course around the Sun, between Mars and Venus, which, according to Copernicus, it marks by the real motion of its own body with the system at rest. Since, then, the harmonic speculation considers the eccentric motions of the planets, as seen from the Sun, one can easily understand that, if an observer were on the Sun, however great the Sun's motion, the Earth, although it were at rest (to grant this for the moment to Brahe), would, nevertheless, seem to him to run its annual course in the space between the planets, and also in a time between the planet's times. Although, therefore, a man may be weak in faith and so unable to conceive of the motion of the Earth among the stars, he may still find it possible to take pleasure in the exalted contemplation of this most divine mechanism; he needs but to apply whatever he hears about the daily motions of the Earth in its eccentric to the appearance of those motions on the Sun, as even Tycho Brahe presents it with the Earth at rest.

The true followers of the Samian philosophy, however, have no just cause for envying such men this participation in a most delightful speculation, for if they accept also the immovability of the Sun and the motion of the Earth, their pleasure will be more exquisite in many ways, since it will be derived from the very consummated perfection of contemplation.

In the first place, therefore, let my readers understand that at the present day among all astronomers it is held to be a well-established fact that all the planets except the Moon, which alone has the Earth as its center, revolve around the Sun; the Moon's orbit or course, be it said, is not large enough to enable it to be drawn on this chart in proper relation to the other orbits. To the other five planets, therefore, is added the Earth as sixth,

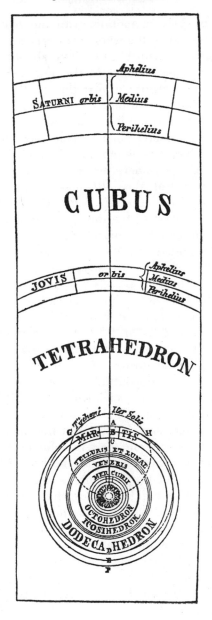

which, either by its own motion, with the Sun stationary, or, itself being at rest while the whole planetary system is in revolution, describes, it too, its orbit, the sixth, about the Sun.

Secondly, the following fact is also established: that all the planets revolve in eccentric orbits; that is, they alter their distances from the Sun, so that in one part of the orbit they are very remote from the Sun, while in the opposite part they come very near the Sun. In the appended scheme there have been made for each planet three circles, no one of which indicates the real eccentric path of the planet; the middle one, however, as, for instance, in the case of Mars, BE, has a diameter equal to the longer diameter of the eccentric orbit; the orbit itself, as AD, touches AF, the highest of the three, in the one quarter, A, and CD the lowest, in the other quarter, D.

The orbit GH, represented by points and drawn through the center of the Sun, indicates the path of the Sun according to Tycho Brahe. If the Sun travels this path, every point of the planetary system here depicted advances in a like path, each in its own; and if one point of it, that is the center of the Sun, stands in one part of its orbit, as here in the lowest part, all parts of the system will stand, each in the lowest part of its own orbit. Owing to the narrowness of the space, the three circles of Venus have run into one, contrary to my intention.

Thirdly, let the reader recall from my "Mysterium Cosmographicum," which I published twenty-two years ago, that the number of the planets, or orbits about the Sun, was derived by the most wise Creator from the five solid figures, about which Euclid so many centuries ago wrote the book which, since it is made up of a series of propositions, is called "Elementa." That there cannot be more regular bodies, that regular plane figures, that is, cannot unite into a solid in more than five ways, was made clear in the second book of the present work.

Fourthly, as regards the relations of the planetary orbits, the relation between two neighboring orbits is always such that, as will easily be seen, each one of the orbits approximates one of the terms of the ratio which exists between the orbits of one of the five solid bodies; the ratio, that is, of the orbit circumscribed about the figure to the orbit inscribed. For when, following the observations of Brahe, I had completed the demonstration of the distances, I discovered this fact: if the angles of the cube are applied to the innermost circle of Saturn, the centers of the planes nearly touch the middle circle of Jupiter, and if the angles of the tetrahedron rest on the innermost circle of Jupiter, the centers of the planes of the tetrahedron nearly touch the outermost circle of Mars; also, if the angles of the octahedron rise from any one of the circles of Venus (for all three are reduced to a very narrow space), the centers of the planes of the octahedron enter and descend below the outermost circle of Mercury; finally, coming to the ratios which exist between the orbits of the dodecahedron and the orbits of the icosahedron, which ratios are equal to each other, we find that the nearest of all to these are the ratios or distances between the circles of Mars and the Earth and between those of the Earth and Venus, and these ratios also, if we reckon from the innermost circle of Mars to the middle circle of the Earth and from the middle circle of the Earth to the middle circle of Venus, are similarly equal to each other; for the middle distance of the Earth is the mean proportional between the smallest distance of Mars and the middle distance of Venus; but these two ratios between the circles of the planets are still larger than are the ratios of those two sets of orbits in the figures, so that the centers of the planes of the dodecahedron do not touch the outermost circle of the Earth, nor do the centers of the planes of the icosahedron touch the outermost circle of Venus; and this hiatus is not filled up by the semidiameter of the orbit of the Moon, added to the greatest distance of the Earth and taken away from the smallest distance. But there is a certain other relation connected with a figure that I notice: if an enlarged dodecahedron to which I have given the name *echinus* [hedgehog] as being formed of twelve five-cornered stars and thereby being very near to the five regular bodies, if, I say, this dodecahedron should place its twelve points on the innermost circle of Mars, then the sides of the pentagons, which **are, respectively, the bases** of the different radii or points, touch the middle circle of Venus.

Briefly: the cube and the octahedron enter somewhat their conjugate planetary orbits, the dodecahedron and the icosahedron do not quite reach their conjugate orbits, the tetrahedron just touches both orbits; in the first case there is a deficiency, in the second case an excess in the last case an equality, in the distances of the planets.

From these considerations it is apparent that the exact relations of the planetary distances were not derived from the regular figures alone; for the Creator, the very fountain head of geometry, who, as Plato says, practices geometry eternally, does not deviate from his archetype. And indeed this fact might be gathered from the consideration that all the planets change their distances through definite periods of time; so that each one has two notable distances from the Sun, the maximum and the minimum; and there may be made between every two planets a fourfold comparison of their distances from the Sun, comparisons of their maximum and of their minimum distances, and comparisons of their mutually opposed distances, those that are farthest apart and those that are nearest together; thus, of all the combinations of two neighboring planets, the comparisons are twenty in number, while on the other hand the solid figures are but five. It is reasonable to believe, however, that the Creator, if he paid attention to the relation of the orbits in their general aspect, paid attention also to the relation of the varying distances of the individual orbits in detail, and that these acts of attention were the same in both cases and were connected with each other. When we duly consider this fact, we shall certainly arrive at the conclusion that for establishing the diameters and the eccentricities of the orbits there are required several principles in combination, besides the principle of the five regular bodies.

Fifthly, to come to the motions, among which are established the harmonies, I again impress upon the reader the fact that it has been shown by me in my Commentaries on Mars, from the exceedingly accurate observations of Brahe, that equal diurnal arcs on one and the same eccentric are not traversed with equal velocities, but that these different times *in equal parts of the eccentric are to each other as the distances from the Sun,* the source of the motion; and, on the other hand, that, the times being supposed equal, as, for instance, one natural day in each case, *the true diurnal arcs corresponding to them in a single eccentric orbit are inversely proportional to the two distances from the Sun.* It has likewise been shown by me that *the orbit of a planet is elliptical, and the Sun, the source of motion, is in one of the foci of this ellipse, and so it results that the planet, when it has completed a quarter of the entire circuit, beginning at the aphelion, is at a distance from the Sun exactly half way between the maximum distance in aphelion and the minimum distance in perihelion.* From these two axioms it results that *the mean diurnal motion of the planet in its eccentric is the same as the real diurnal arc of that eccentric at the moments at which the planet is at the end of the quarter eccentric reckoned from the aphelion, although that true quadrant as yet appears smaller than the exact quadrant.* It follows, further that *any two perfectly exact diurnal arcs of the eccentric, at exactly the same distance, the one from the aphelion, the other from the perihelion, are together equal to two median diurnal arcs;* and consequently, that, *since circumferences are to each other as diameters, one mean diurnal arc is to the sum of all the mean arcs, which are equal to each other, as many as there are in the whole circumference, as one mean diurnal arc is to the sum of all the real eccentric arcs, the same in number but unequal to each other.* And these truths concerning the real diurnal arcs of the eccentric and the real motions must be known beforehand, that now from these we may understand the apparent motions as they are when observed from the Sun.

Sixthly, as regards the apparent arcs as seen from the Sun, it is known even from the ancient astronomy that of real motions, even when they are equal to each other, that which is farther from the center of the universe (as one that is in aphelion) appears to the eye looking at it from that center to be less, and that which is nearer (as one that is in perihelion) seems to be greater. Since, therefore, in addition, the real diurnal arcs which are in proximity are greater still on account of the greater velocity, and the real arcs in the remote aphelion are smaller still on account of the retardation, it results, as I have shown in my Commentaries on Mars, that *the apparent diurnal arcs of one eccentric are almost exactly inversely proportional to the square of their distances from the Sun.* As, for instance, if a planet in one of its days when it is in aphelion is distant from the Sun 10 units, in any measure whatsoever, and in its opposite day, when it is in perihelion, is distant 9 units of exactly the same kind, it is certain that, as seen from the Sun, its apparent progress in aphelion will be to its apparent progress in perihelion as 81 is to 100.

Now this is true with these reservations: first, that the arcs of the eccentric be not large, that they may not have different distances varying greatly, that is, that they may not cause a sensible variation in the distances of their ends from the apsides; secondly that the eccentricity be not very great, for the greater the eccentricity, that is the greater the arc, the greater is the increase of the angle of that appearance in comparison with its own advance toward the Sun, according to Theorem 8 of the "Optics" of Euclid. But there is another reason why I give this warning. The arcs of the eccentric about the middle of the anomalies are observed obliquely from the center of the Sun, and this obliquity diminishes the size of their appearance, while, on the other hand, the arcs around the apsides are presented to the sight, which is supposed to be on the Sun, from directly in front. When, therefore, the eccentricity is very great, the relation of the motions is sensibly disarranged if we apply the mean diurnal motion without diminution to the mean distance, as if it appeared from the mean distance as large as it is; and this will appear below in the case of Mercury. All this matter is treated at greater length in "Epitome Astronomiae Copernicae," Book V, but it had to be given here because it concerns the very terms themselves of the celestial harmonies, when considered apart each by itself.

Seventhly, in case anyone chances to think of those diurnal motions that are apparent, not to the assumed observer on the Sun, but to the observer on the Earth, with regard to which motions Book VI of "Epitome Astronomiae Copernicae" deals, let him know that these do not come under consideration at all in the present enquiry; clearly they should not, since the Earth is not the source of their motion, nor can they, since these motions, being referred to a false appearance, change not only into absolute rest or apparent motionlessness, but even into retrograde motion; whereby all the infinity of relations is attributed to all the planets at one and the same time and equally. That we may determine, therefore, what the inherent relations are that are established by the diurnal motions of the true individual eccentric orbits (although as yet even they are apparent, being supposed to be seen from the Sun, the source of motion), we must first separate from these inherent motions this appearance of extrinsic annual motion common to all five planets, whether that motion is due, as Copernicus holds, to the motion of the Earth itself, or, as Tycho Brahe holds, to the annual motion of the whole system, and these motions peculiar to each planet must be presented to our view freed from what is extraneous.

Eighthly, thus far we have dealt with the various times of arcs of one and the same planet. Now we must deal also with the motions of the planets taken two at a time and compare these motions with each other. And here note the definition of the terms that we shall find it necessary to use. By the *proximate apsides* of two planets we shall mean the perihelion of the higher and the aphelion of the lower, notwithstanding the fact that they turn not toward the same quarter of the heavens, but toward different and possibly opposite quarters. *Extreme motions*, understand to be the slowest and the fastest of the entire planetary circuit; *convergent extreme* or *converse*, those that are in the nearest apsides of two orbits, that is, in the perihelion of the superior, and the aphelion of the inferior; *divergent* or *diverse*, those that are in opposite apsides, that is in the aphelion of the superior, and the perihelion of the inferior. Again, therefore, a part of my "Mysterium Cosmographicum," suspended twenty-two years ago, because I did not then see my way clear, must be completed and introduced here. For, after I had by unceasing toil through a long period of time, using the observations of Brahe, discovered the true distances of the orbits, at last, at last, the true relation of the periodic times to the orbits and, if you ask for the exact time, conceived on the 8th of March of this

> ... though late, yet looked upon me idle
> And after long time came;

year, 1618, but unsuccessfully brought to the test and for that reason rejected as false, but, finally returning on the 15th of May, by a new onset it overcame by storm the shadows of my mind, with such fullness of agreement between my seventeen-years' labor on the observations of Brahe and this present study of mine that I at first believed that I was dreaming and was assuming as an accepted principle what was still a subject of enquiry. But the principle is unquestionably true and quite exact: *the periodic times of any two planets are to each other exactly as the cubes of the square roots of their median distances;* this fact should be observed, however, that the arithmetic mean between the two diameters of the elliptical orbit is a little less than the longer diameter. And so, if one takes from the period, say, of the Earth, which is one year, and from Saturn's period of thirty years, the third part of the ratio, that is the cubic roots, and doubles this ratio by squaring the roots, one has in the resulting numbers the exact ratio of the median distances from the Sun of the Earth and Saturn.[1] For the cubic root of 1 is 1 and the square of that is 1; and the cubic root of 30 is greater than 3, and the square of that, therefore, is greater than 9. And Saturn, when at its mean distance from the Sun, is a little higher than nine times the mean distance of the Earth from the Sun.

Ninthly, if now you wish to measure as by the same ten-foot rule the exact journeys made by each planet daily through the sky, you will have to combine two ratios, one of the real (not apparent) daily arcs of the eccentric, the other of the mean distance of each planet from the Sun, because this is likewise the

---

[1] For in my Commentaries on Mars, Chap. XLIII, fol. 232 (III, 353) I showed that this arithmetic mean is either the diameter itself of the circle which is equal in length to the elliptical orbit or very little less than the diameter.

ratio of the amplitudes of the orbits; that is, the real daily arc of each planet must be multiplied into the semidiameter of its own orbit. This done, there will result numbers suitable for use in ascertaining whether those journeys have harmonic relations.

Tenthly, that you may know how great the apparent length of any such daily journey is when the eye is supposed to be on the Sun—although this may be obtained directly from astronomical observation, still it will also result if you add to the ratio of the journeys the inverse ratio of the mean, not real, distances of any point of the eccentrics, the journey of the superior eccentric being multiplied into the distance from the Sun of the inferior, and, on the other hand, the journey of the inferior being multiplied into the distance from the Sun of the superior.

Eleventhly, furthermore, given the apparent motions, the aphelion of one and the perihelion of the other, or conversely, or alternately, there are elicited ratios of the distances, of the aphelion of one to the perihelion of the other; in which case, however, the mean motions must be known beforehand, that is the inverse ratio of the periodic times, from which is deduced the proportion relating to the orbits found in paragraph VIII. Then, *taking the mean proportional between either apparent motion and its own mean, the result is that, as this mean proportional is to the semidiameter of its orbit* (which is already given), *so is the mean motion to the distance or interval sought.* Let the periodic times of two planets be 27 and 8; then their mean diurnal motions are to each other as 8 is to 27. Therefore, the semidiameters of the orbits will be as 9 is to 4. For the cubic root of 27 is 3, and that of 8 is 2, and the squares of these roots, 3 and 2, are 9 and 4. Now let the apparent motions be, the aphelion of one 2, and the perihelion of the other $33\frac{1}{3}$. The mean proportionals between the mean motions, 8 and 27, and these apparent motions will be 4 and 30. If, therefore, the mean 4 gives the mean distance of the planet 9, then the mean motion 8 gives the aphelion distance 18, corresponding to the apparent motion 2; and if the other mean 30 gives the mean distance of the other planet 4, then the mean motion of that planet 27 gives its perihelion distance $3\frac{3}{5}$. I say, therefore, that the aphelion distance of the former planet is to the perihelion of this as 18 is to 3⅗. From which it is clear that, the harmonies between the extreme motions of two planets having been found, and the periodic times assigned to each, there must result the extreme and mean distances, and, therefore, also the eccentricities.

Twelfthly, it is given also, from different extreme motions of one and the same planet, to find the mean motion. For this is not exactly the arithmetical mean between the extreme motions, nor is it exactly the geometrical mean, but it is as much less than the geometrical mean as the geometrical mean is less than the [arithmetical] mean between the two. Let the two extreme motions be 8 and 10. The mean motion will be less than 9, less even than the root of 80 by a half of the difference between the two, 9 and the root of 80. So, if the aphelion is 20, and the perihelion 24, the mean motion will be less than 22, less even than the root of 480 by a half of the difference between this root and 22.

GUSTAV ROBERT KIRCHHOFF

(1824–1887)

This German physicist is credited (with R. W. Bunsen) with establishing the science of spectrum analysis, which he applied to celestial objects. He enunciated Kirchhoff's law (concerning electric currents in a network, and in optics the emissive power of a body at a definite temperature), and distinguished himself in the fields of thermal conductivity and elasticity.

RESEARCHES ON THE SOLAR SPECTRUM AND THE SPECTRA OF THE CHEMICAL ELEMENTS

IN THE course of the experiments already alluded to, which Foucault instituted on the spectrum of the electric arc formed between the carbon points, this physicist observed that the bright sodium lines present were changed into dark bands in the spectrum produced by the light from one of the carbon poles, which had been allowed to pass through the luminous arc; and when he passed direct sunlight through the arc he noticed that the double D line was seen with an unusual degree of distinctness. No attempt was made to explain or to increase these observations either by Foucault or by any other physicist, and they remained unnoticed by the greatest number of experimentalists. They were unknown to me when Bunsen and I, in the year 1859, commenced our investigations on the spectra of colored flames.

In order to test in the most direct manner possible the truth of the frequently asserted fact of the coincidence of the sodium lines with the lines D, I obtained a tolerably bright solar spectrum, and brought a flame colored by sodium vapor in front of

561

the slit. I then saw the dark lines *D* change into bright ones. The flame of a Bunsen's lamp threw the bright sodium lines upon the solar spectrum with unexpected brilliancy. In order to find out the extent to which the intensity of the solar spectrum could be increased, without impairing the distinctness of the sodium lines, I allowed the full sunlight to shine through the sodium flame upon the slit, and, to my astonishment, I saw that the dark lines *D* appeared with an extraordinary degree of clearness. I then exchanged the sunlight for the Drummond's or oxyhydrogen limelight, which, like that of all incandescent solid or liquid bodies, gives a spectrum containing no dark lines. When this light was allowed to fall through a suitable flame colored by common salt, dark lines were seen in the spectrum in the position of the sodium lines. The same phenomenon was observed if instead of the incandescent lime a platinum wire was used, which being heated in a flame was brought to a temperature

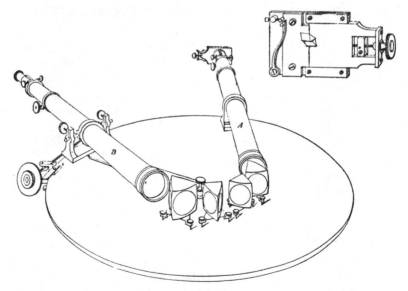

The apparatus employed by Kirchhoff for the observation of the solar spectrum

near to its melting point by passing an electric current through it.

The phenomenon in question is easily explained upon the supposition that the sodium flame absorbs rays of the same degree by the fact, which has long been known, that certain gases, as for instance, nitrous acid and iodine vapor, possess at low temperatures the property of such a selective absorption. The following considerations shew that this is the true explanation of the phenomenon. If a sodium flame be held before an incandescent platinum wire whose spectrum is being examined, the brightness of the light in the neighborhood of the sodium lines would, according to the above supposition, *not* be altered; in the position of the sodium lines themselves, however, the brightness *is* altered, for two reasons; in the first place, the intensity of light emitted by the platinum wire is reduced to a certain fraction of its original amount by absorption in the flame, and secondly, the light of the flame itself is added to that from the wire. It is plain that if the platinum wire emits a sufficient amount of light, the loss of light occasioned by absorption in the flame must be greater than the gain of light from the luminosity of the flame; the sodium lines must then appear darker than the surrounding parts, and by contrast with the neighboring parts they may seem to be quite black, although their degree of luminosity is necessarily greater than that which the sodium flame alone would have produced.

The absorptive power of sodium vapor becomes most apparent when its luminosity is smallest, or when its temperature is lowest. In fact we were unable to produce the dark sodium lines in the spectrum of a Drummond's light, or in that of an incandescent wire, by means of a Bunsen's gas-flame in which common salt was placed; but the experiment succeeded with a flame of aqueous alcohol containing common salt. The following experiment proposed by Crookes likewise very clearly shews this influence of temperature. If a piece of sodium is burnt in a room, and the air thus filled with the vapor of sodium compounds, every flame is seen to burn with the characteristic yellow light. If a small flame in which a bead of soda salt is placed be now fixed in front of a large one, so that the former is seen projected on the latter as a background, the small flame appears to be surrounded with a black smoky mantle. This dark mantle is produced by the absorptive action of the sodium vapors in the outer part of the flame, which are cooler than those in the flame itself. Bunsen and I have produced the dark lines in the spectrum of a common candle-flame, by allowing the rays to pass through a test tube containing a small quantity of sodium-amalgam, which we heated to boiling; so that the sodium vapor effecting the absorption had in this case possessed a temperature far below the red-heat. The same phenomenon is observed in a much more striking manner if a glass tube is used containing some small pieces of sodium first filled with hydrogen, and then rendered vacuous and sealed. The lower end of the tube can be heated so as to vaporize the sodium. By means of this arrangement, which was proposed by Roscoe, the heated vapor of the sodium, when viewed by the sodium-light, is seen as a dark black smoke which throws a deep shadow, but is perfectly invisible when observed by the ordinary gaslight . . .

The sodium flame is characterized beyond that of any other colored flame by the intensity of the lines in its spectrum. Next to it in this respect comes the lithium flame. It is just as easy to reverse the red lithium line, that is, to turn the bright line into a dark one, as it is to reverse the sodium line. If direct sunlight be allowed to pass through a lithium flame, the spectrum exhibits in the place of the red lithium band a black line which in distinctness bears comparison with the most remarkable of Fraunhofer's lines, and disappears when the flame is withdrawn. It is now so easy to obtain the reversal of the spectra of the other metals; nevertheless Bunsen and I have succeeded in reversing the brightest lines of potassium, strontium, calcium, and barium, by exploding mixtures of the chlorates of these metals and milk-sugar in front of the slit of our apparatus whilst the direct solar rays fell on the instrument.

These facts would appear to justify the supposition that each incandescent gas diminishes by absorption the intensity of those rays only which possess degrees of refrangibility equal to those of the rays which it emits; or, in other words, that the spectrum of every incandescent gas must be reversed, when it is penetrated by the rays of a source of light of sufficient intensity giving a continuous spectrum.

RENÉ LAËNNEC

(1781–1826)

Laennec has one important invention to his credit: the stethoscope. A French physician who virtually killed himself with overwork, he was prompted to devise the new instrument for listening to the sounds of the heart and lungs (called auscultation) when confronted by a female patient whose natural endowment was so great that he was unable to hear her heart "by application of the hand and percussion." His account of this discovery is not without charm. His work on the subject, *Traité de l'Auscultation Médiate*, appeared in 1819.

ON MEDIATE AUSCULTATION

In 1816 I was consulted by a young woman presenting general symptoms of disease of the heart. Owing to her stoutness little information could be gathered by application of the hand and percussion. The patient's age and sex did not permit me to resort to the kind of examination I have just described (i.e., direct application of the ear to the chest). I recalled a well-known acoustic phenomenon, namely, if you place your ear against one end of a wooden beam the scratch of a pin at the other extremity is most distinctly audible. It occurred to me that this physical property might serve a useful purpose in the case with which I was then dealing. Taking a sheaf of paper, I rolled it into a very tight roll, one end of which I placed over the praecordial region, while I put my ear to the other. I was both surprised and gratified at being able to hear the beating of the heart with much greater clearness and distinctness than I had ever done before by direct application of my ear.

I at once saw that this means might become a useful method for studying not only the beating of the heart but likewise all movements capable of producing sound in the thoracic cavity, and that consequently it might serve for the investigation of respiration, the voice, râles, and even possibly the movements of a liquid effused into the pleural cavity or pericardium.

With this conviction, I at once began and have continued to the present time, a series of observations at the Hospital Necker. As a result I have obtained many new and certain signs, most of which are striking, easy of recognition, and calculated perhaps to render the diagnosis of nearly all complaints of the lungs, pleurae, and heart both more certain and more circumstantial than the surgical diagnosis obtained by use of the sound or by introduction of the finger. . . .

Before proceeding with my subject I consider it my duty to record the various attempts that I have made to improve upon the exploring instrument I at present use; these attempts have proved almost entirely vain, and if I mention them it is in the hope that any other investigator seeking to perfect the instrument will strike out a fresh path.

The first instrument employed by me consisted of a cylinder or roll of paper, sixteen lines in diameter and one foot long, made of three quires of paper rolled very tightly round, and held in position with gummed paper and filed smooth at both ends. However tight the roll may be, there will always remain a tube three or four lines in diameter running up the center, because the sheets of paper composing it can never be rolled completely on themselves. This fortuitous circumstance gave rise, as will be seen, to an important observation upon my part: I found that for listening to the voice the tube is an indispensable factor. An entirely solid body is the best instrument that can be used for listening to the heart; such an instrument would indeed suffice also for hearing respiratory sounds and râles; yet these last two phenomena yield greater intensity of sound if a perforated cylinder is used, hollowed out at one end into a kind of funnel one and one half inches in depth.

The densest bodies are not, as analogy would lead us to suppose, the best materials for constructing these instruments. Glass and metals, apart from their weight and the sensation of cold that they impart in winter, are not such good carriers of

567

the heartbeats and the sounds produced by breathing and râles, as are bodies of lesser density. . . .

Substances of medium density, such as paper, wood, and cane, are those which have always appeared to me preferable to all others. This result may be in contradiction with an axiom of physics; nonetheless I consider it to be quite established.

I consequently employ at the present time a wooden cylinder with a tube three lines in diameter bored right down its axis; it is divisible into two parts by means of a screw and is thus more portable. One of the parts is hollowed out at its end into a wide funnel-shaped depression one and one half inches deep leading into the central tube. A cylinder made like this is the instrument most suitable for exploring breath sounds and râles. It is converted into a tube of uniform diameter with thick walls all the way, for exploring the voice and the heartbeats, by introducing into the funnel or bell a kind of stopper made of the same wood, fitting it quite closely; this is made fast by means of a small brass tube running through it, entering a certain distance into the tubular space running through the length of the cylinder. This instrument is sufficient for all cases, although, as I have said, a perfectly solid body might perhaps be better for listening to the beating of the heart.

The dimensions indicated above are not altogether unimportant; if the diameter is larger it is not always possible to apply the stethoscope closely against all points of the chest; if the instrument is longer, it becomes difficult to hold it exactly in place; if it were shorter, the physician would often be obliged to adopt an uncomfortable position, which is to be avoided above all things if he desires to carry out accurate observations.

I shall be careful, when discussing each variety of exploration, to mention the positions which experience has taught me to be most favorable for observation and least tiring for both physician and patient.

Suffice it to say for the moment that in all cases the stethoscope should be held like a pen, and that the hand must be placed quite close to the patient's chest in order to make sure that the instrument is properly applied.

JEAN BAPTISTE LAMARCK

(1744–1829)

Promoter of a theory of evolution which antedated Darwin, Lamarck began his career as a military man, turned to medicine and botany because of poor health, and became professor of zoology and custodian of Louis XVI's Jardin des Plantes. There he developed his classification of vertebrates and invertebrates (*Système des Animaux sans Vertèbres*, 1801). At the same time he began his speculations about the origin of species and evolved the theory that variations result from inherited characteristics acquired to meet the needs of the enivironment (*Philosophie Zoologique*, 1809). Lamarck thus provided the general foundation for the now largely accepted (though still unproved) theory of descent. His special theory—that acquired characteristics can be inherited—has, however, been largely rejected.

WHAT IS A SPECIES?

WHAT IS a *species* among living beings?

All those who have much to do with the study of natural history know that naturalists at the present day are extremely embarrassed in defining what they mean by the word "species."

In truth, observation for a long time has shown us, and shows us still in a great number of cases, collections of individuals which resemble each other so much in their organization and by the *ensemble* of their parts that we do not hesitate to regard these collections of similar individuals as constituting so many species.

From this consideration we call *species* every collection of individuals which are alike or almost so, and we remark that the regeneration of these individuals conserves the species and propagates it in continuing successively to reproduce similar individuals.

Formerly it was supposed that each species was immutable, as old as Nature, and that she had caused its special creation by the Supreme Author of all which exists.

But we can impose on Him laws in the execution of His will, and determine the mode which He has been pleased to follow in this respect, so it is only in this way that He permits us to recognize it by the aid of observation. Has not His infinite power created an order of things which successively gives existence to all that we see as well as to all that which exists and which we do not know?

Assuredly, whatever has been His will, the omnipotence of His power is always the same; and in whatever way this supreme will has been manifested, nothing can diminish its greatness. As regards, then, the decrees of this infinite wisdom, I confine myself to the limits of a simple observer of Nature. Then, if I discover anything in the course that Nature follows in her creations, I shall say, without fear of deceiving myself, that it has pleased its author that she possesses this power.

The idea that was held as to species among living bodies was quite simple, easy to grasp, and seemed confirmed by the constancy in the similar form of the individuals which reproduction or generation perpetuated. There still occur among us a very great number of these pretended species which we see every day.

However, the farther we advance in the knowledge of the different organized bodies with which almost every part of the surface of the globe is covered, the more does our embarrassment increase in determining what should be regarded as species, and the greater is the reason for limiting and distinguishing the genera.

As we gradually gather the productions of Nature, as our collections gradually grow richer, we see almost all the gaps filled up, and our lines of demarcation effaced. We find ourselves compelled to make an arbitrary determination, which sometimes leads us to seize upon the slightest differences between varieties to form of them the character of that which we call species, and sometimes one person designates as a variety of such a species individuals a little different, which others regard as constituting a particular species.

I repeat, the richer our collections become, the more numerous are the proofs that all is more or less shaded, that the remarkable differences become obliterated, and that the more often Nature leaves it at our disposal to establish distinctions only minute, and in some degree trivial peculiarities.

But some genera among animals and plants are of such an extent, from the number of species they contain, that the study and the determination of these species are now almost impossible. The species of these genera, arranged in series and placed together according to their natural relations, present, with those allied to them, differences so slight that they shade into each other; and because these species are in some degree confounded with one another they leave almost no means of determining, by expression in words, the small differences which distinguish them.

There are also those who have been for a long time, and strongly, occupied with the determination of the species, and who have consulted rich collections, who can understand up to what point species, among living bodies, merge one into another, and who have been able to convince themselves, in the regions where we see isolated species, that this is only because there are wanting other species which are more nearly related, and which we have not yet collected.

I do not mean to say by this that the existing animals form a very simple series, one everywhere equally graduated; but I say that they form a branching series, irregularly graduated, and which has no discontinuity in its parts, or which at best has not always had, if it is true that it is to be found anywhere. It results from this that the species which terminates each branch of the general series holds a place at least on one side apart from the other allied species which intergrade with them. Behold this state of things, so well known, which I am now compelled to demonstrate.

I have no need of any hypothesis or any supposition for this: I call to witness all observing naturalists. . . .

A great many facts teach us that gradually, as the individuals

571

of one of our species change their situation, climate, mode of life, or habits, they thus receive influences which gradually change the consistence and the proportions of their parts, their form, their faculties, even their organization; so that all of them participate eventually in the changes which they have undergone.

In the same climate very different situations and exposures at first cause simple variations in the individuals which are found exposed there; but as time goes on the continual differences of situation of individuals of which I have spoken, which live and successively reproduce in the same circumstances, give rise among them to differences which are, in some degree, essential to their being, in such a way that at the end of many successive generations these individuals, which originally belonged to another species, are at the end transformed into a new species, distinct from the other.

For example, if the seeds of a grass, or of every other plant natural to a humid field, should be transplanted, by an accident, at first to the slope of a neighboring hill, where the soil, although more elevated, would yet be quite cool, so as to allow the plant to live, and then after having lived there, and passed through many generations there, it should gradually reach the poor and almost arid soil of a mountainside—if the plant should thrive and live there and perpetuate itself during a series of generations, it would then be so changed that the botanists who should find it there would describe it as a separate species.

The same thing happens to animals which circumstances have forced to change their climate, manner of living, and habits; but for these the influences of the causes which I have just cited need still more time than in the case of plants to produce the notable changes in the individuals, though in the long run, however, they always succeed in bringing them about.

The idea of defining under the word "species" a collection of similar individuals which perpetuate the same by generation, and which have existed thus as anciently as Nature, implies the necessity that the individuals of one and the same species cannot mix, in their acts of generation, with the individuals of a different species. Unfortunately observation has proved, and still proves every day, that this consideration has no basis; for the hybrids, very common among plants, and the unions which are often observed between the individuals of very different species among animals, have made us perceive that the limits between these species, supposed to be constant, are not so rigid as is supposed.

In truth, nothing often results from these singular unions, especially when they are very incongruous, as the individuals which result from them are usually sterile; but also, when the disparities are less great, it is known that the drawbacks with which it has to do no longer exist. However, this means alone suffices to gradually create the varieties which have afterwards arisen from races, and which, with time, constitute that which we call *species*. . . .

It appears, as I have already said, that *time* and *favorable conditions* are the two principal means which Nature has employed in giving existence to all her productions. We know that for her time has no limit, and that consequently she has it always at her disposal.

As to the circumstances of which she has had need and of which she makes use every day in order to cause her productions to vary, we can say that they are in a manner inexhaustible.

The essential ones arise from the influence and from all the environing media, from the diversity of local causes, of habits, of movements, of action, finally of means of living, of preserving their lives, of defending themselves, of multiplying themselves, et cetera. Moreover, as the result of these different influences, the faculties, developed and strengthened by use, became diversified by the new habits maintained for long ages, and by slow degrees the structure, the consistence, in a word the nature, the condition of the parts and of the organs consequently participating in all these influences, became preserved and were propagated by generation.

The bird which necessity drives to the water to find there the prey needed for its subsistence separates the toes of its feet when it wishes to strike the water and move on its surface. The skin, which unites these toes at their base, contracts in this way

573

the habit of extending itself. Thus in time the broad membranes which connect the toes of ducks, geese, et cetera, are formed in the way indicated.

But one accustomed to live perched on trees has necessarily the end of the toes lengthened and shaped in another way. Its claws are elongated, sharpened, and are curved and bent so as to seize the branches on which it so often rests.

Likewise we perceive that the shore bird, which does not care to swim, but which, however, is obliged to approach the water to obtain its prey, will be continually in danger of sinking in the mud, but wishing to act so that its body shall not fall into the liquid, it will contract the habit of extending and lengthening its feet. Hence it will result in the generations of these birds which continue to live in this manner that the individuals will find themselves raised as if on stilts, on long naked feet; namely, denuded of feathers up to and often above the thighs.

I could here pass in review all the classes, all the orders, all the genera and species of animals which exist, and make it apparent that the conformation of individuals and of their parts, their organs, their faculties, et cetera, is entirely the result of circumstances to which the race of each species has been subjected by nature.

I could prove that it is not the form either of the body or of its parts which gives rise to habits, to the mode of life of animals, but, on the contrary, it is the habits, the mode of life, and all the influential circumstances which have, with time, made up the form of the body and of the parts of animals. With the new forms new faculties have been acquired, and gradually Nature has reached the state in which we actually see her.

Indeed, we know that all the time that an organ, or a system of organs, is rigorously exercised throughout a long time, not only its power, and the parts which form it, grow and strengthen themselves, but there are proofs that this organ, or system of organs, at that time attracts to itself the principal active forces of the life of the individual, because it becomes the cause which, under these conditions, makes the functions of other organs to be diminished in power.

Thus not only every organ or every part of the body, whether of man or of animals, being for a long period and more vigorously exercised than the others, had acquired a power and facility of action that the same organ could not have had before, and that it has never had in individuals which have exercised less, but also we consequently remark that the excessive employment of this organ diminishes the functions of the others and proportionately enfeebles them.

The man who habitually and vigorously exercises the organ of his intelligence develops and acquires a great facility of attention, of aptitude for thought, et cetera, but he has a feeble stomach and strongly limited muscular powers. He, on the contrary, who thinks little does not easily, and then only momentarily fixes his attention, while habitually giving much exercise to his muscular organs, has much vigor, possesses an excellent digestion, and is not given to the abstemiousness of the savant and man of letters.

Moreover, when one exercises long and vigorously an organ or system of organs, the active forces of life (in my opinion, the nervous fluid) have taken such a habit of acting toward this organ that they have formed in the individual an inclination to exercise which it is difficult for it to overcome.

Hence it happens that the more we exercise an organ, the more we use it with facility, the more does it result that we perceive the need of continuing to use it at the times when it is placed in action. So we remark that the habit of study, of application, of work, or of any other exercise of our organs or of any one of our organs, becomes with time an indispensable need to the individual, and often a passion which it does not know how to overcome. . . .

Thus we are assured that that which is taken for *species* among living bodies, and that all the specific differences which distinguish these natural productions, have no absolute *stability*, but that they enjoy only a relative *stability*; which it is very important to consider in order to fix the limits which we must establish in the determination of that which we must call *species*.

JOHANN HEINRICH LAMBERT

(1728–1777)

Physicist, astronomer, mathematician and philosopher, Lambert investigated notably light, heat and color. His major discovery was a method of measuring the intensity of light (the lambert is a unit of brightness), described in his *Photometria* (1760). He was also interested in cosmology and formulated a theorem relating to the planets (*Kosmologische Briefe*, 1761). In mathematics he demonstrated that π is incommensurable, and introduced hyperbolic functions into trigonometry.

CONCERNING SYSTEMS OF SYSTEMS

BEFORE WE proceed in our enquiry concerning the motion of the fixed stars, we must endeavor to have a just idea of their situation and arrangement in the heavens. While we raise our eyes to the firmament, we see the whole of the stars attached, as it were, to the same vaulted surface; this, however, is an optical illusion; they are, in reality, at very different distances from us, as well as from the Sun, which is the fixed star of our system.

In order to prove this, we shall not have recourse either to the annual paralax of the Earth, which is too inconsiderable to measure such vast distances, nor to the observed motion of the fixed stars, which the observations of several centuries would scarcely be sufficient to discover, even in a small degree.

Our evidence will be derived partly from the apparent as well as real light and magnitude of those stars, and partly from the laws of cosmogony.

One star appears larger than another, not only because it actually is so, or that it is at a smaller distance from the eye;

but, likewise, because it has a greater degree of luster; a circumstance, the reason of which we discover in the pupil of the eye, in the confusion of the image painted in the retina, and in the dispersion of the light on the same organ. Our best glasses, by extinguishing the scattered and tremulous rays, shew us the fixed stars like so many luminous points. For similar reasons, one star seems to shine with a greater brilliancy than another, especially if it has more luster in its own nature. We may presume, also, that their light suffers a diminution in the atmospheres of the Earth and Sun, in the ether itself, in the atmosphere of other fixed stars which it traverses, and in that of the bodies which revolve round themselves. Thus, the more distant a star is, the more pale and feeble will its light become by the time it reaches the eye; but, if all the stars were equally distant, their light would decay proportionally, and this difference would not exist.

If they were all of the same magnitude, and equally brilliant, we should thence infer, that such as appear of the smallest size are the most remote. And, were they all at an equal distance, we ought to conclude that the small ones had, at the same time, an inferior degree of brilliancy. It is observed that the number of stars in the different classes of magnitude increases nearly as the square of the term of each magnitude. There are eighteen of the first magnitude, sixty-eight of the second, two hundred and nine of the third, four hundred and fifty-three of the fourth, &c. It is certain that this progression is much better accounted for by the different distances of the stars, though we are far from contending that they are all equally large and equally luminous.

The Milky Way.—The outline of the milky way seems extremely irregular to the eye, and its breadth very unequally verging from three degrees in some places to 25 degrees in others even to 30 degrees. There are places where it appears broken, lacerated, or split into several pieces, some of which seem to overleap the general boundary. In short, taken all together, it is visibly detached from the rest of the heavens, and the number of its stars, compared with those that are without it, is like the ocean compared to a drop of water.

577

What then is the cause of this apparently feeble light in the stars of the milky way? For all the fixed stars being destined to serve the same end, we see no reason to believe that these have a light originally weaker than the rest. It can only be on account of their distance then, that they make a fainter impression on our senses. The milky way lies in the background of the other stars, at such an immense distance, as prevents our discovering its component stars otherwise than with a telescope. This being the case, no reason can possibly be assigned, why those stars should not be in themselves equally large and luminous with our Sun.

The circumstance of distance leads us to conceive, in like manner, that notwithstanding their apparent proximity, they may be separated from one another by vast intervals. And, in fact, everything concurs to persuade us, that there is a distance between them similar to what exists between the other fixed stars; for example, between the Sun and Sirius, or the fixed star the most contiguous to our system . . .

But if we suppose that those stars are separated by distances equal to those that the other fixed stars hold in respect to one another, we would thence draw this other conclusion, that the stars of the milky way are arranged not in the same line, but the one behind the other in immense serieses . . .

. . . it necessarily follows that the stars in the milky way are some more, some less remote, and that they succeed each other in numberless serieses, stretching progressively into the abyss of the universe. The stars which are out of the tract of the milky way, being also, as we have shewn, at various distances from us, form similar serieses, though less extended in length.

Let us consider at present the whole visible stars in mass, and we shall perceive that this whole does not exhibit a spherical figure, but rather that of a physical plane or disk, whose diameter is much greater than the axis which measures its thickness. In this plane lie the milky way, and all that is without it: it may be regarded as the ecliptic of the other fixed stars. It represents a flattened cylinder, or a spheroid, which for a row of a hundred stars in its thickness, ought to have a train of millions in its length; and it is this that defines the general aspect, or *coup d'œil,* for we see it in an oval form.

Systems of Higher Order.—Our Earth belongs, by a chain of gradations, to several systems, and at last to the system of the universe: all the centers of those systems as well as the universal center, exert their influence over her. The whole of those centers then, ought, in respect of the Earth, to occupy a sensible space in the heavens; at least we have a right to suppose that we ought to see them with the telescope. Nothing but the inconveniencies arising from the transmission of light as detailed above, could intercept our view of them. For as to their magnitude, it is such as it would be necessary to render them visible.

Here then we have all the systems of the universe reduced to order, and enchased in one another. But what is our position amidst those systems? Where are we? As to this point we can speak indefinitely, negatively, and by approximation only.

The Earth is not at the center of the solar system. The Sun is not at the center of his system of fixed stars; a center which is either in the region of Orion or Sirius. This system is neither at the center nor in the plane of the milky way, though it seems to project over it a little; the portion of this way which it approaches the nearest, is that which passes by the colure of Capricorn, where its breadth is double. But where is the milky way itself in relation to other milky ways? Here ends all our science with the utmost stretch of our eyes and instruments.

On the Complication of Celestial Motions.—Hitherto we have proceeded on the supposition that the heavenly bodies revolve in ellipses. The new point of view to which our theory leads us will produce an entire change; and we shall see that we have reviewed a suite of hypotheses which overturn each other, in proportion as we advance in our enquiry.

The Moon, it is said, describes an ellipse round the Earth. This would be true were the Earth at rest; but as she moves round the Sun, and obliges the Moon to participate in her motion, the orbit of this last cannot be an ellipse, but a cycloid. The ellipse of the

579

Earth vanishes for the same reason, the moment the Sun ceases to be immoveable, and is found to describe an orbit round a new center. Then the ellipse of the Earth becomes a cycloid of the first degree, that of the Moon of the second, and the velocity of their motion increases in the same proportion.

But this order continues no longer than the new center, or body of the fourth degree, reckoning from the Moon, is supposed immoveable. As soon as we give motion to it, the ellipse of the sun vanishes in its turn; he then describes a cycloid of the first degree, the Earth of the second, the Moon of the third.

We easily perceive, that what is here said of the Moon, the Earth, and the Sun, applies equally to all the satellites, planets, comets, and fixed stars, without exception. There is not a heavenly body which does not partake of these motions, more or less complex; while each shares them in a degree suited to its particular circumstances.

We observe likewise, that as we pass on from center to center, these motions become more and more complicated; and their combinations only terminate at the universal center, which alone is in a state of real and absolute rest. If, beginning by the Moon, we suppose that the body which occupies that center is in the thousandth, the cycloid of the Earth will be in the nine hundred and ninety-eighth degree. There, and there alone, will be the true orbit of the Earth, while the velocity with which she describes it, will be her true velocity. But who is in condition to determine it, to describe the nature of her cycloid, to trace the perplexed path of our planet, and the strange bounds or skips she makes in the regions of the Heavens?

Nothing, however, is more evident. The Earth as well as all the other globes, revolve, properly speaking, round the universal center alone. With respect to the Sun, she only attends him in the same route, and as his fellow traveler, avails herself of his company, by partaking in his light and heat. She undoubtedly makes many circuitous, and, as they may appear to us, useless trips, but which, as the law of gravitation supplies no other means of keeping two or more bodies together, are nevertheless necessary. She gravitates towards all the centers on which she depends;

with the Moon towards the Sun, with the Sun towards a body of the fourth degree, with this last towards a body of the fifth, or towards the center of the milky way, and so on of the rest.

Thus, from system to system, our cycloid takes new inflections, which increase in magnitude as we advance in our career.

General Conclusion.—Let us recapitulate and have done. The law of gravitation extends universally over all matter. The fixed stars obeying central forces move in orbits. The milky way comprehends several systems of fixed stars; those that appear out of the tract of the milky way form but one system which is our own. The sun being of the number of fixed stars, revolves round a center like the rest. Each system has its center, and several systems taken together have a common center. Assemblages of their assemblages have likewise theirs. In fine, there is a universal center for the whole world round which all things revolve. Those centers are not void, but occupied by opaque bodies. Those bodies may borrow their light from one or more Suns, and hence become visible with phases. Perhaps the pale light seen in Orion is our center. The real orbits of comets, planets, and suns, are not ellipses, but cycloids of different degrees. The orbits of those bodies which are immediately subject to the action of the universal center can alone be ellipses.

SAMUEL P. LANGLEY

(1834–1906)

Precursor of the Wright brothers, Langley is remembered for his invention of the first heavier-than-air machine actually to fly: His nine-pound model airplane stayed in the air for half a mile over the Potomac River in 1896 before running out of fuel. His subsequent attempt to fly a man-carrying machine seven years later ended disastrously just nine days before the Wrights succeeded at Kitty Hawk. His "aerodrome," as he called it, was steam-driven and is on exhibition at the Washington National Museum. Langley also invented a barometer for measuring radiant heat and made important studies in solar physics.

MEMOIR ON MECHANICAL FLIGHT

I ANNOUNCED in 1891, as the result of experiments carried on by me through previous years, that it was possible to construct machines which would give such a velocity to inclined surfaces that bodies indefinitely heavier than the air could be sustained upon it and moved through it with great velocity. In particular, it was stated that a plane surface in the form of a parallelogram of 76.2 cm.×12.2 cm. (30×4.8 inches), weighing 500 grams (1.1 pounds), could be driven through the air with a velocity of 20 meters (65.6 feet) per second in absolutely horizontal flight, with an expenditure of 1/200 horsepower, or, in other terms, that 1 horsepower would propel and sustain in horizontal flight, at such a velocity (that is, about 40 miles an hour), a little over 200 pounds' weight of such surface, where the specific gravity of the plane was a matter of secondary importance, the support being derived from the elasticity and inertia of the air upon which the body is made to run rapidly.

582

It was further specifically remarked that it was not asserted that planes of any kind were the best forms to be used in mechanical flight, nor was it asserted, without restrictions, that mechanical flight was absolutely possible, since this depended upon our ability to get horizontal flight during transport, and to leave the earth and to return to it in safety. Our ability actually to do this, it was added, would result from the practice of some unexplored art or science which might be termed Aerodromics, but on which I was not then prepared to enter. . . .

It is to be remembered that the mechanical difficulties of artificial flight have been so great that, so far as is known, never at any time in the history of the world previous to my experiment of May 1896 had any such mechanism, however actuated, sustained itself in the air for more than a few seconds—never, for instance, a single half minute—and those models which had sustained themselves for these few seconds had been in almost every case actuated by rubber springs, and had been of such size that they should hardly be described as more than toys. This refers to actual flights in free air, unguided by any tract or arm, for, since the most economical flight must always be a horizontal one in a straight line, the fact that a machine has lifted itself while pressed upward against an overhead track which compels the aerodrome to move horizontally and at the proper angle for equilibrium, is no proof at all of real "flight."

I desire to ask the reader's consideration of the fact that even ten years ago [i.e., 1887] the whole subject of mechanical flight was so far from having attracted the general attention of physicists or engineers, that it was generally considered to be a field fitted rather for the pursuits of the charlatan than for those of the man of science. Consequently, he who was bold enough to enter it found almost none of those experimental data which are ready to hand in every recognized and reputable field of scientific labor. Let me reiterate the statement, which even now seems strange, that such disrepute attached so lately to the attempt to make a "flying machine," that hardly any scientific men of position had made even preliminary investigations, and that almost every experiment to be made was made for the first time. To cover so vast a field as that which aerodromics is now seen to open, no lifetime would have sufficed. The preliminary experiments on the primary question of equilibrium and the intimately associated problems of the resistance of the sustaining surfaces, the power of the engines, the method of their application, the framing of the hull structure which held these, the construction of the propeller, the putting of the whole in initial motion, were all to be made, and could not be conducted with the exactness which would render them final models of accuracy.

I beg the reader, therefore, to recall as he reads that everything here has been done with a view to putting a trial aerodrome successfully in flight within a few years, and thus giving an early demonstration of the only kind which is conclusive in the eyes of the scientific man, as well as of the general public—a demonstration that mechanical flight is possible—by actually flying.

All that has been done, has been with an eye principally to this immediate result, and all the experiments given in this book are to be considered only as approximations to exact truth. All were made with a view, not to some remote future, but to an arrival within the compass of a few years at some result in actual flight that could not be gainsaid or mistaken.

Although many experimenters have addressed themselves to the problem within the last few years—and these have included men of education and skill—the general failure to arrive at any actual flight has seemed to throw a doubt over the conclusions which I had announced as theoretically possible.

When, therefore, I was able to state that on May 6, 1896, such a degree of success had been attained that an aerodrome, built chiefly of steel, and driven by a steam engine, had indeed flown for over half a mile—that this machine had alighted with safety, and had performed a second flight on the same day, it was felt that an advance had been made, so great as to constitute the long-desired experimental demonstration of the possibility of mechanical flight. . . .

In all discussions of flight, especially of soaring flight, the first source to which one naturally looks for information is birds. But here correct deductions from even the most accurate of observations are very difficult, because the observation cannot include all of the conditions under which the bird is doing its work. If we could but see the wind, the problem would be greatly simplified, but as the matter stands, it may be said that much less assistance has been derived from studious observations on bird flight than might have been anticipated, perhaps because it has been found thus far impossible to reproduce in the flying machine or aerostatic model the shape and condition of wing with its flexible and controllable connection with the body, and especially the instinctive control of the wing to meet the requirements of flight that are varying from second to second, and which no automatic adjustment can adequately meet.

At the time I commenced these experiments, almost the only flying machine which had really flown was a toylike model, suggested by A. Penaud, a young Frenchman of singular mechanical genius, who contributed to the world many most original and valuable papers on Aeronautics, which may be found in the journal "L'Aeronaute." His aeroplane is a toy in size, with a small propeller whose blades are usually made of two feathers, or of stiff paper, and whose motive power is a twisted strand of rubber. This power maintains it in the air for a few seconds and with an ordinary capacity for flight of fifty feet or so, but it embodies a device for automatically securing horizontal flight, which its inventor was the first to enunciate.

Although Penaud recognized that, theoretically, two screws are necessary in an aerial propeller, as the use of a single one tends to make the apparatus revolve on itself, he adopted the single screw on account of the greater simplicity of construction that it permitted. . . .

My own earliest models employed a light wooden frame with two propellers, which were each driven by a strand of twisted rubber. In later forms, the rubber was enclosed and the end strains taken up by the thinnest tin-plate tubes, or, better still, paper tubes strengthened by shellac.

Little was known to me at that time as to the proper proportions between wing surface, weight, and power; and while I at first sought to infer the relation between wing surface and weight

585

from that of soaring birds, where it varies from one half to one square foot of wing surface to the pound, yet the ratio was successively increased in the earlier models, until it became four square feet to one pound. It may be well to add, however, that the still later experiments with the steam-driven models, in which the supporting surface was approximately two square feet to the pound, proved that the lack of ability of these early rubber-driven models to properly sustain themselves even with four square feet of wing surface to the pound was largely due to the fact that the wings themselves had not been stiff enough to prevent their being warped by the air pressure generated by their forward motion.

During the years I presently describe, these tentative constructions were renewed at intervals without any satisfactory result, though it became clear from repeated failures that the motive power at command would not suffice, even for a few seconds' flight, for models of sufficient size to enable a real study to be made of the conditions necessary for successful flight.

In these earliest experiments everything had to be learned about the relative position of the center of gravity and what I have called the center of pressure. In regard to the latter term, it might at first seem that since the upward pressure of the air is treated as concentrated at one point of the supporting surface, as the weight is at the center of gravity, this point should be always in the same position for the same supporting surface. This relation, however, is never constant. How paradoxical seems the statement that, if ab be such a supporting surface in the form of a plane of uniform thickness and weight, suspended at c (ac being somewhat greater than cb) and subjected to the pressure of a wind in the direction of the arrow, the pressure on the lesser arm cb will overpower that on the greater arm $ac!$ We now know, however, that this must be so, and why, but as it was not known to the writer till determined by experiments published later in "Experiments in Aerodynamics," all this was worked out by trial in the models.

It was also early seen that the surface of support could be advantageously divided into two, with one behind the other, or

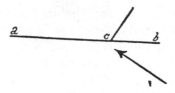

one over the other, and this was often, though not always, done in the models.

At the very beginning another difficulty was met which has proved a constant and ever-increasing one with larger models— the difficulty of launching them in the air. It is frequently proposed by those unfamiliar with this difficulty, to launch the aerodrome by placing it upon a platform car or upon the deck of a steamer, and running the car or boat at an increasing speed until the aerodrome, which is free to rise, is lifted by the wind of advance. But this is quite impracticable without means to prevent premature displacement, for the large surface and slight weight render any model of considerable size unmanageable in the least wind, such as is always present in the open air. It is, therefore, necessary in any launching apparatus that the aerodrome be held rigidly until the very moment of release, and that instant and simultaneous release from the apparatus be made at all the sustaining points at the proper moment.

There is but a very partial analogy in this case to the launching of a ship, which is held to her ways by her great weight. Here, the "ship" is liable to rise from its ways or be turned over laterally at any instant, unless it is securely fastened to them in a manner to prevent its rising, but not to prevent its advancing.

The experiments with rubber-driven models commenced in April 1887 at the Allegheny Observatory were continued at intervals (partly there, but chiefly in Washington) for three or four years, during which time between thirty and forty independent models were constructed, which were so greatly altered in the course of experiment that more nearly one hundred models were in reality tried. The result of all this extended labor was wholly inconclusive, but as subsequent trials of other motors (such as compressed air, carbonic-acid gas, electric batteries,

587

and the like) proved futile, and (before the steam engine) only the rubber gave results, however unsatisfactory, in actual flight, from which anything could be learned, I shall give some brief account of these experiments which preceded and proved the necessity of using the steam engine, or other like energetic motors, even in experimental models.

An early attempt was made in April 1887 with a model consisting of a frame formed of two wooden pieces, each about 1 meter long and 4 cm. wide, made for lightness, of star-shaped section, braced with cross-pieces and carrying two long strips of rubber, each about 1 mm. thick, 30 mm. wide, 2 meters long, doubled, weighing 300 grams. Each of these strips could be wound to about 300 turns, one end being made fast to the front of the frame, the other to the shaft of a four-bladed propeller 30 cm. in diameter. The wings were made of lightest pine frames, over which paper was stretched, and were double, one being superposed upon the other. Each was 15 cm. wide and 120 cm. long. The distance between them was 12 cm. and the total surface a little more than 3,600 sq. cm. (four square feet). In flying, the rubber was so twisted that the propellers were run in opposite directions. The weight of the whole apparatus was not quite one kilogram, or about one pound to two feet of sustaining surface, which proved to be entirely too great a weight for the power of support. When placed upon the whirling table, it showed a tendency to soar at a speed of about ten miles an hour, but its own propellers were utterly insufficient to sustain it.

In this attempt, which was useful only in showing how much was to be learned of practical conditions, the primary difficulty lay in making the model light enough and sufficiently strong to support its power. This difficulty continued to be fundamental through every later form; but besides this, the adjustment of the center of gravity to the center of pressure of the wings, the disposition of the wings themselves, the size of the propellers, the inclination and number of their blades, and a great number of other details, presented themselves for examination. Even in the first model, the difficulty of launching the machine or giving it the necessary preliminary impulse was disclosed—a difficulty which may perhaps not appear serious to the reader, but which in fact required years of experiment to remove. . . .

In June 1889, however, new rubber-driven models were made in which the wooden frames were replaced by tubes of light metal, which, however, were still too heavy, and these subsequently by tubes of paper covered with shellac, which proved to be the lightest and best material in proportion to its strength that has been found. The twisted rubber was carried within these tubes, which were made just strong enough to withstand the end strain it produced. The front end of the rubber being made fast to an extremity of the tube, the other end was attached directly to the shaft of the propeller, which in the early models was still supplied with four blades. . . .

The aerodromes made at this time were too heavy, as well as too large, to be easily launched by hand, and it was not until 1891 that the first one was constructed light enough to actually fly. This first flight was obtained from the north window of the dome of the Allegheny Observatory, on March 28, 1891, and imperfect as it was, served to show that the proper balancing of the aerodrome which would bring the center of gravity under the center of pressure, so as to give a horizontal flight, had yet to be obtained.

From this time on until 1893 experiments continued to be made with rubber-driven models, of which, as has been stated, nearly forty were constructed, some with two propellers, some with one; some with one propeller in front and one behind; some with plane, some with curved, wings; some with single, some with superposed, wings; some with two pairs of wings, one preceding and one following; some with the Penaud tail; and some with other forms. . . .

The wings in general were flat, but in some cases curved. The rubber was usually wound to about one hundred turns, and trouble continually arose from its "kinking" and unequal unwinding, which often caused most erratic flights.

It is sufficient to say of these that, rude as they were, much

589

was learned from them about the condition of the machines in free air, which could never be learned from the whirling table or other constrained flight.

The advantages and also the dangers of curved wings as compared with plane ones were shown, and the general disposition which would secure an even balance was ascertained; but all this was done with extreme difficulty, since the brief flights were full of anomalies, arising from the imperfect conditions of observation. For instance, the motor power was apparently exhausted more rapidly when the propellers were allowed to turn with the model at rest than when it was in motion, though in theory, in the latter case, more power would seem to be expended and a greater speed of revolution obtained in a given time. The longest flights obtainable did not exceed six or eight seconds in time, nor eighty to one hundred feet in distance, and were not only so brief, but, owing to the spasmodic action of the rubber and other causes, so irregular, that it was extremely difficult to obtain even the imperfect results which were actually deduced from them. . . .

The difficulties of these long-continued early experiments were enhanced by the ever-present difficulty which continued through later ones, that it was almost impossible to build the model light enough to enable it to fly, and at the same time strong enough to withstand the strains which flight imposed upon it. The models were broken up by their falls after a few flights, and had to be continually renewed, while owing to the slightness of their construction the conditions of observation could not be exactly repeated; and these flights themselves, as has already been stated, were so brief in time (usually less than six seconds), so limited in extent (usually less than twenty meters), and so wholly capricious and erratic, owing to the nature of the rubber motor and other causes, that very many experiments were insufficient to eliminate these causes of malobservation.

PIERRE SIMON DE LAPLACE

(1749–1827)

This French astronomer's deduction that our planetary system is stable discountenanced Newton's fear that the solar system might disintegrate into disorder, and gave astronomy the "three laws of Laplace." His *Mécanique Céleste* (1799–1825) is a classical statement of the advances in gravitational astronomy since Newton. Laplace's second epoch-making work, *Exposition du Système du Monde* (1796), advanced the famous Nebular Hypothesis, contending that the solar system was the result of a contracting nebula (now replaced by the tidal evolution theory). Laplace also developed a theory of tides, a theory of the surface tension of liquids based on molecular attraction, and worked on the theory of probability (*Théorie Analytique des Probabilités*, 1812).

THE SYSTEM OF THE WORLD

However arbitrary the elements of the system of the planets may be, there exists between them some very remarkable relations, which may throw light on their origin. Considering it with attention, we are astonished to see all the planets move round the Sun from west to east, and nearly in the same plane, all the satellites moving round their respective planets in the same direction, and nearly in the same plane with the planets. Lastly, the Sun, the planets, and those satellites in which a motion of rotation have been observed, turn on their own axes, in the same direction, and nearly in the same plane as their motion of projection.

The satellites exhibit in this respect a remarkable peculiarity. Their motion of rotation is exactly equal to their motion of revolution; so that they always present the same hemisphere to their

591

primary. At least, this has been observed for the Moon, for the four satellites of Jupiter, and for the last satellite of Saturn, the only satellites whose rotation has been hitherto recognized.

Phenomena so extraordinary, are not the effect of irregular causes. By subjecting their probability to computation, it is found that there is more than two thousand to one against the hypothesis that they are the effect of chance, which is a probability much greater than that on which most of the events of history, respecting which there does not exist a doubt, depends. We ought, therefore, to be assured with the same confidence, that a primitive cause has directed the planetary motions.

Another phenomenon of the solar system, equally remarkable, is the small eccentricity of the orbits of the planets and their satellites, while those of comets are very much extended. The orbits of this system present no intermediate shades between a great and small eccentricity. We are here again compelled to acknowledge the effect of a regular cause; chance alone could not have given a form nearly circular to the orbits of all the planets. It is, therefore, necessary that the cause which determined the motions of these bodies, rendered them also nearly circular. This cause then must also have influenced the great eccentricity of the orbits of comets, and their motion in every direction; for, considering the orbits of retrograde comets, as being inclined more than one hundred degrees to the ecliptic, we find that the mean inclination of the orbits of all the observed comets, approaches near to one hundred degrees, which would be the case if the bodies had been projected at random.

What is this primitive cause? In the concluding note of this work I will suggest an hypothesis which appears to me to result with a great degree of probability, from the preceding phenomena, which, however, I present with that diffidence, which ought always to attach to whatever is not the result of observation and computation.

Whatever be the true cause, it is certain that the elements of the planetary system are so arranged as to enjoy the greatest possible stability, unless it is deranged by the intervention of foreign causes. From the sole circumstance that the motions of the planets and satellites are performed in orbits nearly circular, in the same direction, and in planes which are inconsiderably inclined to each other, the system will always oscillate about a mean state, from which it will deviate but by very small quantities. The mean motions of rotation and of revolution of these different bodies are uniform, and their mean distances from the foci of the principal forces which actuate them are constant; all the secular inequalities are periodic. . . .

From the preceding chapter it appears, that we have the five following phenomena to assist us in investigating the cause of the primitive motions of the planetary system. The motions of the planets in the same direction, and very nearly in the same plane; the motions of the satellites in the same direction as those of the planets; the motions of rotation of these different bodies and also of the Sun, in the same direction as their motions of projection, and in planes very little inclined to each other; the small eccentricity of the orbits of the planets and satellites; finally, the great eccentricity of the orbits of the comets, their inclinations being at the same time entirely indeterminate.

Buffon is the only individual that I know of, who, since the discovery of the true system of the world, endeavored to investigate the origin of the planets and satellites. He supposed that a comet, by impinging on the Sun, carried away a torrent of matter, which was reunited far off, into globes of different magnitudes, and at different distances from this star. These globes, when they cool and become hardened, are the planets and their satellites. This hypothesis satisfied the first of the five preceding phenomena; for it is evident that all bodies thus formed should move very nearly in the plane which passes through the center of the Sun, and through the direction of the torrent of matter which has produced them: but the four remaining phenomena appear to me inexplicable on this supposition. Indeed the absolute motion of the molecules of a planet ought to be in the same direction as the motion of its center of gravity; but it by no means follows from this, that the motion of rotation of a planet should be also in the same direction. Thus the Earth may revolve

593

from east to west, and yet the absolute motion of each of its molecules may be directed from west to east. This observation applies also to the revolution of the satellites, of which the direction, in the same hypothesis, is not necessarily the same as that of the motion of projection of the planets.

The small eccentricity of the planetary orbits is a phenomenon, not only difficult to explain on this hypothesis, but altogether inconsistent with it. We know from the theory of central forces, that if a body which moves in a re-entrant orbit about the Sun, passes very near the body of the Sun, it will return constantly to it, at the end of each revolution. Hence it follows that if the planets were originally detached from the Sun, they would touch it, at each return to this star; and their orbits, instead of being nearly circular, would be very eccentric. Indeed it must be admitted that a torrent of matter detached from the Sun, cannot be compared to a globe which just skims by its surface: from the impulsions which the parts of this torrent receive from each other, combined with their mutual attraction, they may, by changing the direction of their motions, increase the distances of their perihelions from the Sun. But their orbits should be extremely eccentric, or at least all the orbits would not be circular, except by the most extraordinary chance. Finally, no reason can be assigned on the hypothesis of Buffon, why the orbits of more than one hundred comets, which have been already observed, should be all very eccentric. This hypothesis, therefore, is far from satisfying the preceding phenomena. Let us consider whether we can assign the true cause.

Whatever may be its nature, since it has produced or influenced the direction of the planetary motions, it must have embraced them all within the sphere of its action; and considering the immense distance which intervenes between them, nothing could have effected this but a fluid of almost indefinite extent. In order to have impressed on them all a motion circular and in the same direction about the Sun, this fluid must environ this star, like an atmosphere. From a consideration of the planetary motions, we are, therefore, brought to the conclusion, that in consequence of an excessive heat, the solar atmosphere originally extended beyond the orbits of all the planets, and that it has successively contracted itself within its present limits.

In the primitive state in which we have supposed the Sun to be, it resembles those substances which are termed nebulæ, which, when seen through telescopes, appear to be composed of a nucleus, more or less brilliant, surrounded by a nebulosity, which, by condensing on its surface, transforms it into a star. If all the stars are conceived to be similarly formed, we can suppose their anterior state of nebulosity to be preceded by other states, in which the nebulous matter was more or less diffuse, the nucleus being at the same time more or less brilliant. By going back in this manner, we shall arrive at a state of nebulosity so diffuse, that its existence can with difficulty be conceived.

For a considerable time back, the particular arrangement of some stars visible to the naked eye, has engaged the attention of philosophers. Mitchel remarked long since how extremely improbable it was that the stars composing the constellation called the Pleiades, for example, should be confined within the narrow space which contains them, by the sole chance of hazard; from which he inferred that this group of stars, and the similar groups which the heavens present to us, are the effects of a primitive cause, or of a primitive law of nature. These groups are a general result of the condensation of nebulæ of several nuclei; for it is evident that the nebulous matter being perpetually attracted by these different nuclei, ought at length to form a group of stars, like to that of the Pleiades. The condensation of nebulæ consisting of two nuclei, will in like manner form stars very near to each other, revolving the one about the other like to the double stars, whose respective motions have been already recognized.

But in what manner has the solar atmosphere determined the motions of rotation and revolution of the planets and satellites? If these bodies had penetrated deeply into this atmosphere, its resistance would cause them to fall on the Sun. We may, therefore, suppose that the planets were formed at its successive limits, by the condensation of zones of vapors, which it must, while it was cooling, have abandoned in the plane of its equator.

Let us resume the results. The Sun's atmosphere cannot

595

extend indefinitely; its limit is the point where the centrifugal force arising from the motion of rotation balances the gravity; but according as the cooling contracts the atmosphere, and condenses the molecules which are near to it, on the surface of the star, the motion of rotation increases; for in virtue of the principle of areas, the sum of the areas described by the radius vector of each particle of the Sun and of its atmosphere, and projected on the plane of its equator, is always the same. Consequently, the rotation ought to be quicker, when these particles approach to the center of the Sun. The centrifugal force arising from this motion becoming thus greater, the point where the gravity is equal to it, is nearer to the center of the Sun. Supposing, therefore, what is natural to admit, that the atmosphere extended at any epoch as far as this limit, it ought, according as it cooled, to abandon the molecules, which are situated at this limit, and at the successive limits produced by the increased rotation of the Sun. These particles, after being abandoned, have continued to circulate about this star, because their centrifugal force was balanced by their gravity. But as this equality does not obtain for those molecules of the atmosphere which are situated on the parallels to the Sun's equator, these have come nearer by their gravity to the atmosphere according as it condensed, and they have not ceased to belong to it, inasmuch as by this motion, they have approached to the plane of this equator.

Let us now consider the zones of vapors, which have been successively abandoned. These zones ought, according to all probability, to form by their condensation, and by the mutual attraction of their particles, several concentrical rings of vapors circulating about the Sun. The mutual friction of the molecules of each ring ought to accelerate some and retard others, until they all had acquired the same angular motion. Consequently, the real velocities of the molecules which are farther from the Sun, ought to be greatest. The following cause ought, likewise, to contribute to this difference of velocities: The most distant particles of the Sun, which, by the effects of cooling and of condensation, have collected so as to constitute the superior part of the ring, have always described areas proportional to the times, because the central force by which they are actuated has been constantly directed to this star; but this constancy of areas requires an increase of velocity, according as they approach more to each other. It appears that the same cause ought to diminish the velocity of the particles, which, situated near the ring, constitute its inferior part.

If all the particles of a ring of vapors continued to condense without separating, they would at length constitute a solid or a liquid ring. But the regularity which this formation requires in all the parts of the ring, and in their cooling, ought to make this phenomenon very rare. Thus the solar system presents but one example of it; that of the rings of Saturn. Almost always each ring of vapors ought to be divided into several masses, which, being moved with velocities which differ little from each other, should continue to revolve at the same distance about the Sun. These masses should assume a spheroidical form, with a rotatory motion in the direction of that of their revolution, because their inferior particles have a less real velocity than the superior; they have, therefore, constituted so many planets in a state of vapor. But if one of them was sufficiently powerful, to unite successively by its attraction, all the others about its center, the ring of vapors would be changed into one sole spheroidical mass, circulating about the Sun, with a motion of rotation in the same direction with that of revolution. This last case has been the most common; however, the solar system presents to us the first case, in the four small planets which revolve between Mars and Jupiter, at least unless we suppose with Olbers, that they originally formed one planet only, which was divided by an explosion into several parts, and actuated by different velocities. Now if we trace the changes which a farther cooling ought to produce in the planets formed of vapors, and of which we have suggested the formation, we shall see to arise in the center of each of them, a nucleus increasing continually, by the condensation of the atmosphere which environs it. In this state, the planet resembles the Sun in the nebulous state, in which we have first supposed it to be; the cooling should, therefore, produce at the different limits of its atmosphere, phenomena similar to those which have been de-

597

scribed, namely, rings and satellites circulating about its center in the direction of its motion of rotation, and revolving in the same direction on their axes. The regular distribution of the mass of rings of Saturn about its center and in the plane of its equator, results naturally from this hypothesis, and, without it, is inexplicable. Those rings appear to me to be existing proofs of the primitive extension of the atmosphere of Saturn, and of its successive condensations. Thus the singular phenomena of the small eccentricities of the orbits of the planets and satellites, of the small inclination of these orbits to the solar equator, and of the identity in the direction of the motions of rotation and revolution of all those bodies with that of the rotation of the Sun, follow from the hypothesis which has been suggested, and render it extremely probable. If the solar system was formed with perfect regularity, the orbits of the bodies which compose it would be circles, of which the planes, as well as those of the various equators and rings, would coincide with the plane of the solar equator. But we may suppose that the innumerable varieties which must necessarily exist in the temperature and density of different parts of these great masses, ought to produce the eccentricities of their orbits, and the deviations of their motions, from the plane of this equator.

In the preceding hypothesis, the comets do not belong to the solar system. If they be considered, as we have done, as small nebulæ, wandering from one solar system to another, and formed by the condensation of the nebulous matter, which is diffused so profusely throughout the universe, we may conceive that when they arrive in that part of space where the attraction of the Sun predominates, it should force them to describe elliptic or hyperbolic orbits. But as their velocities are equally possible in every direction, they must move indifferently in all directions, and at every possible inclination to the ecliptic; which is conformable to observation. Thus the condensation of the nebulous matter, which explains the motions of rotation and revolution of the planets and satellites in the same direction, and in orbits very little inclined to each other, likewise explains why the motions of the comets deviate from this general law.

598

The great eccentricity of the orbits of the comets, is also a result of our hypothesis. If those orbits are elliptic, they are very elongated, since their greater axes are at least equal to the radius of the sphere of activity of the Sun. But these orbits may be hyperbolic. However, with respect to the hundred comets, of which the elements are known, not one appears to move in a hyperbola; hence the chances which assign a sensible hyperbola, are extremely rare relatively to the contrary chances. The comets are so small, that they only become sensible when their perihelion distance is inconsiderable. Hitherto this distance has not surpassed twice the diameter of the Earth's orbit, and most frequently, it has been less than the radius of this orbit. We may conceive, that in order to approach so near to the Sun, their velocity at the moment of their ingress within its sphere of activity, must have an intensity and direction confined within very narrow limits. If we determine by the analysis of probabilities, the ratio of the chances which, in these limits, assign a sensible hyperbola to the chances which assign an orbit, which may without sensible error be confounded with a parabola, it will be found that there is at least six thousand to unity that a nebula which penetrates within the sphere of the Sun's activity so as to be observed, will either describe a very elongated ellipse, or an hyperbola, which, in consequence of the magnitude of its axis will be as to sense confounded with a parabola in the part of its orbit which is observed. It is not, therefore, surprising that hitherto no hyperbolic motions have been recognized.

The attraction of the planets, and perhaps also the resistance of the ethereal media, ought to change several cometary orbits into ellipses, of which the greater axes are much less than the radius of the sphere of the solar activity. It is probable that such a change was produced in the orbit of the comet of 1759, the greater axis of which was not more than thirty-five times the distance of the Sun from the Earth. A still greater change was produced in the orbits of the comets of 1770 and of 1805.

If any comets have penetrated the atmospheres of the Sun and planets at the moment of their formation, they must have described spirals, and consequently fallen on these bodies, and in consequence of their fall, caused the planes of the orbits and of the equators of the planets to deviate from the plane of the solar equator.

If in the zones abandoned by the atmosphere of the Sun, there are any molecules too volatile to be united to each other, or to the planets, they ought, in their circulation about this star, to exhibit all the appearances of the zodiacal light, without opposing any sensible resistance to the different bodies of the planetary system, both on account of their great rarity, and also because their motion is very nearly the same as that of the planets which they meet.

An attentive examination of all the circumstances of this system renders our hypothesis still more probable. The primitive fluidity of the planets is clearly indicated by the compression of their figure, conformably to the laws of the mutual attraction of their molecules; it is, moreover, demonstrated by the regular diminution of gravity, as we proceed from the equator to the poles. This state of primitive fluidity to which we are conducted by astronomical phenomena, is also apparent from those which natural history points out. But in order fully to estimate them, we should take into account the immense variety of combinations formed by all the terrestrial substances which were mixed together in a state of vapor, when the depression of their temperature enabled their elements to unite; it is necessary, likewise, to consider the wonderful changes which this depression ought to cause in the interior and at the surface of the earth, in all its productions, in the constitution and pressure of the atmosphere, in the ocean, and in all substances which it held in a state of solution. Finally, we should take into account the sudden changes, such as great volcanic eruptions, which must at different epochs have deranged the regularity of these changes. Geology, thus studied under the point of view which connects it with astronomy, may, with respect to several objects, acquire both precision and certainty.

One of the most remarkable phenomena of the solar system is the rigorous equality which is observed to subsist between the angular motions of rotation and revolution of each satellite. It is infinity to unity that this is not the effect of hazard. The theory of universal gravitation makes infinity to disappear from this improbability, by shewing that it is sufficient for the existence of this phenomenon, that at the commencement these motions did not differ much. Then, the attraction of the planet would establish between them a perfect equality; but at the same time it has given rise to a periodic oscillation in the axis of the satellite directed to the planet, of which oscillation the extent depends on the primitive difference between these motions. As the observations of Mayer on the libration of the Moon, and those which Bouvard and Nicollet made for the same purpose, at my request, did not enable us to recognize this oscillation; the difference on which it depends must be extremely small, which indicates with every appearance of probability the existence of a particular cause, which has confined this difference within very narrow limits, in which the attraction of the planet might establish between the mean motions of rotation and revolution a rigid equality, which at length terminated by annihilating the oscillation which arose from this equality. Both these effects result from our hypothesis; for we may conceive that the Moon, in a state of vapor, assumed in consequence of the powerful attraction of the earth the form of an elongated spheroid, of which the greater axis would be constantly directed towards this planet, from the facility with which the vapors yield to the slightest force impressed upon them. The terrestrial attraction continuing to act in the same manner, while the Moon is in a state of fluidity, ought at length, by making the two motions of this satellite to approach each other, to cause their difference to fall within the limits, at which their rigorous equality commences to establish itself. Then this attraction should annihilate, by little and little, the oscillation which this equality produced on the greater axis of the spheroid directed towards the earth. It is in this manner that the fluids which cover this planet, have destroyed by their friction and resistance the primitive oscillations of its axis of rotation, which is only now subject to the nutation resulting from the actions of the Sun and Moon. It is easy to be assured that the equality of the motions of rotation and revolution of the satellites ought to oppose the formation of rings and secondary satellites, by the atmospheres of these bodies. Consequently observation has not hitherto indicated the existence of any such. The motions of the three first satellites of Jupiter present a phenomenon still more extraordinary than the preceding; which consists in this, that the mean longitude of the first, minus three times that of the second, plus twice that of the third, is constantly equal to two right angles. There is the ratio of infinity to one, that this equality is not the effect of chance. But we have seen, that in order to produce it, it is sufficient, if at the commencement, the mean motions of these three bodies approached very near to the relation which renders the mean motion of the first, minus three times that of the second, plus twice that of the third, equal to nothing. Then their mutual attraction rendered this ratio rigorously exact, and it has moreover made the mean longitude of the first minus three times that of the second, plus twice that of the third, equal to a semicircumference. At the same time, it gave rise to a periodic inequality, which depends on the small quantity, by which the mean motions originally deviated from the relation which we have just announced. Notwithstanding all the care Delambre took in his observations, he could not recognize this inequality, which, while it evinces its extreme smallness, also indicates, with a high degree of probability, the existence of a cause which makes it to disappear. In our hypothesis, the satellites of Jupiter, immediately after their formation, did not move in a perfect vacuo; the less condensible molecules of the primitive atmospheres of the Sun and planet would then constitute a rare medium, the resistance of which being different for each of the [bodies], might make the mean motions to approach by degrees to the ratio in question; and when these movements had thus attained the conditions requisite, in order that the mutual attraction of the three satellites might render this relation originated, and eventually rendered it insensible. We cannot better illustrate these effects than by comparing them to the motion of a pendulum, which, actuated by a great velocity, moves in a medium, the resistance of which is inconsiderable. It will first describe a great number of circumferences; but at length its motion of circulation perpetually decreasing, it will be converted into an oscillatory motion, which itself diminishing more and more, by the resistance of the medium, will eventually be totally destroyed, and then the pendulum, having attained a state of repose, will remain at rest for ever.

ANTOINE LAURENT LAVOISIER

(1743–1794)

One of the founders of modern chemistry, Lavoisier holds the unhappy distinction of having been executed during the French Revolution—on the charge of having watered the soldiers' tobacco!
(though actually for having been a "farmer of taxes" under the
monarchy). Lavoisier discovered no new elements, made no radical
inventions. His achievement was, rather, to organize and interpret
correctly data already collected. He conducted quantitative experiments, disproving the slow-dying phlogiston theory, explained combustion as the union of a burning substance with oxygen, applied
chemistry to agriculture, and helped introduce a system of chemical
nomenclature which became the basis of our present one. His most
important publication: *Traité Élémentaire de Chimie* (1789).

MEMOIR ON THE NATURE OF THE PRINCIPLE WHICH COMBINES WITH METALS DURING THEIR CALCINATION AND WHICH INCREASES THEIR WEIGHT

ARE THERE different species of air? Is it sufficient that a body
be in a durable state of expansibility [*état d'expansibilité durable*] in order to be a species of air? Finally, are the different
airs which occur in nature or which we may produce separate
substances or merely modifications of the air of the atmosphere?
Such are the principal questions which encompass the plan
which I have formed and whose successive development I propose to bring before the eyes of the Academy. But the time devoted to our public meetings does not permit me to treat any of
these questions extensively, and I will confine myself today to a
particular case and limit myself to showing that the principle
which combines with metals during their calcination, which in-

creases their weight and constitutes them in the state of a calx, is nothing other than the most salubrious and purest portion of the air and such that, if the air, after having engaged in a metallic combination, becomes free again, it appears in an eminently respirable state more capable than the air of the atmosphere of sustaining ignition and combustion.

The majority of metallic calces are not to be reduced, that is, returned to the metallic state, without the immediate contact of a carbonaceous material or any substance whatsoever containing what we call *phlogiston*. The charcoal which is used is completely destroyed in this operation if it be present in suitable proportion; whence it follows that the air which is evolved in metallic reductions with carbon is not a simple substance but in some manner is the result of the combination of the elastic fluid disengaged from the metal and that disengaged from the carbon. Therefore the fact that this fluid is obtained as fixed air gives us no right to conclude that it existed in this form in the metallic calx before its combination with the carbon.

These considerations showed me that in order to clear up the mystery of the reduction of metallic calces it would be necessary to experiment with those calces which are reducible without the addition of anything. The calx of iron offered me this property and actually, of all those calces, either natural or artificial, which we have exposed at the foci of the large burning glasses either of the Regent or of Mr. Trudaine, there have been none which have not been completely reduced without addition.

I tried, consequently, to reduce by means of a burning glass several species of the calx of iron under large glass bells inverted in mercury, and I succeeded in disengaging by this means a large quantity of elastic fluid. But at the same time this elastic fluid became mixed with the common air contained in the bell, and this circumstance threw much uncertainty on my results, so that none of the tests which I conducted upon this air were perfectly conclusive and it was impossible for me to be certain whether the phenomena I obtained arose from the common air, from that disengaged from the calx of iron, or from the combination of the two. The experiments having failed of fully filling my purpose, I omit their details here; they will, however, find their natural place in other memoirs.

As much as these difficulties arise from the nature of iron itself, from the refractory nature of its calces, and from the difficulty of reducing them without addition, I regarded them as insurmountable and therefore thought that I ought to direct my attention to another species of calx, more easily treatable and being, like the calces of iron, reducible without addition. Precipitated mercury per se, which is nothing else than a calx of mercury, as several authors have already advanced and as will appear even more convincingly by the reading of this memoir, precipitated mercury per se, as I said, appeared to me to be completely appropriate for the object which I had in view, for everyone knows today that this substance is reducible without addition at a very medium degree of heat. Although I have repeated a great many times the experiments which I am about to describe, I have not thought it appropriate to give the details of each of them here for fear of extending the memoir too far, and consequently I have combined into a single account the circumstances pertaining to many repetitions of the same experiment.

First, to assure myself that precipitated mercury per se was a genuine metallic calx, that it gave the same results, the same species of air on reduction according to the ordinary method (that is, to use the customary expression, with the addition of phlogiston), I mixed an *once* of this calx with 48 *grains* of powdered charcoal and introduced the mixture into a little glass retort of 2 cubic *pouces* or more capacity. This I placed in a reverberatory furnace of proportionate size. The neck of this retort was about a pied and 3 to 4 *lignes* in diameter and was bent in various places by means of an enameler's lamp in such a manner that its end was disposed beneath an ample glass bell filled with water and inverted in a tub of the same. The apparatus which is here before the eyes of the Academy will suffice to illustrate its operation. This apparatus, simple as it is, is even more accurate in that it has neither joints nor lute nor any passage through which the air may enter or escape.

As soon as a fire was placed beneath the retort and the first effects of the heat felt, the common air which it contained expanded and some little of it passed into the bell. However, in view of the small volume of the empty part of the retort, this air made no sensible error, and its quantity taken at the most can scarcely amount to a cubic *pouce*. As the retort is heated further the air is evolved with much speed and rises through the water in the bell. The operation did not last for more than three-quarters of an hour, the fire being kept up during this interval. When all the calx of mercury had been reduced and the air ceased to come forth, I marked the height of the water in the bell and found that the quantity of air evolved had been 64 cubic *pouces* without counting that which was unavoidably absorbed in traversing the water.

I submitted this air to a large number of tests, the details of which I omit, and found that 1) it can, by shaking, combine with water and give to the water all the properties of acidulated, gaseous, or aerated waters such as those of Seltz, Pougues, Bussang, Pirmont, etc.; 2) it kills in some seconds animals which were placed in it; 3) candles and all combustible bodies in general are extinguished in an instant; 4) it precipitates lime water; 5) it combines with great ease with either fixed or volatile alkalis, depriving them of their causticity and making them capable of crystallizing. All these properties are precisely those of that species of air known under the name of *fixed air* which I obtained by the reduction of minium by powdered charcoal, which calcareous earths and effervescent alkalis evolve in combining with acids, and which vegetable materials evolve in fermenting. It was thus established that precipitated mercury *per se* gives the same products as other metallic calces when reduced with the addition of phlogiston, and that it belongs, therefore, in the general class of metallic calces.

It then only remained to examine this calx alone, to reduce it without adding anything, to see if some elastic fluid were evolved from it, and, supposing there were, to determine its nature. To this end I placed in a retort of 2 cubic *pouces* capacity 1 *once* of precipitated mercury *per se* alone, arranged the apparatus in the same manner as in the preceding experiment, and operated so that all the circumstances would be exactly the same. The reduction took place this time with a little more difficulty than when charcoal was added; more heat was required, and there was no sensible change until the retort began to become slightly red. Then the air was evolved little by little, passed into the bell, and, holding the same degree of fire during two and one-half hours, all the mercury was reduced.

The operation completed, there was found, on the one hand, partly in the neck of the retort and partly in a glass vessel which I placed beneath the water under the exit of the retort, 7 *gros* and 18 *grains* of fluid mercury, and on the other hand, the quantity of the air which had passed into the bell was found to be 78 cubic *pouces;* whence it follows that by supposing that the whole loss of weight should be attributed to the air, each cubic *pouce* should weigh a little less than two-thirds of a *grain*—a value not far removed from that for common air.

After having thus fixed the first results, I had only to submit the 78 cubic *pouces* of air which I had obtained to all the tests necessary to determine its nature, and I found with much surprise

1. That it would not combine with water on shaking
2. That it did not precipitate limewater but only gave it a nearly imperceptible turbidity
3. That it failed to unite at all with fixed or volatile alkalis
4. That it failed entirely to diminish the causticity of these
5. That it could be used again to calcine metals
6. Finally, that it had none of the properties of fixed air

In contrast to the latter, animals did not perish in it and it seemed more suitable to their respiration. Candles and inflamed materials were not only not extinguished, but the flame widened in a very remarkable manner and shed much more light and brilliancy than in common air. Charcoal burned therein with a brilliance nearly like that of phosphorus. and all combustible materials in general were consumed with astonishing rapidity. All these circumstances have fully convinced me that this air, far from being fixed air, is in a more respirable, more combustible state and in consequence is more pure even than the air which sustains us.

It appears to be proved from the above that the principle which combines with and increases the weight of metals when they are calcined is nothing other than the purest portion of the air itself which surrounds us and which we breathe—this it is which in calcination passes from the expansible state to the solid one. If, then, this principle is obtained in the form of fixed air in all metallic reductions where carbon is used, it follows that this is due to the combination of this latter with the pure portion of the air, and it is very probable that all metallic calces would, like mercury, give only eminently respirable air if we could reduce them all as we do precipitated mercury per se.

All that has been said of the air of metallic calces applies naturally to that which is obtained from niter by explosion. It is known from a number of experiments already published, and which I have in greatest part repeated, that the major part of this air is in the state of fixed air, is deadly to animals which breathe it, and has the property of uniting easily with lime and the alkalis, rendering them mild and capable of crystallizing. But since, at the same time, the explosion of niter takes place only with the addition of carbon or any substance which contains phlogiston, one can hardly doubt that, under these circumstances, eminently respirable air is converted into fixed air. From this it would follow that the air combined in niter which produces the terrible explosions of gunpowder is the respirable portion of the air of the atmosphere deprived of its expansibility and is one of the constituent principles of nitric acid.

Since charcoal disappears completely in the revivification of the calx of mercury, and since one retrieves in this operation only mercury and fixed air, one is forced to conclude that the principle to which has been given till now the name of *fixed air* is the result of the combination of the eminently respirable portion of the air with charcoal. I propose to develop this in a more satisfying manner in a series of memoirs which I shall give on the topic.

EXPERIMENTS ON THE RESPIRATION
OF ANIMALS

OF ALL the phenomena of the animal economy, none is more striking, none more worthy the attention of philosophers and physiologists than those which accompany respiration. Little as our acquaintance is with the object of this singular function, we are satisfied that it is essential to life and that it cannot be suspended for any time without exposing the animal to the danger of immediate death. . . .

The experiments of some philosophers, and especially those of Messrs. Hales and Cigna, had begun to afford some light on this important object; and Dr. Priestley has lately published a treatise in which he has greatly extended the bounds of our knowledge; and has endeavored to prove, by a number of very ingenious, delicate, and novel experiments, that the respiration of animals has the property of phlogisticating air, in a similar manner to what is effected by the calcination of metals and many other chemical processes; and that the air ceases not to be respirable till the instant when it becomes surcharged, or at least saturated, with phlogiston.

However probable the theory of this celebrated philosopher may at first sight appear; however numerous and well conducted may be the experiments by which he endeavors to support it, I must confess I have found it so contradictory to a great number of phenomena that I could not but entertain some doubts of it. I have accordingly proceeded on a different plan and have found myself led irresistibly, by the consequences of my experiments, to very different conclusions.

Now air which has served for the calcination of metals is, as we have already seen, nothing but the mephitic residuum of atmospheric air, the highly respirable part of which has combined with the mercury, during the calcination: and the air which has served the purposes of respiration, when deprived of the fixed air, is exactly the same; and, in fact, having combined with the latter residuum about one half of its bulk of dephlogisticated air, extracted from the calx of mercury, I re-established it in its former state and rendered it equally fit for respiration, combustion, et cetera, as common air, by the same method as that I pursued with air vitiated by the calcination of mercury.

The result of these experiments is that, to restore air that has been vitiated by respiration to the state of common respirable air, two effects must be produced: first, to deprive it of the fixed air (carbon dioxide) it contains, by means of quicklime or caustic alkali; secondly, to restore to it a quantity of highly respirable or dephlogisticated air, equal to that which it has lost. Respiration, therefore, acts inversely to these two effects, and I find myself in this respect led to two consequences equally probable, and between which my present experience does not enable me to pronounce. . . .

The first of these opinions is supported by an experiment which I have already communicated to the Academy. For I have shown in a memoir, read at our public Easter meeting, 1775, that dephlogisticated air (oxygen) may be wholly converted into fixed air by an addition of powdered charcoal; and in other memoirs I have proved that this conversion may be effected by several other methods: it is possible, therefore, that respiration may possess the same property, and that dephlogisticated air, when taken into the lungs, is thrown out again as fixed air. . . . Does it not then follow, from all these facts, that this pure species of air has the property of combining with the blood and that this combination constitutes its red color? But whichever of these two opinions we embrace, whether that the respirable portion of the air combines with the blood, or that it is changed into fixed air in passing through the lungs; or lastly, as I am inclined to believe, that both these effects take place in the act of respiration, we may, from facts alone, consider as proved:

I. That respiration acts only on the portion of pure or dephlogisticated air contained in the atmosphere; that the residuum or mephitic part is an merely passive medium which enters into the lungs and departs from them nearly in the same state, without change or alteration.

II. That the calcination of metals, in a given quantity of

atmospheric air, is effected, as I have already often declared, only in proportion as the dephlogisticated air, which it contains, has been drained and combined with the metal.

III. That, in like manner, if an animal be confined in a given quantity of air, it will perish as soon as it has absorbed, or converted into fixed air, the major part of the respirable portion of air, and the remainder is reduced to a mephitic state.

IV. That the species of mephitic air, which remains after the calcination of metals, is in no wise different, according to all the experiments I have made, from that remaining after the respiration of animals; provided always that the latter residuum has been freed from its fixed air; that these two residuums may be substituted for each other in every experiment, and that they may each be restored to the state of atmospheric air by a quantity of dephlogisticated air equal to that of which they had been deprived. A new proof of this last fact is that, if the proportion of this highly respirable air, contained in a given quantity of the atmospheric, be increased or diminished, in such proportion will be the quantity of metal which we shall be capable of calcining in it, and, to a certain point, the time which animals will be capable of living in it.

ANTON VAN LEEUWENHOEK

(1632-1723)

"First of the microbe hunters" is a title often applied to this Dutch naturalist who constructed his own microscope and was the first to see and describe the minute living creatures we call bacteria or germs. He had a consuming interest in everything he saw under the lens, from red blood corpuscles to spermatozoa, from the lens of the eye to the starch granules in tissue. He disproved cases of supposed spontaneous generation, but noted that the aphis reproduces parthogenetically, without a male. His copious observations were recorded in letters published in the *Philosophical Transactions of the Royal Society*, London.

THE OBSERVATIONS OF MR. ANTONY LEEUWENHOEK, ON ANIMALCULES ENGENDERED IN THE SEMEN

(A letter from the observer to the right honourable the Viscount Brouncker; written in Latin; and dated November, 1677; which the editor considered should be published in the very words in which it was sent)

After the distinguished Professor of Medicine Craanen had himself many times honoured me with a visit, he besought me, in a letter, to demonstrate some of my observations to his kinsman Mr. Ham. On the second occasion when this Mr. Ham visited me [in August, 1677], he brought with him, in a small glass phial, the spontaneously discharged semen of a man who had lain with an unclean woman and was suffering from gonorrhoea; saying that, after a very few minutes (when the matter had become so far liquefied that it could be introduced into a small glass tube) he had seen living animalcules in it which he

613

believed to have arisen by some sort of putrefaction. He judged these animalcules to possess tail, and not to remain alive above twenty-four hours. He also reported that he had noticed that the animalcules were dead after the patient had taken turpentine.

In the presence of Mr. Ham, I examined some of this matter which I had introduced into a glass tube, and saw some living creatures in it: but when I examined the same matter more carefully by myself, I observed that they were dead after the lapse of two or three hours.

I have divers times examined the same matter (human semen) from a healthy man (not from a sick man, nor spoiled by keeping for a long time, and not liquefied after the lapse of some minutes; but immediately after ejaculation, before six beats of the pulse had intervened): and I have seen so great a number of living creatures in it, that sometimes more than a thousand were moving about in an amount of material the size of a grain of sand. I saw this vast number of living animalcules not all through the semen, but only in the liquid matter which seemed adhering to the surface of the thicker part. In the thicker matter of the semen, however, the animalcules lay apparently motionless. And I conceived the reason of this to be, that the thicker matter consisted of so many coherent particles that the animalcules could not move in it. These animalcules were smaller than the corpuscles which impart a red colour to the blood; so that I judge a million of them would not equal in size a large grain of sand. Their bodies were rounded, but blunt in front and running to a point behind, and furnished with a long thin tail, about five or six times as long as the body, and very transparent, and with the thickness of about one twenty-fifth that of the body; so that I can best liken them in form to a small earthnut with a long tail. The animalcules moved forward with a snake like motion of the tail, as eels do when swimming in water: and in the somewhat thicker matter, they lashed their tails some eight or ten times in advancing a hair's breadth. I have sometimes fancied that I could even discern different parts in the bodies of these animalcules: but forasmuch as I have not always been able to do so, I will say no more. Among these animalcules there were some still smaller particles, to which I can ascribe nothing but a globular form.

I remember that some three or four years ago I examined seminal fluid at the request of the late Mr. Oldenburg, Secretary of the Royal Society. Looking into the matter I find that he wrote asking me to do so from London, on the 24th of April, 1674: and among other things, he besought me also to examine saliva, chyle, sweat, etc.: but at that time I took the animalcules just described for globules. Yet as I felt averse from making further inquiries, and still more so from writing about them, I did nothing more at that time. What I here describe was not obtained by any sinful contrivance on my part, but the observations were made upon the excess with which Nature provided me in my conjugal relations. And if your Lordship should consider such matters either disgusting, or likely to seem offensive to the learned, I earnestly beg that they be regarded as private, and either published or suppressed as your Lordship's judgment dictates.

I have already many times observed with wonder the parts themselves whereof the denser substance of the semen is mainly made up. They consist of all manner of great and small vessels, so various and so numerous that I misdoubt me not that they be nerves, arteries, and veins. Nay, I have indeed observed these vessels in such great numbers, that I believe I have seen more in a single drop of semen than an anatomist would meet with in a whole day's dissection of any object. And when I saw them, I felt convinced that, in no full-grown human body, are there any vessels which may not be found likewise in sound semen.

Once I fancied I saw a certain form, about the size of a sand grain, which I could compare with some inward part of our body. When this matter had been exposed to the air for some moments, the mass of vessels aforesaid was turned into a watery substance mingled with large oily globules, such as I have formerly described as lying among the vessels of the spinal marrow. On seing these oily globules, I conceived that

615

the vessels might perhaps serve for the conveyance of the animal spirits, and that they are composed of such a soft substance in order that, as the humour or animal spirits continually flowed through them, they might thereby become consolidated into oily globules of sundry sizes—especially when they are exposed to the air.

Moreover, when this matter had stood a little while, there appeared therein some three-sided bodies terminating at either end in a point, and of the length of the smallest grains of sand, though some may have been a bit bigger. And these were furthermore as bright and clear as if they had been crystals.

LITTLE ANIMALS IN RAIN WATER

In the year 1675 I discovered very small living creatures in rain water, which had stood but few days in a new earthen pot glazed blue within. This invited me to view this water with great attention, especially those little animals appearing to me ten thousand times less than those represented by Monsieur Swammerdam, and by him called water fleas, or water lice, which may be perceived in the water with the naked eye.

The first sort I several times observed to consist of five, six, seven, or eight clear globules without being able to discern any film that held them together, or contained them. When these animalcula or living atoms moved, they put forth two little horns, continually moving. The space between these two horns was flat, though the rest of the body was roundish, sharpening a little toward the end, where they had a tail, near four times the length of the whole body, of the thickness, by my microscope, of a spider's web; at the end of which appeared a globule of the size of one of those which made up the body. These little creatures, if they chanced to light on the least filament or string, or other particle, were entangled therein, extending their body in a long round and endeavoring to disentangle their tail. Their motion of extension and contraction continued awhile; and I have seen several thousands of these poor little creatures, within the space of a grain of gross sand, lie fast clustered together in a few filaments.

I also discovered a second sort, of an oval figure; and I imagined their head to stand on a sharp end. These were a little longer than the former. The inferior part of their body is flat, furnished with several extremely thin feet, which moved very nimbly. The upper part of the body was round, and had within eight, ten, or twelve globules, where they were very clear. These little animals sometimes changed their figure into a perfect round, especially when they came to lie on a dry place. Their body was also very flexible; for as soon as they struck against the smallest fibre or string their body was bent in, which bending presently jerked out again. When I put any of them on a dry place I observed that, changing themselves into a round, their body was raised pyramidal-wise, with an extant point in the middle; and having lain thus a little while, a motion of their feet, they burst asunder, and the globules were presently diffused and dissipated, so that I could not discern the least thing of any film, in which the globules had doubtless been enclosed; and at this time of their bursting asunder I was able to discover more globules than when they were alive.

I observed a third sort of little animals that were twice as long as broad, and to my eye eight times smaller than the first. Yes, I thought I discerned little feet, whereby they moved very briskly, both in round and straight line.

There was a fourth sort, which were so small that I was not able to give them any figure at all. These were a thousand times smaller than the eye of a large louse. These exceeded all the former in celerity. I have often observed them to stand still as it were on a point, and then turn themselves about with that swiftness, as we see a top turn round, the circumference they made being no larger than that of grain of small sand, and then extending themselves straight forward, and by and by lying in a bending posture. I discovered also several other sorts of animals; these were generally made up of such soft parts, as the former, that they burst asunder as soon as they came to want water.

617

May 26, it rained hard; the rain growing less, I caused some of that rain water running down from the housetop to be gathered in a clean glass, after it had been washed two or three times with water. And in this I observed some few very small living creatures, and seeing them, I thought they might have been produced in the leaded gutters in some water that had remained there before.

I perceived in pure water, after some days, more of those animals, as also some that were somewhat larger. And I imagine that many thousands of these little creatures do not equal an ordinary grain of sand in bulk; and comparing them with a cheese mite, which may be seen to move with the naked eye, I make the proportion of one of these small water creatures to a cheese mite to be like that of a bee to a horse; for the circumference of one of these little animals in water is not so large as the thickness of a hair in a cheese mite.

In another quantity of rain water, exposed for some days to the air, I observed some thousands of them in a drop of water, which were of the smallest sort that I had seen hitherto. And in some time after I observed, besides the animals already noted, a sort of creatures that were eight times as large, of almost a round figure; and as those very small animalcula swam gently among each other, moving as gnats do in the air, so did these larger ones move far more swiftly, tumbling round as it were, and then making a sudden downfall.

In the waters of the river Maese I saw very small creatures of different kinds and colors, and so small that I could very hardly discern their figures; but the number of them was far less than those found in rain water. In the water of a very cold well in the autumn I discovered a very great number of living animals, very small, that were exceedingly clear, and a little larger than the smallest I ever saw. In sea water I observed at first a little blackish animal, looking as if it had been made up of two globules. This creature had a peculiar motion, resembling the skipping of a flea on white paper, so that it might very well be called a water flea; but it was far less than the eye of that little animal, which Dr. Swammerdam calls the water flea. I also discovered little creatures therein that were clear, of the same size with the former animal, but of an oval figure, having a serpentine motion. I further noticed a third sort, which were very slow in their motion; their body was of a mouse color, clear toward the oval point; and before the head and behind the body there stood out a sharp little point anglewise. This sort was a little larger. But there was yet a fourth somewhat longer than oval. Yet of all these sorts there were but a few of each. Some days after viewing this water I saw a hundred where before I had seen but one; but these were of another figure, and not only less, but they were also very clear, and of an oblong oval figure, only with this difference, that their heads ended sharper; and although they were a thousand times smaller than a small grain of sand, yet when they lay out of the water in a dry place they burst in pieces and spread into three or four very little globules, and into some aqueous matter, without any other parts appearing in them.

Having put about one third of an ounce of whole pepper in water, and it having lain about three weeks in the water, to which I had twice added some snow water, the other water being in great part exhaled, I discerned in it with great surprise an incredible number of little animals, of divers kinds, and among the rest, some that were three or four times as long as broad; but their whole thickness did not much exceed the hair of a louse. They had a very pretty motion, often tumbling about and sideways; and when the water was let to run off from them they turned round like a top; at first their body changed into an oval, and afterwards, when the circular motion ceased, they returned to their former length. The second sort of creatures discovered in this water were of a perfect oval figure, and they had no less pleasing or nimble a motion than the former; and these were in far greater numbers. There was a third sort, which exceeded the two former in number, and these had tails like those I had formerly observed in rain water. The fourth sort, which moved through the three former sorts, were incredibly small, so that I judged that if one hundred of them lay one by another they would not equal the length of a grain of coarse sand; and according to this estimate, one million of them could not equal the dimensions of a grain of such coarse sand. There was discovered a fifth sort, which had near the thickness of the former, but almost twice the length.

In snow water, which had been about three years in a glass bottle well stopped, I could discover no living creatures; and having poured some of it into a porcelain teacup, and put therein half an ounce of whole pepper, after some days I observed some animalcula, and those exceedingly small ones, whose body seemed to me twice as long as broad, but they moved very slowly, and often circularly. I observed also a vast multitude of oval-figured animalcula, to the number of eight thousand in a single drop.

GOTTFRIED VON LEIBNIZ
(1646-1716)

Another great German philosopher who was interested in mathematics and science, Leibniz is famous for his theory that substance exists in the form of self-contained atoms or monads. Of more practical consequence for science was his invention (possibly with the assistance of ideas borrowed from Newton—a disputed point) of differential calculus (1684). Leibniz was also interested in languages, law, politics, history and theology, and attempted to reconcile Protestantism and Catholicism in his *Systema Theologicum* (1686). Essays on many subjects appear in his *Acta Eruditorium* (1686).

QUANTITY OF MOTION

A short demonstration of a remarkable error made by Descartes and others in that they affirm it to be a law of nature that always the same quantity of motion is conserved by God; which law they make improper use of in applying it to mechanics.

Most mathematicians, when they see, in the cases of the five mechanical powers, that velocity and mass are mutually compensated, generally estimated the motive force by the quantity of motion or by the product of the mass of the body into its velocity. Or to speak more mathematically, the forces of two bodies (of the same sort) which are set in motion, and which act both by reason of their masses and their motions, they say, are in a ratio compounded of the bodies or masses and of the velocities which they possess. And so it may be agreeable to reason that the same totality of motive power is conserved in

621

nature: and is neither diminished, since we see that no force is lost by a body, but is transferred to some other body; nor increased, because surely perpetual mechanical motion never occurs and no machine or even the world is able to maintain its force without a new external impulse; whence it happens that Descartes, who considered *motive force* and *quantity of motion* as equivalent, affirmed that the same quantity of motion was always conserved by God in the world.

But I, that I may show how much difference there is between these two ideas, assume, *first*, that a body falling from a certain height acquires a force sufficient to raise it to the same height, if it is given the proper direction and no external forces interfere: for example, that a pendulum will return precisely to the height from which it has been released, unless the resistance of the air and other slight obstacles absorb some of its strength, which we need not consider. I assume, *secondly*, that as much force is needed to raise a body A weighing one pound to the height CD of four ells, as to raise a body B weighing four pounds to the height EF of one ell. These assumptions are conceded by the Cartesians as well as by other philosophers and mathematicians of our times. Hence it follows that the body A (Fig. 1) let fall from the height CD acquires exactly as much force as the body B let fall from the height EF. For the body A, after that by its fall from C it reaches D, there has the force of ascending again to C, by assumption 1, that is, the force sufficient to raise a body weighing one pound (that is, its own body) to the height of four ells. And similarly the body B, after that by its fall E it reaches F, there has the force of ascending again to E by assumption 1, that is, the force sufficient to raise a body weighing four pounds (that is its own body) to the height of one ell. Therefore by assumption 2 the force of the body A when it reaches D and the force of the body B when it reaches F are equal.

Now let us see if the quantity of motion also is the same for both. And here quite unexpectedly a great difference appears. This I show as follows: It has been demonstrated by Galileo that the velocity acquired by the fall CD is twice the

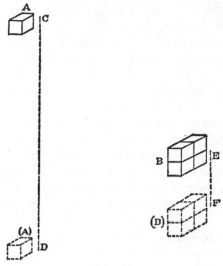

Fig. 1

velocity acquired by the fall *EF*. If therefore we multiply the body A, which may be taken as one, by its velocity, which may be taken as two, the product or the quantity of motion will be two. Again if we multiply the body *B*, which may be taken as four, by its velocity, which may be taken as one, the product or the quantity of motion will be four. Therefore the quantity of motion of the body *A* when at the point *D* is half that of the body *B* when at the point *F*, and yet just now the forces of both of these bodies have been found to be equal. And so there is a great difference between motive force and quantity of motion, so that one of these magnitudes cannot be determined from the other; which we have undertaken to show. From this it appears in what way the force should be estimated, from the quantity of the effect which it is able to produce; for example, from the height to which it can lift a heavy body of known magnitude and nature, not from the velocity which it can impress on the body. For there is need not of twice the force but more than that to give twice the velocity to the same body. No one should be surprised that in ordinary machines,

623

such as the lever, the wheel and axle, the pulley, the wedge, the screw, and the like, there is equilibrium when the size of one body is compensated by the velocity of the other, which is brought about by the arrangement, of the machine; or when the magnitudes (the same sort of body being assumed) are reciprocally as the velocities, or when the same quantity of motion is produced in any other way, for then it will happen that there will be the same quantity of effect in both the bodies, or the same height of ascent or descent, on whichever side of the equilibrated system you choose to produce the motion. And so by accident it happens in this case that the force can be estimated from the quantity of motion. But other cases occur, such as that which we have previously dealt with, where they are not the same.

While there is nothing more simple than our demonstration, it is strange that it never came into the minds of DesCartes or of his learned followers. But too great confidence in his own ingenuity led him astray, and the others were led astray by their confidence in him. For DesCartes, by an error common to great men, became a little too confident. And I fear not a few of his followers have been imitating the Peripatetics whom they laugh at, that is, they have been depending upon consulting the books of their master, rather than on right reason and the nature of things.

Therefore we may say that forces are in the compound ratio of the bodies (of the same specific gravity or density) and of the heights productive of velocity, that is, the heights by falling from which they can acquire such velocities; or more generally (since no velocity has really been produced) of the heights that will produce them: but not generally of the velocities themselves, although this seems plausible at first sight, and has so seemed to many; from which many errors have arisen, which are contained in the works on mathematical mechanics of RR.P. Honoratus Faber and Claudius des Chales, and also of Joh. Alph. Borelli and of other men, otherwise distinguished in such matters. Hence also I think it has happened, that doubts have been thrown by some learned men on the theorem of

624

Huygens about the center of oscillation of a pendulum, which however is certainly valid.

THE EARTH ORIGINALLY MOLTEN

In agreement with these views, some savants developed an hypothesis that serves to explain more clearly the order of the world. They suggest that vast globes, self-luminous like the fixed stars or our sun, or projected from a luminous body, after reaching the last stages of ebullition, were covered with socriae like bubbling foam. It is as if the spots by which the ancients suspected the sun could be altered and some day obscured, and which our optical instruments have allowed us to see, should increase in amount until they veiled the face of that orb. For the greater part they believe, in effect (as the sacred writers, in their way, tend to imply), that *there are raging fires at the center of the earth from which flames can break forth in eruption.*

Existing traces of the primitive aspect of nature support these conjectures, for *all scoria* resulting from fusion is *a sort of glass.* And the crust which covered the molten matter of the globe and which hardened from the fused condition would be like scoria, as happens with metals in the furnace. If the great framework of the earth, the exposed rocks, the imperishable silicates, are almost entirely vitrified, does that not prove that they arose from fusion of the bodies, brought about by the powerful action of nature's fire on still soft material? And as the action of that fire infinitely surpasses that of our furnace, both in intensity and duration, is it a matter of astonishment that it led to a result that men cannot attain now? . . . It is everywhere true that the most simple and primitive material in the composition of the earth, that which represents most accurately the true nature of rock, is that which most resists fire, which melts under an excessive heat, and finishes by vitrifying. . . .

. . . At the same time it is readily believed that at the origin of things, before the separation of the opaque material from

625

the luminous, *when our globe was incandescent,* the fire drove the humidity into the air, acting like a distillation. That is to say, as a result of the lowering of the temperature, it was converted into aqueous vapors. These vapors, finding themselves in contact with the chilled surface of the earth, condensed to water. The water, working over the debris of the recent conflagration, took up the fixed salts, giving rise to *a sort of lixivium,* which soon formed the sea. . . .

Finally it is credible that the consolidation of the crust of the globe, on cooling—as takes place with metals and other bodies which become more porous with fusion—has left *enormous bubbles* accordant in grandeur with the planet; that is to say, *cavities* enclosing water or air were formed under its immense vaults. It is also probable that other parts stretched out in the form of beds and that, by the diversity of material and the [irregular] distribution of heat, *the masses were not equally compressed and have burst, here and there, so that certain portions subsided to form the trough of valleys, whereas others, more solid, have remained upright like columns and, for that reason, constituted the mountains.*

To these causes would be added the action of the waters, which by their weight tended to furrow stream beds in the still soft surface. Then the vaults of the earth breaking, either from the weight of the material or from the explosion of gases, the water would be forced from the depths of the abyss across the wreckage, and, joining that which was flowing naturally from the high places, would give rise to vast inundations which would leave abundant sediment at divers points. These sediments would harden, and with repetition of the same condition sedimentary beds would be superimposed. The face of the earth, still only slightly firm, has thus been often renewed until, the causes of disturbance having been exhausted or balanced, *a more stable state was finally produced.* These facts should make us understand *the double origin of solid bodies,* first by their chilling after igneous fusion, and then by new aggregations after their solution in the waters.

626

JUSTUS VON LIEBIG
(1803-1873)

Founder of agricultural chemistry and discoverer of chloroform, Liebig left an impressive mark on organic chemistry. He founded the first sizable chemical laboratory in Europe for teaching and research, at Giessen. He was the first to prove that body heat is the product of the combustion of food, and the first to divide foods into fats, carbohydrates and proteins. He produced extracts of meat and other foodstuffs which became famous as baby foods. In agriculture he introduced artificial fertilizers, and taught that plants absorb mineral elements from the soil and carbon and nitrogen from the air. Works: *Animal Chemistry* (1842), *Organic Chemistry* (1843), *Researches on Flesh and Its Preparation* (1847), *Agricultural Chemistry* (1855).

THE POLYBASIC ACIDS

DAVY'S THEORY arose from the behavior of potassium chlorate and iodate. The decomposition of these salts at an elevated temperature into oxygen and potassium chloride without change of neutrality made it necessary, he thought, to conclude that the potassium was not present as the action in these salts. In connection with potassium iodate it is particularly certain that potash is not decomposed by iodine nor oxygen displaced by iodine. Davy concluded as follows: hydrochloric acid is a compound of chlorine and hydrogen $Cl_2 + H_2$.

The radical of hydrochloric acid may take up one or several atoms of oxygen without changing its saturation capacity for, according to him, this faculty is dependent only upon the hydrogen of the acid which is located outside the radical.

627

Hydrochloric acid . . . . . Cl_2O $+ H_2$
Hypochlorous acid. . . . . $Cl_2O_2 + H_2$
Chlorous acid. . . . . $Cl_2O_4 + H_2$
Chloric acid. . . . . $Cl_2O_6 + H_2$
Perchloric acid . . . . $Cl_2O_3 + H_2$

Acids are, according to this view, hydrogen compounds in which the hydrogen may be replaced by metals.

Neutral *salts* are compounds of the same class wherein the hydrogen has been replaced by an equivalent of a metal. Those substances which we at present call anhydrous acids generally acquire their property of forming salts with metal oxides only on treatment with water, but there are some compounds which decompose the oxides at higher temperatures.

On combining an acid with a metallic oxide hydrogen is in most cases separated in the form of water. As far as the constitution of the new compound is concerned it is a matter of indifference how we think of the formation of this water. In many cases it is formed by the reduction of the oxide; in others, maybe, at the expense of the elements of the acid—we know not which.

We only know that without water at ordinary temperatures no salt can be formed and that the constitution of salts is analogous to the hydrogen compounds that we call acids. In the examination of Davy's theory the principle which should preferably be kept in mind is, accordingly, that he makes the saturation capacity of an acid dependent on its hydrogen content or on a portion of its hydrogen so that if the remaining elements of the acid together be called its radical, the composition of the radical has not the most distant influence on this capacity. . . .

If we apply Davy's view to the phosphorus acids we find the following relations:

Phosphorus combines in several proportions with hydrogen; the best known of these compounds is composed according to the formula

$$P_2 + H_6.$$

If eight atoms of oxygen be taken up in this phosphorus hydride, ordinary phosphoric acid is formed. $P_2O_8 + H_6$. According to this, it must form salts wherein all or part of the hydrogen is replaced by equivalents of metals. Brought together with metal oxides, the hydrogen will be reduced by the oxygen of the oxide to water; those oxides in which oxygen is the most weakly attached will undergo this reaction more easily than others. Silver oxide stands above all others in this respect.

With the oxides of the alkalies which have a great affinity for oxygen this reaction proceeds with more difficulty. In proportion as the hydrogen of the acid is removed and replaced, the affinity of the radical for the remaining hydrogen increases and only by means of an increased mass of alkali can this reduction be completed. With many acids similar to phosphoric acid in composition this can only be done by silver oxide. The salts of phosphoric acid receive the following form:

$$P_2O_8 + H_6 \quad \ldots\ldots \quad \text{phosphoric acid}$$

$$P_2O_8 + \left. \begin{matrix} H_2 \\ 2K \end{matrix} \right\} \quad \ldots\ldots \quad \text{so-called neutral salt}$$

$$P_2O_8 + \left. \begin{matrix} H_4 \\ K \end{matrix} \right\} \quad \ldots\ldots \quad \text{acid salt}$$

$$P_2O_8 + 3K \quad \ldots\ldots \quad \text{so-called basic salt}$$

$$P_2O_8 + 3Ag \quad \ldots\ldots \quad \text{silver salt.}$$

According to the composition of lead phosphite, phosphorous acid is

$$P_2O_6 + 6H$$

Of the 6 atoms of hydrogen which it contains only 4 may be replaced by metals. The lead salt is

$$P_2O_6 + \left. \begin{matrix} H_2 \\ Pb_2 \end{matrix} \right\}$$

If phosphoric acid be exposed to a higher temperature a part of the hydrogen outside the radical combines with an equivalent of oxygen of the latter, water is formed and evolved and two new acids, pyro- and metaphosphoric acid, are formed.

$$P_2O_7 + H_4 \text{ pyrophosphoric acid}$$
$$P_2O_9 + H_2 \text{ metaphosphoric acid}$$

All the properties of cyanuric, meconic and citric acids indicate that they contain no water in the dry state and, from Davy's view, their composition is as follows: $Cy_6O_6 + 6H$ cyanuric acid, $C_{14}H_2O_{14} + 6H$ meconic acid.

The salts of these acids are composed in a manner analogous to the phosphorus acids. I have mentioned their relations to the modifications of phosphoric acid in the foregoing.

CAROLUS LINNAEUS

(1707–1778)

This Swedish botanist is the father of modern systematic botany, for his system of naming according to biological classification brought order out of the chaos of a million uncatalogued plants and animals. His identification of man as *Homo sapiens* is an instance of his binomial nomenclature which remains in use to this day. Linnaeus was a great traveler and collector, and his many works and catalogues include: *Systema Natura* (1737), *Genera Plantarum* (1737), *Critica Botanica* (1737), *Classes Plantarum* (1737), and the work in which he announced his system of nomenclature, *Species Plantarum* (1753).

CRITICA BOTANICA

What difficulty has been caused to botanists from the revival of the sciences down to the present day by the invention of new names is known to everyone who has handled the subject; accordingly, when at the beginning of the last century the invasion of barbarism threatened by the vast horde of names in use was stemmed by C. Bauhin, by the general consent of botanists anyone who should in future dare to introduce new names was stigmatized with a black mark, and this was well advised, since, in the circumstances, the stage of learning which the science had at that time reached did not make it possible to frame better names.

When at length the commonwealth of botany had been brought by Morison under an ordered constitution, and an eternal law, taken from nature's book, had been promulgated any who should offend against or transgress this law were branded as ignoramuses. No exception was then allowed: all specific names which did not suit the genus in question were to be banned by an inexorable

631

decree of fate. Alas! What widespread wild confusion ensued toward the end of the last century, while the citizens of the commonwealth of botany were distracted by internal strife beneath the triumvirate of Ray, Tournefort, and Rivinus; Tournefort and Rivinus bestowing different names on each genus and the genera being distributed in one way by the one, and in another by the other. At length Tournefort obtained the victory in regard to genera, and, peace being restored, the world of botanists from that time forward fought shy of the making of any more new names.

However, citizens of the commonwealth never ceased to bring in every day new supplies from foreign lands, to distinguish them as they arrived with more suitable names, to restore what was lacking, to repair previous disasters, to become wiser and devise better counsels, and to provide for the general well-being of the commonwealth, though not one of them took upon himself to introduce a complete reformation of its constitution (for Vaillant died just as he began to do so) or to bestow new names. Nevertheless by slow and almost imperceptible steps from Tournefort's time down to the present day more new names have crept in than were ever bestowed at the bidding of any dictator; this is obvious if one brings into comparison the new names of Feuillée, Commelin, Boerhaave, Vaillant, Pontedera, Dillenius, Ruppius, Scheuchzer, Knaut, Montius, Heucher, Buxbaum, Micheli, Kramer, Burman, et cetera. An inevitable necessity compels men to run on rocks which they have not learned to avoid; sound reason enjoins that they should refuse the road by which it is unsafe to travel; and so also it is fated that botanists should impose wrong names, so long as the science remains an untilled field, so long as laws and rules have not been framed on which they [can] erect as on firm foundations the science of botany; and so the aforesaid botanists have, under pressure of necessity, corrected most wisely the faulty names given by their predecessors.

As I turn over the laborious works of the authorities I observe them busied all day long with discovering plants, describing them, drawing them, bringing them under genera and classes; I find, however, among them few philosophers, and hardly any who have attempted to develop nomenclature, one of the two foundations of botany, though that a name should remain unshaken is quite as essential as attention to genera. That they can find no rules given by the ancients for the bestowal of names, no demonstrations or settled principles, is the complaint of novices, and equally of men practiced in the science. For any rules of nomenclature which botanists have brought in from time to time are too specialized for any certain conclusion to be drawn from them. Again there is so much disagreement between the authorities that the reader can hardly determine to which in preference to the others he should give his allegiance, since satisfactory principles are not everywhere to be seen. Wherefore it is not surprising if, when the novice has developed into a mature botanist, appearing the while to have done all that was possible, he in his work makes mistakes over nomenclature and so comes to burden botany with wrong names.

Wherefore we can never hope for a lasting peace and better times till botanists come to an agreement among themselves about the fixed laws in accordance with which judgment can be pronounced on names, that is to say, good names can be absolutely distinguished from bad ones, the good ones maintained and the bad ones banished without any exception, so that botany firmly built on immovable principles may remain a fortress inviolable and unshaken.

Before botanists can admit such laws it is necessary that someone among them should take upon himself to offer proposals to be examined by other botanists, so that if they are good they may be confirmed, if unsound they may be convicted of unsoundness and abandoned, while something better is put in their place. But, so long as botanists refuse to make this beginning, so long also will they remain in doubt and uncertainty, and false names will accumulate every day to burden botany. Now as hitherto no one has thought fit to undertake this self-denying task, I have determined to make the attempt; for if a citizen in a free commonwealth may speak his mind it will be at least allowable for me to state my principles among botanists! I have not reached

633

such an extreme of hardihood as to believe that all my reasoning is so firmly based but that someone else may propound reasoning much more mature; still, mine will be true until some other principles are shown to be truer. To you, my dearly beloved botanists, I submit my rules, the rules which I have laid down for myself, and in accordance with which I intend to walk. If they seem to you worthy, let them be used by you also; if not, please propound something better!

Half a year ago, when my *"Genera"* came out, I was advised by not a few to publish my observations on nomenclature, since the principles underlying my *"Fundamenta Botanica,"* were regarded as proved by few, indeed by very few. I was prevented from complying with this request by the laborious and exacting charge of the *"Hortus Cliffortianus"* which I had taken on my shoulders; this charge robbed me of not only all my working hours, but also of the rest necessary to health: for the fixing of the day on which I was to strike camp demanded that the web which I had begun to weave should be completely finished. Hence scarcely a moment was left in which to put my notes together or, having done so, to add the finishing touch. Certain friends to whom I was under deep obligations were of opinion that these observations were essential and that, before going on to the species, I should bring them to the light of day. In obedience to the advice of these gentlemen, to whom I felt morally bound to refuse nothing, I corrected my sketchy observations and handed them over to the publisher. And so it was chiefly lack of time which prevented me from giving the work the final touches of a leisurely pen and thus securing favor for what I had said. I was unwilling, however, to keep back the work merely to avoid the shafts of malevolence, which I have never taken pains to conciliate. For I knew that wiser men, to whose judgment I commit my views, do not fall under the spell of meretricious language, but have regard only to principles and examples, and weigh the value of the practice which follows from these. Further, I knew that, when I was endeavoring to be of use, they would not call me to account for shortcomings caused by lack of time.

634

Another not less formidable cause of delay confronted me, as no method was open to me save that of examples. For even if I had piled up several volumes on names, and had reveled in argument to an immoderate extent, without at the same time giving examples, few would have gathered my meaning; while from the examples alone, without arguments, all would easily have understood me, the facts before them speaking for themselves. How could I indicate the plants without giving names? How give the names without the authority for them? And so, in giving examples, I was bound also to cite authorities, and in the course of doing so I foresaw that I should readily lose the favor of those whom I was most anxious to please. I myself, who have been the lifelong foe of critics, was bound to be reckoned among the critics. By "critics" I mean those botanists— alas, too many—who, like despots, busy themselves with gaining honor and authority for themselves from the disasters of others, who do not trouble to share some little observation of their own with the learned world, unless they can at the same time point out that another more learned than themselves has failed to observe these facts; or again who, like pygmies taking their stand on the shoulders of giants, boast that they can see further —not realizing that it is not given to all to see everything, that one has excelled in describing, another in drawing pictures, another in synonyms, another in minute observations, another in genera, others again in other departments, since the life of an individual man is not long enough to cover the whole ground, yet in the meantime notable additions have been made [to the science] while each has attended to or has restored some one branch of it.

Wherefore, so as not to injure anyone, I determined to cite only the wiser authorities and those "whose intellects Prometheus formed of superior clay," feeling assured that from these men of superior learning I should win indulgence, as I knew that they would never have attained to such solid learning had they not preferred the advancement of botany to every other consideration, and that these wiser persons do not defend their own views out of a blind affection for authority, but make the prosperity of botany their only concern. However, if I should wound other botanists of inferior rank, I ask their pardon, having set this down not out of malice but guided by my love of botany.

Accordingly I have written this "Critique" which I offer to the kind reader as a sequel to Chapters VII-X of my *"Fundamenta Botanica,"* by way of explaining §§ 210-324; and I have appended a considerable number of examples, so that anyone may in accordance with them refer names to the laws which apply to them. However, in the section on specific names I have quoted scarcely any examples, since but few worthy ones are in existence, and even at the present time when we are proud of the vigorous growth of botany few, indeed very few botanists, feel certain what plants are species and what varieties. Wherefore in my *"Hortus Cliffortianus,"* which through the bounty of the generous owner of the garden will presently appear, I have endeavored to mark species with specific names.

I would have the reader know that these rules, subject to considerations hereafter to be taken into account, hold good in the mineral and animal kingdoms, fully as much as in botany, and I crave his favor for my venture.

SYSTEMA NATURAE

Man, when he enters the world, is naturally led to enquire who he is; whence he comes; whither he is going; for what purpose he is created; and by whose benevolence he is preserved. He finds himself descended from the remotest creation; journeying to a life of perfection and happiness; and led by his endowments to a contemplation of the works of nature.

Like other animals who enjoy life, sensation, and perception; who seek for food, amusements, and rest, and who prepare habitations convenient for their kind, he is curious and inquisitive: but, above all other animals, he is noble in his nature, in as much as, by the powers of his mind, he is able to reason justly upon whatever discovers itself to his senses; and to look, with reverence and wonder, upon the works of Him who created all things.

That existence is surely contemptible, which regards only the gratification of instinctive wants, and the preservation of a body made to perish. It is therefore the business of a thinking being, to look forward to the purposes of all things; and to remember that the end of creation is, that God may be glorified in all his works.

Hence it is of importance that we should study the works of nature, than which, what can be more useful, what more interesting? For, however large a portion of them lies open to our present view; a still greater part is yet unknown and undiscovered.

All things are not within the immediate reach of human capacity. Many have been made known to us, of which those who went before us were ignorant; many we have heard of, but know not what they are; and many must remain for the diligence of future ages.

It is the exclusive property of man, to contemplate and to reason on the great book of nature. She gradually unfolds herself to him, who with patience and perseverance, will search into her misteries; and when the memory of the present and of past generations shall be entirely obliterated, he shall enjoy the high privilege of living in the minds of his successors, as he has been advanced in the dignity of his nature, by the labours of those who went before him.

The UNIVERSE comprehends whatever exists; whatever can come to our knowledge by the agency of our senses. The *Stars,* the *Elements,* and this our *Globe.*

The STARS are bodies remote, lucid, revolving in perpetual motion. They shine, either by their own proper lights, as the *Sun,* and the remoter *fixed Stars;* or are *Planets* receiving light from others. Of these the primary planets are solar; *Saturn, Jupiter, Mars,* the *Earth, Venus, Mercury,* and *Georgium Sidus:* the secondary are those subservient to, and rolling round the primary, as the *Moon* round the earth.

637

The ELEMENTS are bodies simple, constituting the atmosphere of, and probably filling the spaces between the stars.

Fire;	lucid,	resilient,	warm,	evolant,	vivifying.
Air;	transparent,	elastic,	dry,	encircling,	generating.
Water;	diaphanous,	fluid,	moist,	gliding,	conceiving.
Earth;	opaque,	fixed,	cold,	quiescent,	sterile.

The EARTH is a planetary sphere, turning round its own axis, once in 24 hours, and round the sun once a year; surrounded by an *atmosphere* of elements, and covered by a stupendous crust of *natural bodies*, which are the objects of our studies. It is terraqueous; having the depressed parts covered with waters; the elevated parts gradually dilated into dry and habitable continents. The *land* is moistened by *vapours*, which rising from the waters, are collected into *clouds:* these are deposited upon the tops of mountains; form small *streams*, which unite into *rivulets*, and reunite into those ever-flowing *rivers*, which pervading the thirsty earth, and affording moisture to the productions growing for the support of her living inhabitants, are at last returned into their parent *sea*.

The study of natural history, simple, beautiful, and instructive, consists in the collection, arrangement, and exhibition of the various productions of the earth.

These are divided into the three grand kingdoms of nature, whose boundaries meet together in the Zoophytes.

MINERALS inhabit the interior parts of the earth in rude and shapeless masses; are generated by salts, mixed together promiscuously, and shaped fortuitously.

They are bodies *concrete*, without life or sensation.

VEGETABLES clothe the surface with verdure, imbibe nourishment through bibulous roots, breathe by quivering leaves, celebrate their nuptials in a genial metamorphosis, and continue their kind by the dispersion of seed within prescribed limits.

They are bodies *organized*, and have *life* and not sensation.

ANIMALS adorn the exterior parts of the earth, respire, and generate eggs; are impelled to action by hunger, congeneric affections, and pain; and by preying on other animals and

638

vegetables, restrain within proper proportion the numbers of both.

They are bodies *organized,* and have *life, sensation,* and the power of locomotion.

MAN, the last and best of created works, formed after the image of his Maker, endowed with a portion of intellectual divinity, the governor and subjugator of all other beings, is, by his wisdom alone, able to form just conclusions from such things as present themselves to his senses, which can only consist of bodies merely natural. Hence the first step of wisdom is to know these bodies; and to be able, by those marks imprinted on them by nature, to distinguish them from each other, and to affix to every object its proper name.

These are the elements of all science; this is the great alphabet of nature: for if the name be lost, the knowledge of the object is lost also; and without these, the student will seek in vain for the means to investigate the hidden treasures of nature.

METHOD, the soul of Science, indicates that every natural body may, by inspection, be known by its own peculiar name; and this name points out whatever the industry of man has been able to discover concerning it: so that amidst the greatest apparent confusion, the greatest order is visible.

SYSTEM is conveniently divided into five branches, each subordinate to the other: *class, order, genus, species,* and *variety,* with their names and characters. For he must first know the name who is willing to investigate the object.

The science of nature supposes an exact knowledge of the nomenclature, and a systematic arrangement of all natural bodies. In this arrangement, the *classes* and *orders* are arbitrary; the *genera* and *species* are natural. All true knowledge refers to the species, all solid knowledge to the genus.

Of these three grand divisions the *animal* kingdom ranks highest in comparative estimation, next the *vegetable,* and the last and lowest is the *mineral* kingdom.

ANIMALS enjoy *sensation* by means of a living organization, animated by a medullary substance; *perception* by nerves; and *motion* by the exertion of the will.

They have *members* for the different purposes of life; *organs* for their different senses; and *faculties* or powers for the application of their different perceptions.

They all originate from an *egg*.

Their external and internal structure; their comparative anatomy, habits, instincts, and various relations to each other, are detailed in authors who professedly treat on these subjects.

The natural *division* of animals is into 6 *classes*, formed from their internal structure.

2 ventricles;			
Heart with 2 auricles,	viviparous.	MAMMALIA.	1.
blood warm, red.	oviparous.	BIRDS.	2.
Heart with 1 auricle,	lungs voluntary.	AMPHIBIA.	3.
1 ventricle;			
blood cold, red.	external gills.	FISHES.	4.
Heart with 1 auricle,	have antennae.	INSECTS.	5.
ventricle 0;			
sanies cold, white.	——tentacula.	WORMS.	6.

1. MAMMALIA. *Lungs* respire alternately; *jaws* incumbent, covered; *teeth* usually within; *teats* lactiferous; *organs* of sense, tongue, nostrils, eyes, ears, and papillae of the skin; *covering*, hair, which is scanty in warm climates, and hardly any on aquatics; *supporters*, 4 feet, except in aquatics; and in most a *tail: walk* on the *earth*, and *speak*.

2. BIRDS. *Lungs* respire alternately; *jaws* incumbent, naked, extended, without teeth; *eggs* covered with a calcareous shell; *organs* of sense, tongue, nostrils, eyes, and ears without auricles; *covering*, incumbent, imbricate feathers; *supporters*, feet 2, wings 2; and a heart-shaped rump; *fly* in the *air*, and *sing*.

3. AMPHIBIA.   *Jaws* incumbent; *penis* (frequently) double;
eggs (usually) membranaceous; *organs* of
sense, tongue, nostrils, eyes, ears; *covering*,
a naked skin; *supporters* various, in some
0; *creep* in *warm* places and *hiss*.

4. FISHES.   *Jaws* incumbent; *penis* (usually) 0; *eggs*
without white; *organs* of sense, tongue,
nostrils? eyes, ears; *covering*, imbricate
scales; *supporters*, fins; *swim* in the *water*,
and *smack*.

5. INSECTS.   *Spiracles*, lateral pores; *jaws*, lateral; *organs*
of sense, tongue, eyes, antennae on the
head, brain 0, ears 0, nostrils 0; *covering*,
a bony coat of mail; *supporters*, feet, and
in some, wings; *skip* on *dry* ground, and
buzz.

6. WORMS.   *Spiracles*, obscure; *jaws*, various; frequently *hermaphrodites; organs* of sense
tentacula, (generally) eyes, brain 0, ears
0, nostrils 0; *covering*, calcareous or 0,
except spines; *supporters*, feet 0, fins 0;
crawl in *moist* places, and are *mute*.

JOSEPH LISTER

(1827—1912)

Even before Pasteur, Joseph Lister was convinced of the importance of cleanliness in the operating room. A practicing surgeon in
Edinburgh and London, he introduced carbolic acid as an antiseptic with immediate and remarkable success, losses in patients
undergoing amputation, for instance, being reduced from 43 per
cent to 15 per cent. He thus revolutionized the modern practice of
surgery. Lister was also president of the Royal Society and surgeon
to Queen Victoria.

ON THE ANTISEPTIC PRINCIPLE OF THE
PRACTICE OF SURGERY

IN THE COURSE of an extended investigation into the nature of
inflammation, and the healthy and morbid conditions of the
blood in relation to it, I arrived several years ago at the conclusion that the essential cause of suppuration in wounds is
decomposition brought about by the influence of the atmosphere
upon blood or serum retained within them, and, in the case of
contused wounds, upon portions of tissue destroyed by the violence of the injury.

To prevent the occurrence of suppuration with all its attendant risks was an object manifestly desirable, but till lately
apparently unattainable, since it seemed hopeless to attempt to
exclude the oxygen which was universally regarded as the agent
by which putrefaction was effected. But when it had been shown
by the researches of Pasteur that the septic properties of the
atmosphere depended not on the oxygen, or any gaseous constituent, but on minute organisms suspended in it, which owed their
energy to their vitality, it occurred to me that decomposition in

642

the injured part might be avoided without excluding the air, by applying as a dressing some material capable of destroying the life of the floating particles. Upon this principle I have based a practice of which I will now attempt to give a short account.

The material which I have employed is carbolic or phenic acid, a volatile organic compound, which appears to exercise a peculiarly destructive influence upon low forms of life, and hence is the most powerful antiseptic with which we are at present acquainted.

The first class of cases to which I applied it was that of compound fractures, in which the effects of decomposition in the injured part were especially striking and pernicious. The results have been such as to establish conclusively the great principle that all local inflammatory mischief and general febrile disturbances which follow severe injuries are due to the irritating and poisonous influence of decomposing blood or sloughs. For these evils are entirely avoided by the antiseptic treatment, so that limbs which would otherwise be unhesitatingly condemned to amputation may be retained, with confidence of the best results.

In conducting the treatment, the first object must be the destruction of any septic germs which may have been introduced into the wounds, either at the moment of the accident or during the time which has since elapsed. This is done by introducing the acid of full strength into all accessible recesses of the wound by means of a piece of rag held in dressing forceps and dipped into the liquid.[1] This I did not venture to do in the earlier cases; but experience has shown that the compound which carbolic acid forms with the blood, and also any portions of tissue killed by its caustic action, including even parts of the bone, are disposed of by absorption and organisation, provided they are afterwards kept from decomposing. We are thus enabled to employ the antiseptic treatment efficiently at a period after the occurrence of the injury at which it would otherwise probably fail. Thus I have now under my care, in Glasgow Infirmary, a boy who was admitted with compound fracture of the leg as late as eight and

[1] The addition of a few drops of water to a considerable quantity of the acid, induces it to assume permanently the liquid form.

one-half hours after the accident, in whom, nevertheless, all local and constitutional disturbance was avoided by means of carbolic acid, and the bones were soundly united five weeks after his admission.

The next object to be kept in view is to guard effectually against the spreading of decomposition into the wound along the stream of blood and serum which oozes out during the first few days after the accident, when the acid originally applied has been washed out or dissipated by absorption and evaporation. This part of the treatment has been greatly improved during the past few weeks. The method which I have hitherto published (see Lancet for Mar. 16th, 23rd, 30th, and April 27th of the present year) consisted in the application of a piece of lint dipped in the acid, overlapping the sound skin to some extent and covered with a tin cap, which was daily raised in order to touch the surface of the lint with the antiseptic. This method certainly succeeded well with wounds of moderate size; and indeed I may say that in all the many cases of this kind which have been so treated by myself or my house-surgeons, not a single failure has occurred. When, however, the wound is very large, the flow of blood and serum is so profuse, especially during the first twenty-four hours, that the antiseptic application cannot prevent the spread of decomposition into the interior unless it overlaps the sound skin for a very considerable distance, and this was inadmissible by the method described above, on account of the extensive sloughing of the surface of the cutis which it would involve. This difficulty has, however, been overcome by employing a paste composed of common whiting (carbonate of lime), mixed with a solution of one part of carbolic acid in four parts of boiled linseed oil so as to form a firm putty. This application contains the acid in too dilute a form to excoriate the skin, which it may be made to cover to any extent that may be thought desirable, while its substance serves as a reservoir of the antiseptic material. So long as any discharge continues, the paste should be changed daily, and, in order to prevent the chance of mischief occurring during the process, a piece of rag dipped in the solution of carbolic acid in oil is put on next the skin, and maintained there permanently, care being taken to avoid raising it along with the putty. This rag is always kept in an antiseptic condition from contact with the paste above it, and destroys any germs which may fall upon it during the short time that should alone be allowed to pass in the changing of the dressing. The putty should be in a layer about a quarter of an inch thick, and may be advantageously applied rolled out between two pieces of thin calico, which maintain it in the form of a continuous sheet, which may be wrapped in a moment round the whole circumference of a limb if this be thought desirable, while the putty is prevented by the calico from sticking to the rag which is next the skin.[2] When all discharge has ceased, the use of the paste is discontinued, but the original rag is left adhering to the skin till healing by scabbing is supposed to be complete. I have at present in the hospital a man with severe compound fracture of both bones of the left leg, caused by direct violence, who, after the cessation of the sanious discharge under the use of the paste, without a drop of pus appearing, has been treated for the last two weeks exactly as if the fracture was a simple one. During this time the rag, adhering by means of a crust of inspissated blood collected beneath it, has continued perfectly dry, and it will be left untouched till the usual period for removing the splints in a simple fracture, when we may fairly expect to find a sound cicatrix beneath it.

We cannot, however, always calculate on so perfect a result as this. More or less pus may appear after the lapse of the first week, and the larger the wound, the more likely this is to happen. And here I would desire earnestly to enforce the necessity of persevering with the antiseptic application in spite af the appearance of suppuration, so long as other symptoms are favorable. The surgeon is extremely apt to suppose that any suppuration is an indication that the antiseptic treatment has

[2] In order to prevent evaporation of the acid, which passes readily through any organic tissue, such as oiled silk or gutta percha, it is well to cover the paste with a sheet of block tin, or tinfoil strengthened with adhesive plaster. The thin sheet lead used for lining tea chests will also answer the purpose, and may be obtained from any wholesale grocer.

failed, and that poulticing or water dressing should be resorted to. But such a course would in many cases sacrifice a limb or a life. I cannot, however, expect my professional brethren to follow my advice blindly in such a matter, and therefore I feel it necessary to place before them, as shortly as I can, some pathological principles intimately connected, not only with the point we are immediately considering, but with the whole subject of this paper.

If a perfectly healthy granulating sore be well washed and covered with a plate of clean metal, such as block tin, fitting its surface pretty accurately, and overlapping the surrounding skin an inch or so in every direction and retained in position by adhesive plaster and a bandage, it will be found, on removing it after twenty-four or forty-eight hours, that little or nothing that can be called pus is present, merely a little transparent fluid, while at the same time there is an entire absence of the unpleasant odour invariably perceived when water dressing is changed. Here the clean metallic surface presents no recesses like those of porous lint for the septic germs to develop in, the fluid exuding from the surface of the granulations has flowed away undecomposed, and the result is the absence of suppuration. This simple experiment illustrates the important fact that granulations have no inherent tendency to form pus, but do so only when subjected to preternatural stimulus. Further, it shows that the mere contact of a foreign body does not of itself stimulate granulations to suppurate; whereas the presence of decomposing organic matter does. These truths are even more strikingly exemplified by the fact that I have elsewhere recorded (Lancet, March 23rd, 1867), that a piece of dead bone free from decomposition may not only fail to induce the granulations around it to suppurate, but may actually be absorbed by them; whereas a bit of dead bone soaked with putrid pus infallibly induces suppuration in its vicinity.

Another instructive experiment is, to dress a granulating sore with some of the putty above described, overlapping the sound skin extensively; when we find, in the course of twenty-four hours, that pus has been produced by the sore, although the application has been perfectly antiseptic; and, indeed, the larger the amount of carbolic acid in the paste, the greater is the quantity of pus formed, provided we avoid such a proportion as would act as a caustic. The carbolic acid, though it prevents decomposition, induces suppuration—obviously by acting as a chemical stimulus; and we may safely infer that putrescent organic materials (which we know to be chemically acrid) operate in the same way.

In so far, then, carbolic acid and decomposing substances are alike; viz., that they induce suppuration by chemical stimulation, as distinguished from what may be termed simple inflammatory suppuration, such as that in which ordinary abscesses originate —where the pus appears to be formed in consequence of an excited action of the nerves, independently of any other stimulus. There is, however, this enormous difference between the effects of carbolic acid and those of decomposition; viz., that carbolic acid stimulates only the surface to which it is at first applied, and every drop of discharge that forms weakens the stimulant by diluting it; but decomposition is a self-propagating and self-aggravating poison, and, if it occur at the surface of a severely injured limb, it will spread into all its recesses so far as any extravasated blood or shreds of dead tissue may extend, and lying in those recesses, it will become from hour to hour more acrid, till it requires the energy of a caustic sufficient to destroy the vitality of any tissues naturally weak from inferior vascular supply, or weakened by the injury they sustained in the accident.

Hence it is easy to understand how, when a wound is very large, the crust beneath the rag may prove here and there insufficient to protect the raw surface from the stimulating influence of the carbolic acid in the putty; and the result will be first the conversion of the tissues so acted on into granulations, and subsequently the formation of more or less pus. This, however, will be merely superficial, and will not interfere with the absorption and organisation of extravasated blood or dead tissues in the interior. But, on the other hand, should decomposition set in before the internal parts have become securely consolidated, the most disastrous results may ensue.

I left behind me in Glasgow a boy, thirteen years of age, who, between three and four weeks previously, met with a most severe injury to the left arm, which he got entangled in a machine at a fair. There was a wound six inches long and three inches broad, and the skin was very extensively undermined beyond its limits, while the soft parts were generally so much lacerated that a pair of dressing forceps introduced at the wound and pushed directly inwards appeared beneath the skin at the opposite aspect of the limb. From this wound several tags of muscle were hanging, and among them was one consisting of about three inches of the triceps in almost its entire thickness; while the lower fragment of the bone, which was broken high up, was protruding four inches and a half, stripped of muscle, the skin being tucked in under it. Without the assistance of the antiseptic treatment, I should certainly have thought of nothing else but amputation at the shoulder-joint; but, as the radial pulse could be felt and the fingers had sensation, I did not hesitate to try and save the limb and adopted the plan of treatment above described, wrapping the arm from the shoulder to below the elbow in the antiseptic application, the whole interior of the wound, together with the protruding bone, having previously been freely treated with strong carbolic acid. About the tenth day, the discharge, which up to that time had been only sanious and serous, showed a slight admixture of slimy pus; and this increased till (a few days before I left) it amounted to about three drachms in twenty-four hours. But the boy continued as he had been after the second day, free from swelling, redness, or pain. I, therefore, persevered with the antiseptic dressing; and, before I left, the discharge was already somewhat less, while the bone was becoming firm. I think it likely that, in that boy's case, I should have found merely a superficial sore had I taken off all the dressing at the end of the three weeks; though, considering the extent of the injury, I thought it prudent to let the month expire before disturbing the rag next to the skin. But I feel sure that, if I had resorted to ordinary dressing when the pus first appeared, the progress of the case would have been exceedingly different.

The next class of cases to which I have applied the antiseptic treatment is that of abscesses. Here also the results have been extremely satisfactory, and in beautiful harmony with the pathological principles indicated above. The pyogenic membrane, like the granulations of a sore, which it resembles in nature, forms pus, not from any inherent disposition to do so, but only because it is subjected to some preternatural stimulation. In an ordinary abscess, whether acute or chronic, before it is opened the stimulus which maintains the suppuration is derived from the presence of pus pent up within the cavity. When a free opening is made in the ordinary way, this stimulus is got rid of, but the atmosphere gaining access to the contents, the potent stimulus of decomposition comes into operation, and pus is generated in greater abundance than before. But when the evacuation is effected on the antiseptic principle, the pyogenic membrane, freed from the influence of the former stimulus without the substitution of a new one, ceases to suppurate (like the granulations of a sore under metallic dressing), furnishing merely a trifling amount of clear serum, and, whether the opening be dependent or not, rapidly contracts and coalesces. At the same time any constitutional symptoms previously occasioned by the accumulation of the matter are got rid of without the slightest risk of the irritative fever or hectic hitherto so justly dreaded in dealing with large abscesses.

In order that the treatment may be satisfactory, the abscess must be seen before it is opened. Then, except in very rare and peculiar cases,[3] there are no septic organisms in the contents, so that it is needless to introduce carbolic acid into the interior. Indeed, such a procedure would be objectionable, as it would stimulate the pyogenic membrane to unnecessary suppuration. All that is requisite is to guard against the introduction of living atmospheric germs from without, at the same time that free opportunity is afforded for the escape of the discharge from within.

---

[3] As an instance of one of these exceptional cases, I may mention that of an abscess in the vicinity of the colon, and afterwards proved by post-mortem examination to have once communicated with it. Here the pus was extremely offensive when evacuated, and exhibited under the microscope.

I have so lately given elsewhere a detailed account of the method by which this is effected (Lancet, July 27th, 1867), that I shall not enter into it at present further than to say that the means employed are the same as those described above for the superficial dressing of compound fractures; viz., a piece of rag dipped into the solution of carbolic acid in oil to serve as an antiseptic curtain, under cover of which the abscess is evacuated by free incision, and the antiseptic paste to guard against decomposition occurring in the stream of pus that flows out beneath it; the dressing being changed daily until the sinus is closed.

The most remarkable results of this practice in a pathological point of view have been afforded by cases where the formation of pus depended on disease of bone. Here the abscesses, instead of forming exceptions to the general class in the obstinacy of the suppuration, have resembled the rest in yielding in a few days only a trifling discharge, and frequently the production of pus has ceased from the moment of the evacuation of the original contents. Hence it appears that caries, when no longer labouring as heretofore under the irritation of decomposing matter, ceases to be an opprobrium of surgery, and recovers like other inflammatory affections. In the publication before alluded to, I have mentioned the case of a middle-aged man with a psoas abscess depending in diseased bone, in whom the sinus finally closed after months of patient perseverance with the antiseptic treatment. Since that article was written I have had another instance of abscess equally gratifying, but the differing in the circumstance that the disease and the recovery were more rapid in their course. The patient was a blacksmith, who had suffered four and a half months before I saw him from symptoms of ulceration of cartilage in the left elbow. These had latterly increased in severity so as to deprive him entirely of his night's rest and of appetite. I found the region of the elbow greatly swollen, and on careful examination found a fluctuating point at the outer aspect of the articulation. I opened it on the antiseptic principle, the incision evidently penetrating to the joint, giving exit to a few drachms of pus. The medical gentleman under whose care he was (Dr. Macgregor, of Glasgow) supervised the daily dressing with the carbolic acid paste till the patient went to spend two or three weeks at the coast, when his wife was entrusted with it. Just two months after I opened the abscess, he called to show me the limb, stating that the discharge had been, for at least two weeks, as little as it was then, a trifling moisture upon the paste, such as might be accounted for by the little sore caused by the incision. On applying a probe guarded with an antiseptic rag, I found that the sinus was soundly closed, while the limb was free from swelling or tenderness; and, although he had not attempted to exercise it much, the joint could already be moved through a considerable angle. Here the antiseptic principle had effected the restoration of a joint, which, on any other known system of treatment, must have been excised.

Ordinary contused wounds are, of course, amenable to the same treatment as compound fractures, which are a complicated variety of them. I will content myself with mentioning a single instance of this class of cases. In April last, a volunteer was discharging a rifle when it burst, and blew back the thumb with its metacarpal bone, so that it could be bent back as on a hinge at the trapezial joint, which had evidently been opened, while all the soft parts between the metacarpal bones of the thumb and forefinger were torn through. I need not insist before my present audience on the ugly character of such an injury. My house-surgeon, Mr. Hector Cameron, applied carbolic acid to the whole raw surface, and completed the dressing as if for compound fracture. The hand remained free from pain, redness or swelling, and with the exception of a shallow groove, all the wound consolidated without a drop of matter, so that if it had been a clean cut, it would have been regarded as a good example of primary union. The small granulating surface soon healed, and at present a linear cicatrix alone tells of the injury he has sustained, while his thumb has all its movements and his hand a fine grasp.

If the severest forms of contused and lacerated wounds heal thus kindly under the antiseptic treatment, it is obvious that its application to simple incised wounds must be merely a matter of detail. I have devoted a good deal of attention to this class, but I have not as yet pleased myself altogether with any of the methods I have employed. I am, however, prepared to go so far as to say that a solution of carbolic acid in twenty parts of water, while a mild and cleanly application, may be relied on for destroying any septic germs that may fall upon the wound during the performance of an operation; and also that, for preventing the subsequent introduction of others, the paste above described, applied as for compound fractures, gives excellent results. Thus I have had a case of strangulated inguinal hernia in which it was necessary to take away half a pound of thickened omentum, heal without any deep-seated suppuration or any tenderness of the sac or any fever; and amputations, including one immediately below the knee, have remained absolutely free from constitutional symptoms.

Further, I have found that when the antiseptic treatment is efficiently conducted, ligatures may be safely cut short and left to be disposed of by absorption or otherwise. Should this particular branch of the subject yield all that it promises, should it turn out on further trial that when the knot is applied on the antiseptic principle, we may calculate as securely as if it were absent on the occurrence of healing without any deep-seated suppuration, the deligation of main arteries in their continuity will be deprived of the two dangers that now attend it, viz., those of secondary hæmorrhage and an unhealthy state of the wound. Further, it seems not unlikely that the present objection to tying an artery in the immediate vicinity of a large branch may be done away with; and that even the innominate, which has lately been the subject of an ingenious experiment by one of the Dublin surgeons, on account of its well-known fatality under the ligature of secondary hæmorrhage, may cease to have this unhappy character when the tissues in the vicinity of the thread, instead of becoming softened through the influence of an irritating decomposing substance, are left at liberty to consolidate firmly near an unoffending though foreign body.

It would carry me far beyond the limited time which, by the rules of the Association, is alone at my disposal, were I to enter into the various applications of the antiseptic principle in the several special departments of surgery.

There is, however, one point more that I cannot but advert to, viz., the influence of this mode of treatment upon the general healthiness of an hospital. Previously to its introduction the two large wards in which most of my cases of accident and of operation are treated were among the unhealthiest in the whole surgical division of the Glasgow Royal Infirmary, in consequence apparently of those wards being unfavorably placed with reference to the supply of fresh air; and I have felt ashamed when recording the results of my practice, to have so often to allude to hospital gangrene or pyæmia. It was interesting, though melancholy, to observe that whenever all or nearly all the beds contained cases with open sores, these grievous complications were pretty sure to show themselves; so that I came to welcome simple fractures, though in themselves of little interest either for myself or the students, because their presence diminished the proportion of open sores among the patients. But since the antiseptic treatment has been brought into full operation, and wounds and abscesses no longer poison the atmosphere with putrid exhalations, my wards, though in other respects under precisely the same circumstances as before, have completely changed their character; so that during the last nine months not a single instance of pyæmia, hospital gangrene, or erysipelas has occurred in them.

As there appears to be no doubt regarding the cause of this change, the importance of the fact can hardly be exaggerated.

CHARLES LYELL

(1797–1875)

Lyell's *Principles of Geology* (1830–33) is generally regarded as establishing the basis of modern geology, the equivalent in its field to Darwin's great work in his. Lyell, a Scottish geologist, attacked the popular theory that geologic changes were caused by catastrophic convulsions, and suggested that the greatest changes were produced by forces still at work, and that history must be reckoned in terms, not of thousands, but of millions of years. He divided the Tertiary system into the Eocene, Miocene, Pliocene and Pleistocene. Other works: *The Elements of Geology* (1838), *Travels in North America, with Geological Observations* (1845), and *The Antiquity of Man* (1863), a critique of Darwinism.

PRINCIPLES OF GEOLOGY

I. GEOLOGY DEFINED

GEOLOGY is the science which investigates the successive changes that have taken place in the organic and inorganic kingdoms of nature; it inquires into the causes of these changes, and the influence which they have exerted in modifying the surface and external structure of our planet.

Geology is intimately related to almost all the physical sciences, as history is to the moral. An historian should, if possible, be at once profoundly acquainted with ethics, politics, jurisprudence, the military art, theology; in a word, with all branches of knowledge by which any insight into human affairs, or into the moral and intellectual nature of man, can be obtained. It would be no less desirable that a geologist should be well versed in chemistry, natural philosophy, mineralogy, zoology, compa-

654

rative anatomy, botany; in short, in every science relating to organic and inorganic nature. With these accomplishments, the historian and geologist would rarely fail to draw correct and philosophical conclusions from the various monuments transmitted to them of former occurrences. They would know to what combination of causes analogous effects were referable, and they would often be enabled to supply, by inference, information concerning many events unrecorded in the defective archives of former ages. But as such extensive acquisitions are scarcely within the reach of any individual, it is necessary that men who have devoted their lives to different departments should unite their efforts; and as the historian receives assistance from the antiquary, and from those who have cultivated different branches of moral and political science, so the geologist should avail himself of the aid of many naturalists, and particularly of those who have studied the fossil remains of lost species of animals and plants.

The analogy, however, of the monuments consulted in geology, and those available in history, extends no farther than to one class of historical monuments—those which may be said to be *undesignedly* commemorative of former events. The canoes, for example, and stone hatchets found in our peat bogs, afford an insight into the rude arts and manners of the earliest inhabitants of our island; the buried coin fixes the date of the reign of some Roman emperor; the ancient encampment indicates the districts once occupied by invading armies, and the former method of constructing military defences: the Egyptian mummies throw light on the art of embalming, the rites of sepulture, or the average stature of the human race in ancient Egypt. This class of memorials yields to no other in authenticity, but it constitutes a small part only of the resources on which the historian relies, whereas in geology it forms the only kind of evidence which is at our command. For this reason we must not expect to obtain a full and connected account of any series of events beyond the reach of history. But the testimony of geological monuments, if frequently imperfect, possesses at least the advantage of being free from all intentional misrepresentation. We may be deceived in the inferences which we draw, in the same manner as we often mistake the nature and import of phenomena observed in the daily course of nature; but our liability to err is confined to the interpretation, and, if this be correct, our information is certain.

II. PREJUDICES WHICH HAVE RETARDED THE PROGRESS OF GEOLOGY

IF WE REFLECT on the history of the progress of geology, we perceive that there have been great fluctuations of opinion respecting the nature of the causes to which all former changes of the earth's surface are referable. The first observers conceived the monuments which the geologist endeavors to decipher to relate to an original state of the earth, or to a period when there were causes in activity, distinct, in kind and degree, from those now constituting the economy of nature. These views were gradually modified, and some of them entirely abandoned in proportion as observations were multiplied, and the signs of former mutations more skilfully interpreted. Many appearances, which had for a long time been regarded as indicating mysterious and extraordinary agency, were finally recognized as the necessary result of the laws now governing the material world; and the discovery of this unlooked-for conformity has at length induced some philosophers to infer that, during the ages contemplated in geology, there has never been any interruption to the agency of the same uniform laws of change. The same assemblage of general causes, they conceive, may have been sufficient to produce, by their various combinations, the endless diversity of effects, of which the shell of the earth has preserved the memorials; and, consistently with these principles, the recurrence of analogous changes is expected by them in time to come.

Prepossessions in regard to the duration of past time.—Now the reader may easily satisfy himself that, however undeviating

656

the course of nature may have been from the earliest epochs, it was impossible for the first cultivators of geology to come to such a conclusion, so long as they were under a delusion as to the age of the world, and the date of the first creation of animate beings. However fantastical some theories of the sixteenth century may now appear to us—however unworthy of men of great talent and sound judgment—we may rest assured that, if the same misconception now prevailed in regard to the memorials of human transactions, it would give rise to a similar train of absurdities. Let us imagine, for example, that Champollion, and the French and Tuscan literati lately engaged in exploring the antiquities of Egypt, had visited that country with a firm belief that the banks of the Nile were never peopled by the human race before the beginning of the nineteenth century, and that their faith in this dogma was as difficult to shake as the opinion of our ancestors, that earth was never the abode of living beings until the creation of the present continents, and of the species now existing—it is easy to perceive what extravagant systems they would frame, while under the influence of this delusion, to account for the monuments discovered in Egypt. The sight of the pyramids, obelisks, colossal statues, and ruined temples, would fill them with such astonishment, that for a time they would be as men spellbound—wholly incapable of reasoning with sobriety. They might incline at first to refer the construction of such stupendous works to some superhuman powers of a primeval world. A system might be invented resembling that so gravely advanced by Manetho, who relates that a dynasty of gods originally ruled in Egypt, of whom Vulcan, the first monarch, reigned nine thousand years; after whom came Hercules and other demigods, who were at last succeeded by human kings.

These speculations, if advocated by eloquent writers, would not fail to attract many zealous votaries, for they would relieve men from the painful necessity of renouncing preconceived opinions. But when one generation had passed away, and another, not compromised to the support of antiquated dogmas, had succeeded, they would review the evidence afforded by mummies more impartially, and would no longer controvert the preliminary question, that human beings had lived in Egypt before the nineteenth century: so that when a hundred years perhaps had been lost, the industry and talents of the philosopher would be at last directed to the elucidation of points of real historical importance.

But the above arguments are aimed against one only of many prejudices with which the earlier geologists had to contend. Even when they conceded that the earth had been peopled with animate beings at an earlier period than was at first supposed, they had no conception that the quantity of time bore so great a proportion to the historical era as is now generally conceded. How fatal every error as to the quantity of time must prove to the introduction of rational views concerning the state of things in former ages may be conceived by supposing the annals of the civil and military transactions of a great nation to be perused under the impression that they occurred in a period of one hundred instead of two thousand years. Such a portion of history would immediately assume the air of a romance; the events would seem devoid of credibility, and inconsistent with the present course of human affairs. A crowd of incidents would follow each other in thick succession. Armies and fleets would appear to be assembled only to be destroyed, and cities built merely to fall in ruins. There would be the most violent transitions from foreign or intestine war to periods of profound peace, and the works effected during the years of disorder or tranquility would appear alike superhuman in magnitude.

We should be warranted in ascribing the erection of the great pyramid to superhuman power, if we were convinced that it was raised in one day; and if we imagine, in the same manner, a continent or mountain chain to have been elevated, during an equally small fraction of the time which was really occupied in upheaving it, we might then be justified in inferring that the subterranean movements were once far more energetic than in our own times. We know that during one earthquake the coast of Chili may be raised for a hundred miles to the average height of about three feet. A repetition of two thousand shocks, of equal violence, might produce a mountain chain one hundred miles long and six thousand feet high. Now, should one or two only of these convulsions happen in a century, it would be consistent with the order of events experienced by the Chilians from the earliest times: but if the whole of them were to occur in the next hundred years, the entire district must be depopulated, scarcely any animals or plants could survive, and the surface would be one confused heap of ruin and desolation.

Prejudices arising from our peculiar position as inhabitants of the land.—The sources of prejudice hitherto considered may be deemed peculiar for the most part to the infancy of the science, but others are common to the first cultivators of geology and to ourselves, and are all singularly calculated to produce the same deception and to strengthen our belief that the course of nature in the earlier ages differed widely from that now established.

The first and greatest difficulty consists in an habitual unconsciousness that our position as observers is essentially unfavourable, when we endeavour to estimate the nature and magnitude of the changes now in progress. In consequence of our inattention to this subject, we are liable to serious mistakes in contrasting the present with former states of the globe. As dwellers on the land, we inhabit about a fourth part of the surface; and that portion is almost exclusively a theatre of decay, and not of reproduction. We know, indeed, that new deposits are annually formed in seas and lakes, and that every year some new igneous rocks are produced in the bowels of the earth, but we cannot watch the progress of their formation; and as they are only present to our minds by the aid of reflection, it requires an effort both of the reason and the imagination to appreciate duly their importance. It is, therefore, not surprising that we estimate very imperfectly the result of operations thus invisible to us; and that, when analogous results of former epochs are presented to our inspection, we cannot immediately recognise the analogy. He who has observed the quarrying of stone from a rock, and has seen it shipped for some distant port, and then endeavours to conceive what kind of edifice will be raised by the materials, is in the same predicament as a geologist, who, while he is confined to the land, sees the decomposition of rocks, and the transportation of matter by rivers to the sea, and then endeavours to picture to himself the new strata which Nature is building beneath the waters.

Prejudices arising from our not seeing subterranean changes. —Nor is his position less unfavourable when, beholding a volcanic eruption, he tries to conceive what changes the column of lava has produced, in its passage upwards, on the intersected strata; or what form the melted matter may assume at great depths on cooling; or what may be the extent of the subterranean rivers and reservoirs of liquid matter far beneath the surface. It should, therefore, be remembered that the task imposed on those who study the earth's history requires no ordinary share of discretion; for we are precluded from collating the corresponding parts of the system of things as it exists now and as it existed at former periods. If we were inhabitants of another element—if the great ocean were our domain, instead of the narrow limits of the land—our difficulties would be considerably lessened; while, on the other hand, there can be little doubt, although the reader may, perhaps, smile at the bare suggestion of such an idea, that an amphibious being, who should possess our faculties, would still more easily arrive at sound theoretical opinions in geology, since he might behold, on the one hand, the decomposition of rocks in the atmosphere or the transportation of matter by running water; and, on the other, examine the deposition of sediment in the sea and the imbedding of animal and vegetable remains in new strata. He might ascertain, by direct observation, the action of a mountain torrent as well as of a marine current; might compare the products of volcanos poured out upon the land with those ejected beneath the waters; and might mark, on the one hand, the growth of the forest, and, on the other, that of the coral reef. Yet, even with these advantages, he would be liable to fall into the greatest errors, when endeavouring to reason on rocks of subterranean origin. He would seek in vain, within the sphere of his observation, for any direct analogy to the process of their formation, and would therefore be in danger of attributing them, wherever they are upraised to view, to some "primeval state of nature."

For more than two centuries the shelly strata of the Sub-Apennine hills afforded matter of speculation to the early geologists of Italy, and few of them had any suspicion that similar deposits were then forming in the neighbouring sea. Some imagined that the strata, so rich in organic remains, instead of being due to secondary agents, had been so created in the beginning by the fiat of the Almighty. Others ascribed the imbedded fossil bodies to some plastic power which resided in the earth in the early ages of the world. In what manner were these dogmas at length exploded? The fossil relics were carefully compared with their living analogues, and all doubts as to their organic origin were eventually dispelled. So, also, in regard to the containing beds of mud, sand, and limestone: those parts of the bottom of the sea were examined where shells are now becoming annually entombed in new deposits. Donati explored the bed of the Adriatic and found the closest resemblance between the strata there forming and those which constituted hills above a thousand feet high in various parts of the Italian peninsula. He ascertained by dredging that living testacea were there grouped together in precisely the same manner as were their fossil analogues in the inland strata; and while some of the recent shells of the Adriatic were becoming incrusted with calcareous rock, he discovered that others had been newly buried in sand and clay, precisely as fossil shells occur in the Sub-Apennine hills.

The establishment, from time to time, of numerous points of identification drew at length from geologists a reluctant admission that there was more correspondence between the condition of the globe at former eras and now, and more uniformity in the laws which have regulated the changes of its surface, than they at first imagined. If, in this state of the science, they still despaired of reconciling every class of geological phenomena to the operations of ordinary causes, even by straining analogy to the utmost limits of credibility, we might have expected, at least, that the balance of probability would now have been presumed

661

to incline toward the close analogy of the ancient and modern causes. But, after repeated experience of the failure of attempts to speculate on geological monuments, as belonging to a distinct order of things, new sects continued to persevere in the principles adopted by their predecessors. They still began, as each new problem presented itself, whether relating to the animate or inanimate world, to assume an original and dissimilar order of nature; and when at length they approximated, or entirely came round to an opposite opinion, it was always with the feeling that they were conceding what they had been justified *a priori* in deeming improbable. In a word, the same men who, as natural philosophers, would have been most incredulous respecting any deviations from the known course of nature, if reported to have happened *in their own time*, were equally disposed, as geologists, to expect the proofs of such deviation at every period of the past.

III. DOCTRINE OF THE DISCORDANCE OF THE ANCIENT AND MODERN CAUSES OF CHANGE CONTROVERTED

Climate of the northern hemisphere formerly different.—Proofs of former revolutions in climate, as deduced from fossil remains have afforded one of the most popular objections to the theory which endeavours to explain all geological changes by reference to those now in progress on the earth. The probable causes, therefore, of fluctuations in climate may first be treated of.

That the climate of the northern hemisphere has undergone an important change, and that its mean annual temperature must once have more nearly resembled that now experienced within tropics, was the opinion of some of the first naturalists who investigated the contents of the ancient strata. Their conjecture became more probable when the shells and corals of the older tertiary and many secondary rocks were carefully examined; for the organic remains of these formations were found to be intimately connected by generic affinity with species now living in warmer latitudes. At a later period, many reptiles, such as turtles, tortoises, and large saurian animals, were discovered in

European formations in great abundance; and they supplied new and powerful arguments, from analogy, in support of the doctrine that the heat of the climate had been great when our secondary strata were deposited. Lastly, when the botanist turned his attention to the specific determination of fossil plants, the evidence acquired still further confirmation; for the flora of a country is peculiarly influenced by temperature: and the ancient vegetation of the earth might have been expected more readily than the forms of animals to have afforded conflicting proofs, had the popular theory been without foundation. When the examination of fossil remains was extended to rocks in the most northern parts of Europe and North America, and even to the Arctic regions, indications of the same revolution in climate were discovered.

Proofs from fossil shells in tertiary strata.— In Sicily, Calabria, and in the neighbourhood of Naples, the fossil testacea of the most modern tertiary formations belong almost entirely to species now inhabiting the Mediterranean; but as we proceed northwards in the Italian peninsula we find in the strata called Sub-Apennine an assemblage of fossil shells departing somewhat more widely from the type of the neighbouring seas. The proportion of species identifiable with those now living in the Mediterranean is still considerable; but it no longer predominates, as in the South of Italy and part of Sicily, over the unknown species. Although occurring in localities which are removed several degrees farther from the equator (as at Siena, Parmi, Asti, &c.), the shells yield clear indications of a warmer climate. This evidence is of great weight, and is not neutralized by any facts of a conflicting character; such, for instance, as the association, in the same group, of individuals referable to species now confined to arctic regions.

On comparing the fossils of the tertiary deposits of Paris and London with those of Bordeaux, and these again with the more modern strata of Sicily, we should at first expect that they would each indicate a higher temperature in proportion as they are situated farther to the south. But the contrary is true; of the shells

663

belonging to these several groups, whether freshwater or marine, some are of extinct, others of living species. Those found in the older, or Eocene, deposits of Paris and London, although six or seven degrees to the north of the Miocene strata at Bordeaux, afford evidence of a warmer climate; while those of Bordeaux imply that the sea in which they lived was of a higher temperature than that of Sicily, where the shelly strata were formed six or seven degrees nearer to the equator. In these cases the greater antiquity of the several formations (the Parisian being the oldest and the Sicilian the newest) has more than counterbalanced the influence which latitude would otherwise exert, and this phenomenon clearly points to a gradual and successive refrigeration of climate.

Siberian mammoths.—It will naturally be asked whether some recent geological discoveries bringing evidence to light of a colder, or, as it has been termed, "glacial epoch," towards the close of the tertiary periods throughout the northern hemisphere, does not conflict with the theory above alluded to, of a warmer temperature having prevailed in the eras of the Eocene, Miocene, and Pliocene formations. In answer to this enquiry, it may certainly be affirmed that an oscillation of climate has occurred in times immediately antecedent to the peopling of the earth by man; but proof of the intercalation of a less genial climate at an era when nearly all the marine and terrestrial testacea had already become specifically the same as those now living by no means rebuts the conclusion previously drawn, in favour of a warmer condition of the globe, during the ages which elapsed while the tertiary strata were deposited. In some of the most superficial patches of sand, gravel, and loam, scattered very generally over Europe, and containing recent shells, the remains of extinct species of land quadrupeds have been found, especially in places where the alluvial matter appears to have been washed into small lakes or into depressions in the plains bordering ancient rivers. Among the extinct mammalia thus entombed, we find species of the elephant, rhinoceros, hippopotamus, bear, hyaena, lion, tiger, monkey (macacus), and many others; consisting partly of genera now confined to warmer regions.

It is certainly probable that when some of these quadrupeds abounded in Europe, the climate was milder than that now experienced. The hippopotamus, for example, is now only met with where the temperature of the water is warm and nearly uniform throughout the year, and where the rivers are never frozen over. Yet when the great fossil species (*Hippopotamus major* Cuv.) inhabited England, the testacea of our country were nearly the same as those now existing, and the climate cannot be supposed to have been very hot.

The mammoth also appears to have existed in England when the temperature of our latitudes could not have been very different from that which now prevails; for remains of this animal have been found at North Cliff, in the county of York, in a lacustrine formation, in which all the land and freshwater shells, thirteen in number, can be identified with species and varieties now existing in that county. Bones of the bison also, an animal now inhabiting a cold or temperate climate, have been found in the same place. That these quadrupeds, and the indigenous species of testacea associated with them, were all contemporary inhabitants of Yorkshire has been established by unequivocal proof.

Recent investigations have placed beyond all doubt the important fact that a species of tiger, identical with that of Bengal, is common in the neighbourhood of Lake Aral, near Sussac, in the forty-fifth degree of north latitude; and from time to time this animal is now seen in Siberia in a latitude as far north as the parallel of Berlin and Hamburg.

Now, if the Indian tiger can range in our own times to the southern borders of Siberia or skirt the snows of the Himalaya, and if the puma can reach the fifty-third degree of latitude in South America, we may easily understand how large species of the same genera may once have inhabited our temperate climate. The mammoth E (*primigenius*), already alluded to, as occurring fossil in England, was decidedly different from the

665

two existing species of elephants, one of which is limited to Asia, south of the thirty-first degree of north latitude, the other to Africa, where it extends as far south as the Cape of Good Hope.

Pallas and other writers describe the bones of the mammoth as abounding throughout all the Lowland of Siberia, stretching in a direction west and east, from the borders of Europe to the extreme point nearest America, and south and north, from the base of the mountains of Central Asia to the shores of the Arctic Sea. Within this space, scarcely inferior in area to the whole of Europe, fossil ivory has been collected almost everywhere, on the banks of the Irtish, Obi, Yenesei, and other rivers. But it is not on the Obi nor the Yenesei, but on the Lena, farther to the east, where, in the same parallels of latitude, the cold is far more intense, that fossil remains have been found in the most wonderful state of preservation. In 1772, Pallas obtained from Wiljuiskoi, in latitude 64°, from the banks of the Wiljui, a tributary of the Lena, the carcass of a rhinoceros (*R. tichorhinus*), taken from the sand in which it must have remained congealed for ages, the soil of that region being always frozen to within a slight depth of the surface. This carcass was compared to a natural mummy, and emitted an odour like putrid flesh, part of the skin being still covered with black and grey hairs.

After more than thirty years, the entire carcass of a mammoth (or extinct species of elephant) was obtained in 1803, by Mr. Adams, much farther to the north. It fell from a mass of ice, in which it had been encased, on the banks of the Lena, in latitude 70°; and so perfectly had the soft parts of the carcass been preserved that the flesh, as it lay, was devoured by wolves and bears. This skeleton is still in the museum of St. Petersburg, the head retaining its integument and many of the ligaments entire. The skin of the animal was covered, first, with black bristles, thicker than horsehair, from twelve to sixteen inches in length; secondly, with hair of a reddish-brown colour, about four inches long; and thirdly, with wool of the same colour as the hair, about an inch in length. Of the fur, upwards of thirty pounds' weight were gathered from the wet sand-bank. The individual was nine feet high and sixteen feet long, without reckoning the large curved tusks: a size rarely surpassed by the largest living male elephants.

It is evident, then, that the mammoth, instead of being naked, like the living Indian and African elephants, was enveloped in a thick shaggy covering of fur, probably as impenetrable to rain and cold as that of the vicissitudes of a northern climate; and it is certain that, from the moment when the carcasses, both of the rhinoceros and elephant, above described, were buried in Siberia, in latitudes 64° and 70° north, the soil must have remained frozen and the atmosphere nearly as cold as at this day.

On considering all the facts above enumerated, it seems reasonable to imagine that a large region in Central Asia, including, perhaps, the southern half of Siberia, enjoyed, at no very remote period in the earth's history, a temperate climate, sufficiently mild to afford food for numerous herds of elephants and rhinoceroses, *of species distinct from those now living*. But the age of this fauna was comparatively modern in the earth's history. It appears that when the oldest or Eocene tertiary deposits were formed, a warm temperature pervaded the European seas and lands. Shells of the genus Nautilus and other forms characteristic of tropical latitudes; fossil reptiles, such as the crocodile, turtle, and tortoise; plants, such as palms, some of them allied to the cocoanut, the screw pine, the custard apple, and the acacia, all lead to this conclusion. This flora and fauna were followed by those of the Miocene formation, in which indications of a southern, but less tropical, climate are detected. Finally, the Pliocene deposits, which come next in succession, exhibit in their organic remains a much nearer approach to the state of things now prevailing in corresponding latitudes. It was towards the close of this period that the seas of the northern hemisphere became more and more filled with floating icebergs often charged with erratic blocks, so that the waters and the atmosphere were chilled by the melting ice, and an arctic fauna enabled, for a time, to invade the temperate latitudes both of North America and Europe. The extinction of a considerable number of land quadrupeds and aquatic mollusca was gradually brought about by the increasing severity of the cold; but many species survived this revolution in climate, either by their capacity of living under a variety of conditions, or by migrating for a time to more southern lands and seas. At length, by modifications in the physical geography of the northern regions, and the cessation of floating ice on the eastern side of the Atlantic, the cold was moderated, and a milder climate ensued, such as we now enjoy in Europe.

Proofs from fossils in secondary and still older strata.—A great interval of time appears to have elapsed between the formation of the secondary strata, which constitute the principal portion of the elevated land in Europe, and the origin of the Eocene deposits. If we examine the rocks from the chalk to the new red sandstone inclusive, we find many distinct assemblages of fossils entombed in them, all of unknown species, and many of them referable to genera and families now most abundant between the tropics. Among the most remarkable are reptiles of gigantic size; some of them herbivorous, others carnivorous, and far exceeding in size any now known even in the torrid zone. The genera are for the most part extinct, but some of them, as the crocodile and monitor, have still representatives in the warmer parts of the earth. Coral reefs also were evidently numerous in the seas of the same periods, composed of species often belonging to genera now characteristic of a tropical climate. The number of large chambered shells also, including the nautilus, leads us to infer an elevated temperature; and the associated fossil plants, although imperfectly known, tend to the same conclusion, the Cycadeæ constituting the most numerous family.

But it is from the more ancient coal deposits that the most extraordinary evidence has been supplied in proof of the former existence of a very different climate, a climate which seems to have been moist, warm, and extremely uniform, in those very latitudes which are now the colder, and in regard to temperature the most variable regions of the globe. We learn from the researches of Adolphe Brongniart, Goeppert, and other botanists that in the flora of the Carboniferous era there was a great predominance of ferns, some of which were arborescent; as, for example, Caulopteris, Protopteris, and Psarronius; nor can this be accounted for, as some have supposed, by the greater power which ferns possess of resisting maceration in water. This prevalence of ferns indicates a moist, equable, and temperate climate, and the absence of any severe cold; for such are the conditions which, at the present day, are found to be most favourable to that tribe of plants. It is only in the islands of the tropical oceans, and of the southern temperate zone, such as Norfolk Island, Otaheite, the Sandwich Islands, Tristan d'Acunha, and New Zealand, that we find any near approach to that remarkable preponderance of ferns which is characteristic of the carboniferous flora. It has been observed that tree ferns and other forms of vegetation which flourished most luxuriantly within the tropics extend to a much greater distance from the equator in the southern hemisphere than in the northern, being found even as far as 46° south latitude in New Zealand. There is little doubt that this is owing to the more uniform and moist climate occasioned by the greater proportional area of sea. Next to ferns and pines, the most abundant vegetable forms in the coal formation are the Calamites, Lepidodendra, Sigillariæ, and Stigmariæ. These were formerly considered to be so closely allied to tropical genera, and to be so much greater in size than the corresponding tribes now inhabiting equatorial latitudes, that they were thought to imply an extremely hot as well as humid and equable climate. But recent discoveries respecting the structure and relations of these fossil plants have shown that they deviated so widely from all existing types in the vegetable world that we have more reason to infer from this evidence a widely different climate in the Carboniferous era, as compared to that now prevailing, than a temperature extremely elevated. Palms, if not entirely wanting when the strata of the carboniferous group were deposited, appear to have been exceedingly rare. The Coniferæ, on the other hand, so abundantly met with in the coal, resemble Araucariæ in structure, a family of the fir tribe characteristic at present of the milder regions of the southern hemisphere, such as Chile, Brazil, New Holland, and Norfolk Island.

"In regard to the geographical extent of the ancient vegetation, it was not confined," says M. Brongniart, "to a small space, as to Europe, for example; for the same forms are met with again at great distances. Thus the coal plants of North America are, for the most part, identical with those of Europe, and all belong to the same genera. Some specimens, also, from Greenland, are referable to ferns, analogous to those of our European coal mines."

To return, therefore, from this digression—the flora of the coal appears to indicate a uniform and mild temperature in the air, while the fossils of the contemporaneous mountain limestone, comprising abundance of lamelliferous corals, large chambered cephalopods, and crinoidea, naturally lead us to infer a considerable warmth in the waters of the northern sea of the Carboniferous period. So also in regard to strata older than the coal, they contain in high northern latitudes mountain masses of corals which must have lived and grown on the spot, and large chambered univalves, such as Orthocerata and Nautilus, all seeming to indicate, even in regions bordering on the arctic circle, the former prevalence of a temperature more elevated than that now prevailing.

The warmth and humidity of the air, and the uniformity of climate, both in the different seasons of the year and in different latitudes appear to have been most remarkable when some of the oldest of the fossiliferous strata were formed. The approximation to a climate similar to that now enjoyed in these latitudes does not commence till the era of the formations termed tertiary; and while the different tertiary rocks were deposited in succession, from the Eocene to the Pliocene, the temperature seems to have been lowered, and to have continued to diminish even after the appearance upon the earth of a considerable number of the existing species, the cold reaching its maximum of intensity in European latitudes during the glacial epoch, or the epoch immediately antecedent to that in which all the species now contemporary with man were in being.

THOMAS ROBERT MALTHUS

(1766–1834)

Although Malthus' place is primarily among the great economic
theorists, both Darwin and Wallace were indebted to him for the
idea of natural selection. (Malthus, in turn, admitted that he took
the idea from Benjamin Franklin!) Malthus, an English clergyman,
aroused a storm of protest with his *Essay on the Principle of Population* (1798), containing the pessimistic proposition that disease,
war, poverty and vice appear to be necessary checks on the growth
of population, which otherwise would outdistance the means of
subsistence.

ESSAY ON THE PRINCIPLE OF POPULATION

QUESTION STATED. *Little prospect of a determination of it, from
the enmity of the opposing parties. The principal argument
against the perfectibility of man and of society has never been
fairly answered. Nature of the difficulty arising from population.
Outline of the principal argument of the essay.*

The great and unlooked-for discoveries that have taken place
of late years in natural philosophy; the increasing diffusion of
general knowledge from the extension of the art of printing; the
ardent and unshackled spirit of inquiry that prevails throughout the lettered and even unlettered world; the new and extraordinary lights that have been thrown on political subjects, which
dazzle and astonish the understanding; and particularly that tremendous phenomenon in the political horizon, the French Revolution, which like a blazing comet, seems destined either to inspire with fresh life and vigor or to scorch up and destroy the
shrinking inhabitants of the earth, have all concurred to lead
many able men into the opinion that we were touching on a period

big with the most important changes—changes that would in some measure be decisive of the future fate of mankind.

It has been said that the great question is now at issue whether man shall henceforth start forward with accelerated velocity toward illimitable and hitherto unconceived improvement; or be condemned to a perpetual oscillation between happiness and misery, and after every effort remain still at an immeasurable distance from the wished-for goal.

Yet, anxiously as every friend of mankind must look forward to the termination of this painful suspense, and eagerly as the inquiring mind would hail every ray of light that might assist its view into futurity, it is much to be lamented that the writers on each side of this momentous question still keep far aloof from each other. Their mutual arguments do not meet with a candid examination. The question is not brought to rest on fewer points, and even in theory scarcely seems to be approaching to a decision.

The advocate for the present order of things is apt to treat the sect of speculative philosophers either as a set of artful and designing knaves, who preach up ardent benevolence and draw captivating pictures of a happier state of society, only the better to enable them to destroy the present establishments and to forward their own deep-laid schemes of ambition; or as wild and mad-headed enthusiasts whose silly speculations and absurd paradoxes are not worth the attention of any reasonable man.

The advocate for the perfectibility of man and of society retorts on the defender of establishments a more than equal contempt. He brands him as the slave of the most miserable and and narrow prejudices; or as the defender of the abuses of civil society, only because he profits by them. He paints him either as a character who prostitutes his understanding to his interest, or as one whose powers of mind are not of a size to grasp anything great and noble; who cannot see above five yards before him; and who must therefore be utterly unable to take in the views of the enlightened benefactor of mankind.

In this unamicable contest the cause of truth cannot but suffer. The really good arguments on each side of the question are not allowed to have their proper weight. Each pursues his own theory, little solicitous to correct or improve it by an attention to what is advanced by his opponents.

The friend of the present order of things condemns all political speculations in the gross. He will not even condescend to examine the grounds from which the perfectibility of society is inferred. Much less will he give himself the trouble in a fair and candid manner to attempt an exposition of their fallacy.

The speculative philosopher equally offends against the cause of truth. With eyes fixed on a happier state of society, the blessings of which he paints in the most captivating colors, he allows himself to indulge in the most bitter invectives against every present establishment, without applying his talents to consider the best and safest means of removing abuses, and without seeming to be aware of the tremendous obstacles that threaten, even in theory, to oppose the progress of man toward perfection.

It is an acknowledged truth in philosophy that a just theory will always be confirmed by experiment. Yet so much friction and so many minute circumstances occur in practice, which it is next to impossible for the most enlarged and penetrating mind to foresee, that on few subjects can any theory be pronounced just that has not stood the test of experience. But an untried theory cannot fairly be advanced as probable, much less as just, till all the arguments against it have been maturely weighed and clearly and consistently refuted.

I have read some of the speculations on the perfectibility of man and of society with great pleasure. I have been warmed and delighted with the enchanting picture which they hold forth. I ardently wish for such happy improvements. But I see great and, to my understanding, unconquerable difficulties in the way to them. These difficulties it is my present purpose to state; declaring at the same time that, so far from exulting in them as a cause of triumph over the friends of innovation, nothing would give me greater pleasure than to see them completely removed.

The most important argument that I shall adduce is certainly not new. The principles on which it depends have been explained in part by Hume, and more at large by Dr. Adam Smith. It has been advanced and applied to the present subject, though not

673

with its proper weight, or in the most forcible point of view, by Mr. Wallace; and it may probably have been stated by many writers that I have never met with. I should certainly therefore not think of advancing it again, though I mean to place it in a point of view in some degree different from any that I have hitherto seen, if it had ever been fairly and satisfactorily answered.

The cause of this neglect on the part of the advocates for the perfectibility of mankind is not easily accounted for, I cannot doubt the talents of such men as Godwin and Condorcet. I am unwilling to doubt their candor. To my understanding, and probably to that of most others, the difficulty appears insurmountable. Yet these men of acknowledged ability and penetration scarcely deign to notice it, and hold on their course in such speculations with unabated ardor and undiminished confidence. I have certainly no right to say that they purposely shut their eyes to such arguments. I ought rather to doubt the validity of them, when neglected by such men, however forcibly their truth may strike my own mind. Yet in this respect it must be acknowledged that we are all of us too prone to err. If I saw a glass of wine repeatedly presented to a man, and he took no notice of it, I should be apt to think that he was blind or uncivil. A juster philosophy might teach me rather to think that my eyes deceived me and that the offer was not really what I conceived it to be.

In entering upon the argument I must premise that I put out of the question, at present, all mere conjectures; that is, all suppositions, the probable realization of which cannot be inferred upon any just philosophical grounds. A writer may tell me that he thinks man will ultimately become an ostrich. I cannot properly contradict him. But before he can expect to bring any reasonable person over to his opinion he ought to show that the necks of mankind have been gradually elongating; that the lips have grown harder and more prominent; that the legs and feet are daily altering their shape; and that the hair is beginning to change into stubs of feathers. And till the probability of so wonderful a conversion can be shown, it is surely lost time and lost eloquence to expatiate on the happiness of man in such a state; to describe his powers, both of running and flying; to paint him in a condition where all narrow luxuries would be contemned; where he would be employed only in collecting the necessaries of life; and where, consequently, each man's share of labor would be light and his portion of leisure ample.

I think I may fairly make two postulata.

First, that food is necessary to the existence of man.

Secondly, that the passion between the sexes is necessary and will remain nearly in its present state.

These two laws ever since we have had any knowledge of mankind appear to have been fixed laws of our nature; and as we have not hitherto seen any alteration in them, we have no right to conclude that they will ever cease to be what they now are, without an immediate act of power in that Being who first arranged the system of the universe; and for the advantage of His creatures still executes, according to fixed laws, all its various operations.

I do not know that any writer has supposed that on this earth man will ultimately be able to live without food. But Mr. Godwin has conjectured that the passion between the sexes may in time be extinguished. As, however, he calls this part of his work a deviation into the land of conjecture, I will not dwell longer upon it at present than to say that the best arguments for the perfectibility of man are drawn from a contemplation of the great progress that he has already made from the savage state and the difficulty of saying where he is to stop. But toward the extinction of the passion between the sexes no progress whatever has hitherto been made. It appears to exist in as much force at present as it did two thousand or four thousand years ago. There are individual exceptions now as there always have been. But as these exceptions do not appear to increase in number it would surely be a very unphilosophical mode of arguing to infer merely from the existence of an exception that the exception would, in time, become the rule, and the rule the exception.

Assuming then, my postulata as granted, I say that the power of population is indefinitely greater than the power in the earth to produce subsistence for man.

Population, when unchecked, increases in a geometrical ratio. Subsistence increases only in a arithmetical ratio. A slight acquaintance with numbers will show the immensity of the first power in comparison to the second.

By that law of our nature which makes food necessary to the life of man the effects of these two unequal powers must be kept equal.

This implies a strong and constantly operating check on population from the difficulty of subsistence. This difficulty must fall somewhere; and must necessarily be severely felt by a large portion of mankind.

Through the animal and vegetable kingdoms Nature has scattered the seeds of life abroad with the most profuse and liberal hand. She has been comparatively sparing in the room and the nourishment necessary to rear them. The germs of existence contained in this spot of earth, with ample food, and ample room to expand in, would fill millions of worlds in the course of a few thousand years. Necessity, that imperious all-pervading law of nature, restrains them within the prescribed bounds. The race of plants and the race of animals shrink under this great restrictive law. And the race of man cannot, by any efforts of reason, escape from it. Among plants and animals its effects are waste of seed, sickness, and premature death. Among mankind, misery and vice. The former, misery, is an absolutely necessary consequence of it. Vice is a highly probable consequence, and we therefore see it abundantly prevail; but it ought not, perhaps, to be called an absolutely necessary consequence. The ordeal of virtue is to resist all temptation to evil.

This natural inequality of the two powers of population and of production in the earth, and that great law of our nature which must constantly keep their effects equal, form the great difficulty that to me appears insurmountable in the way to the perfectibility of society. All other arguments are of slight and subordinate consideration in comparison of this. I see no way by which man can escape from the weight of this law which pervades all animated nature. No fancied equality, no agrarian regulations in their utmost extent, could remove the pressure of it even for a single century. And it appears, therefore, to be decisive against the possible existence of a society, all the members of which should live in ease, happiness, and comparative leisure, and feel no anxiety about providing the means of subsistence for themselves and families.

Consequently, if the premises are just, the argument is conclusive against the perfectibility of the mass of mankind.

I have thus sketched the general outline of the argument; but I will examine it more particularly; and I think it will be found that experience, the true source and foundation of all knowledge, invariably confirms its truth.

GUGLIELMO MARCONI

(1874–1937)

Son of an Italian father and Irish mother, this student of Hertz did not invent the wireless telegraphy, but produced the first instrument to send messages on a commercial scale. The record of his transmissions reads: messages sent for nine miles in England (1896); across the English Channel (1898); across the Atlantic from Cornwall to Newfoundland (1901). He invented a magnetic detector and a horizontal directional aerial, and in 1909 received (with Karl Ferdinand Braun) the Nobel prize for physics. He later worked on short-wave communication.

My first tests were carried out with an ordinary Hertz oscillator and a Branly coherer as detector, but I soon found out that the Branly coherer was far too erratic and unreliable for practical work.

After some experiments I found that a coherer consisting of nickel and silver filings placed in a small gap between two silver plugs in a tube, was remarkably sensitive and reliable. This improvement together with the inclusion of the coherer in a circuit tuned to the wave-length of the transmitted radiation, allowed me to gradually extend up to about a mile the distance at which I could affect the receiver.

Another, now well-known, arrangement which I adopted was to place the coherer in a circuit containing a voltaic cell and a sensitive telegraph relay actuating another circuit, which worked a tapper or trembler and a recording instrument. By means of a Morse telegraph key placed in one of the circuits of the oscillator or transmitter it was possible to emit long or short successions of electric waves, which would affect the receiver at a distance and accurately reproduce the telegraphic signs transmitted through space by the oscillator.

With such apparatus I was able to telegraph up to a distance of about a half a mile.

Some further improvements were obtained by using reflectors with both transmitters and receivers, the transmitter being in this case a Righi oscillator.

This arrangement made it possible to send signals in one definite direction, but was inoperative if hills or any large obstacle happened to intervene between the transmitter and receiver.

In August 1895 I discovered a new arrangement which not only greatly increased the distance over which I could communicate, but also seemed to make the transmission independent from the effects of intervening obstacles.

This arrangement consisted in connecting one terminal of the Hertzian oscillator, or spark producer, to earth and the other terminal to a wire or capacity area placed at a height above the ground, and in also connecting at the receiving end one terminal of the coherer to earth and the other to an elevated conductor (Figs. 2 and 3).

I then began to examine the relation between the distance at which the transmitter could affect the receiver and the elevation of the capacity areas above the earth, and I very soon definitely ascertained that the higher the wires or capacity areas, the greater the distance over which it was possible to telegraph.

Thus I found that when using cubes of tin of about 30 cms. side as elevated conductors or capacities, placed at the top of poles 2 meters high, I could receive signals at 30 meters distance, and when placed on poles 4 meters high, at 100 meters, and at 8 meters high at 400 meters. With larger cubes 100 cms. side, fixed at a height of 8 meters, signals could be transmitted 2,400 meters all round.

These experiments were continued in England, where in September 1896 a distance of 1¾ miles was obtained in tests carried out for the British Government at Salisbury. The distance of communication was extended to 4 miles in March 1897, and in May of the same year to 9 miles. . . .

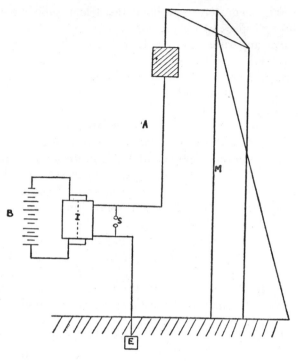

Marconi's Fig. 2

In all these experiments a very small amount of electrical power was used, the high tension current being produced by an ordinary Ruhmkorff coil. . . .

From the beginning of 1898, instead of joining the coherer or detector directly to the aerial and earth, I connected it between the ends of a secondary of a suitable oscillation transformer containing a condenser and tuned to the period of the electrical waves received. The primary of this oscillation transformer was connected to the elevated wire and to earth (Fig. 6).

This arrangement allowed of a certain degree of syntony, as by varying the period of oscillation of the transmitting antennae, it was possible to send messages to a tuned receiver without interfering with others differently syntonized. . . .

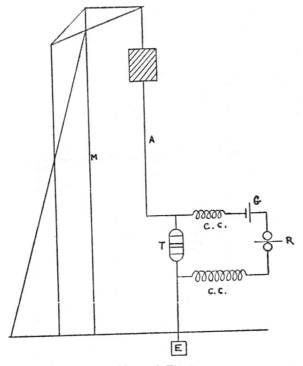

Marconi's Fig. 3

In 1900 I constructed and patented a complete system of transmitters and receivers which consisted of the usual kind of elevated capacity area and earth connection, but these were inductively coupled to an oscillation circuit containing a condenser, an inductance, and a spark gap or detector, the conditions which I found essential for efficiency being that the periods of electrical oscillation of the elevated wire or conductor should be in tune or resonance with that of the condenser circuit, and that of the two circuits of the transmitter (Fig. 8).

The circuits consisting of the oscillating circuit and the radiating circuit were more or less loosely 'coupled' by varying the distance between them. By the adjustment of the inductance inserted in the elevated conductor and by the variation of capacity

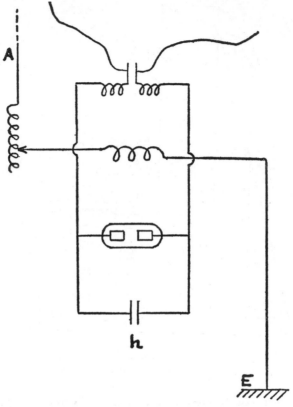

Marconi's Fig. 6

of the condenser circuit, the two circuits were brought into resonance, a condition . . . essential in order to obtain efficient radiation.

Part of my work regarding the utilisation of condenser circuits in association with the radiating antennae was carried out simultaneously to that of Professor Braun, without, however, either of us knowing at the time anything of the contemporary work of the other. . . .

The belief that the curvature of the earth would not stop the propagation of the waves, and the success obtained by syntonic

682

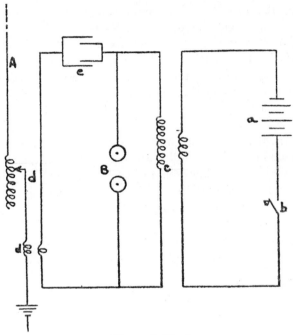

Marconi's Fig. 8

methods in preventing mutual interference, led me in 1900 to decide to attempt the experiment . . . to detect electric waves over a distance of 4000 kilometers, which, if successful, would immediately prove the possibility of telegraphing without wires between Europe and America.

. . . I was convinced that . . . the exact knowledge of the real conditions under which telegraphy over such distances could be carried out, would do much to improve our understanding of the phenomena connected with wireless transmission.

The transmitter erected at Poldhu, on the coast of Cornwall, was similar in principle to the one I have already referred to, but on a very much larger scale than anything previously attempted.

The power of the generating plant was about 25 kilowatts. . . .

My previous tests had convinced me that when endeavouring

683

to extend the distance of communication, it was not merely sufficient to augment the power of the electrical energy of the sender, but that it was also necessary to increase the area or height of the transmitting and receiving elevated conductors.

As it would have been too expensive to employ vertical wires of great height, I decided to increase their number and capacity, which seemed likely to make possible the efficient utilization of large amounts of energy.

The arrangement of transmitting antennae which was used at Poldhu consisted of a fan-like arrangement of wires supported by an insulated stay between masts only 48 meters high and 60 meters apart. These wires converged together at the lower end and were connected to the transmitting apparatus contained in a building. . . .

The tests were commenced early in December 1901 and on the 12th of that month the signals transmitted from England were clearly and distinctly received at the temporary station at St. John's in Newfoundland. . . .

A result of scientific interest which I first noticed during the tests on S.S. *Philadelphia* and which is a most important factor in long distance Radiotelegraphy, was the very marked and detrimental effect of daylight on the propagation of electric waves at great distances, the range by night being usually more than double that attainable during daytime.

I do not think that this effect has yet been satisfactorily investigated or explained. . . .

I am now inclined to believe that the absorption of electric waves during the daytime is due to the electrons propagated into space by the sun, and that if these are continually falling like a shower upon the earth, in accordance with the hypothesis of Professor Arrhenius, then that portion of the earth's atmosphere which is facing the sun will have in it more electrons than the part which is not facing the sun, and therefore it may be less transparent to electric waves.

Sir J. J. Thomson has shown . . . that if electrons are distributed in a space traversed by electric waves, these will tend to move the electrons in the direction of the wave, and will therefore absorb some of the energy of the wave. Hence, as Professor [J. A.] Fleming has pointed out, . . . a medium through which electrons or ions are distributed acts as a slightly turbid medium to long electric waves.

Apparently the length of wave and amplitude of the electrical oscillations have much to do with this interesting phenomenon, long waves and small amplitudes being subject to the effect of daylight to a much lesser degree than short waves and large amplitudes.

According to Professor Fleming the daylight effect should be more marked on long waves, but this has not been my experience. Indeed, in some very recent experiments in which waves of about 8000 meters long were used, the energy received by day was usually greater than at night.

The fact remains, however, that for comparatively short waves, such as are used for ship communication, clear sunlight and blue skies, though transparent to light, act as a kind of fog to these waves. . . .

JAMES CLERK MAXWELL

(1831–1879)

The proof that electromagnetic waves pass through the ether at the velocity of light—the basis of radio, radar and television transmission—was first given by this Scottish physicist-astronomer. His great work, *Treatise on Electricity and Magnetism* (1873), was largely ignored until in 1888 Hertz produced experimental evidence of electromagnetic waves longer than light waves. Maxwell is also famous in astronomical circles for his paper, *On the Stability of Saturn's Rings* (1859), proving that the rings were neither solid nor continuous. He investigated color vision, color-blindness, and the kinetic theory of gases, and is the author of a well-known text, *Matter and Motion* (1876).

A TREATISE ON ELECTRICITY AND MAGNETISM

THE NATURE OF ELECTRICITY

LET a piece of glass and a piece of resin be rubbed together. They will be found to attract each other. If a second piece of glass be rubbed with a second piece of resin, it will be found that the two pieces of glass repel each other and that the two pieces of resin are also repelled from one another, while each piece of glass attracts each piece of resin. These phenomena of attraction and repulsion are called electrical phenomena, and the bodies which exhibit them are said to be "electrified," or to be "charged with electricity."

Bodies may be electrified in many other ways, as well as by friction. When bodies not previously electrified are observed to be acted on by an electrified body, it is because they have become "electrified by induction." If a metal vessel be electrified by induction, and a second metallic body be suspended by silk threads near it, and a metal wire be brought to touch simultaneously the electrified body and the second body, this latter body will be found to be electrified. Electricity has been transferred from one body to the other by means of the wire.

There are many other manifestations of electricity, all of which have been more or less studied, and they lead to the formation of theories of its nature, theories which fit in, to a greater or less extent, with the observed facts. The electrification of a body is a physical quantity capable of measurement, and two or more electrifications can be combined experimentally with a result of the same kind as when two quantities are added algebraically. We, therefore, are entitled to use language fitted to deal with electrification as a quantity as well as a quality, and to speak of any electrified body as "charged with a certain quantity of positive or negative electricity."

While admitting electricity to the rank of a physical quantity, we must not too hastily assume that it is, or is not, a substance, or that it is, or is not, a form of energy, or that it belongs to any known category of physical quantities. All that we have proved is that it cannot be created or annihilated, so that if the total quantity of electricity within a closed surface is increased or diminished, the increase or diminution must have passed in or out through the closed surface.

This is true of matter, but it is not true of heat, for heat may be increased or diminished within a closed surface, without passing in or out through the surface, by the transformation of some form of energy into heat, or of heat into some other form of energy. It is not true even of energy in general if we admit the immediate action of bodies at a distance.

There is, however, another reason which warrants us in asserting that electricity, as a physical quantity, synonymous with the total electrification of a body, is not, like heat, a form of energy. An electrified system has a certain amount of energy, and this energy can be calculated. The physical qualities, "electricity" and "potential," when multiplied together, produce the quantity, "energy." It is impossible, therefore, that electricity and energy should be quantities of the same category, for electricity is only one of the factors of energy, the other factor being "potential."

Electricity is treated as a substance in most theories of the subject, but as there are two kinds of electrification, which, being combined, annul each other, a distinction has to be drawn between free electricity and combined electricity, for we cannot conceive of two substances annulling each other. In the two-fluid theory, all bodies, in their unelectrified state, are supposed to be charged with equal quantities of positive and negative electricity. These quantities are supposed to be so great that no process of electrification has ever yet deprived a body of all the electricity of either kind. The two electricities are called "fluids" because they are capable of being transferred from one body to another, and are, within conducting bodies, extremely mobile.

In the one-fluid theory everything is the same as in the theory of two fluids, except that, instead of supposing the two substances equal and opposite in all respects, one of them, generally the negative one, has been endowed with the properties and name of ordinary matter, while the other retains the name of the electric fluid. The particles of the fluid are supposed to repel each other and attract those of electricity. This theory requires us, however, to suppose the mass of the electric fluid so small that no attainable positive or negative electrification has yet perceptibly increased or diminished the mass or the weight of a body, and it has not yet been able to assign sufficient reasons why the positive rather than the negative electrification should be supposed due to an *excess* quantity of electricity.

For my own part, I look for additional light on the nature of electricity from a study of what takes place in the space intervening between the electrified bodies. Some of the phenomena are explained equally by all the theories, while others merely indicate the peculiar difficulties of each theory. We may conceive the relation into which the electrified bodies are thrown, either as the result of the state of the intervening medium, or as the result of a direct action between the electrified bodies at a distance. If we adopt the latter conception, we may determine the law of the action, but we can go no further in speculating on its cause.

If, on the other hand, we adopt the conception of action through a medium, we are led to inquire into the nature of that action in each part of the medium. If we calculate on this hypothesis the total energy residing in the medium, we shall find it equal to the energy due to the electrification of the conductors on the hypothesis of direct action at a distance. Hence, the two hypotheses are mathematically equivalent.

On the hypothesis that the mechanical action observed between electrified bodies is exerted through and by means of the medium, as the action of one body on another by means of the tension of a rope or the pressure of a rod, we find that the medium must be in a state of mechanical stress. The nature of the stress is, as Faraday pointed out, a tension along the lines of force combined with an equal pressure in all directions at right angles to these lines. This distribution of stress is the only one consistent with the observed mechanical action on the electrified bodies, and also with the observed equilibrium of the fluid dielectric which surrounds them. I have, therefore, assumed the actual existence of this state of stress.

Every case of electrification or discharge may be considered as a motion in a closed circuit, such that at every section of the circuit the same quantity of electricity crosses in the same time; and this is the case, not only in the voltaic current, where it has always been recognised, but in those cases in which electricity has been generally supposed to be accumulated in certain places. We are thus led to a very remarkable consequence of the theory which we are examining, namely, that the motions of electricity are like those of an *incompressible* fluid, so that the total quantity within an imaginary fixed closed surface remains always the same.

The peculiar features of the theory as developed in this book are as follows.

That the energy of electrification resides in the dielectric medium, whether that medium be solid or gaseous, dense or rare, or even deprived of ordinary gross matter, provided that it be still capable of transmitting electrical action.

That the energy in any part of the medium is stored up in the form of a constraint called polarisation, dependent on the resultant electromotive force (the difference of potentials between two conductors) at the place.

That electromotive force acting on a dielectric produces what we call electric displacement.

That in fluid dielectrics the electric polarisation is accompanied by a tension in the direction of the lines of force combined with an equal pressure in all directions at right angles to the lines of force.

That the surfaces of any elementary portion into which we may conceive the volume of the dielectric divided must be conceived to be electrified, so that the surface density at any point of the surface is equal in magnitude to the displacement through that point of the surface *reckoned inwards*.

That, whatever electricity may be, the phenomena which we have called electric displacement is a movement of electricity in the same sense as the transference of a definite quantity of electricity through a wire.

THEORIES OF MAGNETISM

Certain bodies—as, for instance, the iron ore called loadstone, the earth itself, and pieces of steel which have been subjected to certain treatment—are found to possess the following properties, and are called magnets.

If a magnet be suspended so as to turn freely about a vertical axis, it will in general tend to set itself in a certain azimuth, and, if disturbed from this position, it will oscillate about it.

It is found that the force which acts on the body tends to cause a certain line in the body—called the axis of the magnet —to become parallel to a certain line in space, called the "direction of the magnetic force."

The ends of a long thin magnet are commonly called its poles, and like poles repel each other; while unlike poles attract each other. The repulsion between the two magnetic poles is in the straight line joining them, and is numerically equal to the products of the strength of the poles divided by the square of the distance between them; that is, it varies as the inverse square of the distance. Since the form of the law of magnetic action is identical with that of electric action, the same reasons which can be given for attributing electric phenomena to the action of one "fluid," or two "fluids" can also be used in favour of the existence of a magnetic matter, fluid or otherwise, provided new laws are introduced to account for the actual facts.

At all parts of the earth's surface, except some parts of the polar regions, one end of a magnet points in a northerly direction and the other in a southerly one. Now a bar of iron held parallel to the direction of the earth's magnetic force is found to become magnetic. Any piece of soft iron placed in a magnetic field is found to exhibit magnetic properties. These are phenomena of *induced* magnetism. Poisson supposes the magnetism of iron to consist in a separation of the magnetic fluids within each magnetic molecule. Weber's theory differs from this in assuming that the molecules of the iron are always magnets, even before the application of the magnetising force, but that in ordinary iron the magnetic axes of the molecules are turned indifferently in every direction, so that the iron as a whole exhibits no magnetic properties; and this theory agrees very well with what is observed.

The theories establish the fact that magnetisation is a phenomenon, not of large masses of iron, but of molecules; that is to say, of portions of the substance so small that we cannot by any mechanical method cut them in two, so as to obtain a north pole separate from the south pole. We have arrived at no explanation, however, of the nature of a magnetic molecule, and we have therefore to consider the hypothesis of Ampère—that the magnetism of the molecule is due to an electric current constantly circulating in some closed path within it.

Ampère concluded that if magnetism is to be explained by means of electric currents, these currents must circulate within

691

the molecules of the magnet, and cannot flow from one molecule to another. As we cannot experimentally measure the magnetic action at a point within the molecule, this hypothesis cannot be disproved in the same way that we can disprove the hypothesis of sensible currents within the magnet. In spite of its apparent complexity, Ampère's theory greatly extends our mathematical vision into the interior of the molecules.

THE ELECTRO-MAGNETIC THEORY OF LIGHT

We explain electro-magnetic phenomena by means of mechanical action transmitted from one body to another by means of a medium occupying the space between them. The undulatory theory of light also assumes the existence of a medium. We have to show that the properties of the electro-magnetic medium are identical with those of the luminiferous medium.

To fill all space with a new medium whenever any new phenomena are to be explained is by no means philosophical, but if the study of two different branches of science has independently suggested the idea of a medium; and if the properties which must be attributed to the medium in order to account for electro-magnetic phenomena are of the same kind as those which we attribute to the luminiferous medium in order to account for the phenomena of light, the evidence for the physical existence of the medium is considerably strengthened.

According to the theory of emission, the transmission of light energy is effected by the actual transference of light-corpuscles from the luminous to the illuminated body. According to the theory of undulation there is a material medium which fills the space between the two bodies, and it is by the action of contiguous parts of this medium that the energy is passed on, from one portion to the next, till it reaches the illuminated body. The luminiferous medium is therefore, during the passage of light through it, a receptacle of energy. This energy is supposed to be partly potential and partly kinetic, and our theory agrees with the undulatory theory in assuming the existence of a medium capable of becoming a receptacle for two forms of energy.

Now, the properties of bodies are capable of quantitative measurement. We therefore obtain the numerical value of some property of the medium—such as the velocity with which a disturbance is propagated in it, which can be calculated from experiments, and also observed directly in the case of light. If it be found that the velocity of propagation of electro-magnetic disturbance is the same as the velocity of light, we have strong reasons for believing that light is an electro-magnetic phenomenon.

It is, in fact, found that the velocity of light and the velocity of propagation of electro-magnetic disturbance are quantities of the same order of magnitude. Neither of them can be said to have been determined accurately enough to say that one is greater than the other. In the meantime, our theory asserts that the quantities are equal, and assigns a physical reason for this equality, and it is not contradicted by the comparison of the results, such as they are.

Lorenz has deduced from Kirchhoff's equations of electric currents a new set of equations, indicating that the distribution of force in the electro-magnetic field may be considered as arising from the mutual action of contiguous elements, and that waves, consisting of transverse electric currents, may be propagated, with a velocity comparable with that of light, in non-conducting media. These conclusions are similar to my own, though obtained by an entirely different method.

The most important step in establishing a relation between electric and magnetic phenomena and those of light must be the discovery of some instance in which one set of phenomena is affected by the other. Faraday succeeded in establishing such a relation, and the experiments by which he did so are described in the nineteen series of his "Experimental Researches." Suffice it to state here that he showed that in the case of a ray of plane-polarised light the effect of the magnetic force is to turn the plane of polarisation round the direction of the ray as an axis, through a certain angle.

693

The action of magnetism on polarised light leads to the conclusion that in a medium under the action of a magnetic force, something belonging to the same mathematical class as an angular velocity, whose axis is in the direction of the magnetic force, forms part of the phenomenon. This angular velocity cannot be any portion of the medium of sensible dimensions rotating as a whole. We must, therefore, conceive the rotation to be that of very small portions of the medium, each rotating on its own axis.

This is the hypothesis of molecular vortices. The displacements of the medium during the propagation of light will produce a disturbance of the vortices, and the vortices, when so disturbed, may react on the medium so as to affect the propagation of the ray. The theory proposed is of a provisional kind, resting as it does on unproved hypotheses relating to the nature of molecular vortices, and the mode in which they are affected by the displacement of the medium.

ACTION AT A DISTANCE

There appears to be some prejudice, or *a priori* objection, against the hypothesis of a medium in which the phenomena of radiation of light and heat, and the electric actions at a distance, take place. It is true that at one time those who speculated as to the cause of physical phenomena were in the habit of accounting for each kind of action at a distance by means of a special æthereal fluid, whose function and property it was to produce these actions. They filled all space three and four times over with æthers of different kinds, the properties of which consisted merely to "save appearances," so that more rational inquirers were willing to accept not only Newton's definite law of attraction at a distance, but even the dogma of Cotes that action at a distance is one of the primary properties of matter, and that no explanation can be more intelligible than this fact. Hence the undulatory theory of light has met with much opposition, directed not against its failure to explain the phenomena, but against its assumption of the existence of a medium in which light is propagated.

The mathematical expression for electro-dynamic action led, in the mind of Gauss, to the conviction that a theory of the propagation of electric action would in time be found to be the very keystone of electro-dynamics. Now, we are unable to conceive of propagation in time, except either as the flight of a material substance through space or as the propagation of a condition of motion or stress in a medium already existing in space.

In the theory of Neumann, the mathematical conception called potential, which we are unable to conceive as a material substance, is supposed to be projected from one particle to another, in a manner which is quite independent of a medium, and which, as Neumann has himself pointed out, is extremely different from that of the propagation of light. In other theories it would appear that the action is supposed to be propagated in a manner somewhat more similar to that of light.

But in all these theories the question naturally occurs: "If something is transmitted from one particle to another at a distance, what is its condition after it had left the one particle, and before it reached the other?" If this something is the potential energy of the two particles, as in Neumann's theory, how are we to conceive this energy as existing in a point of space coinciding neither with the one particle nor with the other? In fact, whenever energy is transmitted from one body to another in time, there must be a medium or substance in which the energy exists after it leaves one body, and before it reaches the other, for energy, as Torricelli remarked, "is a quintessence of so subtle a nature that it cannot be contained in any vessels except the inmost substance of material things."

Hence all these theories lead to the conception of a medium in which the propagation takes place, and if we admit this medium as an hypothesis, I think we ought to endeavour to construct a mental representation of all the details of its action, and this has been my constant aim in this treatise.

695

A DYNAMICAL THEORY OF THE ELECTROMAGNETIC FIELD

The most obvious mechanical phenomenon in electrical and magnetical experiments is the mutual action by which bodies in certain states set each other in motion at a sensible distance. The first step, therefore, is to ascertain the magnitude and direction of the force acting between the bodies. This force depends on the relative position of the bodies and on their electric or magnetic condition. Hence it seems at first sight natural to explain the facts by assuming the existence of something either at rest or in motion in each body. This "something," which constitutes the electric or magnetic state of the body, is capable of acting at a distance according to mathematical laws.

Mathematical theories of statical electricity, magnetism, mechanical action between conductors, and induction of currents have thus been formed. These theories do not expressly consider the surrounding medium. They assume particles which have the property of acting on one another at a distance by attraction and repulsion. Monsieur W. Weber has found it necessary to assume further that the force between two electric particles depends on their relative velocity as well. The mechanical difficulties involved prevent me from considering this theory as an ultimate one, though it may yet be useful.

I have therefore preferred to seek an explanation of the facts in another direction, by supposing them to be produced by actions which go on in the surrounding medium as well as in the excited bodies.

The theory I propose may therefore be called a theory of the *electromagnetic field,* because it has to do with the space in the neighborhood of electric or magnetic bodies. It may also be called a *dynamical* theory, because it assumes matter in motion—producing observed electromagnetic phenomena—in that space.

The electromagnetic field is that part of space which contains and surrounds bodies in electric or magnetic conditions. It may be filled with any kind of matter or empty of gross matter, as in the case of vacuums. There is always enough matter left to receive and transmit the undulations of light and heat. The undulations are those of an ethereal substance, not of gross matter whose presence merely modifies in some way the motion of the ether.

From the phenomena of heat and light we receive data giving us some reason to believe in the existence of a pervading medium, of small but real density, capable of being set in motion and of transmitting motion from one part to another with great, but not infinite, velocity.

The parts of this pervading medium must be so connected that the motion of one part depends on the motion of the rest. At the same time these connections must be capable of a certain kind of elastic yielding, since the communication of motion is not instantaneous but occupies time.

The medium is therefore capable of receiving and storing up two kinds of energy: namely, "actual" energy, depending on the motion of its parts, and "potential" energy, consisting of work done in recovering from displacement by virtue of its elasticity.

The propagation of undulations consists in the continual transformation of one of these forms of energy into the other, alternately. At any instant the amount of energy in the whole medium is equally divided, so that half is energy of motion and half is elastic resilience.

According to the theory which I propose to explain, electromotive force—which will produce a current, heat, or decompose a body—is the force called into play during the communication of motion from one part of the medium to another.

But when electromotive force acts on a dielectric substance, such as glass, sulphur, or air, it produces a state of polarization, described as a state in which every particle has its opposite poles in opposite conditions. In a dielectric under electromotive force we may conceive that the electricity in each molecule is displaced. One side is rendered positively and the other negatively electrical. But the electricity remains entirely connected with the molecule and does not pass from one molecule to another.

697

The effect of this action on the whole dielectric mass is to produce a general displacement of electricity in a certain direction. This displacement does not amount to a current, because when it has reached a certain value it becomes constant. But it is the commencement of a current.

Electric displacement according to our theory is a kind of elastic yielding to the action of electromotive force. It is similar to that which takes place in structures and machines owing to the want of perfect rigidity in the connections. Electric displacement explains why a dielectric does not instantly return to its primitive state when the electromotive force is removed. This phenomenon, exhibited by almost all solid dielectric substances, gives rise to the residual charge in the Leyden jar and to several phenomena of electric cables.

It appears, therefore, that certain phenomena in electricity and magnetism lead to the same conclusion as those of optics, namely:

There is an ethereal medium pervading all bodies and modified only in degree by their presence.

The parts of this medium are capable of being set in motion by electric currents and magnets.

This motion is communicated from one part of the medium to another by forces arising from the connections of those parts.

Under the action of these forces there is a certain yielding, depending on the elasticity of these connections.

Therefore energy in two different forms may exist in the medium. One form is the actual energy of the motion of its parts; the other is the potential energy stored up in the connections by virtue of their elasticity.

Thus, then, we are led to the conception of a complicated mechanism capable of a vast variety of motion but at the same time subject to the general laws of dynamics. We ought to be able to work out all the consequences of its motion, provided we know the form of the relation between the motions of the parts. The induction of one current by another and the mechanical action between conductors carrying currents give the clue. The phenomenon of the induction of currents has been deduced from their mechanical action by Helmholtz and Thomson [Lord Kelvin]. I have followed the reverse order and deduced the mechanical action from the laws of induction. I have then described experimental methods of determining the quantities, L, M, N, on which these phenomena depend.

I then apply the phenomena of induction and attraction of currents to the exploration of the electromagnetic field with a magnet. I show the distribution of its equipotential magnetic surfaces, cutting the lines of force at right angles.

In order to bring these results within the power of symbolical calculation I then express them in the form of the general equations of the electromagnetic field. There are twenty of these equations in all, involving twenty variable quantities, such as electric displacement, electromotive force, strength of a current and its electromagnetic effect, and free electricity.

I then express in terms of these quantities the intrinsic energy of the electromagnetic field. This depends partly on its magnetic and partly on its electric polarization at every point.

From this I determine the mechanical force acting, first, on a movable conductor carrying an electric current; secondly, on a magnetic pole; thirdly, on an electrified body.

The last result—namely, the mechanical force acting on an electrified body—gives rise to an independent method of electrical measurement. It is founded on electrostatic effects. The relation between the units of measurement depends on what I have called the "electric elasticity" of the medium. It is a velocity, which has been experimentally determined by Messieurs Weber and Kohlrausch.

I then show how to calculate the electrostatic capacity of a condenser and the specific inductive capacity of a dielectric.

The general equations are next applied to the case of a magnetic disturbance propagated through a non-conducting field. It is shown that the only disturbances which can be so propagated are those transverse to the direction of propagation. The velocity of propagation is the velocity v, found from experiments such as those of Weber. It expresses the number of electrostatic units of electricity which are contained in one electro-magnetic unit.

The velocity is so nearly that of light that it seems we have strong reason to conclude that light itself (including radiant heat and other radiations if any) is an electromagnetic disturb-ance in the form of waves propagated through the electro-magnetic field according to electromagnetic laws.

The conceptions of the propagation of transverse magnetic disturbances to the exclusion of normal ones is distinctly set forth by Professor Faraday in his "Thoughts on Ray Vibra-tions." The electromagnetic theory of light, as proposed by him, is the same in substance as that which I have begun to develop, except that in 1846 there were no data to calculate the velocity of propagation.

ILLUSTRATIONS OF THE DYNAMICAL THEORY OF GASES

So many of the properties of matter, especially when in the gaseous form, can be deduced from the hypothesis that their minute parts are in rapid motion, the velocity increasing with the temperature, that the precise nature of this motion becomes a subject of rational curiosity. Daniel Bernoulli, Herapath, Joule, Krönig, Clausius, etc. have shown that the relations between pressure, temperature, and density in a perfect gas can be ex-plained by supposing the particles to move with uniform velocity in straight lines, striking against the sides of the containing vessel and thus producing pressure. It is not necessary to sup-pose each particle to travel to any great distance in the same straight line; for the effect in producing pressure will be the same if the particles strike against each other; so that the straight line described may be very short. M. Clausius has determined the mean length of path in terms of the average distance of the particles, and the distance between the centres of two particles when collision takes place. We have at present no

700

means of ascertaining either of these distances; but certain phaenomena, such as the internal friction of gases, the conduction of heat through a gas, and the diffusion of one gas through another, seem to indicate the possibility of determining accurately the mean length of path which a particle describes between two successive collisions. In order to lay the foundation of such investigations on strict mechanical principles, I shall demonstrate the laws of motion of an indefinite number of small, hard, and perfectly elastic spheres acting on one another only during impact.

If the properties of such a system of bodies are found to correspond to those of gases, an important physical analogy will be established, which may lead to more accurate knowledge of the properties of matter. If experiments on gases are inconsistent with the hypothesis of these propositions, then our theory, though consistent with itself, is proved to be incapable of explaining the phaenomena of gases. In either case it is necessary to follow out the consequences of the hypothesis.

Instead of saying that the particles are hard, spherical, and elastic, we may if we please say that the particles are centres of force, of which the action is insensible except at a certain small distance, when it suddenly appears as a repulsive force of very great intensity. It is evident that either assumption will lead to the same results. For the sake of avoiding the repetition of a long phrase about these repulsive forces, I shall proceed upon the assumption of perfectly elastic spherical bodies. If we suppose those aggregate molecules which move together to have a bounding surface which is not spherical, then the rotatory motion of the system will store up a certain proportion of the whole *vis viva*, as has been shown by Clausius, and in this way we may account for the value of the specific heat being greater than on the more simple hypothesis. . . .

Prop. IV. To find the average number of particles whose velocities lie between given limits, after a great number of collisions among a great number of equal particles.

Let N be the whole number of particles. Let x, y, z, be the components of the velocity of each particle in three rectangular directions, and let the number of particles for which x lies between x and $x + dx$ be $Nf(x)dx$, where $f(x)$ is a function of x to be determined.

The number of particles for which y lies between y and $y + dy$ will be $Nf(y)dy$; and the number for which z lies between z and $z + dz$ will be $Nf(z)dz$, where f always stands for the same function.

Now the existence of the velocity x does not in any way affect that of the velocities y or z, since these are all at right angles to each other and independent, so that the number of particles whose velocity lies between x and $x + dx$, and also between y and $y + dy$, and also between z and $z + dz$, is

$$Nf(x)f(y)f(z)\,dx\,dy\,dz.$$

If we suppose the N particles to start from the origin at the same instant, then this will be the number in the element of volume $(dx\,dy\,dz)$ after unit of time, and the number referred to unit of volume will be

$$Nf(x)f(y)f(z).$$

But the directions of the coordinates are perfectly arbitrary, and therefore this number must depend on the distance from the origin alone, that is

$$f(x)f(y)f(z) = \phi(x^2 + y^2 + z^2).$$

Solving this functional equation, we find

$$f(x) = Ce^{Ax^2}, \phi(r^2) = C^3 e^{Ar^2}$$

If we make A positive, the number of particles will increase with the velocity, and we should find the whole number of particles infinite. We therefore make A negative and equal to $-1/\alpha^2$, so that the number between x and $x + dx$ is

702

$$NCe^{-\dfrac{x^2}{\alpha^2}} dx.$$

Integrating from $x = -\infty$ to $x = +\infty$, we find the whole number of particles,

$$NC\sqrt{\pi}\alpha = N, \quad \therefore C = \frac{1}{\alpha\sqrt{\pi}},$$

$f(x)$ is therefore

$$\frac{1}{\alpha\sqrt{\pi}}e^{-\dfrac{x^2}{\alpha^2}}$$

Whence we may draw the following conclusions:—

1st. The number of particles whose velocity, resolved in a certain direction, lies between x and $x + dx$ is

$$N\frac{1}{\alpha\sqrt{\pi}}e^{-\dfrac{x^2}{\alpha^2}} dx \ldots \ldots \ldots \ldots (1)$$

2nd. The number whose actual velocity lies between v and $v + dv$ is

$$N\frac{4}{\alpha^3\sqrt{\pi}}v^2 e^{-\dfrac{v^2}{\alpha^2}} dv \ldots \ldots \ldots \ldots (2)$$

3rd. To find the mean value of v, add the velocities of all the particles together and divide by the number of particles; the result is

$$\text{Mean velocity} = \frac{2\alpha}{\sqrt{\pi}} \ldots \ldots \ldots \ldots (3)$$

4th. To find the mean value of v^2, add all the values together and divide by N,

$$\text{mean value of } v^2 = 3/2\alpha^2 \dots \dots \dots \dots (4)$$

This is greater than the square of the mean velocity, as it ought to be.

It appears from this proposition that the velocities are distributed among the particles according to the same law as the errors are distributed among the observations in the theory of the "method of least squares." The velocities range from 0 to ∞, but the number of those having great velocities is comparatively small. In addition to these velocities, which are in all directions equally, there may be a general motion of translation of the entire system of particles which must be compounded with the motion of the particles relatively to one another. We may call the one the motion of translation, and the other the motion of agitation.

GREGOR JOHANN MENDEL

(1822–1884)

Mendel's law—regarding the inheritance of "dominant" and "recessive" characteristics—was the consequence of eight years' hybridization experiments on many generations of peas in a monastery garden. Its author was an Austrian biologist who became the abbot of a cloister in Brünn. First read to the members of the local Natural History Society (1865), Mendel's paper was virtually forgotten until revived by De Vries around 1900. It is now considered of almost equal importance with the findings of Darwin.

EXPERIMENTS IN PLANT-HYBRIDIZATION

Introductory Remarks

EXPERIENCE of artificial fertilization, such as is effected with ornamental plants in order to obtain new variations in colour, has led to the experiments which will here be discussed. The striking regularity with which the same hybrid forms always reappeared whenever fertilization took place between the same species induced further experiments to be undertaken, the object of which was to follow up the developments of the hybrids in their progeny.

Those who survey the work done in this department will arrive at the conviction that among all the numerous experiments made, not one has been carried out to such an extent and in such a way as to make it possible to determine the number of different forms under which the offspring of hybrids appear, or to arrange these forms with certainty according to their separate generations, or definitely to ascertain their statistical relations.

It requires indeed some courage to undertake a labour of

705

such far-reaching extent; this appears, however, to be the only right way by which we can finally reach the solution of a question the importance of which cannot be overestimated in connection with the history of the evolution of organic forms.

The paper now presented records the results of such a detailed experiment. This experiment was practically confined to a small plant group, and is now, after eight years' pursuit, concluded in all essentials. Whether the plan upon which the separate experiments were conducted and carried out was the best suited to attain the desired end is left to the friendly decision of the reader.

SELECTION OF THE EXPERIMENTAL PLANTS

The value and utility of any experiment are determined by the fitness of the material to the purpose for which it is used, and thus in the case before us it cannot be immaterial what plants are subjected to experiment and in what manner such experiments are conducted.

The selection of the plant group which shall serve for experiments of this kind must be made with all possible care if it be desired to avoid from the outset every risk of questionable results.

The experimental plants must necessarily—

1. Possess constant differentiating characters.

2. The hybrids of such plants must, during the flowering period, be protected from the influence of all foreign pollen, or be easily capable of such protection.

The hybrids and their offspring should suffer no marked disturbance in their fertility in the successive generations.

Accidental impregnation by foreign pollen, if it occurred during the experiments and were not recognized, would lead to entirely erroneous conclusions. Reduced fertility or entire sterility of certain forms, such as occurs in the offspring of many hybrids, would render the experiments very difficult or entirely frustrate them. In order to discover the relations in which the

706

hybrid forms stand towards each other and also towards their progenitors it appears to be necessary that all members of the series developed in each successive generation should be, *without exception*, subjected to observation.

At the very outset special attention was devoted to the *Leguminosae* on account of their peculiar floral structure. Experiments which were made with several members of this family led to the results that the genus *Pisum* was found to possess the necessary qualifications.

Some thoroughly distinct forms of this genus possess characters which are constant, and easily and certainly recognizable, and when their hybrids are mutually crossed they yield fertile progeny. Furthermore, a disturbance through foreign pollen cannot easily occur, since the fertilizing organs are closely packed inside the keel and the anther bursts within the bud, so that the stigma becomes covered with pollen even before the flower opens. This circumstance is of special importance. As additional advantages worth mentioning, there may be cited the easy culture of these plants in the open ground and in pots, and also their relatively short period of growth. Artificial fertilization is certainly a somewhat elaborate process, but nearly always succeeds. For this purpose the bud is open before it is perfectly developed, the keel is removed, and each stamen carefully extracted by means of forceps, after which the stigma can at once be dusted over with the foreign pollen.

DIVISION AND ARRANGEMENT OF THE EXPERIMENTS

If two plants which differ constantly in one or several characters be crossed, numerous experiments have demonstrated that the common characters are transmitted unchanged to the hybrids and their progeny; but each pair of differentiating characters, on the other hand, unite in the hybrid to form a new character, which in the progeny of the hybrid is usually variable. The object of the experiment was to observe these variations in the case of each pair of differentiating characters, and to deduce the law according to which they appear in the successive generations. The experiment resolves itself therefore into just as many separate experiments as there are constantly differentiating characters presented in the experimental plants.

The various forms of Peas selected for crossing showed differences in the length and colour of the stem; in the size and form of the leaves; in the position, colour, and size of the flowers; in the length of the flower stalk; in the colour, form, and size of the pods; in the form and size of the seeds; and in the colour of the seed coats and of the albumen [cotyledons]. Some of the characters noted do not permit of a sharp and certain separation, since the difference is of a "more or less" nature, which is often difficult to define. Such characters could not be utilized for the separate experiments; these could only be applied to characters which stand out clearly and definitely in the plants. Lastly, the result must show whether they, in their entirety, observe a regular behaviour in their hybrid unions, and whether from these facts any conclusion can be come to regarding those characters which possess a subordinate significance in the type.

The characters which were selected for experiment relate:

1. To the *difference in the form of the ripe seeds*. These are either round or roundish, the depressions, if any, occur on the surface, being always only shallow; or they are irregularly angular and deeply wrinkled (*P. quadratum*).

2. To the *difference in the colour of the seed albumen* (endosperm). The albumen of the ripe seeds is either pale yellow, bright yellow and orange coloured, or it possesses a more or less intense green tint. This difference of colour is easily seen in the seeds as their coats are transparent.

3. To the *difference in the colour of the seed coat*. This is either white, with which character white flowers are constantly correlated; or it is grey, grey-brown, leather-brown, with or without violet spotting, in which case the colour of the standards is violet, that of the wings purple, and the stem in the axils of the leaves is of a reddish tint. The grey seed coats become dark brown in boiling water.

4. To the *difference in the form of the ripe pods.* These are either simply inflated, not contracted in places; or they are deeply constricted between the seeds and more or less wrinkled (*P. saccharatum*).

5. To the *difference in the colour of the unripe pods.* They are either light to dark green, or vividly yellow, in which colouring the stalks, leaf veins, and calyx participate.

6. To the *difference in the position of the flowers.* They are either axial, that is, distributed along the main stem; or they are terminal, that is, bunched at the top of the stem and arranged almost in a false umbel; in this case the upper part of the stem is more or less widened in section (*P. umbellatum*).

7. To the *difference in the length of the stem.* The length of the stem is very various in some forms; it is, however, a constant character for each, in so far that healthy plants, grown in the same soil, are only subject to unimportant variations in this character.

In experiments with this character, in order to be able to discriminate with certainty, the long axis of 6 to 7 ft. was always crossed with the short one of ¾ ft. to 1½ ft.

Each two of the differentiating characters enumerated above were united by cross-fertilization. There were made for the

1st trial	60	fertilizations	on	15	plants.
2nd "	58	"	"	10	"
3rd "	35	"	"	10	"
4th "	40	"	"	10	"
5th "	23	"	"	5	"
6th "	34	"	"	10	"
7th "	37	"	"	10	"

Furthermore, in all the experiments reciprocal crossings were effected in such a way that each of the two varieties which in one set of fertilizations served as seed bearer in the other set was used as the pollen plant.

The plants were grown in garden beds, a few also in pots, and were maintained in their naturally upright position by means of sticks, branches of trees, and strings stretched between.

For each experiment a number of pot plants were placed during the blooming period in a greenhouse, to serve as control plants for the main experiment in the open as regards possible disturbance by insects. Among the insects which visit Peas the beetle *Bruchus pisi* might be detrimental to the experiments should it appear in numbers. The female of this species is known to lay the eggs in the flower, and in so doing opens the keel; upon the tarsi of one specimen, which was caught in a flower, some pollen grains could clearly be seen under a lens.

The risk of false impregnation by foreign pollen is, however, a very slight one with *Pisum*, and is quite incapable of disturbing the general result. Among more than 10,000 plants which were carefully examined there were only a very few cases where an indubitable false impregnation had occurred. Since in the greenhouse such a case was never remarked, it may well be supposed that *Bruchus pisi*, and possibly also abnormalities in the floral structure, were to blame.

[F₁] The Forms of the Hybrids

Experiments which in previous years were made with ornamental plants have already afforded evidence that the hybrids, as a rule, are not exactly intermediate between the parental species. With some of the more striking characters, those, for instance, which relate to the form and size of the leaves, the pubescence of the several parts, etc., the intermediate, indeed, is nearly always to be seen; in other cases, however, one of the two parental characters is so preponderant that it is difficult, or quite impossible, to detect the other in the hybrid.

This is precisely the case with the Pea hybrids. In the case of each of the seven crosses the hybrid character resembles that of one of the parental forms so closely that the other either escapes observation completely or cannot be detected with certainty. This circumstance is of great importance in the determination and classification of the forms under which the offspring of the hybrids appear. Henceforth in this paper those characters which are transmitted entire, or almost unchanged in the hybridization, and therefore in themselves constitute the characters of the hybrid, are termed the *dominant,* and those which become latent in the process *recessive.* The expression "recessive" has been chosen because the characters thereby designed withdraw or entirely disappear in the hybrids, but nevertheless reappear unchanged in their progeny, as will be demonstrated later on.

It was furthermore shown by the whole of the experiments that it is perfectly immaterial whether the dominant characters belong to the seed bearer or to the pollen parent; the form of the hybrid remains identical in both cases.

Of the differentiating characters which were used in the experiments the following are dominant:

1. The round or roundish form of the seed with or without shallow depressions.

2. The yellow colouring of the seed albumen [cotyledons].

3. The grey, grey-brown, or leather-brown colour of the seed coat, in association with violet-red blossoms and reddish spots in the leaf axils.

4. The simply inflated form of the pod.

5. The green colouring of the unripe pod in association with the same colour in the stems, the leaf veins, and the calyx.

6. The distribution of the flowers along the stem.

7. The greater length of stem.

With regard to this last character it must be stated that the longer of the two parental stems is usually exceeded by the hybrid, a fact which is possibly only attributable to the greater luxuriance which appears in all parts of plants when stems of very different length are crossed. Thus, for instance, in repeated experiments, stems of 1 ft. and 6 ft. in length yielded without exception hybrids which varied in length between 6 ft. and 7½ ft.

[F₂] THE FIRST GENERATION [BRED] FROM THE HYBRIDS

In this generation there reappear, together with the dominant characters, also the recessive ones with their peculiarities fully developed, and this occurs in the definitely expressed average proportion of three to one, so that among each four plants of this generation three display the dominant character and one the recessive. This relates without exception to all the characters which were investigated in the experiments. The angular wrinkled form of the seed, the green colour of the albumen, the white colour of the seed coats and the flowers, the constrictions of the pods, the yellow colour of the unripe pod, of the stalk, of the calyx, and of the leaf venation, the umbel-like form of the inflorescence, and the dwarfed stem, all reappear in the numerical proportion given, without any essential alteration. *Transitional forms were not observed in any experiment.*

Since the hybrids resulting from reciprocal crosses are formed alike and present no appreciable difference in their subsequent development, consequently the results [of the reciprocal crosses] can be reckoned together in each experiment. The relative numbers which were obtained for each pair of differentiating characters are as follows:

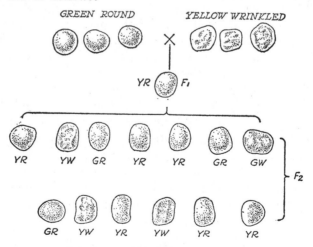

Inheritance of Seed Characters in Pea

The seed of a green round variety fertilized by pollen of a yellow wrinkled variety are yellow and round (F_1). The reciprocal cross would give the same result. Two pods of F_2 seed borne by the F_1 plant are shown. There were 6 yellow round, 3 green round, 3 yellow wrinkled, 1 green wrinkled.

Expt. 1. Form of seed.—From 253 hybrids 7,324 seeds were obtained in the second trial year. Among them were 5,474 round or roundish ones and 1,850 angular wrinkled ones. Therefrom the ratio 2.96 to 1 is deduced.

Expt. 2. Colour of albumen.—258 plants yielded 8,023 seeds, 6,022 yellow, and 2,001 green; their ratio, therefore, is as 3.01 to 1.

In these two experiments each pod yielded usually both kinds of seed. In well-developed pods which contained on the average six to nine seeds, it often happened that all the seeds were round (Expt. 1) or all yellow (Expt. 2); on the other hand there were never observed more than five wrinkled or five green ones in one pod. It appears to make no difference whether the pods are developed early or later in the hybrid or whether they spring from the main axis or from a lateral one. In some few plants only a few seeds developed in the first formed pods, and these possessed exclusively one of the two characters, but in the subsequently developed pods the normal proportions were maintained nevertheless.

These two experiments are important for the determination of the average ratios, because with a smaller number of experimental plants they show that very considerable fluctuations may occur. In counting the seeds, also, especially in Expt. 2, some care is requisite, since in some of the seeds of many plants the green colour of the albumen is less developed, and at first may be easily overlooked. The cause of this partial disappearance of the green colouring has no connection with the hybrid character of the plants, as it likewise occurs in the parental variety. This peculiarity [bleaching] is also confined to the individual and is not inherited by the offspring. In luxuriant plants this appearance was frequently noted. Seeds which are damaged by insects during their development often vary in colour and form, but, with a little practice in sorting, errors are easily avoided. It is almost superfluous to mention that the pods must remain on the plants until they are thoroughly ripened and have become dried, since it is only then that the shape and colour of the seed are fully developed.

Expt. 3. Colour of the seed coats.—Among 929 plants 705 bore violet-red flowers and grey-brown seed coats; 224 had white flowers and white seed coats, giving the proportion 3.15 to 1.

Expt. 4. Form of pods.—Of 1,181 plants 882 had them simply inflated, and in 299 they were constricted. Resulting ratio, 2.95 to 1.

Expt. 5. Colour of the unripe pods.—The number of trial plants was 580, of which 428 had green pods and 152 yellow ones. Consequently these stand in the ratio 2.82 to 1.

Expt. 6. Position of flowers.—Among 858 cases 651 had inflorescences axial and 207 terminal. Ratio, 3.14 to 1.

Expt. 7. Length of stem.—Out of 1,064 plants, in 787 cases the stem was long, and in 277 short. Hence a mutual ratio of 2.84 to 1. In this experiment the dwarfed plants were carefully lifted and transferred to a special bed. This precaution was necessary, as otherwise they would have perished through being overgrown by their tall relatives. Even in their quite young state they can be easily picked out by their compact growth and thick dark-green foliage.

If now the results of the whole of the experiments be brought together, there is found, as between the number of forms with the dominant and recessive characters, an average ratio of 2.98 to 1, or 3 to 1.

The dominant character can have here a *double signification* —viz. that of a parental character, or a hybrid character. In which of the two significations it appears in each separate case can only be determined by the following generation. As a parental character it must pass over unchanged to the whole of the offspring; as a hybrid character, on the other hand, it must maintain the same behaviour as in the first generation [F_2].

[F_3] THE SECOND GENERATION [BRED] FROM THE HYBRIDS

Those forms which in the first generation [F_2] exhibit the recessive character do not further vary in the second generation

[F_3] as regards this character; they remain constant in their offspring.

It is otherwise with those which possess the dominant character in the first generation [bred from the hybrids]. Of these *two* thirds yield offspring which display the dominant and recessive characters in the proportion of 3 to 1, and thereby show exactly the same ratio as the hybrid forms, while only *one* third remains with the dominant character constant.

The separate experiments yielded the following results:

Expt. 1. Among 565 plants which were raised from round seeds of the first generation, 193 yielded round seeds only, and remained therefore constant in this character; 372, however, gave both round and wrinkled seeds, in the proportion of 3 to 1. The number of the hybrids, therefore, as compared with the constants is 1.93 to 1.

Expt. 2. Of 519 plants which were raised from seeds whose albumen was of yellow colour in the first generation, 166 yielded exclusively yellow, while 353 yielded yellow and green seeds in the proportion of 3 to 1. There resulted, therefore, a division into hybrid and constant forms in the proportion of 2.13 to 1.

For each separate trial in the following experiments 100 plants were selected which displayed the dominant character in the first generation, and in order to ascertain the significance of this, ten seeds of each were cultivated.

Expt. 3. The offspring of 36 plants yielded exclusively grey-brown seed coats, while of the offspring of 64 plants some had grey-brown and some had white.

Expt. 4. The offspring of 29 plants had only simply inflated pods; of the offspring of 71, on the other hand, some had inflated and some constricted.

Expt. 5. The offspring of 40 plants had only green pods; of the offspring of 60 plants some had green, some yellow ones.

Expt. 6. The offspring of 33 plants had only axial flowers; of the offspring of 67, on the other hand, some had axial and some terminal flowers.

715

Expt. 7. The offspring of 28 plants inherited the long axis, and those of 72 plants some the long and some the short axis.

In each of these experiments a certain number of the plants came constant with the dominant character. For the determination of the proportion in which the separation of the forms with the constantly persistent character results, the two first experiments are of especial importance, since in these a larger number of plants can be compared. The ratios 1.93 to 1 and 2.13 to 1 gave together almost exactly the average ratio of 2 to 1. The sixth experiment gave a quite concordant result; in the others the ratio varies more or less, as was only to be expected in view of the smaller number of 100 trial plants. Experiment 5, which shows the greatest departure, was repeated, and then, in lieu of the ratio of 60 and 40, that of 65 and 35 resulted. *The average ratio of 2 to 1 appears, therefore, as fixed with certainty.* It is therefore demonstrated that, of those forms which possess the dominant character in the first generation, two thirds have the hybrid character, while one third remains constant with the dominant character.

The ratio of 3 to 1, in accordance with which the distribution of the dominant and recessive characters results in the first generation, resolves itself therefore in all experiments into the ratio of 2 : 1 : 1 if the dominant character be differentiated according to its significance as a hybrid character or as a parental one. Since the members of the first generation [F_2] spring directly from the seed of the hybrids [F_1], *it is now clear that the hybrids form seeds having one or other of the two differentiating characters, and of these one half develop again the hybrid form, while the other half yield plants which remain constant and receive the dominant or the recessive characters [respectively] in equal numbers.*

THE SUBSEQUENT GENERATIONS [BRED] FROM THE HYBRIDS

The proportions in which the descendants of the hybrids develop and split up in the first and second generations presumably hold good for all subsequent progeny. Experiments 1 and 2 have already been carried through six generations, 3 and 7 through five, and 4, 5, and 6 through four, these experiments being continued from the third generation with a small number of plants, and no departure from the rule has been perceptible. The offspring of the hybrids separated in each generation in the ratio of 2 : 1 : 1 into hybrids and constant forms.

If A be taken as denoting one of the two constant characters, for instance the dominant, a, the recessive, and Aa the hybrid form in which both are conjoined, the expression

$$A+2Aa+a$$

shows the terms in the series for the progeny of the hybrids of two differentiating characters.

The observation made by Gärtner, Kölreuter, and others, that hybrids are inclined to revert to the parental forms, is also confirmed by the experiments described. It is seen that the number of the hybrids which arise from one fertilization, as compared with the number of forms which become constant, and their progeny from generation to generation, is continually diminishing, but that nevertheless they could not entirely disappear. If an average equality of fertility in all plants in all generations be assumed, and if, furthermore, each hybrid forms seed of which one half yields hybrids again, while the other half is constant to both characters in equal proportions, the ratio of numbers for the offspring in each generation is seen by the following summary, in which A and a denote again the two parental characters, and Aa the hybrid forms. For brevity's sake it may be assumed that each plant in each generation furnishes only 4 seeds.

				RATIOS				
Generation	A	Aa	a	A	:	Aa	:	a
1	1	2	1	1	:	2	:	1
2	6	2	6	3	:	2	:	3
3	28	8	28	7	:	2	:	7
4	120	16	120	15	:	2	:	15
5	496	32	496	31	:	2	:	32
n				2^n-1	:	2	:	2^n-1

717

In the tenth generation, for instance, $2^n-1=1023$. There result, therefore, in each 2,048 plants which arise in this generation, 1,023 with the constant dominant character, 1,023 with the recessive character, and only two hybrids.

THE OFFSPRING OF HYBRIDS IN WHICH SEVERAL DIFFERENTIATING CHARACTERS ARE ASSOCIATED

In the experiments above described plants were used which differed only in one essential character. The next task consisted in ascertaining whether the law of development discovered in these applied to each pair of differentiating characters when several diverse characters are united in the hybrid by crossing. As regards the form of the hybrids in these cases, the experiments showed throughout that this invariably more nearly approaches to that one of the two parental plants which possesses the greater number of dominant characters. If, for instance, the seed plant has a short stem, and constricted pods; the hybrid resembles the seed parent only in the form of the pod; in the other characters it agrees with the pollen parent. Should one of the two parental types possess only dominant characters, then the hybrid is scarcely or not at all distinguishable from it.

Two experiments were made with a considerable number of plants. In the first experiment the parental plants differed in the form of the seed and in the colour of the albumen; in the second in the form of the seed, in the colour of the albumen, and in the colour of the seed coats. Experiments with seed characters give the result in the simplest and most certain way.

In order to facilitate study of the data in these experiments, the different characters of the seed plant will be indicated by A, B, C, those of the pollen plant by a, b, c, and the hybrid forms of the characters by Aa, Bb, and Cc.

Expt. 1.—AB, seed parents; ab, pollen parents;
          A, form round; a, form wrinkled;
          B, albumen yellow. b, albumen green.

The fertilized seeds appeared round and yellow like those of the seed parents. The plants raised therefrom yielded seeds of four sorts, which frequently presented themselves in one pod. In all, 556 seeds were yielded by 15 plants, and of these there were:

> 315 round and yellow,
> 101 wrinkled and yellow,
> 108 round and green,
> 32 wrinkled and green.

All were sown the following year. Eleven of the round yellow seeds did not yield plants, and three plants did not form seeds. Among the rest:

> 38 had round yellow seeds .... *AB*
> 65 round yellow and green seeds .... *ABb*
> 60 round yellow and wrinkled yellow seeds .... *AaB*
> 138 round yellow and green, wrinkled yellow and
>   green seeds .... *AaBb.*

From the wrinkled yellow seeds 96 resulting plants bore seed, of which:

> 28 had only wrinkled yellow seeds .... *aB*
> 68 wrinkled yellow and green seeds .... *aBb.*

From 108 round green seeds 102 resulting plants fruited, of which:

> 35 had only round green seeds .... *Ab*
> 67 round and wrinkled green seeds .... *Aab.*

The wrinkled green seeds yielded 30 plants which bore seeds all of like character; they remained constant *ab.*

The offspring of the hybrids appeared therefore under nine different forms, some of them in very unequal numbers. When these are collected and co-ordinated we find:

38 plants with the sign *AB*
35   ,,   ,,   ,,   *Ab*
28   ,,   ,,   ,,   *aB*
30   ,,   ,,   ,,   *ab*
65   ,,   ,,   ,,   *ABb*
68   ,,   ,,   ,,   *aBb*
60   ,,   ,,   ,,   *AaB*
67   ,,   ,,   ,,   *Aab*
138   ,,   ,,   ,,   *AaBb.*

The whole of the forms may be classed into three essentially different groups. The first includes those with the signs *AB, Ab, aB,* and *ab:* they possess only constant characters and do not vary again in the next generation. Each of these forms is represented on the average thirty-three times. The second group includes the signs *ABb, aBb, AaB, Aab:* these are constant in one character and hybrid in another, and vary in the next generation only as regards the hybrid character. Each of these appears on an average sixty-five times. The form *AaBb* occurs 138 times: it is hybrid in both characters, and behaves exactly as do the hybrids from which it is derived.

If the numbers in which the forms belonging to these classes appear be compared, the ratios of 1, 2, 4 are unmistakably evident. The numbers 32, 65, 138 present very fair approximations to the ratio numbers of 33, 66, 132.

The developmental series consists, therefore, of nine classes, of which four appear therein always once and are constant in both characters; the forms *AB, ab,* resemble the parental forms, the two others present combinations between the conjoined characters *A, a, B, b,* which combinations are likewise possibly constant. Four classes appear always twice, and are constant in one character and hybrid in the other. One class appears four times, and is hybrid in both characters. Consequently the offspring of the hybrids, if two kinds of differentiating characters are combined therein, are represented by the expression

$$AB+Ab+aB+ab+2ABb+2aBb+2AaB+2Aab+4AaBb.$$

This expression is indisputably a combination series in which the two expressions for the characters A and a, B and b are combined. We arrive at the full number of the classes of the series by the combination of the expressions:

$$A+2Aa+a$$
$$B+2Bb+b.$$

Expt. 2.

ABC, seed parents;	abc, pollen parents;
A, form round;	a, form wrinkled;
B, albumen yellow;	b, albumen green;
C, seed coat grey-brown.	c, seed coat white.

This experiment was made in precisely the same way as the previous one. Among all the experiments it demanded the most time and trouble. From 24 hybrids 687 seeds were obtained in all: these were all either spotted, grey-brown or grey-green, round or wrinkled. From these in the following year 639 plants fruited, and, as further investigation showed, there were among them:

8	plants	ABC	22	plants	$ABCc$	45	plants	$ABbCc$
14	"	ABc	17	"	$AbCc$	36	"	$aBbCc$
9	"	AbC	25	"	$aBCc$	38	"	$AaBCc$
11	"	Abc	20	"	$abCc$	40	"	$AaBCc$
8	"	aBC	15	"	$ABbC$	49	"	$AaBbC$
10	"	aBc	18	"	$ABbc$	48	"	$AaBbc$
10	"	abC	19	"	$aBbC$			
7	"	abc	24	"	$aBbc$			
			14	"	$AaBC$	78	"	$AaBbCc$
			18	"	$AaBc$			
			20	"	$AabC$			
			16	"	$Aabc$			

The whole expression contains 27 terms. Of these 8 are constant in all characters, and each appears on the average 10 times;

12 are constant in two characters and hybrid in the third; each appears on the average 19 times; 6 are constant in one character and hybrid in the other two; each appears on the average 43 times. One form appears 78 times and is hybrid in all of the characters. The ratios 10, 19, 43, 78 agree so closely with the ratios 10, 20, 40, 80, or 1, 2, 4, 8, that this last undoubtedly represents the true value.

The development of the hybrids when the original parents differ in three characters results therefore according to the following expression:

$$ABC + ABc + AbC + Abc + aBC + aBc + abC + abc + 2ABCc$$
$$+ 2AbCc + 2aBCc + 2abCc + 2ABbC + 2ABbc + 2aBbC +$$
$$2aBbc + 2AaBC + 2AaBc + 2AabC + 2Aabc + 4ABbCc +$$
$$+ 4AaBCc + 4AabCc + 4AaBbC + 4AaBbc + 8AaBbCc.$$

Here also is involved a combination series in which the expressions for the characters A and a, B and b, C and c, are united. The expressions give all the classes of the series. The constant

$$A+2Aa+a$$
$$B+2Bb+b$$
$$C+2Cc+c$$

combinations which occur therein agree with all combinations which are possible between the characters A, B, C, a, b, c; two thereof, ABC and abc, resemble the two original parental stocks.

In addition, further experiments were made with a smaller number of experimental plants in which the remaining characters by twos and threes were united as hybrids: all yielded approximately the same results. There is therefore no doubt that for the whole of the characters involved in the experiments the principle applies that *the offspring of the hybrids in which several essentially different characters are combined exhibit the terms of a series of combinations, in which the developmental series for each pair of differentiating characters are united.* It is demonstrated at the same time that *the relation of each pair of different char-*

acters in hybrid union is independent of the other differences in the two original parental stocks.

If n represent the number of the differentiating characters in the two original stocks, 3^n gives the number of terms of the combination series, 4^n the number of individuals which belong to the series, and 2^n the number of unions which remain constant. The series therefore contains, if the original stocks differ in four characters, $3^4=81$ classes, $4^4=256$ individuals, and $2^4=16$ constant forms; or, which is the same, among each 256 offspring of the hybrids there are 81 different combinations, 16 of which are constant.

All constant combinations which in Peas are possible by the combination of the said seven differentiating characters were actually obtained by repeated crossing. Their number is given by $2^7=128$. Thereby is simultaneously given the practical proof *that the constant characters which appear in the several varieties of a group of plants may be obtained in all the associations which are possible according to the [mathematical] laws of combination, by means of repeated artificial fertilization.*

If we endeavour to collate in a brief form the results arrived at, we find that those differentiating characters, which admit of easy and certain recognition in the experimental plants, all behave exactly alike in their hybrid associations. The offspring of the hybrids of each pair of differentiating characters are, one half, hybrid again, while the other half are constant in equal proportions having the characters of the seed and pollen parents respectively. If several differentiating characters are combined by cross-fertilization in a hybrid, the resulting offspring form the terms of a combination series in which the combination series for each pair of differentiating characters are united.

The uniformity of behaviour shown by the whole of the characters submitted to experiment permits, and fully justifies, the acceptance of the principle that a similar relation exists in the other characters which appear less sharply defined in plants, and therefore could not be included in the separate experiments. An experiment with peduncles of different lengths gave on the whole a fairly satisfactory result, although the differentiation and serial arrangement of the forms could not be effected with that certainty which is indispensable for correct experiment.

THE REPRODUCTIVE CELLS OF THE HYBRIDS

The results of the previously described experiments led to further experiments, the results of which appear fitted to afford some conclusions as regards the composition of the egg and pollen cells of hybrids. An important clue is afforded in *Pisum* by the circumstance that among the progeny of the hybrids constant forms appear, and that this occurs, too, in respect of all combinations of the associated characters. So far as experience goes, we find it in every case confirmed that constant progeny can only be formed when the egg cells and the fertilizing pollen are of like character, so that both are provided with the material for creating quite similar individuals, as is the case with the normal fertilization of pure species. We must therefore regard it as certain that exactly similar factors must be at work also in the production of the constant forms in the hybrid plants. Since the various constant forms are produced in *one* plant, or even in *one* flower of a plant, the conclusion appears logical that in the ovaries of the hybrids there are formed as many sorts of egg cells, and in the anthers as many sorts of pollen cells, as there are possible constant combination forms, and that these egg and pollen cells agree in their internal composition with those of the separate forms.

In point of fact it is possible to demonstrate theoretically that this hypothesis would fully suffice to account for the development of the hybrids in the separate generations, if we might at the same time assume that the various kinds of egg and pollen cells were formed in the hybrids on the average in equal numbers.

In order to bring these assumptions to an experimental proof, the following experiments were designed. Two forms which were constantly different in the form of the seed and the colour of the albumen were united by fertilization.

If the differentiating characters are again indicated as *A*, *B*, *a*, *b*, we have:

AB, seed parent;	*ab*, pollen parent;
A, form round;	*a*, form wrinkled;
B, albumen yellow.	*b*, albumen green.

The artificially fertilized seeds were sown together with several seeds of both original stocks, and the most vigorous examples were chosen for the reciprocal crossing. There were fertilized:

1. The hybrids with the pollen of *AB*.
2. The hybrids   ”   ”   ”   ” *ab*.
3. *AB*   ”   ”   ”   ” the hybrids.
4. *ab*   ”   ”   ”   ” the hybrids.

For each of these four experiments the whole of the flowers on three plants were fertilized. If the above theory be correct, there must be developed on the hybrids egg and pollen cells of the forms *AB*, *Ab*, *aB*, *ab*, and there would be combined:

1. The egg cells *AB*, *Ab*, *aB*, *ab* with the pollen cells *AB*.
2. The egg cells *AB*, *Ab*, *aB*, *ab* with the pollen cells *ab*.
3. The egg cells *AB* with the pollen cells *AB*, *Ab*, *aB*, *ab*.
4. The egg cells *ab* with the pollen cells *AB*, *Ab*, *aB*, *ab*.

From each of these experiments there could then result only the following forms:

1. *AB*, *ABb*, *AaB*, *AaBb*.
2. *AaBb*, *Aab*, *aBb*, *ab*.
3. *AB*, *ABb*, *AaB*, *AaBb*.
4. *AaBb*, *Aab*, *aBb*, *ab*.

If, furthermore, the several forms of the egg and pollen cells of the hybrids were produced on an average in equal numbers, then in each experiment the said four combinations should stand in the same ratio to each other. A perfect agreement in the numerical relations was, however, not to be expected, since in each fertilization, even in normal cases, some egg cells remain undeveloped or subsequently die, and many even of the well-formed seeds fail to germinate when sown. The above assumption is also limited in so far that, while it demands the formation of an equal number of the various sorts of egg and pollen cells, it does not require that this should apply to each separate hybrid with mathematical exactness.

The first and second experiments had primarily the object of proving the composition of the hybrid egg cells, while the third and fourth experiments were to decide that of the pollen cells. As is shown by the above demonstration, the first and third experiments and the second and fourth experiments should produce precisely the same combinations, and even in the second year the result should be partially visible in the form and colour of the artificially fertilized seed. In the first and third experiments the dominant characters of form and colour, *A* and *B*, appear in each union, and are also partly constant and partly in hybrid union with the recessive characters *a* and *b*, for which reason they must impress their peculiarity upon the whole of the seeds. All seeds should therefore appear round and yellow, if the theory be justified. In the second and fourth experiments, on the other hand, one union is hybrid in form and in colour, and consequently the seeds are round and yellow; another is hybrid in form, but constant in the recessive character of colour, whence the seeds are round and green; the third is constant in the recessive character of form but hybrid in colour, consequently the seeds are wrinkled and yellow; the fourth is constant in both recessive characters, so that the seeds are wrinkled and green. In both these experiments there were consequently four sorts of seed to be expected—viz. round and yellow, round and green, wrinkled and yellow, wrinkled and green.

The crop fulfilled these expectations perfectly. There were obtained in the

1st Experiment, 98 exclusively round yellow seeds;
3rd　　 ”　　 94　　 ”　　 ”　　 ”　　 ”

In the 2nd Experiment, 31 round and yellow, 26 round and green, 27 wrinkled and yellow, 26 wrinkled and green seeds.

In the 4th Experiment, 24 round and yellow, 25 round and green, 22 wrinkled and yellow, 27 wrinkled and green seeds.

There could scarcely be now any doubt of the success of the experiment; the next generation must afford the final proof. From the seed sown there resulted for the first experiment 90 plants, and for the third 87 plants which fruited: these yielded for the

1st Exp.	3rd Exp.		
20	25	round yellow seeds....................	AB
23	19	round yellow and green seeds...........	ABb
25	22	round and wrinkled yellow seeds........	AaB
22	21	round and wrinkled green and yellow seeds	$AaBb$

In the second and fourth experiments the round and yellow seeds yielded plants with round and wrinkled yellow and green seeds, $AaBb$.

From the round green seeds plants resulted with round and wrinkled green seeds, Aab.

The wrinkled yellow seeds gave plants with wrinkled yellow and green seeds, aBb.

From the wrinkled green seeds plants were raised which yielded again only wrinkled and green seeds, ab.

Although in these two experiments likewise some seeds did not germinate, the figures arrived at already in the previous year were not affected thereby, since each kind of seed gave plants which, as regards their seed, were like each other and different from the others. There resulted therefore from the

2nd Exp.	4th Exp.					
31	24	plants of the form				$AaBb$
26	25	"	"	"	"	AaB
27	22	"	"	"	"	aBb
26	27	"	"	"	"	ab

In all the experiments, therefore, there appeared all the forms which the proposed theory demands, and they came in nearly equal numbers.

In a further experiment the characters of flower colour and length of stem were experimented upon, and selection was so made that in the third year of the experiment each character ought to appear in half of all the plants if the above theory were correct. *A, B, a, b* serve again as indicating the various characters.

A, violet-red flowers.	*a*, white flowers.
B, axis long.	*b*, axis short.

There subsequently appeared

The violet-red flower-colour	(*Aa*)	in	85	plants.
” white ” ”	(*a*)	in	81	”
” long stem	(*Bb*)	in	87	”
” short ”	(*b*)	in	79	”

The theory adduced is therefore satisfactorily confirmed in this experiment also.

For the characters of form of pod, colour of pod, and position of flowers experiments were also made on a small scale, and results obtained in perfect agreement. All combinations which were possible through the union of the differentiating characters duly appeared, and in nearly equal numbers.

Experimentally, therefore, the theory is confirmed that *the pea hybrids form egg and pollen cells which, in their constitution, represent in equal numbers all constant forms which result from the combination of the characters united in fertilization.*

The difference of the forms among the progeny of the hybrids, as well as the respective ratios of the numbers in which they are observed, find a sufficient explanation in the principle above deduced. The simplest case is afforded by the developmental series of each pair of differentiating characters. This series is represented by the expression $A+2Aa+a$, in which A and a signify

728

the forms with constant differentiating characters, and Aa the hybrid form of both. It includes in three different classes four individuals. In the formation of these, pollen and egg cells of the form A and a take part on the average equally in the fertilization; hence each form [occurs] twice, since four individuals are formed. There participate consequently in the fertilization

The pollen cells $A+A+a+a$
The egg cells $A+A+a+a.$

It remains, therefore, purely a matter of chance which of the two sorts of pollen will become united with each separate egg cell. According, however, to the law of probability, it will always happen, on the average of many cases, that each pollen form A and a, consequently one of the two pollen cells A in the fertilization will meet with the egg cell A and the other with an egg cell a, and so likewise one pollen cell a will unite with an egg cell A, and the other with egg cell a.

The result of the fertilization may be made clear by putting the signs for the conjoined egg and pollen cells in the form of fractions, those for the pollen cells above and those for the egg cells below the line. We then have

$$\frac{A}{A}+\frac{A}{a}+\frac{a}{A}+\frac{a}{a}.$$

In the first and fourth term the egg and pollen cells are of like kind, consequently the product of their union must be constant, viz. A and a; in the second and third, on the other hand, there again results a union of the two differentiating characters of the stocks, consequently the forms resulting from these fertilizations are identical with those of the hybrid from which they sprang. *There occurs accordingly a repeated hybridization.* This explains the striking fact that the hybrids are able to produce, besides the two parental forms, offspring which are like themselves; — and — both give the same union Aa, since, as already

$$\frac{A}{a} \quad \frac{a}{A}$$

remarked above, it makes no difference in the result of fertilization to which of the two characters the pollen or egg cells belong. We may write then

$$\frac{A}{A} + \frac{A}{a} + \frac{a}{A} + \frac{a}{a} = A + 2Aa + a.$$

This represents the average result of the self-fertilization of the hybrids when two differentiating characters are united in them. In individual flowers and in individual plants, however, the ratios in which the forms of the series are produced may suffer not inconsiderable fluctuations. Apart from the fact that the numbers in which both sorts of egg cells occur in the seed vessels can only be regarded as equal on the average, it remains purely a matter of chance which of the two sorts of pollen may fertilize each separate egg cell. For this reason the separate values must necessarily be subject to fluctuations, and there are even extreme cases possible, as were described earlier in connection with the experiments on the form of the seed and the colour of the albumen. The true ratios of the numbers can only be ascertained by an average deduced from the sum of as many single values as possible; the greater the number the more are merely chance effects eliminated.

The developmental series for hybrids in which two kinds of differentiating characters are united contains among sixteen individuals nine different forms, viz.:

$$AB + Ab + aB + ab + 2ABb + 2aBb + 2AaB + 2Aab + 4AaBb.$$

Between the differentiating characters of the original stocks Aa and Bb four constant combinations are possible, and consequently the hybrids produce the corresponding four forms of egg and pollen cells AB, Ab, aB, ab, and each of these will on the average figure four times in the fertilization, since sixteen individuals are included in the series. Therefore the participators in the fertilization are

Pollen cells $AB+AB+AB+AB+Ab+Ab+Ab+Ab+aB+aB+aB+$ $aB+ab+ab+ab+ab$.

Egg cells $AB+AB+AB+AB+Ab+Ab+Ab+Ab+aB+aB+aB+$ $aB+ab+ab+ab+ab$.

In the process of fertilization each pollen form unites on an average equally often with each egg cell form, so that each of the four pollen cells AB unites once with one of the forms of egg cell AB, Ab, aB, ab. In precisely the same way the rest of the pollen cells of the forms Ab, aB, ab unite with all the other egg cells. We obtain therefore

$$AB + ABb + AaB + AaBb + ABb + Ab + AaBb + Aab + AaB$$
$$+ AaBb + aB + aBb + AaBb + Aab + aBb + ab = AB + Ab+$$
$$aB + ab + 2ABb + 2aBb + 2AaB + 2Aab + 4AaBb.$$

In precisely similar fashion is the developmental series of hybrids exhibited when three kinds of differentiating characters are conjoined in them. The hybrids form eight various kinds of egg and pollen cells—ABC, ABc, AbC, Abc, aBC, aBc, abC, abc— and each pollen form unites itself again on the average once with each form of egg cell.

The law of combination of different characters which governs the development of the hybrids finds therefore its foundation and explanation in the principle enunciated, that the hybrids produce egg cells and pollen cells which in equal numbers represent all constant forms which result from the combinations of the characters brought together in fertilization.

CONCLUDING REMARKS

It can hardly fail to be of interest to compare the observations made regarding *Pisum* with the results arrived at by the two authorities in this branch of knowledge, Kölreuter and Gärtner, in their investigations. According to the opinion of both, the hybrids in outward appearance present either a form intermediate between the original species or they closely resemble either the one or the other type, and sometimes can hardly be discriminated from it. From their seeds usually arise, if the fertilization was effected by their own pollen, various forms which differ from the normal type. As a rule, the majority of individuals obtained by one fertilization maintain the hybrid form, while some few others come more like the seed parent, and one or other individual approaches the pollen parent. This, however, is not the case with all hybrids without exception. Sometimes the offspring have more nearly approached, some the one and some the other of the two original stocks, or they all incline more to one or the other side; while in other cases *they remain perfectly like the hybrid* and continue constant in their offspring. The hybrids of varieties behave like hybrids of species, but they possess greater variability of form and a more pronounced tendency to revert to the original types.

With regard to the form of the hybrids and their development, as a rule an agreement with the observations made in *Pisum* is unmistakable. It is otherwise with the exceptional cases cited. Gärtner confesses even that the exact determination whether a form bears a greater resemblance to one or to the other of the two original species often involved great difficulty, so much depending upon the subjective point of view of the observer. Another circumstance could, however, contribute to render the results fluctuating and uncertain, despite the most careful observation and differentiation. For the experiments plants were mostly used which rank as good species and are differentiated by a large number of characters. In addition to the sharply defined characters, where it is a question of greater or less similarity, those characters must also be taken into account which are often difficult to define in words, but yet suffice, as every plant specialist knows, to give the forms a peculiar appearance. If it be accepted that the development of hybrids follows the law which is valid for *Pisum,* the series in each separate experiment must contain very many forms, since the number of the terms, as is known, increases with the number of the differentiating characters as the powers of three. With a relatively small number of experimental plants the result therefore could only be approximately right, and in single cases might fluctuate considerably. If, for instance, the two original stocks differ in seven characters, and 100 and 200 plants were raised from the seeds of their hybrids to determine the grade of relationship of the offspring, we can easily see how uncertain the decision must become, since for seven differentiating characters the combination series contains 16,384 individuals under 2187 various forms; now one and then another relationship could assert its predominance, just according as chance presented this or that form to the observer in a majority of cases.

If, furthermore, there appear among the differentiating characters at the same time *dominant* characters, which are transmitted entire or nearly unchanged to the hybrids, then in the terms of the developmental series that one of the two original parents which possesses the majority of dominant characters must always be predominant. In the experiment described relative to *Pisum,* in which three kinds of differentiating characters were concerned, all the dominant characters belonged to the seed parent. Although the terms of the series in their internal composition approach both original parents equally, yet in this experiment the type of the seed parent obtained so great a preponderance that out of each sixty-four plants of the first generation fifty-four exactly resembled it, or only differed in one character. It is seen how rash it must be under such circumstances to draw from the external resemblances of hybrids conclusions as to their internal nature.

Gärtner mentions that in those cases where the development was regular, among the offspring of the hybrids the two original species were not reproduced, but only a few individuals which approached them. With very extended developmental series it could not in fact be otherwise. For seven differentiating characters, for instance, among more than 16,000 individuals—offspring of the hybrids—each of the two original species would occur only once. It is therefore hardly possible that these should appear at all among a small number of experimental plants; with some probability, however, we might reckon upon the appearance in the series of a few forms which approach them.

We meet with an *essential difference* in those hybrids which remain constant in their progeny and propagate themselves as truly as the pure species. According to Gärtner, to this class belong the *remarkably fertile hybrids Aquilegia atropurpurea canadensis, Lavatera pseudolbia thuringiaca, Geum urbano-rivale,* and some *Dianthus* hybrids; and, according to Wichura, the hybrids of the Willow family. For the history of the evolution of plants this circumstance is of special importance, since constant hybrids acquire the status of new species. The correctness of the facts is guaranteed by eminent observers, and cannot be doubted. Gärtner had an opportunity of following up *Dianthus Armeria deltoides* to the tenth generation, since it regularly propagated itself in the garden.

With *Pisum* it was shown by experiment that the hybrids form egg and pollen cells of *different* kinds, and that herein lies the reason of the variability of their offspring. In other hybrids, likewise, whose offspring behave similarly we may assume a like cause; for those, on the other hand, which remain constant the assumption appears justifiable that their reproductive cells are all alike and agree with the foundation cell [fertilized ovum] of the hybrid. In the opinion of renowned physiologists, for the purpose of propagation one pollen cell and one egg cell unite in Phanerogams into a single cell, which is capable by assimilation and formation of new cells to become an independent organism. This development follows a constant law, which is founded on the material composition and arrangement of the elements which meet in the cell in a vivifying union. If the reproductive cells be of the same kind and agree with the foundation cell [fertilized ovum] of the mother plant, then the development of the new individual will follow the same law which rules the mother plant. If it chance that an egg cell unites with a *dissimilar* pollen cell, we must then assume that between those elements of both cells, which determine opposite characters, some sort of compromise is effected. The resulting compound cell becomes the foundation of the hybrid organism, the development of which necessarily follows a different scheme from that obtaining in each of the two original species. If the compromise be taken to be a complete one, in the sense, namely, that the hybrid embryo is formed from two similar cells, in which the differences are *entirely and permanently accommodated* together, the further result follows that the hybrids, like any other stable plant species, reproduce themselves truly in their offspring. The reproductive cells which are formed in their seed vessels and anthers are of one kind, and agree with the fundamental compound cell [fertilized ovum].

With regard to those hybrids whose progeny is *variable* we may perhaps assume that between the differentiating elements of the egg and pollen cells there also occurs a compromise, in so far that the formation of a cell as foundation of the hybrid becomes possible; but, nevertheless, the arrangement between the conflicting elements is only temporary and does not endure throughout the life of the hybrid plant. Since in the habit of the plant no changes are perceptible during the whole period of vegetation, we must further assume that it is only possible for the differentiating elements to liberate themselves from the enforced union when the fertilizing cells are developed. In the formation of these cells all existing elements participate in an entirely free and equal arrangement, by which it is only the differentiating ones which mutually separate themselves. In this way the production would be rendered possible of as many sorts of egg and pollen cells as there are combinations possible of the formative elements.

The attribution attempted here of the essential difference in the development of hybrids to *a permanent or temporary union* of the differing cell elements can, of course, only claim the value of an hypothesis for which the lack of definite data offers a wide scope. Some justification of the opinion expressed lies in the evidence afforded by *Pisum* that the behaviour of each pair of differentiating characters in hybrid union is independent of the other differences between the two original plants, and, further, that the hybrid produces just so many kinds of egg and pollen cells as there are possible constant combination forms. The differentiating characters of two plants can finally, however, only depend upon differences in the composition and grouping of the elements which exist in the foundation cells [fertilized ova] of the same in vital interaction.

In conclusion, the experiments carried out by Kölreuter, Gärtner, and others with respect to *the transformation of one species into another by artificial fertilization* merit special mention. Particular importance has been attached to these experiments, and Gärtner reckons them among "the most difficult of all in hybridization."

If a species *A* is to be transformed into a species *B*, both must be united by fertilization and the resulting hybrids then be fertilized with the pollen of *B*; then, out of the various offspring resulting, that form would be selected which stood in nearest relation to *B* and once more be fertilized with *B* pollen, and so continuously until finally a form is arrived at which is like *B* and constant in its progeny. By this process the species *A* would change into the species *B*. Gärtner alone has effected thirty such experiments with plants of genera *Aquilegia, Dianthus, Geum, Lavatera, Lychnis, Malva, Nicotiana,* and *Oenothera.* The period of transformation was not alike for all species. While with some a triple fertilization sufficed, with others this had to be repeated five or six times, and even in the same species fluctuations were observed in various experiments. Gärtner ascribes this difference to the circumstance that "the specific [*typische*] power by which a species, during reproduction, effects the change and transformation of the maternal type varies considerably in different plants, and that, consequently, the periods within which the one species is changed into the other must also vary, as also the number of generations, so that the transformation in some species is perfected in more, and in others in fewer generations." Further, the same observer remarks "that in these transformation experiments a good deal depends upon which type and which individual be chosen for further transformation."

If it may be assumed that in these experiments the constitution of the forms resulted in a similar way to that of *Pisum*, the entire process of transformation would find a fairly simple explanation. The hybrid forms as many kinds of egg cells as there are constant combinations possible of the characters conjoined therein, and one of these is always of the same kind as that of the fertilizing pollen cells. Consequently there always exists the possibility with all such experiments that even from the second fertilization there may result a constant form identical with that of the pollen parent. Whether this really be obtained depends in each separate case upon the number of the experimental plants, as well as upon the number of differentiating characters which are united by the fertilization. Let us, for instance, assume that the plants selected for experiment differed in three characters, and the species *ABC* is to be transformed into the other species *abc* by repeated fertilization with the pollen of the latter; the hybrids resulting from the first cross form eight different kinds of egg cells, viz.:

$$ABC, ABc, AbC, aBC, Abc, aBc, abC, abc.$$

These in the second year of experiment are united again with the pollens cells *abc*, and we obtain the series

$$AaBbCc+AaBbc+AabCc+aBbCc+Aabc+aBbc+abCc+abc.$$

Since the form *abc* occurs once in the series of eight terms, it is consequently little likely that it would be missing among the experimental plants, even were these raised in a smaller number, and the transformation would be perfected already by a second fertilization. If by chance it did not appear, then the fertilization must be repeated with one of those forms nearest akin, *Aabc*, *aBbc*, *abCc*. It is perceived that such an experiment must extend the farther *the smaller the number of experimental plants and the larger the number of differentiating characters* in the two original species; and that, furthermore, in the same species there can easily occur a delay of one or even of two generations such as Gärtner observed. The transformation of widely divergent species could generally only be completed in five or six years of experiment, since the number of different egg cells which are formed in the hybrid increases as the power of two with the number of differentiating characters.

DMITRI IVANOVICH MENDELEEV

(1834–1907)

Son of a Siberian teacher, Mendeleev had a difficult time acquiring an education in St. Petersburg, but eventually became a professor there, as well as director of the Bureau of Weights and Measures. His major contribution to science was his statement of the periodic law, a classification of chemical elements which made possible the prediction of elements not yet discovered. His best-known work is the *Principles of Chemistry* (1868, translated 1905).

THE RELATION BETWEEN THE PROPERTIES AND ATOMIC WEIGHTS OF ELEMENTS

. . . In UNDERTAKING to prepare a textbook called "Principles of Chemistry," I wished to establish some sort of system of simple bodies in which their distribution is not guided by chance, as might be thought instinctively, but by some sort of definite and exact principle. We previously saw that there was an almost complete absence of numerical relations for establishing a system of simple bodies, but in the end any system based on numbers which can be determined exactly will deserve preference over other systems which do not have numerical support, since the former leave little room for arbitrary choices. The numerical data for simple bodies are limited at the present time. If for some of them the physical properties are determined with certainty, yet this applies only to a very small number of the elementary bodies. For example, such properties as optical, or even electrical or magnetic, ones, cannot in the end serve as a support for a system because one and the same body can show different values for these properties, depending on the state in which they occur. In this regard, it is enough to recall graphite

739

and diamond, ordinary and red phosphorus, and oxygen and ozone. Not only do we not know the density in the vapor state for most of them, by which to determine the weight of the particles of the simple bodies, but this density is subject to alteration exactly like those polymeric alterations which have been noted for complex bodies. Oxygen and sulfur show this effect positively, but the relations between nitrogen, phosphorus, and arsenic offer further confirmation because these similar elements have particle weights of N_2, P_4, and As_4, unequal in the number of atoms among themselves. A number of the properties of the simple bodies must change with these polymeric changes. Thus we cannot be sure that for any element, even for platinum, there may not occur another state, and the location of an element in a system based on its physical properties would then be changed. Besides this, anyone understands that no matter how the properties of a simple body may change in the free state, *something* remains constant, and when the elements form compounds, this *something* has a material value and establishes the characteristics of the compounds which include the given element. In this respect, we know only one constant peculiar to an element, namely, the atomic weight. The size of the atomic weight, by the very essence of the matter, is a number which is not related to the state of division of the simple body but to the material part which is common to the simple body and all its compounds. The atomic weight belongs not to coal or the diamond, but to carbon. The property which Gerhardt and Cannizzaro determined as the atomic weight of the elements is based on such a firm and certain assumption that for most bodies, especially for those simple bodies whose heat capacity in the free state has been determined, there remains no doubt of the atomic weight, such as existed some years ago, when the atomic weights were so often confused with the equivalents and determined on the basis of varied and often contradictory ideas.

This is the reason I have chosen the system on the size of the atomic weights of the elements.

The first attempt which I made in this way was the following: I selected the bodies with the lowest atomic weights and arranged them in the order of the size of their atomic weights. This showed that there existed a period in the properties of the simple bodies, and even in terms of their atomicity the elements followed each other in the order of arithmetic succession of the size of their atoms:

Li=7; Be=9.4; B = 11; C = 12; N = 14; O = 16; F=19
Na = 23; Mg = 24; Al = 27.4; Si = 28; P = 31; S = 32; Cl=35.3
K = 39; Ca = 40;........ Ti = 50; V = 51 ....

In the arrangement of elements with atoms greater than 100, we meet an entirely analogous continuous order:

Ag = 108; Cd = 112; Ur = 116; Sn = 118; Sb = 122; Te = 128; I = 127.

It has been shown that Li, Na, K, and Ag are related to each other, as are C, Si, Ti, Sn, or as are N, P, V, Sb, etc. This at once raises the question whether the properties of the elements are expressed by their atomic weights and whether a system can be based on them. An attempt at such a system follows.

In the assumed system, the atomic weight of the element, unique to it, serves as a basis for determining the place of the element. Comparison of the groups of simple bodies known up to now according to the weights of their atoms leads to the conclusion that the distribution of the elements according to their atomic weights does not disturb the natural similarities which exist between the elements but, on the contrary, shows them directly. . . .

All the comparisons which I have made in this direction lead me to conclude that *the size of the atomic weight determines the nature of the elements,* just as the weight of the molecules determines the properties and many of the reactions of complex bodies. If this conclusion is confirmed by further applications of this approach to the study of the elements, then we are near an epoch in understanding the existing differences and the reasons for the similarity of elementary bodies.

I think that the law established by me does not run counter to the general direction of natural science, and that until now it has not been demonstrated, although already there have been hints of it. Henceforth, it seems to me, there will be a new interest in determining atomic weights, in discovering new elementary bodies, and in finding new analogies between them.

I now present one of many possible systems of elements based on their atomic weights. It serves only as an attempt to express those results which can be obtained in this way. I myself see that this attempt is not final, but it seems to me that it clearly expresses the applicability of my assumptions to all combinations of elements whose atoms are known with certainty. In this I have also wished to establish a general system of the elements. Here is this attempt:

			Ti = 50	Zr = 90	? = 180
			V = 51	Nb = 94	Ta = 182
			Cr = 52	Mo = 96	W = 186
			Mn = 55	Rh = 104, 4	Pt = 197, 4
			Fe = 56	Ru = 104, 4	Ir = 198
		Ni = Co = 59	Pd = 106, 6	Os = 199	
H = 1			Cu = 63, 4	Ag = 108	Ilg = 200
	Be = 9, 4	Mg = 24	Zn = 65, 2	Cd = 112	
	B = 11	Al = 27, 4	? = 68	Ur = 116	Au = 197?
	C = 12	Si = 28	? = 70	Sn = 118	
	N = 14	P = 31	As = 75	Sb = 122	Bi = 210?
	O = 16	S = 32	Se = 79, 4	Te = 128?	
	F = 19	Cl = 35, 5	Br = 80	J = 127	
Li = 7	Na = 23	K = 39	Rb = 85, 4	Cs = 133	Tl = 204
		Ca = 40	Sr = 87, 6	Ba = 137	Pb = 207
		? = 45	Ce = 92		
		?Er = 56	La = 94		
		?Yt = 60	Di = 95		
		?In = 75, 6	Th = 118?		

Periodic table according to D. I. Mendeleev, 1869.

In conclusion, I consider it advisable to recapitulate the results of the above work.

1. Elements arranged according to the size of their atomic weights show clear *periodic* properties.

2. Elements which are similar in chemical function either have atomic weights which lie close together (like Pt, Ir, Os) or show a uniform increase in atomic weight (like K, Rb, Cs). The uniformity of such an increase in the different groups is taken from previous work. In such comparisons, however, the workers did not make use of the conclusions of Gerhardt, Regnault, Cannizzaro, and others who established the true value of the atomic weights of the elements.

3. Comparisons of the elements or their groups in terms of size of their atomic weights establish their so-called "atomicity" and, to some extent, differences in chemical character, a fact which is clearly evident in the group Li, Be, B, C, N, O, F, and is repeated in the other groups.

4. The simple bodies which are most widely distributed in nature have small atomic weights, and all the elements which have small atomic weights are characterized by the specificity of their properties. They are therefore the typical elements. Hydrogen, as the lightest element, is in justice chosen as typical of itself.

5. The *size* of the atomic weight determines the character of the element, just as the size of the molecule determines the properties of the complex body, and so, when we study compounds, we should consider not only the properties and amounts of the elements, not only the reactions, but also the weight of the atoms. Thus, for example, compounds of S and Te, Cl and I, etc., although showing resemblances, also very clearly show differences.

6. We should still expect to discover many *unknown* simple bodies; for example, those similar to Al and Si, elements with atomic weights of 65 to 75.

7. Some *analogies* of the elements are discovered from the size of the weights of their atoms. Thus uranium is shown to be analogous to boron and aluminum, a fact which is also justified when their compounds are compared.

The purpose of my paper will be entirely attained if I succeed in turning the attention of investigators to the same relationships in the size of the atomic weights of nonsimilar elements, which have, as far as I know, been almost entirely neglected until now. Assuming that in problems of this nature lies the solution of one of the most important questions of our science, I myself, as my time will permit, will turn to a comparative study of lithium, beryllium, and boron.

. . . And now, in order to clarify the matter further, I wish to draw some conclusions as to the chemical and physical properties of those elements which have not been placed in the system and which are still undiscovered but whose discovery is very probable. I think that until now we have not had any chance to foresee the absence of these or other elements, because we have had no order for their arrangement, and even less have we had occasion to predict the properties of such elements. With the periodic and atomic relations now shown to exist between all the atoms and the properties of their elements, we see the possibility not only of noting the absence of some of them but even of determining, and with great assurance and certainty, the properties of these as yet unknown elements; it is possible to predict their atomic weight, density in the free state or in the form of oxides, acidity or basicity, degree of oxidation, and ability to be reduced and to form double salts and to describe the properties of the metalloorganic compounds and chlorides of the given element; it is even possible also to describe the properties of some compounds of these unknown elements in still greater detail. Although at the present time it is not possible to say when one of these bodies which I have predicted will be discovered, yet the opportunity exists for finally convincing myself and other chemists of the truth of those hypotheses which lie at the base of the system I have drawn up. Personally, for me these assumptions have become so strong that, as in the case of indium, there is justification for the ideas which are based on the periodic law which lies at the base of all this study.

Among the ordinary elements, the *lack* of a number of *analogues of boron and aluminum* is very striking, that is, in group III, and it is certain that we lack an element of this group immediately following aluminum; this must be found in the even, or second, series, immediately after potassium and calcium. Since the atomic weights of these latter are near 40, and since then in this row the element of group IV, titanium, Ti = 50, follows, then the atomic weight of the missing element should be nearly 45. Since this element belongs to an even series, it should have more basic properties than the lower elements of group III, boron or aluminum, that is, its oxide, R_2O_3, should be a stronger base. An indication of this is that the oxide of titanium, TiO_2, with the properties of a very weak acid, also shows many signs of being clearly basic. On the basis of these properties of titanium dioxide; compared to aluminum, this oxide should have a more strongly basic character, and therefore, probably, it should not decompose water, and it should combine with acids and alkalis to form simple salts; ammonia will not dissolve it, but perhaps the hydrate will dissolve weakly in potassium hydroxide, although the latter is doubtful, because the element belongs to the even series and to a group of elements whose oxides contain a small amount of oxygen. I have decided to give this element the preliminary name of *ekaboron*, deriving the name from this, that it follows boron as the first element of the even group, and the syllable *eka* comes from the Sanskrit word meaning "one." Eb = 45. Ekaboron should be a metal with an atomic volume of about 15, because in the elements of the second series, and in all the series, the atomic volume falls quickly as we go from the first group to the following ones. Actually, the volume of potassium is nearly 50, calcium nearly 25, titanium and vanadium nearly 9, and chromium, molybdenum, and iron nearly 7; thus the specific gravity of the metal should be close to 3.0, since its atomic weight = 45. The metal will be nonvolatile, because all the metals in the even series of all the groups (except group I) are nonvolatile; hence it can hardly be discovered by the ordinary method of spectrum analysis. It should not decompose water at ordinary temperature, but at somewhat raised temperatures it should decompose it, as do many other metals of this series which form basic oxides. Finally, it will dissolve in acids. Its chloride $EbCl_3$ (perhaps Eb_2Cl_6), should be a volatile substance but a salt, since it corresponds to a basic oxide. Water will act on it as it does on the chlorides of calcium and magnesium, that is, ekaboron chloride will be a hygroscopic body and will be able to evolve hydrogen chloride without having the character of a hydrochloride. Since the volume of calcium chloride $= 49$ and that of titanium chloride $= 109$, the volume of ekaboron chloride should be close to 78, and therefore its specific gravity will probably be about 2.0. Ekaboron oxide, Eb_2O_3, should be a nonvolatile substance and probably should not fuse; it should be insoluble in water, because even calcium oxide is very lightly soluble in water, but it will probably dissolve in acid. Its specific volume should be about 39, because in the series potassium oxide has a volume of 35, $CaO = 18$, $TiO = 20$, and $CrO_3 = 36$; that is, considered on the basis of a content of one atom of oxygen, the volume quickly falls to the right, thus, for potassium $= 35$, for calcium $= 18$, for titanium $= 10$, for chromium $= 12$; and therefore the volume for ekaboron oxide containing one atom of oxygen should be nearly 13, and so the formula Eb_2O_3 should correspond to a volume of about 39, and therefore anhydrous ekaboron oxide will have a specific gravity close to 3.5. Since it is a sufficiently strong base, this oxide should show little tendency to form alums, although it will probably give alum-forming compounds, that is, double salts with potassium sulfate. Finally, ekaboron will not form metalloorganic compounds, since it is one of the metals of an even series. Judging by the data now known for the elements which accompany cerium, none of them belong in the place which is assigned to ekaboron, so that this metal is certainly not one of the members of the cerium complex which is now known.

THOMAS HUNT MORGAN

(1866–1945)

The science of genetics, begun with Mendel's cultivation of garden peas and continued with De Vries' work on rosebushes, came to maturity with Morgan's laboratory experiments with the fruit fly. Professor of biology at Bryn Mawr, Columbia and the California Institute of Technology, he received the Nobel prize for medicine in 1933 for his discoveries about genes and chromosomes, the carriers of inheritable characteristics. His important works include: *A Critique of the Theory of Evolution* (1916), *The Physical Bases of Heredity* (1919), *The Theory of the Gene* (1926), and *Embryology and Genetics* (1933).

A CRITIQUE OF THE THEORY OF EVOLUTION

WHY DO BIOLOGISTS throughout the world today agree that Mendel's discovery is one of first rank?

A great deal might be said in this connection. What is essential may be said in a few words. Biology had been, and is still, largely a descriptive and speculative science. Mendel showed by experimental proof that heredity could be explained by a simple mechanism. His discovery has been exceedingly fruitful.

Science begins with naïve, often mystic conceptions of its problems. It reaches its goal whenever it can replace its early guessing by verifiable hypotheses and predictable results. This is what Mendel's law did for heredity. . . .

Within the last five or six years, from a common wild species of fly, the fruit fly, *Drosophila ampelophila*, which we have brought into the laboratory, have arisen over a hundred and twenty-five new types whose origin is completely known. Let me call attention to a few of the more interesting of these types and their modes of inheritance, comparing them with wild types in order to show that the kinds of inheritance found in domesticated races occur also in wild types. The results will show beyond dispute that the characters of wild types are inherited in precisely the same way as are the characters of the mutant types—a fact that is not generally appreciated except by students of genetics, although it is of the most far-reaching significance for the theory of evolution.

A mutant appeared in which the eye color of the female was different from that of the male. The eye color of the mutant female is a dark eosin color, that of the male yellowish eosin. From the beginning this difference was as marked as it is today. Breeding experiments show that eosin eye color differs from the red color of the eye of the wild fly by a single mutant factor. Here then at a single step a type appeared that was sexually dimorphic.

Zoologists know that sexual dimorphism is not uncommon in wild species of animals, and Darwin proposed the theory of sexual selection to account for the difference between the sexes. He assumed that the male preferred certain kinds of females differing from himself in a particular character, and thus in time through sexual selection the sexes came to differ from each other. . . .

THE FACTUAL THEORY OF HEREDITY AND THE COMPOSITION OF THE GERM PLASM

The discovery that Mendel made with edible peas concerning heredity has been found to apply everywhere throughout the plant and animal kingdoms—to flowering plants, to insects, snails, crustacea, fishes, amphibians, birds, and mammals (including man).

There must be something that these widely separated groups of plants and animals have in common—some simple mechanism perhaps—to give such definite and orderly series of results. There is, in fact, a mechanism, possessed alike by animals and plants, that fulfills every requirement of Mendel's principles.

THOMAS HUNT MORGAN

THE CELLULAR BASIS OF ORGANIC EVOLUTION AND HEREDITY

In order to appreciate the full force of the evidence, let me first pass rapidly in review a few familiar historical facts that preceded the discovery of the mechanism in question.

Throughout the greater part of the last century, while students of evolution and of heredity were engaged in what I may call the more general, or, shall I say, the grosser aspects of the subject, there existed another group of students who were engaged in working out the minute structure of the material basis of the living organism. They found that organs such as the brain, the liver, the lungs, the kidneys, et cetera, are not themselves the units of structure, but that all these organs can be reduced to a simpler unit that repeats itself a thousandfold in every organ. We call this unit a cell.

The egg is a cell, and the spermatozoon is a cell. The act of fertilization is the union of two cells. Simple as the process of fertilization appears to us today, its discovery swept aside a vast amount of mystical speculation concerning the role of the male and of the female in the act of procreation.

Within the cell a new microcosm was revealed. Every cell was found to contain a spherical body called the nucleus. Within the the nucleus is a network of fibers, a sap fills the interstices of the network. The network resolves itself into a definite number of threads at each division of the cell. These threads we call chromosomes. Each species of animals and plants possesses a characteristic number of these threads which have a definite size and sometimes a specific shape and even characteristic granules at different levels. Beyond this point our strongest microscopes fail to penetrate. Observation has reached, for the time being, its limit.

The story is taken up at this point by a new set of students who have worked in an entirely different field. Certain observations and experiments that we have not time to consider now led a number of biologists to conclude that the chromosomes are the bearers of the hereditary units. If so, there should be many such units carried by *each* chromosome, for the number of chromosomes is limited while the number of independently inherited characters is large. In *Drosophila* it has been demonstrated not only that there are exactly as many groups of characters that are inherited together as there are pairs of chromosomes, but even that it is possible to locate one of these groups in a particular chromosome and to state the *relative position* there of the factors for the characters. If the validity of this evidence is accepted, the study of the cell leads us finally in a mechanical, but not in a chemical sense, to the ultimate units about which the whole process of the transmission of the hereditary factors centers.

But before plunging into this somewhat technical matter (that is difficult only because it is unfamiliar), certain facts which are familiar for the most part should be recalled, because on these turns the whole of the subsequent story.

The thousands of cells that make up the cell state that we call an animal or plant come from the fertilized egg. An hour or two after fertilization the egg divides into two cells. Then each half divides again. Each quarter next divides. The process continues until a large number of cells is formed and out of these organs mold themselves.

At every division of the cell the chromosomes also divide. Half of these have come from the mother, half from the father. Every cell contains, therefore, the sum total of all the chromosomes, and if these are the bearers of the hereditary qualities, every cell in the body, whatever its function, has a common inheritance.

At an early stage in the development of the animal certain cells are set apart to form the organs of reproduction. In some animals these cells can be identified early in the cleavage.

The reproductive cells are at first like all the other cells in the body in that they contain a full complement of chromosomes, half paternal and half maternal in origin. They divide as do the other cells of the body for a long time. At each division each chromosome splits lengthwise and its halves migrate to opposite poles of the spindle.

But there comes a time when a new process appears in the germ cells. It is essentially the same in the egg and in the sperm

750

cells. The discovery of this process we owe to the laborious researches of many workers in many countries. The list of their
names is long, and I shall not even attempt to repeat it. The
chromosomes come together in pairs. Each maternal chromosome mates with a paternal chromosome of the same kind.

Then follow two rapid divisions. At one of the divisions the
double chromosomes separate so that each resulting cell comes
to contain some maternal and some paternal chromosomes, i.e.,
one or the other member of each pair. At the other division each
chromosome simply splits as in ordinary cell division.

The upshot of the process it that the ripe eggs and the ripe
spermatozoa come to contain only half the total number of chromosomes.

When the eggs are fertilized the whole number of chromosomes is restored again.

The Mechanism of Mendelian Heredity Discovered in the Behavior of the Chromosomes

If the factors in heredity are carried in the chromosomes and
if the chromosomes are definite structures, we should anticipate
that there should be as many *groups* of character as there are
kinds of chromosomes. In only one case has a sufficient number
of characters been studied to show whether there is any correspondence between the number of hereditary groups of characters
and the number of chromosoomes. In the fruit fly, *Drosophila
ampelophila,* we have found about a hundred and twenty-five
characters that are inherited in a perfectly definite way. . . .

If the factors for these characters are carried by the chromosomes, then we should expect that those factors that are carried
by the same chromosomes would be inherited together, provided
the chromosomes are definite structures in the cell.

In the chromosome group of *Drosophila* there are four pairs of
chromosomes, three of nearly the same size and one much smaller.
Not only is there agreement between the number of hereditary
groups and the number of the chromosomes, but even the size

relations are the same, for there are three great groups of characters and three pairs of large chromosomes, and one small group of characters and one pair of small chromosomes. . . .

CONCLUSIONS

I have passed in review a long series of researches as to the nature of the hereditary material. We have in consequence of this work arrived within sight of a result that seemed a few years ago far beyond our reach. The mechanism of heredity has, I think, been discovered—discovered not by a flash of intuition but as the result of patient and careful study of the evidence itself.

With the discovery of this mechanism I venture the opinion that the problem of heredity has been solved. We know how the factors carried by the parents are sorted out to the germ cells. The explanation does not pretend to state how factors arise or how they influence the development of the embryo. But these have never been an integral part of the doctrine of heredity. The problems which they present must be worked out in their own field. So, I repeat, the mechanism of the chromosomes offers a satisfactory solution of the traditional problem of heredity.

HERMANN WALTHER NERNST

(1864–1941)

A German chemist and physicist, Nernst was interested primarily in theories of ions, chemical equilibrium and solutions. He developed a theory of the solution pressure of ions to explain the production of electromotive force in the galvanic cell. He also formulated the principle of the solubility product, to explain the precipitation of salts from saturated solutions by the addition of a common ion. In thermodynamics he formulated the Nernst heat theorem concerning the energy change in a reaction. Nobel prize winner for chemistry in 1921.

ON THE PROCESS OF SOLUTION OF SOLID BODIES

THE FACT that when solid or liquid bodies evaporate, their molecules are forced into a space in which they occur under a definite pressure, the partial pressure of the gas resulting from this process, made it possible to attribute to the evaporating bodies the power of expansion; the pressure under which the gaseous evaporation product is found when equilibrium conditions are attained was called the *vapor pressure* of these bodies.

If, now, in terms of the van't Hoff theory we assume that the molecules of a body in solution are also under a definite pressure, then we must likewise attribute an expansion power to a dissolved substance in contact with the solvent, because here also its molecules are forced into a space in which they are under a certain pressure; obviously, such bodies will go into solution until the osmotic partial pressure of the molecules which results from the process becomes equal to the "solution pressure" of the body.

Accordingly, we have, in evaporation and solution, processes which can be regarded as entirely analogous, as they have been many times; although without knowledge of the osmotic pressure, a sound basis is lacking.

These considerations are so simple and almost self-evident that they lead directly to some far-reaching and noteworthy conclusions which permit a test of the van't Hoff theory from an entirely new standpoint; here, however, they will be considered only for their importance for our immediate purpose.

As we can obviously find for each gas either a solid or a liquid body whose vapor or dissociation pressure agrees with the pressure of this gas, developed either by evaporation or decomposition, so for each molecule occurring in solution or indeed in a freely movable state, that is, for each ion, we must assume the existence of a substance from whose solution molecules of this kind will result. This approaches and perhaps offers the possibility of maintaining the idea just expressed, that of attributing to the metals the power to go into solution as ions. According to this, each metal possesses in water an individual solution pressure whose magnitude can be called P.

We will now consider what happens if we dip a metal with an electrolytic solution pressure P into a solution of a salt formed from this metal in which the ion of the metal exists under a pressure p. First, if $P > p$, then immediately on contact, driven by this pressure, a number of positively charged metallic ions go into solution. Since a certain positive amount of electricity is transported by the latter from the metal into solution, the liquid acquires a positive charge and the positive ions contained in it are arranged in a pattern on its surface; and naturally, a corresponding amount of negative electricity will be free in the metal, which also is arranged on the surface. It can be seen directly that at the place of contact between metal and electrolyte, both electricities must accumulate in the form of a double layer, whose existence had been made known some time ago in another way by Herr v. Helmholtz.

This double layer now gives rise to a component of force which is directed perpendicular to the contact surface of metal and solution and seeks to drive the metallic ion from the electrolyte to the metal, thus working in opposition to the electrolytic solution pressure.

The equilibrium condition will obviously be such that both these forces are present; as a final result we get the appearance of an electromotive force between metal and electrolyte which causes a galvanic current in the direction from metal to liquid if by any sort of an apparatus its occurrence is possible.

If $P < p$ the reverse process naturally occurs; metallic ions are driven from the electrolyte and precipitate on the metal until the electrostatic force of the liquid, resulting here, and the osmotic-pressure excess reach an equilibrium. With this there again appears an electromotive force between metal and electrolyte which here, however, under suitable conditions, will cause a galvanic current in the opposite direction. In both cases, corresponding to the unusually great electrostatic capacity of the ions, the mass of metal which goes into solution or precipitates is very small.

Finally, if $P = p$, there also occurs at the first instant of contact of metal and electrolyte an equilibrium; no potential difference occurs on this between the two. If we formulate these conditions mathematically, we obtain in a new way at once the equations (6) and (7).

$$(6) \quad E = p_0 \, ln \, \frac{p}{P} \qquad\qquad (7) \quad E = 0.860T \, ln \, \frac{p}{P} \times 10^{-4} \, \text{volt}$$

Since P in the nature of things must always have a positive value, it follows that for $p = O$, that is, in pure water, all metals are infinitely strongly charged negatively; this result stands in closest relation to the recent results of Herr v. Helmholtz, according to which for a concentration cell one of whose poles is bathed by pure water, an infinitely strong electromotive force is given which seeks to cause a flowing galvanic current in the cell from one pole to the other. This condition, which forces us to a physically impossible infinite potential difference, naturally means that metals and pure water cannot exist together; this agrees very well with the above argument in which we attribute to all metals the ability to go into solution to form traces of ions.

The analogous method of thinking which we have just established for "electrodes of the first class" is naturally applicable for "electrodes reversible with respect to anions"; instead of the metal, the electronegative ion enters here, and accordingly we have, for example, in the mercury electrode covered with calomel, a dissociation pressure relative to the chloride ion, that is, we must ascribe to it "an electronegative solution pressure." In this way we again get equation (8).

$$(8) \qquad E' = p_0 ln \frac{p}{p'} = 0.860T \, ln \frac{p}{p'} \times 10^{-4} \, \text{volt}$$

Naturally, p', the electronegative solution pressure, always here also has a positive value for pressure; these electrodes may suitably be called "electrodes of the second class."

The method given here for explaining the experimentally established facts of formation of a potential difference between metals and electrolytes is perhaps not so very different from the earlier theories of the origin of the current in a galvanic battery as at first glance appears; but it leads farther than the methods used before inasmuch as it gives simple, formal relations for the questionable potential difference. Whether, for the explanation of this, we attribute to the metals a specific attraction of electricity, as Herr v. Helmholtz does, or, as Herr G. Wiedemann does, we explain the facts by an attractive force between the metals and ions of the electrolyte as actually occurring, or, as I have done here, assume that metals tend to drive their ions into solution through forces analogous to the usual vapor pressure, the explanation is perhaps not so important, if only we admit, as has been done before, that a transport of electricity occurs by contact of metal and electrolyte, producing an equilibrium condition, and that this transport of electricity is inseparably bound up with a transport of material particles. Which sort of forces cause this can to a certain extent be left doubtful for a time; it is much more important first to calculate the work production connected with them. In this matter, I think we are justified in considering it more closely, just as with osmotic pressure we introduce ideas and calculations on the basis of phenomena established by almost certain facts, and here we need not concern ourselves with the question of whether the origin lies in some attractive force between solvent and dissolved body or in the reciprocal relations between the molecules of dissolved bodies. Similarly also, we may venture to use the idea of "electrolytic solution pressure," even if the physical meaning is still somewhat uncertain. I will conclude the discussion of the nature of the forces which drive the ions from the metal into solution with other questions, namely, how does osmotic pressure occur, in what form does the ion remain bound, and finally how the latter is related to its solution. These are not essential and we must content ourselves with showing that the introduction of the electrolytic solution pressure leads to formal relationships which are in agreement with the facts. This will be shown in many ways in the following chapters.

THE RECIPROCAL EFFECT OF THE SOLUBILITY
OF SALTS

. . . 4. We will consider for simplicity a binary electrolyte which is not very soluble in water, as, for example, potassium chlorate. The saturated solution of this substance contains about half a gram-molecule per liter at room temperature and for the most part occurs in the state of free ions K and ClO_3: If then we add either K or ClO_3 ions to this solution, the solubility of potassium chlorate must decrease, and therefore solid salt precipitates. Now we cannot add K or ClO_3 ions alone to the solution, because of their electrical charge, but only along with a negative or positive ion. This we do when we mix a strongly dissociated potassium salt or chlorate with the solution. The negative radical of the first or the positive of the second is without influence, since, as we saw above, indifferent substances do not alter the dissociation tension.

5. I actually observed that when I added some drops of a very concentrated KOH or KCl solution to 10 cubic centimeters of saturated potassium chlorate, in the first case (where the content of the solution could be made much stronger because of the great solubility of KOH) there was an immediate strong separation of $KClO_3$, and in the second case, a separation after a few minutes; the process here is that the concentration and therefore the osmotic partial pressure of the K ion is increased by the addition; the solution pressure of the solid salt $KClO_3$ no longer has the power to hold this increased pressure in equilibrium, the K ion will be forced out of the solution and will precipitate itself on the solid salt, naturally in combination with its equivalent amount of ClO_3 ion, as a solid, because in a solution the opposite ion must always act in an amount electrically equivalent.

The same thing occurs when instead of K ions, ClO_3 ions are added to the solution, and indeed by the addition of a very concentrated $NaClO_3$ solution. Here also a clear crystallization of $KClO_3$ occurred as soon as expected. This experiment was fully analogous to the one in which Horstmann used ammonium carbaminate; in place of the vapor tension we have here the solution tension, in place of the gaseous decomposition product, the ions which occur in solution.

I made an analogous experiment with silver acetate, which at room temperature dissolves to a content of about 0.06 normal, and here also I easily recognized qualitatively the effects demanded by the theory; with addition of either silver nitrate or sodium acetate solid, crystalline AgAc separated. I have followed this case quantitatively in order to test the correctness of the formula which I develop later.

6. The reciprocal effects of solubility of salts have been, up to now, the subject of repeated intensive investigations, without the advancing of any simple law to date. Thus, recently Engel stated that thanks to these intensive investigations no general rule can be established for the action which a chemical compound exerts on the saturated solution of another. We have seen that this may very well be possible, and have therefore proceeded to a proportionally simpler case. The fact that such a rule has re-

mained hidden until now is explained by the fact that up to the present the work has been almost exclusively with easily soluble salts and with correspondingly very concentrated solutions. Since a pressure prevails in these which equals hundreds of atmospheres, the gas laws lose their validity, and therefore naturally simple relations fail. The qualitative character of the phenomenon that the solubility of a salt decreases steadily with the addition of another with a common ion would always be admitted under these conditions, were it not that another complication frequently enters. In the above and in the following considerations it is always assumed that the molecular condition of the solid salt in contact with the saturated solution will not be altered by addition of another salt; if there should be some change in crystal form or crystal water content, or if something should crystallize with the added salt, then, in general, this new solid body would have a new solution pressure for the conditions of which our considerations will permit us no conclusions, but which could be calculated by the introduction of a new constant in the equation. If such a further complication enters, the experimenter can easily distinguish it in the particular case. . . .

8. The formula for use in the above cases is derived directly from the dissociation theory; if we assume that the electrolyte is completely dissociated into its ions, then according to the law of mass action the product of the active masses must be constant and indeed must be equal to the square of the solubility m_0 of the salt without any other additions. If we designate by m the solubility of the salt after addition and by x the added amount (in gram-molecules per liter), then

$$(1) \quad m(m+x) = m_0{}^2$$

ISAAC NEWTON

(1642–1727)

Newton's *Principia,* one of the landmarks in scientific history, was published by Halley in 1687. In this work the English mathematician set forth the theory of universal gravitation, for the first time in history bringing the whole visible world, heaven and earth, into one indivisible unity. The story of the falling apple comes from Voltaire and may or may not be apocryphal. Among Newton's other discoveries was the connection between color and light, though he mistakenly believed that the dispersion of light was proportional to its refraction (*New Theory of Light and Colour,* 1672). His optical researches are summarized in his *Optics* (1704). In mathematics he introduced the binomial theorem, and after his collaboration with Leibniz a celebrated controversy arose as to which was the actual inventor of differential calculus (although probably each developed his own methods independently). Born less than a year after Galileo's death, Newton's work embraced the achievements of such scientists as Copernicus, Tycho and Kepler, and mathematicians from Euclid to Descartes, to bring science across the threshold into the modern era.

PRINCIPIA

OUR DESIGN not respecting arts but philosophy, and our subject not manual but natural powers, we consider those things which relate to gravity, levity, elastic force, the resistance of fluids and the like forces, whether attractive or impulsive; and, therefore, we offer this work as the mathematical principles of philosophy, for all the difficulty of philosophy seems to consist in this—from the phenomena of motions to investigate the forces of nature, and from these forces to demonstrate the other

760

phenomena, and to this end the general propositions in the first and second book are directed. In the third book, we give an example of this in the explication of the system of the world; for by the propositions mathematically demonstrated in the former books, we in the third derive from the celestial phenomena the forces of gravity with which bodies tend to the sun and the several planets. Then from these forces, by other propositions which are also mathematical, we deduce the motions of the planets, the comets, the moon, and the sea.

Upon this subject I had composed the third book in a popular method, that it might be read by many, but afterward, considering that such as had not sufficiently entered into the principles could not easily discern the strength of the consequences, nor lay aside the prejudices to which they had been many years accustomed, therefore, to prevent the disputes which might be raised upon such accounts, I chose to reduce the substance of this book into the form of Propositions (in the mathematical way). So that this third book is composed both "in popular method" and in the form of mathematical propositions. . . .

THE SYSTEM OF THE WORLD

It was the ancient opinion of not a few in the earliest ages of philosophy that the fixed stars stood immovable in the highest parts of the world; that under the fixed stars the planets were carried about the sun; that the earth, as one of the planets, described an annual course about the sun, while, by a diurnal motion, it was in' the meantime revolved about its own axis; and that the sun, as the common fire which served to warm the whole, was fixed in the center of the universe. It was from the Egyptians that the Greeks derived their first, as well as their soundest notions of philosophy. It is not to be denied that Anaxagoras, Democritus and others would have it that the earth possessed the center of the world, but it was agreed on both sides that the motions of the celestial bodies were performed in spaces altogether free and void of resistance. The whim of solid

761

orbs was[1] of later date, introduced by Eudoxus, Calippus and Aristotle, when the ancient philosophy began to decline.

As it was the unavoidable consequence of the hypothesis of solid orbs while it prevailed that the comets must be thrust down below the moon, so no sooner had the late observations of astronomers restored the comets to their ancient places in the higher heavens than these celestial spaces were at once cleared of the encumbrance of solid orbs, which by these observations were broken to pieces and discarded for ever.

Whence it was that the planets came to be retained within any certain bounds in these free spaces, and to be drawn off from the rectilinear courses, which, left to themselves, they should have pursued, into regular revolutions in curvilinear orbits, are questions which we do not know how the ancients explained; and probably it was to give some sort of satisfaction to this difficulty that solid orbs were introduced.

The later philosophers pretend to account for it either by the action of certain vortices, as Kepler and Descartes, or by some other principle of impulse or attraction, for it is most certain that these effects must proceed from the action of some force or other. This we will call by the general name of a centripetal force, as it is a force which is directed to some center; and, as it regards more particularly a body in that center, we call it circum-solar, circum-terrestrial, circum-jovial.

CENTRE-SEEKING FORCES

That by means of centripetal forces the planets may be retained in certain orbits we may easily understand if we consider the motions of projectiles, for a stone projected is by the pressure of its own weight forced out of the rectilinear path, which, by the projection alone, it should have pursued, and made to describe a curve line in the air; and through that crooked way is at last brought down to the ground, and the greater the velocity is with

---

[1] Azure transparent spheres conceived by the ancients to surround the earth one within another, and to carry the heavenly bodies in their revolutions.

which it is projected the further it goes before it falls to earth. We can, therefore, suppose the velocity to be so increased that it would describe an arc of 1, 2, 5, 10, 100, 1,000 miles before it arrived at the earth, till, at last exceeding the limits of the earth, it should pass quite by it without touching it.

And because the celestial motions are scarcely retarded by the little or no resistance of the spaces in which they are performed, to keep up the parity of cases, let us suppose either that there is no air about the earth or, at least, that it is endowed with little or no power of resisting.

And since the areas which by this motion it describes by a radius drawn to the centre of the earth have previously been shown to be proportional to the times in which they are described, its velocity when it returns to the point from which it started will be no less than at first; and, retaining the same velocity, it will describe the same curve over and over by the same law.

But if we now imagine bodies to be projected in the directions of lines parallel to the horizon from greater heights, as from 5, 10, 100, 1,000 or more miles, or, rather, as many semi-diameters of the earth, those bodies according to their different velocity and the different force of gravity in different heights will describe arcs either concentric with the earth or variously eccentric, and go on revolving through the heavens in those trajectories just as the planets do in their orbs.

As when a stone is projected obliquely, the perpetual deflection thereof towards the earth is a proof of its gravitation to the earth no less certain than its direct descent when suffered to fall freely from rest, so the deviation of bodies moving in free spaces from rectilinear paths and perpetual deflection therefrom towards any place, is a sure indication of the existence of some force which from all quarters impels those bodies towards that place.

That there are centripetal forces actually directed to the bodies of the sun, of the earth, and other planets, I thus infer.

The moon revolves about our earth, and by radii drawn to its centre describes areas nearly proportional to the times in which they are described, as is evident from its velocity compared with its apparent diameter; for its motion is slower when its diameter is less (and therefore its distance greater), and its motion is swifter when its diameter is greater.

The revolutions of the satellites of Jupiter about the planet are more regular; for they describe circles concentric with Jupiter by equable motions, as exactly as our senses can distinguish.

And so the satellites of Saturn are revolved about this planet with motions nearly circular and equable, scarcely disturbed by any eccentricity hitherto observed.

That Venus and Mercury are revolved about the sun is demonstrable from their moon-like appearances. And Venus, with a motion almost uniform, describes an orb nearly circular and concentric with the sun. But Mercury, with a more eccentric motion, makes remarkable approaches to the sun and goes off again by turns; but it is always swifter as it is near to the sun, and therefore by a radius drawn to the sun still describes areas proportional to the times.

Lastly, that the earth describes about the sun, or the sun about the earth, by a radius from one to the other, areas exactly proportional to the times is demonstrable from the apparent diameter of the sun compared with its apparent motion.

These are astronomical experiments; from which it follows that there are centripetal forces actually directed to the centres of the earth, of Jupiter, of Saturn, and of the sun.[1]

That these forces decrease in the duplicate proportion of the distances from the centre of every planet appears by Cor. vi., Prop. iv., Book I,[2] for the periodic times of the satellites of

---

[1] Book I., Prop. i. The areas which revolving bodies describe by radii drawn to an immovable centre of force do lie in the same immovable planes and are proportional to the times in which they are described.

Prop. ii. Every body that moves in any curve line described in a plane and by a radius drawn to a point either immovable or moving forward with a uniform rectilinear motion describes about that point areas proportional to the times is urged by a centripetal force direced to that point.

Prop. iii. Every body that, by a radius drawn to another body, howsoever moved, describes areas about that centre proportional to the times is urged by a force compounded out of the centripetal force tending to that other body and of all the accelerative force by which that other body is impelled.

[2] If the periodic times are in the sesquiplicate ratio of the radii, and therefore the velocities reciprocally in the subduplicate ratio of the radii, the centri-

Jupiter are one to another in the sesquiplicate proportion of their distances from the centre of this planet. Cassini assures us that the same proportion is observed in the circum-Saturnal planets. In the circumsolar planets Mercury and Venus, the same proportional holds with great accuracy.

That Mars is revolved about the sun is demonstrated from the phases which it shows and the proportion of its apparent diameters; for from its appearing full near conjunction with the sun and gibbous in its quadratures,[3] it is certain that it travels round the sun. And since its diameter appears about five times greater when in opposition to the sun than when in conjunction therewith, and its distance from the earth is reciprocally as its apparent diameter, that distance will be about five times less when in opposition to than when in conjunction with the sun; but in both cases its distance from the sun will be nearly about the same with the distance which is inferred from its gibbous appearance in the quadratures. And as it encompasses the sun at almost equal distances, but in respect of the earth is very unequally distant, so by radii drawn to the sun it describes areas nearly uniform; but by radii drawn to the earth it is sometimes swift, sometimes stationary, and sometimes retrograde.

That Jupiter in a higher orbit than Mars is likewise revolved about the sun with a motion nearly equable as well in distance as in the areas described, I infer from Mr. Flamsted's observations of the eclipses of the innermost satellite; and the same thing may be concluded of Saturn from his satellite by the observations of Mr. Huyghens and Mr. Halley.

If Jupiter was viewed from the sun it would never appear retrograde or stationary, as it is seen sometimes from the earth, but always to go forward with a motion nearly uniform. And from the very great inequality of its apparent geocentric motion we infer—as it has been previously shown that we may infer—

---

petal forces will be in the duplicate ratio of the radii inversely; and the converse.

[3] *I.e.*, showing convexity when in such a position as that, to an observer on the earth, a line drawn between it and the sun would subtend an angle of 90° or thereabouts.

that the force by which Jupiter is turned out of a rectilinear course and made to revolve in an orbit is not directed to the centre of the earth. And the same argument holds good in Mars and in Saturn. Another centre of these forces is, therefore, to be looked for, about which the areas described by radii intervening may be equable; and that this is the sun, we have proved already in Mars and Saturn nearly, but accurately enough in Jupiter.

The distances of the planets from the sun come out the same whether, with Tycho, we place the earth in the centre of the system, or the sun with Copernicus; and we have already proved that these distances are true in Jupiter. Kepler and Bullialdus have with great care determined the distances of the planets from the sun, and hence it is that their tables agree best with the heavens. And in all the planets, in Jupiter and Mars, in Saturn and the earth, as well as in Venus and Mercury, the cubes of their distances are as the squares of their periodic times; and, therefore, the centripetal circum-solar force throughout all the planetary regions decreases in the duplicate proportion of the distances from the sun. Neglecting those little fractions which may have arisen from insensible errors of observation, we shall always find the said proportion to hold exactly; for the distances of Saturn, Jupiter, Mars, the Earth, Venus, and Mercury from the sun, drawn from the observations of astronomers, are (Kepler) as the numbers 951,000, 519,650, 152,350, 100,000, 70,000, 38,806; or (Bullialdus) as the numbers 954,198, 522,-520, 152,350, 100,000, 72,398, 38,585; and from the periodic times they come out 953,806, 520,116, 152,399, 100,000, 72,333, 38,710. Their distances, according to Kepler and Bullialdus, scarcely differ by any sensible quantity, and where they differ most the differences drawn from the periodic times fall in between them.

EARTH AS A CENTRE

That the circum-terrestrial force likewise decreases in the duplicate proportion of the distances, I infer thus:

The mean distance of the moon from the centre of the earth is, we may assume, sixty semi-diameters of the earth; and its periodic time in respect of the fixed stars 27 days 7 hr. 43 min. Now, it has been shown in a previous book that a body revolved in our air, near the surface of the earth supposed at rest, by means of a centripetal force which should be to the same force at the distance of the moon in the reciprocal duplicate proportion of the distances from the centre of the earth, that is, as 3,600 to 1, would (secluding the resistance of the air) complete a revolution in 1 hr. 24 min. 27 sec.

Suppose the circumference of the earth to be 123,249,600 Paris feet, then the same body deprived of its circular motion and falling by the impulse of the same centripetal force as before would in one second of time describe $15^1/_{12}$ Paris feet. This we infer by a calculus formed upon Prop. xxxvi. ("To determine the times of the descent of a body falling from a given place"), and it agrees with the results of Mr. Huyghens's experiments of pendulums, by which he demonstrated that bodies falling by all the centripetal force with which (of whatever nature it is) they arc impelled near the surface of the earth do in one second of time describe $15^1/_{12}$ Paris feet.

But if the earth is supposed to move, the earth and moon together will be revolved about their common centre of gravity. And the moon (by Prop. lx.) will in the same periodic time, 27 days 7 hr. 43 min., with the same circum-terrestrial force diminished in the duplicate proportion of the distance, describe an orbit whose semi-diameter is to the semi-diameter of the former orbit, that is, to the sixty semi-diameters of the earth, as the sum of both the bodies of the earth and moon to the first of two mean proportionals between this sum and the body of the earth; that is, if we suppose the moon (on account of its mean apparent diameter $31\frac{1}{2}$ min.) to be about $^1/_{42}$ of the earth, as 43 to $\sqrt[3]{42+42^2}$, or as about 128 to 127. And, therefore, the semi-diameter of the orbit—that is, the distance of the centres of the moon and earth—will in this case be $60\frac{1}{2}$ semi-diameters of the earth, almost the same with that assigned by Copernicus; and, therefore, the duplicate proportion of the decrement of the force holds good in this distance. (The action of the sun is here disregarded as inconsiderable.)

This proportion of the decrement of the forces is confirmed from the eccentricity of the planets, and the very slow motion of their apsides; for in no other proportion, it has been established, could the circum-solar planets once in every revolution descend to their least, and once ascend to their greatest distance from the sun, and the places of those distances remain immovable. A small error from the duplicate proportion would produce a motion of the apsides considerable in every revolution, but in many enormous.

THE TIDES

While the planets are thus revolved in orbits about remote centres, in the meantime they make their several rotations about their proper axes: the sun in 26 days, Jupiter in 9 hr. 56 min., Mars in 24⅔ hr., Venus in 23 hr., and in like manner is the moon revolved about its axis in 27 days 7 hr. 43 min.; so that this diurnal motion is equal to the mean motion of the moon in its orbit; upon which account the same face of the moon always respects the centre about which this mean motion is performed —that is, the exterior focus of the moon's orbit nearly.

By reason of the diurnal revolutions of the planets the matter which they contain endeavours to recede from the axis of this motion; and hence the fluid parts, rising higher towards the equator than about the poles, would lay the solid parts about the equator under water if those parts did not rise also; upon which account the planets are something thicker about the equator than about the poles.

And from the diurnal motion and the attractions of the sun and moon our sea ought twice to rise and twice to fall every day, as well lunar as solar. But the two motions which the two luminaries raise will not appear distinguished but will make a certain mixed motion. In the conjunction or opposition of the luminaries their forces will be conjoined and bring on the greatest flood and ebb. In the quadratures the sun will raise the waters which the

768

moon depresseth and depress the waters which the moon raiseth; and from the difference of their forces the smallest of all tides will follow.

But the effects of the luminaries depend upon their distances from the earth, for when they are less distant their effects are greater and when more distant their effects are less, and that in the triplicate proportion of their apparent diameters. Therefore it is that the sun in winter time, being then in its perigee, has a greater effect, whether added to or subtracted from that of the moon, than in the summer season, and every month the moon, while in the perigee raiseth higher tides than at the distance of fifteen days before or after when it is in its apogee.

The fixed stars being at such vast distances from one another, can neither attract each other sensibly nor be attracted by our sun.

COMETS

There are three hypotheses about comets. For some will have it that they are generated and perish as often as they appear and vanish; others that they come from the regions of the fixed stars, and are near by us in their passage through the system of our planets; and, lastly, others that they are bodies perpetually revolving about the sun in very eccentric orbits.

In the first case, the comets, according to their different velocities, will move in conic sections of all sorts; in the second they will describe hyperbolas; and in either of the two will frequent indifferently all quarters of the heavens, as well those about the poles as those towards the ecliptic; in the third their motions will be performed in eclipses very eccentric and very nearly approaching to parabolas. But (if the law of the planets is observed) their orbits will not much decline from the plane of the ecliptic; and, so far as I could hitherto observe, the third case obtains; for the comets do indeed chiefly frequent the zodiac, and scarcely ever attain to a heliocentric latitude of 40 degrees. And that they move in orbits very nearly parabolical, I infer from their velocity; for the velocity with which a parabola is described is everywhere to the velocity with which a comet or planet may be revolved about the sun in a circle at the same distance in the subduplicate ratio of 2 to 1; and, by my computation, the velocity of comets is found to be much about the same. I examined the thing by inferring nearly the velocities from the distances, and the distances both from the parallaxes and the phenomena of the tails, and never found the errors of excess or defect in the velocities greater than what might have arisen from the errors in the distances collected after that manner.

GEORG SIMON OHM

(1787–1854)

As with many another scientist, Ohm's pioneering work in electricity was not immediately recognized, and the German physicist spent most of his life either in retirement or teaching. It was he who discovered the relationship between the intensity of an electrical current and the resistance of a circuit, known as Ohm's law. The unit of electrical resistance is named after him. He also worked on acoustics and crystal interference.

OHM'S LAW

I TURNED to the use of the thermo-electric battery, the suitability of which for my purposes was suggested by Herr Poggendorf; and since the results obtained in this way give the law of conduction in a definite manner, I think it not superfluous to describe my apparatus at length, so that the degree of confidence which can be placed in the results obtained with it can be more easily estimated.

A piece of bismuth was cast in the form of a rectangular brace *abb'a'* (Fig. 1) whose longer side was 6½ inches long, and whose shorter legs *ab*, *a'b'* were each 3½ inches long. It was throughout 9 lines broad and 4 lines thick. On each of the two legs I fastened with two screws copper strips *abcd*, *a'b'c'd'*, which were 9 lines broad, 1 line thick, and together were 28 inches long. These were so bent, that their free ends *cd*, *c'd'* were immersed in mercury contained in two cups *m*, *m'* which stood on the wooden base *fghi*.

On the upper plate of the base was placed the torsion balance, in the description of which I shall be a little diffuse, since its

771

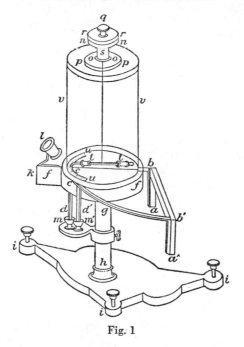

Fig. 1

construction differs somewhat from the ordinary. The glass cylinder *vv*, on which it is set, is 6 inches high and 4½ inches wide. It itself consists of two parts, one of which *nop* is provided with a slightly conical socket, and is cemented fast to the upper plate of the glass cylinder; the other, *qrs*, with a conical projection 8 lines thick fitting closely in the socket, and with a plate *rr* 3 inches wide resting on the plate *nn* of the first part of the same width. The midpoint of the projection *qs* was marked with great care on the lathe by a slight conical depression, and the metal was then filed off for a half inch of its length until the plane surfaces which are thus developed show the conical depression as a complete triangle. By a special arrangement the thread by which the needle is suspended is fastened to the projection so that its midpoint falls exactly in the apex of the triangle. The magnetic needle *tt* is made of steel wire 0.8 lines thick and is not quite 2 inches long. Its two ends are inserted

772

in cylindrical pieces of ivory, to one of which is attached a brass wire, cut to a fine point and bent slightly downward. This brass pointer, which serves as an indicator, comes close to a brass arc *uu*, standing on the base and divided into degrees. At the start I made the magnet so long that its end moved immediately over the graduated scale; but the sluggishness of its motion, as shown by the small number of its vibrations, reminded me of the experiment lately made by Arago, and led me to choose the other arrangement.

The needle thus prepared is suspended by a strip of flattened gold wire 5 inches long, which is fastened to the torsion balance exactly in the axis of rotation. These ribbon-like strips of metal are in my judgment much better fitted for experiments with the torsion balance than cylindrical wires. The strip which I used in my torsion balance, not to mention its shortness, which in many respects is so desirable, possesses in so high a degree all the requirements for investigations with the torsion balance, that the needle, after the strip has experienced a strain of more than three complete revolutions, will again resume its old position after it is released from the strain. Nevertheless after each experiment I examined the needle in the position of rest, so as to be assured that the apparatus had undergone no change. Furthermore I think I should remark that experiments carried out with a similar needle of brass convinced me that small and great vibrations (I examined them from two whole revolutions down to a few degrees) are made in exactly the same time, so that in this respect also there is nothing to be feared.

The torsion balance was cemented to the upper plate of the base in such a way that a straight line drawn down the width of the copper strip *bc* in the direction of the midpoint of the divided arc *uu* and of a simple silk thread set perpendicularly before this arc, was in the magnetic meridian and the magnetic needle also, when its pointer marked zero on the scale. On a projection *k* of the base was carried a convex lens *l* of an inch focal length, set in such a position that the lower divided scale could be observed, and in order to avoid parallax, the eye was always so placed during an observation that the silk thread and the midpoint of the scale coincided. The observations were made in the following manner: whenever the needle was deflected by the electric current in the apparatus, the strip was twisted in the opposite sense by the rotating part of the balance until the brass pointer of the needle stood behind the silk thread on the midpoint of the scale; then the torsion was read off in hundredths of a revolution on the upper scale, which number as is well known gives the force which acts on the needle.

The ends of the conductors which were used in the experiment were dipped in the mercury cups m, m' above which for greater security a simple arrangement secured that the ends of each of the conductors were always put in contact with the mercury in a similar manner. In addition the ends of the conductors, so far up as there was any reason to fear contact with the mercury,

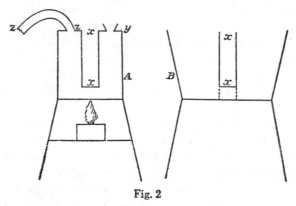

Fig. 2

were coated with rosin, and the end surfaces were filed off clean with a fine file, and were renewed every time. A perfect metallic contact of the several parts is an indispensable condition in researches of this sort, since otherwise the observations will not agree with one another.

Finally, in order to bring the parts of the apparatus where the bismuth and copper are in contact to the proper difference of temperature, I had prepared two tin vessels, whose cross sections are represented on a larger scale in Fig. 2. Each of them had in its middle part a space *xx*, open at the top, and otherwise completely enclosed to receive the parts *ab*, *a'b'*. In one of them, marked *A*, water was kept constantly boiling; this had at *y* a hole that could be closed with a cork, through which water could be introduced into the vessel, and on the other side a tube *zz* through which the steam could escape. In the other vessel *B* snow or cracked ice was placed. The parts *ab*, *a'b'* were sewed up in thin but closely woven silk, were then pushed down into the spaces *xx*, and these were then filled up to the height of about an inch with small shot, and then packed to their tops with powdered glass. In this way all points of contact of the bismuth and the copper were in the space filled with lead, which conducted heat well, and the layer of glass protected this region from rapid changes of temperature from surrounding air.

After this elaborate description of the apparatus I come to the experiments which I made with it. I had prepared 8 different conductors, which in the future I shall distinguish as 1, 2, 3, 4, 5, 6, 7, 0, which were respectively 2, 4, 6, 10, 18, 34, 66, 130, inches long, ⅞ inches thick, cut from one specimen of so called plated copper wire, prepared in the way formerly described. After the water had been boiling for half an hour, these wires were introduced into the circuit one after the other. Between any two sets of experiments, which lasted from 3 to 4 hours, there was always a pause of one hour, while some fresh water already warmed was poured in, which soon began to boil, and then the conductors were again introduced into the circuit in series, but in the opposite order. I thus obtained the following results.

Time of the observations	Set of experiments	Conductors							
		1	2	3	4	5	6	7	8
Jan. 8	I	326¾	300¾	277¾	238¼	190¾	134½	83¼	48½
Jan. 11 {	II	311¼	287	267	230¼	183½	129¼	80	46
	III	307	284	263¾	226¼	181	128¾	79	44½
Jan. 15 {	IV	305¼	281½	259	224	178½	124¾	79	44½
	V	305	282	258¼	223½	178	124¾	78	44

It appears that the force fell off perceptibly from one day to another. Whether the reason for this is to be sought in a change in the surfaces of contact or perhaps in the fact that the 8th and 11th of January were very cold days, and the ice box stood by the window of a poorly heated and badly protected room, I do not dare to decide; I think I should add that from the 15th on I observed no more such differences.

Special emphasis should be laid upon the fact that no trace of fluctuations can be detected, such as appeared when the hydroelectric battery was in circuit. When the needle was brought to rest, it remained in its place without further motion. I have often watched it for half an hour after a set of observations was concluded without perceiving the slightest change of position. Indeed when the needle with conductor 1 was brought to equilibrium and was kept in the same position by a stop placed on one side of it, and then the circuit was completed again with the same conductor, which had been removed from the circuit for some time, there was not the slightest motion toward the opposite side. This justifies the conclusion that the fluctuations have their origin in changes in the fluid, which are conditioned by the electric current itself and rise and fall with it. It seems as if a separation of certain constituents of the fluid was brought about by the moving electricity, which takes place in accordance with exactly the same laws as those which have been determined for the action of electricity at rest; an increase of the force results in an increased separation of the constituents, a decrease of the force permits a partial reunion, which becomes complete when the force vanishes. It is very probable, and we shall later find support for this view, that this separation of the fluid by the current produces a change not only in the exciting force of the circuit, but also in the conductivity of the fluid, and it is just this variability in the hydroelectric circuit which makes the law of conduction in it so confused and so hard to unravel. It appears clearly at once that when we are trying to determine only the influence of the metals in the conduction of the electric current, the hydroelectric circuit is not suited for the purpose, because it gives rise to so many irregularities; whereas the thermo-electric circuit is perfectly fitted for this purpose. We shall now see what it gives.

The numbers already given can be represented very satisfactorily by the equation

$$X = \frac{a}{b+x}$$

in which X is the strength of the magnetic action when the conductor is used whose length is x, and a and b are constants which represent magnitudes depending on the exciting force and the resistance of the rest of the circuit. If for example we set b equal to $20\frac{1}{4}$ and a in the different series equal to 7285, 6965, 6885, 6800, 6800, we obtain by calculation the following results.

Series	Conductors							
	1	2	3	4	5	6	7	8
I	328	300½	277½	240¾	190½	134½	84¼	48½
II	313	287¼	265⅓	230¼	182	128⅓	80¾	46⅓
III	309½	284	262⅓	228	180	127	79¾	45¾
IV	305½	280½	259	224¾	177¾	125¼	79	45
V	305½	280½	259	224¾	177¾	125¼	79	45

If we compare these numbers found by calculation with the former set found by experiment, it will appear that the differences are very small, and are of the order that one might expect in researches of this kind. I shall not delay over this point, but proceed to prove the correctness of the formula in extreme cases, a method which is most serviceable in establishing the general applicability of a law which has been deduced from a few instances.

To this end I made four conductors, a, b, c, d, in order 2, 4, 8, 16 inches long, from the brass wire 0.3 lines thick, which I had used in my previous researches with the hydroelectric circuit; these gave in the circuit the numbers 111½, 64¾, 37, 19¾, while the conductor 1 gave 305. From the above equation the lengths may be determined which correspond to these numbers. We find them to be 40¾, 84¾, 163½, 324, which numbers in general agreement show that an inch of the brass wire is equivalent to 20½ inches of the plated copper wire. After this preliminary work, I introduced into the circuit a conductor of the same brass wire, 23 feet long, which I designated as 5 in this set; it gave 1¼. And we actually get this number almost exactly if we use for x in the equation $23 \cdot 12 \cdot 20\frac{1}{2} = 5658$. We see by this example that the equation fits with experiment very accurately nearly up to the extinction of the force by the resistance of the conductors.

Furthermore I kept one end of the copper-bismuth couple at the temperature of 0° by the use of ice, while the other end was exposed to the temperature of the room, which was shown to be steadily 7½°R. by a thermometer hanging near the apparatus during the observations. The conductors, brought into the circuit in the following order, 1, 2, 3, 4, 5, 6, 7, 8, 7, 6, 5, 4, 3, 2, 1, gave the numbers: 27, 25, 23½, 20, 15½, 10¾, 6½, 3⅔, 6½, 10¾, 15½, 20, 23½, 25¼, 27¾. If we set in our equation $b = 20\frac{1}{4}$, and so determined a that $a/22\frac{1}{4} = 27\frac{3}{8}$, we obtain by calculation numbers which in no case differ from the above by more than half a division; from which it appears that the equation holds for any value of the exciting force. From this last investigation two additional important points are evident. First there is the noteworthy circumstance that the value of b remains unchanged, while the force is more than 10 times less, so that a appears to depend only on the exciting force, and b only on the unchanged part of the circuit. Secondly it seems to follow from these experiments that the force of the thermo-electric circuit is exactly proportional to the difference of temperature between its two ends.

I cannot avoid mentioning here, at the close of this research, an observation which in a more direct way confirms Davy's conclusion that the conductivity of metals is increased by lowering the temperature. I took a 4 inch brass conductor, and brought it into the circuit; it gave 159 divisions. When I heated it in the middle with an alcohol flame, the force gradually decreased by 20 or more divisions, and the action was the same if I moved the flame more toward one or the other end of the conductor; but when I placed on it a layer of snow the force increased by 2 divisions. The temperature of the room was $8\frac{1}{4}°$ Reaumur. This fact is not out of place here, because it may give rise to slight anomalies.

WILHELM FRIEDRICH OSTWALD

(1853–1932)

Winner of the Nobel prize for chemistry in 1909, this German physical chemist was the discoverer of the dilution law which bears his name, stating the relation between molecular conductivity and dilution. His most immediately practical achievement was his work on nitric acid manufacture from ammonia, which accelerated industrial production of nitrates, of such importance to German munitions making during World War I. His laboratory at Leipzig became world-famous, and Ostwald is considered one of the leading names in electrochemistry.

OSTWALD'S DILUTION LAW

THE RESEARCHES of van't Hoff, Planck, and Arrhenius on dilute solutions have in recent times led to the recognition of a complete analogy of these with gases. One of the most valuable advances of these studies is that the compounds usually spoken of as held together by the strongest affinities, such as, for example, potassium chloride, hydrogen chloride, or potassium hydroxide, must actually be regarded in dilute solutions as very largely dissociated.

Since this result is derived according to the laws of thermodynamics on the basis of a hypothesis which is at least very plausible, if not positive, it does not leave much to say against it, so much does it satisfy the usual views. But before deciding on such a change in viewpoint, we have the duty to apply the strongest tests possible for its verification.

One such test is to deduce the broadest possible consequences of the theory, to compare them with practice. The following lines attempt to develop such consequences, and this preliminary communication reports the results of the test.

If the electrolytes are dissociated in water solution and therefore obey laws which are analogous to the gas laws, then the dissociation laws which have been learned for gases will also find use for solutions. In the simplest case, where a molecule decomposes into two, the theory now leads to the following formula which is valid for gases:

$$R \log \frac{p}{p_1 p_2} = \frac{p}{T} + \text{const.},$$

which for a constant temperature and the case where no decomposition products are left over accords with the law

$$p/p_1^2 = C$$

where p is the pressure of the undecomposed part, p_1 of the decomposed part, and C is a constant.

Now, according to the work mentioned above, it is permissible to place the pressure in solution proportional to the actual masses u and u_1 of the substance and inversely proportional to the volume; the equation then becomes

$$p:p_1 = \frac{u}{v} : \frac{u_1}{v}, \text{ and so } \frac{u}{u_1} - v = C.$$ Further, the masses u and u_1

can be calculated from the electrical conductivity, as Arrhenius has shown. If we call the molecular conductivity of volume v, μ_v, and the limit of conductivity of infinite dilution μ_∞, then $u:u_1 = \mu_\infty - \mu_v : \mu_v$, since the conductivity μ_v is proportional to the dissociated mass of electrolyte u_1. From this follows the dilution law, valid for all binary electrolytes:

$$\frac{\mu_\infty - \mu_v}{u_v^2} v = \text{const.}$$

781

The test of this conclusion can be performed with great assurance in the acids and bases, for which numerous measurements of electrical conductivity exist. Since I will publish future communications on this subject, I will content myself now with pointing out that the results of my calculations speak favorably for the theory. The formula expresses not only an altogether general law, which I have earlier found empirically for the influence of dilution on acids and bases, as well as over a hundred substances but it leads also to numerical results which in part agree completely, in part show a variation whose size is of the same order of magnitude as has been established in gases.

THEORY OF CATALYSIS

AFTER A historical introduction the author [Stohmann] brings together the essential values for the heat of combustion of the most important ingredients of nutrients as determined by him and his students. Some general considerations of this are discussed in which the author points out in a praiseworthy manner the great significance of catalytic phenomena for physiology. After a summary of the views of different investigations on this problem, he formulates his own, in which he defines *catalysis* in the following way:

"Catalysis is a condition of movement of the atoms in a molecule of a labile body which follows the entrance of the energy emitted from one body into another and leads to the formation of more stable bodies with loss of energy."

The abstractor has several objections to make to this definition. First, the assumption of a "condition of movement of the atoms in a molecule" is hypothetical and therefore not suitable for purposes of definition. Also, that is plainly not a loss of energy. What is more, in describing characteristic conditions of catalysis, a loss of free energy can follow under conditions even of absolute energy uptake.

If the abstractor were to formulate for himself the problem of characterizing the phenomenon of catalysis in a general way, he would consider the following expression as probably most suitable: Catalysis is the acceleration of a chemical reaction, which proceeds slowly, by the presence of a foreign substance. It would then be necessary to give the following explanations.

There are numerous substances or combinations of substances which in themselves are not stable but undergo slow change and only seem stable to us because their changes occur so slowly that during the usual short period of observation they do not strike us. Such substances or systems often attain an increased reaction rate if certain foreign substances, that is, substances which are not in themselves necessary for the reaction, are added. This acceleration occurs without alteration of the general energy relations, since after the end of the reaction the foreign body can again be separated from the field of the reaction, so that the energy used up by the addition can once more be obtained by the separation, or the reverse. However, these processes, like all natural ones, must always occur in such a direction that the free energy of the entire system is decreased.

It is therefore misleading to consider catalytic action as a force which produces something which would not occur without the substance which acts catalytically; still less can it be assumed that the latter performs work. It will perhaps contribute to an understanding of the problem if I especially mention that time is not involved in the ideas of chemical energy; thus if the chemical energy relations are such that a definite process must occur, then it is only the initial and final states, as well as the whole series of intermediate given states which must be passed through, which must occur, but in no way is the time during which the reaction takes place of concern. Time is here dependent on conditions which lie outside the two chief laws of energetics. The only form of energy which contains time in its definition is kinetic energy, which is proportional to the mass and the square of the velocity. All cases in which such energies take a fixed part are therefore completely determined in time if the conditions are given; but all cases in which the vibrational energy does not play this role are independent of time, that is, they can occur without violating the laws of energy in any given time. Catalytic processes are empirically found to be of the type in which this last property is observed; the existence of catalytic processes is to me therefore a positive proof that chemical processes cannot have a kinetic nature.

PARACELSUS

(1493?–1541)

Theophrastus Bombastus von Hohenheim—who called himself Paracelsus after Celsus, an admired Roman physician of the second century—wrote in the esoteric and often absurd language of the medieval alchemist. He nonetheless appears to have been a thinker of some stature, capable of genuine scientific investigation. Typical of the alchemists, he was especially interested in metals, in the mechanics of mining and in their use in the treatment of disease. He appears to have introduced therapeutic mineral baths and prescribed opium, mercury, lead, sulfur, iron and arsenic for medicinal purposes. In spite of his iconoclastic rejection of Galen and Avicenna, his addiction to alchemy and his troublesome disposition, Paracelsus made distinct contributions to pharmacy and therapeutics.

THE SCIENCE AND NATURE OF ALCHEMY

YOU WHO ARE SKILLED in alchemy, and as many others as promise yourselves great riches or chiefly desire to make gold and silver, which alchemy in different ways promises and teaches; equally, too, you who willingly undergo toil and vexations, and wish not to be freed from them until you have attained your rewards and the fulfillment of the promises made to you: experience teaches this every day, that out of thousands of you not even one accomplishes his desire. Is this a failure of nature or of art? I say no; but it is rather the fault of fate, or of the unskillfulness of the operator. . . .

HOW TO MAKE GOLD AND SILVER (SOL AND LUNA)

What, then, shall we say about the receipts of alchemy, and about the diversity of its vessels and instruments? These are

785

furnaces, glasses, jars, waters, oils, limes, sulphurs, salts, salt-peters, alums, vitriols, chrysocolae, copper greens, atraments, auri-pigments, fel vitri, ceruse, red earth, thucia, wax, lutum sapien-tiae, pounded glass, verdigris, soot, crocus of Mars, soap, crystal, arsenic, antimony, minium, elixir, lazarium, gold leaf, salt niter, sal ammoniac, calamine stone, magnesia, bolus armensus, and many other things. Moreover, [what shall we say] concerning preparations, putrefactions, digestions, probations, solutions, cementings, filtrations, reverberations, calcinations, graduations, rectifications, amalgamations, purgations, etc. with which these alchemical books are crammed. Then, again, concerning herbs, roots, seeds, woods, stones, animals, worms, bone dust, snail shells, other shells, and pitch. These and the like, whereof there are some very farfetched in alchemy, are mere incumbrances of work; since even if Sol and Luna could be made by them they rather hinder and delay than further one's purpose. But it is not from these—to say the truth—that the art of making Sol and Luna is to be learned. So, then, all these things should be passed by, because they have no effect with the five metals, so far as Sol and Luna are concerned. Someone may ask, "What, then, is this short and easy way, which involves no difficulty, and yet whereby Sol and Luna can be made?" Our answer is: this has been fully and openly explained in the Seven Canons. It would be lost labor should one seek further to instruct one who does not understand these. It would be impossible to convince such a person that these matters could be so easily understood, but in an occult rather than in an open sense.

The art is this: after you have made heaven, or the sphere of Saturn, with its life to run over the earth, place it on all the planets or such, one or more, as you wish, so that the portion of Luna may be the smallest. Let all run, until heaven, or Saturn, has entirely disappeared. Then all those planets will remain dead with their old corruptible bodies, having meanwhile obtained another new, perfect, and incorruptible body.

That body is the spirit of heaven. From it these planets again receive a body and life, and live as before. Take this body from the life and the earth. Keep it. It is Sol and Luna. Here you have the art altogether, clear and entire. If you do not yet understand it, or are not practiced therein, it is well. It is better that it should be kept concealed, and not made public.

CONCERNING THE THREE PRIME ESSENCES

Everything which is generated and produced of its elements is divided into three, namely, into Salt, Sulphur, Mercury. Out of these a conjunction takes place, which constitutes one body and an united essence. This does not concern the body in its outward aspect, but only the internal nature of the body.

Its operation is threefold. One of these is the operation of Salt. This works by purging, cleansing, balsaming, and by other ways, and rules over that which goes off in putrefaction. The second is the operation of Sulphur. Now, sulphur either governs the excess which arises from the two others, or it is dissolved. The third is of Mercury, and it removes that which changes into consumption. Learn the form which is peculiar to these three. One is liquor, and this is the form of mercury; one is oiliness, which is the form of sulphur; one is alcali, and this is from salt. Mercury is without sulphur and salt; sulphur is devoid of salt and mercury; salt is without mercury or sulphur. In this manner each persists in its own potency.

But concerning the operations which are observed to take place in complicated maladies, notice that the separation of things is not perfect, but two are conjoined in one, as in dropsy and other similar complaints. For those are mixed diseases which transcend their sap and tempered moisture. Thus, mercury and sulphur sometimes remove paralysis, because the bodily sulphur unites therewith, or because there is some lesion in the immediate neighbourhood. Observe, consequently, that every disease may exist in a double or triple form. This is the mixture, or complication, of disease. Hence the physician must consider, if he deals with a given simple, what is its grade in liquor, in oil, in salt, and how along with the disease it reaches the borders of the lesion. According to the grade, so must the liquor, salt, and sulphur be extracted and administered, as is required. The following short rule must be observed: Give one medicine to the lesion, another to the disease.

Salts purify, but after various manners, some by secession, and of these there are two kinds—one the salt of the thing, which digests things till they separate—the other the salt of Nature, which expels. Thus, without salt, no excretion can take place. Hence it follows that the salt of the vulgar assists the salts of Nature. Certain salts purge by means of vomiting. Salts of this kind are exceedingly gross, and, if they do not pass off in digestion, will produce strangulation in the stomach. Some salts purge by means of perspiration. Such is that most subtle salt which unites with the blood. Now, salts which produce evacuation and vomiting do not unite with the blood, and, consequently, produce no perspiration. Then it is the salt only which separates. Other salts purge through the urine, and urine itself is nothing but a superfluous salt, even as dung is superfluous sulphur. No liquor superfluously departs from the body, for the same remains within. Such are all the evacuations of the body, moisture expelled by salt through the nostrils, the ears, the eyes, and other ways. This is understood to take place by means of the Archeus from these evacuations. Now, as out of the Archeus a laxative salt comes forth, of which one kind purges the stomach because it proceeds from the stomach of the Archeus, so another purges the spleen because it comes from the spleen of the Archeus; and it is in like manner with the brain, the liver, the lungs, and other members, every member of the Archeus acting upon the corresponding member of the Microcosmus.

The species of salt are various. One is sweet as cassia, and this is a separated salt which is called antimony among minerals. Another is like vinegar, as sal gemmae; yet another is acid, as ginger. Another is bitter, as in rhubarb or colocynth. So, also, with alkali; there is some that is generated, as harmel; some extracted, as scammony; some coagulated, as absinth. In the same way, certain salts purge by perspiration alone, certain others by consuming alone, and so on. Wherever there is a peculiar savour, there is also a peculiar operation and expulsion. The operation is of two kinds—that which belongs to the thing and the extinct operation.

CONCERNING THE MASS AND THE MATTER OUT OF WHICH MAN WAS MADE

It follows next in order to consider how it comes about that external causes are so powerful in man.

It must be realised, first of all, that God created all things in heaven and on earth—day and night, all elements, and all animals. When all these were created, God then made man. And here, on the subject of creation, two remarks have to be made. First, all things were made of nothing, by a word only, save man alone. God made man out of *something*, that is to say, from a mass, which was a body, a substance—a *something*. What it was—this mass—we will briefly enquire.

God took the body out of which He built up man from those things which He created from nothingness into something. That mass was the extract of all creatures in heaven and earth, just as if one should extract the soul or spirit, and should take that spirit or that body. For example, man consists of flesh and blood, and besides that of a soul, which is the man, much more subtle than the former. In this manner, from all creatures, all elements, all stars in heaven and earth, all properties, essences, and natures, that was extracted which was most subtle and most excellent in all, and this was united into one mass. From this mass man was afterwards made. Hence man is now a microcosm, or a little world, because he is an extract from all the stars and planets of the whole firmament, from the earth and the elements; and so he is their quintessence. The four elements are the universal world, and from these man is constituted. In number, therefore, he is fifth, that is, the fifth or quintessence, beyond the four elements out of which he has been extracted as a nucleus. But between the macrocosm and the microcosm this difference occurs, that the form, image, species, and substance of man are diverse therefrom. In man the earth is flesh, the water is blood, fire is

789

the heat thereof, and air is the balsam. These properties have not been changed, but only the substance of the body. So man is man, not a world, yet made from the world, made in the likeness, not of the world, but of God. Yet man comprises in himself all the qualities of the world. Whence the Scripture rightly says we are dust and ashes, and into ashes we shall return; that is, although man, indeed, is made in the image of God, and has flesh and blood, and is not like the world, but more than the world, still, nevertheless, he is earth and dust and ashes. And he should lay this well to heart lest from his figure he should suffer himself to be led astray; but he should think what he has been, what he now is, and what hereafter he shall be.

Attend, therefore, to these examples. Since man is nothing else than what he was, and out of which he was made, let him not, even in imagination, be led astray. The knowledge of the fact tends to force upon him the confession that he is nothing but a mass drawn forth from the great universe. This being the case, he must know that he cannot be sustained and nourished therefrom. His body is from the world, and therefore must be fed and nourished by that world from which he has sprung. So it is that his food and his drink and all his aliment grow from the ground. The great universe contributes less to his food and nourishment. If man were not from the great world but from heaven, then he would take celestial bread from heaven along with the angels. He has been taken from the earth and from the elements, and therefore must be nourished by these. Without the great world he could not live, but would be dead, and so he is like the dust and ashes of the great world. It is settled, then, that man is sustained from the four elements, and that he takes from the earth his food, from the water his drink, from the fire his heat, and from the air his breath. But these all make for the sustentation of the body only, of the flesh and the blood.

Now, man is not only flesh and blood, but there is within him the intellect which does not, like the complexion, come from the elements, but from the stars. And the condition of the stars is this, that all the wisdom, intelligence, industry of the animal, and all the arts peculiar to man are contained in them. From the stars man has these same things, and that is called light of Nature; in fact, it is whatever man has found by the light of Nature. Let us illustrate our position by an example. The body of man takes its food from the earth, to which food it is destined by its conception and natural agreement. This is the reason why one person likes one kind of food, and another likes another, each deriving his pleasure from the earth. Animals do the same, hunting out the food and drink for their bodies which has been implanted in the earth. Now as there is in man a special faculty for sustaining his body, that is, his flesh and blood, so is it with his intellect. He ought equally to sustain that with its own familiar food and drink, though not from the elements, since the senses are not corporal but are of the spirit as the stars are of the spirit. He then attracts by the spirit of his star, in whom that spirit is conceived and born. For the spirit in man is nourished just as much as the body. This special feature was engrafted on man at his creation, that although he shares the divine image, still he is not nourished by divine food, but by elemental. He is divided into two parts; into an elemental body, that is, into flesh and blood, whence that body must be nourished; and into spirit, whence he is compelled to sustain his spirit from the spirit of the star. Man himself is dust and ashes of the earth. Such, then, is the condition of man, that, out of the great universe he needs both elements and stars, seeing that he himself is constituted in that way.

And now we must speak of the conception of man, how he is begotten and made. The first man was made from the mass, extracted from the machinery of the whole universe. Then there was built up from him a woman, who corresponds to him in his likeness to the universe. For the future, there proceeds from the man and the woman the generation of all children, of all men. Moreover, the hand of God made the first man after God's own image in a wonderful manner, but still composed of flesh and blood, that he may be very man. Afterwards the first man and his wife were subjected to Nature, and so far separated from the hand of God that man was no longer built up miraculously by God's hand, but by Nature. The generation of man, therefore, has been entrusted to Nature and conferred on one mass from which he had proceeded. That mass in Nature is called semen. Most certain it is, however, that a man and woman only cannot beget a man, but along with those two, the elements also and the spirit of the stars. These four make up the man. The semen in not in the man, save in so far as it enters into him elementary. When, in the act of conception, the elements do not operate, no body is begotten. Where the star does not operate, no spirit is produced. Whatever is produced without the elements and the spirit of the stars is a monster, a mola, an abortion contrary to Nature. As God took the mass and infused life into it, so must the composition perpetually proceed from those four and from God, in whose hand all things are placed. The body and the spirit must be there. These two constituents make up the man—the human being, that is, the man with the woman, and the semen, which comes from without, and is, as it were, an aliment, something which the man has not within himself, but attracts from without, just as though it were a potion. Such as the principle of food and drink is, such is also that of the sperm, which the elements from without contribute to the body as a mass. The star, by means of its spirit, confers the senses. The father and mother are the instruments of the externals by which these are perfected. In order to make this intelligible, I will adduce an example: In the earth nothing grows unless the higher stars contribute their powers. What are these powers? They are such that one cannot exist without the other, but of necessity one must act in conjunction with the other. As those without are, such are those within, so far as man is concerned. Hence it is inferred that the first man was miraculously made, and so existed as the work of God. After that, man was subjugated to Nature, so that he should beget children in connection with her. Now, Nature means the external world in the elements and in the stars. Now it is evident from this that those elements have their prescribed course and mode of operation, just as the stars, too, have their daily course.

They proceed in their daily agreement, and at particular epochs Nature puts forth new ones. Now, if this form of operation— if the father and mother —with this concordance meet together for the work of conception, then the foetus is allotted the Nature of those from whom it is born, namely, of the four parents—the father, the mother, the elements, the stars. From the father and mother proceed a like image and essence of flesh and blood. Besides this, from their imagination, which is the human star, there is allotted the intellect, in proportion wherein the concordance and constellation have exhibited themselves. So, too, from the elements there is allotted the complexion and the quality of the nature. So, too, from the external stars their intelligence. As these meet, the influence which is stronger than the others, preponderates in the foetus, or else there is a mutual commingling of all. Thus man becomes a microscosm. The father and mother are made from the universe, and the universe is constantly contributing to the generation of man. In this way, there is constituted a single body, but a double nature, a single spirit, but a twofold sense. At length the body returns to its primal body, and the senses to the primal sense. They die, pass away, and depart, never to return. The ashes cannot again be made wood, neither can man from that state in which he is ashes be brought back so as to be man again.

Now we have traced the generation of man to this point as a general and universal probation of the whole of astronomy, in order that it might be understood from thence why the astronomer studies and gets to know men by the stars, namely, because man is from the stars. As every son is known by his father, so is it here; and this science is very useful if a man knows who is from heaven, from the elements, from father and mother. The knowledge of the father and mother lies at the root. The knowledge of the elements pertains to medicine. The knowledge of the stars is astrological. There are many reasons why these cognitions are useful and good. Many men are mere brutes, and yet make themselves out angels. Many speak from their mother, calling themselves Samuels or Maccabees. Many in their earthly complexion fast and pray, and call themselves divine. Many handle those things which are not really what they are said to be. Anyone who is an astrologer knows what that spirit is which speaks and is seen. It is matter for regret that many hesitate between the two lights, culling and stealing from each in order to make themselves conspicuous. The spirits are known, indeed, to each, but in a different way, and this should not be so. But though things are thus, man is the work of God, but one only is His very son, that is, Adam. Others are sons of Nature, as Luke in his genealogy recounts of Joseph, that he was the Son of Helus, which Helus was the son of Mathat, which Mathat was the son of Levi, and so on back to Adam; yet there is no mention of the son of God. Thus man is a son in Nature, and does not desert his race, but follows the nature of his parents, the stars. Now, he who knows the father and mother of the stars and of the elements, and also the father and mother of the flesh and blood, he is in a position to discuss concerning that offspring, concerning its nature, essence, properties, in a word, concerning its whole condition. And as a physician compounds all simples into one, preparing a single remedy out of all, which cannot be made up without these numerous ingredients, so God performs His much more notable miracle by concocting man into one compound of all the elements and stars, so that man becomes heaven, firmament, elements, in a word, the nature of the whole universe, shut up and concealed in a slender body. And though God could have made man out of nothing by His one word "Fiat," He was pleased rather to build man up in Nature and to subject him to Nature as its son, but still so that He also subjected Nature to man, though still Nature was man's father. Hence it results that the astronomer knows man's conception by man's parentage. This is the reason why man can be healed by Nature through the agency of a physician, just as a father helps a son who has fallen into a pit. In this way Nature is subjected to man as to its own flesh and blood, its own son, its own fruit produced from itself; in the body of the elements wherein diseases exist; in the body of the spirit, where flourish the intelligence and reason; and the elements, indeed, by means of medi-

794

cine, but the stars by their own knowledge and wisdom. Now, this wisdom in the sight of God is nothing; but the Divine wisdom is preeminent above all. So the names of wisdom differ. That wisdom which comes from Nature is called animal, because it is mortal. That which comes from God is named eternal, because it is free from mortality.

AMBROISE PARÉ

* (1517?–1590)

Paré is called the father of modern surgery because to control bleeding he substituted the ligature of arteries for the cauterization of
wounds with red-hot irons or oil, customary before his time. A member of the barber-surgeons guild of Paris, he served as physician to
five French kings, from Francis I to Henry IV. He wrote many volumes on anatomy, surgery, treatment of wounds, obstetrics, and mon-
sters, of which the best-known is the *Cinq Livres de Chirurgie* (1562).

JOURNEYS IN DIVERS PLACES

MOREOVER, I will here show to my readers the towns and places
where I have been enabled to learn the art of surgery, always
the better to instruct the young surgeon.

And first in the year 1536 the great King François sent a
great army to Turin to recover the cities and castles which had
been taken by the Marquis de Guast, lieutenant general of the
Emperor.

There Monsieur the Constable, then grand master, was lieutenant general of the army, and Monsieur de Montejan was colonel
general of the infantry, to whom I was then surgeon. A great
part of the army having arrived at the Pass of Suze, we found
the enemy holding the passage and having made certain forts and
trenches insomuch that to make them dislodge and quit the place,
it was necessary to fight, where there were many killed and
wounded, as many on one side as the other, but the enemy were
constrained to retire and gain the castle, which was taken in part
by Captain Le Rat, who climbed with many soldiers from his
company on a little hill, from whence they fired directly on the
enemy. He received a shot from an arquebus in the ankle of his

right foot, wherewith he suddenly fell to the ground and then said, "Now the Rat is taken." I dressed him, and God healed him.

We thronged into the city and passed over the dead bodies and some that were not yet dead, hearing them cry under the feet of our horses, which made a great pity in my heart, and truly I repented that I had gone forth from Paris to see so pitiful a spectacle. Being in the city, I entered a stable thinking to lodge my horse and that of my man, where I found four dead soldiers and three who were propped against the wall, their faces wholly disfigured, and they neither saw, nor heard, nor spake, and their clothes yet flaming from the gunpowder which had burnt them. Beholding them with pity there came an old soldier who asked me if there was any means of curing them. I told him no. At once he approached them and cut their throats gently and without anger. Seeing this great cruelty, I said to him that he was a bad man. He answered me that he prayed God that when he should be in such a case, he might find someone who would do the same for him, to the end that he might not languish miserably.

And to return to our discourse, the enemy was summoned to surrender, which they did, and went forth, their lives only saved, and a white staff in their hands, but the greater part went to gain the Château de Villaine, where there were about two hundred Spaniards. Monsieur the Constable would not leave them in his rear in order to render the road free. The château is seated upon a little mountain, which gave great assurance to those within that we could not place the artillery so as to bear upon them. . . .

Now all the said soldiers at the château, seeing our men coming with a great fury, did all they could to defend themselves, and killed and wounded a great number of our soldiers with pikes, arquebuses, and stones, where the surgeons had much work cut out for them. Now I was at that time a fresh-water soldier, I had not yet seen wounds made by gunshot at the first dressing. It is true that I had read in Jean de Vigo, first book, "Of Wounds in General," Chapter Eight, that wounds made by firearms participate of venenosity, because of the powder, and for their cure he commands to cauterize them with oil of elder, scalding hot, in which should be mixed a little theriac and in order not to err before using the said oil, knowing that such a thing would bring great pain to the patient, I wished to know first, how the other surgeons did for the first dressing which was to apply the said oil as hot as possible, into the wound with tents and setons, of whom I took courage to do as they did. At last my oil lacked and I was constrained to apply in its place a digestive made of the yolks of eggs, oil of roses and turpentine. That night I could not sleep at my ease, fearing by lack of cauterization that I should find the wounded on whom I had failed to put the said oil dead or empoisoned, which made me rise very early to visit them, where beyond my hope, I found those upon whom I had put the digestive medicament feeling little pain, and their wounds without inflammation or swelling having rested fairly well throughout the night; the others to whom I had applied the said boiling oil, I found feverish, with great pain and swelling about their wounds. Then I resolved with myself never more to burn thus cruelly poor men wounded with gunshot.

Being at Turin, I found a surgeon who was famous above all for good treatment of gunshot wounds, into whose grace I found means to insinuate myself, to have the recipe which he called his balm, with which he treated gunshot wounds, and he made me court him for years before I could draw his recipe from him. At last by gifts and presents he gave it to me, which was to boil in oil of lilies, little puppies just born, with earthworms prepared with Venetian turpentine. Then I was joyful and my heart made glad, to have understood his remedy, which was like to that which I had obtained by chance.

See how I learned to treat wounds made by gunshot, not from books.

BLAISE PASCAL

(1623–1662)

Pascal was a mathematical prodigy as a child, completing an original treatise on conic sections at the age of sixteen. He later contributed to infinitesimal calculus, and with Fermat founded the theory of probability. His treatise on the equilibrium of fluids makes him one of the founders of hydrodynamics. Various mathematical propositions and demonstrations have been named after him, such as Pascal's law, Pascal's arithmetical triangle, Pascal's mystic hexagram. He turned to philosophy as he grew older, and the famous *Pensées* were first published (in garbled form) seven years after his death.

EXPERIMENTS WITH THE BAROMETER

(A LETTER BY PASCAL'S BROTHER-IN-LAW, PÉRIER)

September 22nd, 1648

WE THEREFORE met on that day at eight o'clock in the morning in the garden of the Pères Minimes, which is in almost the lowest part of the town, where the experiment was begun in the following way:

First, I poured into a vessel sixteen pounds of quicksilver, which I had purified during the three preceding days; and taking two tubes of glass of equal size, each about four feet long, hermetically sealed at one end and open at the other, I made with each of them the ordinary experiment of the vacuum in the same vessel, and when I brought the two tubes near each other without lifting them out of the vessel, it was found that the quicksilver which remained in each of them was at the

799

same level, and that it stood in each of them above the quick-silver in the vessel twenty-six inches three lines and a half. I repeated this experiment twice in the same place, with the same tubes, with the same quicksilver and in the same vessel; and found always that the quicksilver in the tubes was still at the same level and the same height as I found it the first time.

When this had been done, I left one of the two tubes in the vessel, for continual observation: I marked on the glass the height of the quicksilver, and leaving the tube in its place, I begged the Rev. Father Chastin, one of the inmates of the house, a man as pious as he is capable, who thinks very clearly in matters of this sort, to take the trouble to observe it from time to time during the day, so as to see if any change occurred. And with the other tube and a part of the same quicksilver, I ascended with all these gentlemen to the top of the Puy-de-Dôme, which is higher than the Minimes by about five hundred toises, where, when we made the same experiments in the same way as I had at the Minimes, it was found that there remained in the tube no more than twenty-three inches two lines of quick-silver, whereas at the Minimes there was found in the same tube a height of twenty-six inches, three lines and a half; and so there was between the heights of the quicksilver in these experiments a difference of three inches one line and a half: this result so filled us with admiration and astonishment, and so much surprised us, that for our own satisfaction we wished to repeat it. I therefore tried the same thing five times more, with great accuracy, at different places on the top of the moun-tain, once under cover in the little chapel which is there, once in a shelter, once in the wind, once in good weather, and once during the rain and the mists, which came over us sometimes, having taken care to get rid of the air in the tube every time; and in all these trials there was found the same height of the quicksilver, twenty-three inches two lines, which makes a dif-ference of three inches one line and a half from the twenty-six inches three lines and a half which were found at the Minimes; this result fully satisfied us. . . .

(PASCAL'S COMMENT ON THIS LETTER)

This account cleared up all my difficulties and I do not conceal the fact that I was greatly delighted with it; and since I noticed that the distance of twenty toises in height made a difference of two lines in the height of the quicksilver, and that six or seven toises made one of about half a line, a fact which it was easy to test in this city, I made the ordinary experiment of the vacuum at the top and at the bottom of the tower of Saint-Jacques de-la-Boucherie, which is from twenty-four to twenty-five toises high: I found a difference of more than two lines in the height of the quicksilver; and then I made the same experiment in a private house, with ninety-six steps in the stairs, where I found very plainly a difference of half a line; which agrees perfectly with the account of Périer.

THE EQUILIBRIUM OF LIQUIDS

WHY THE WEIGHT OF LIQUIDS IS IN PROPORTION TO THEIR HEIGHT

We see by all these examples that a small filament of water may keep a great weight in equilibrium: it remains to show what is the reason for this increase of force; we proceed to do this by the following experiment (Fig. 1):

If a vessel full of water, otherwise completely closed, has two openings, one of which is one hundred times as large as the other; by putting in each of these a piston which fits it exactly, a man pushing on the small piston will exert a force equal to that of one hundred men who are pushing on the piston which is one hundred times as large, and will overcome the force of ninety-nine men.

Whatever proportion there is between these openings, if the forces which are applied to the pistons are proportional to the openings, they will be in equilibrium. Hence it appears that a

801

vessel full of water is a new principle of mechanics, and a new machine to multiply forces to any degree we please, since a man in this way can lift any load that is given to him.

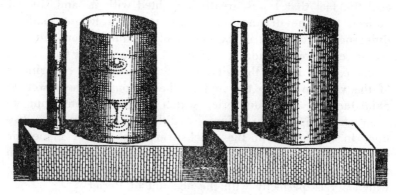

FIG. 1

And it is truly admirable that there is encountered in the new machine the constant rule which appears in all the older machines, such as the lever, the wheel and axle, the endless screw, etc., which is, that the path is increased in the same proportion as the force; for it is clear that, since one of these openings is one hundred times as large as the other, if the man who pushes on the small piston moves it forward an inch, he will push out the other one only one one-hundredth part of an inch, for, since this movement occurs because of the continuity of the water which acts between the pistons, so that the one of them cannot move without moving the other, it is evident that, when the small piston is moved through an inch of water, which has been pushed forward by it, and which pushes the other piston, since the opening through which it moves is one hundred times as large, it will occupy only one one-hundredth of the height. So that the path is to the path as the force to the force; and this rule we may consider as the true cause of this effect: it is clear that it is the same thing to make one hundred pounds of water move one inch as to make one pound of water move one hundred inches; and thus when a pound of water is so situated in relation to one hundred pounds of water that the one hundred pounds cannot move an inch without making the pound move one hundred inches, they must remain in equilibrium, a pound having as much force to make one hundred pounds move an inch as one hundred pounds have to make a pound move one hundred inches.

It may be added, for greater clearness, that the water is under equal pressure under the two pistons; for if one of them has one hundred times more weight than the other it also touches one hundred times as many parts of the liquid, and so each part is equally pressed; therefore all parts ought to be at rest, because there is no reason why one should yield rather than the other. So that if a vessel has only a single opening, an inch across for example, in which there is a piston loaded with a pound weight, this weight presses against all parts of the vessel generally, because of the continuity and the fluidity of the water: but to determine the pressure of each part we have the following rule: Each part an inch large, like the opening, is subjected to as much pressure as if it were pushed by a pound weight (without counting the weight of the water, of which I do not here speak, for I am speaking only of the weight of the piston), because the weight of a pound presses the piston which is in the opening, and each portion of the vessel more or less great is subjected to pressure precisely more or less in proportion to its size, whether this portion is opposite the opening or at the side, far or near; for the continuity and the fluidity of the water make all these things equal and indifferent; so that it is necessary that the material of which the vessel is made should have sufficient resistance in all its parts to sustain all these forces; if the resistance is less in any one of these places, it yields; if it is greater, it provides all the necessary force and the rest remains useless in the circumstances; so that if a new opening is made in the vessel there would be needed to check the water which would gush out, a force equal to the resistance which this part ought to present, that is to say, a force which should be to the force of a pound as this last opening is to the first.

EXAMPLES AND REASONS FOR THE EQUILIBRIUM

If a vessel full of water has two openings, to each one of which is fastened a vertical tube; if water is poured into the one and into the other to the same height, the columns of water will be in equilibrium. (Fig. 1).

For since their heights are equal, they will be in proportion to their magnitudes, that is to say, to their openings, therefore the two masses of water in these tubes are properly two pistons whose weights are proportional to their openings; therefore they will be in equilibrium, by the preceding demonstration.

Hence it follows that, if we pour water into one of these tubes only, it will make the water rise in the other one until it has come to the same height, and then the water will remain in equilibrium, for then the water columns will be two pistons, the weight of which are in proportion to their openings.

This is the reason why water rises as high as its source.

If different liquids are placed in the tubes, such as water in the one and quicksilver in the other, these two liquids will be in equilibrium when their heights are inversely proportional to their weights; that is to say, when the height of the water is fourteen times as great as the height of the quicksilver, because quicksilver weighs fourteen times as much as water does; for then there will be two pistons, one of water and one of quicksilver, of which the weights are proportional of the openings.

And even when the tube full of water is one hundred times narrower than that in which the quicksilver is, this little thread of water will hold in equilibrium all the great mass of quicksilver, provided that it is fourteen times as high.

All that we have said up to this point about tubes can be applied to any vessel whatever, regular or not; for the same equilibrium occurs in any case: so that, if, in place of these two tubes that we have represented at the two openings, there are two vessels used; which are applied also to these openings but which are large in some places, narrow in others, and indeed entirely irregular in all their extent; when liquids have been poured in to the heights which we have described, these liquids will also be in equilibrium in these irregular tubes, just as they were in the uniform tubes, because the weight of liquids is measured only by their heights and not by their sizes.

On Bodies Which Are Immersed in Water

We see by the former chapter that water pushes upward those bodies which it touches from below; that it pushes downward those bodies which it touches from above; and that it pushes toward one side those which it touches on the opposite side: from which it is easy to conclude that when a body is entirely immersed in water, since the water touches it above, below and on all its sides, it strives to push the body upward, downward and in every direction: but since its height is the measure of its force in all these actions, it is easy to see which of all these forces ought to prevail.

For it appears, first, that since it has the same height of water on all the faces of its sides, they will be pushed equally; and therefore the body will not be moved sideways in any direction, any more than a weather-vane between two equal winds. But since the water has more height on the lower face than on the upper face, it is clear that it will push the body more upward than downward: since the difference of these heights of the water is the height of the body itself, it is easy to understand that the water pushes it more upward than downward with a force equal to the weight of the volume of water equal to that of the body.

So that a body which is in water is borne up, in the same way as if it were in one scale of a balance, and the other were loaded with a volume of water equal to its own, from which it appears that a body of copper or of any other matter which weighs more than an equal volume of water, will sink; for its weight exceeds that which counterbalances it.

If a body is of wood, or of some other matter lighter than

an equal volume of water, it rises with the force by which the weight of the water is greater than its weight.

And if it is of equal weight, it neither sinks nor rises; as wax does, which stays almost in the same place in water when it is once put there.

LOUIS PASTEUR

(1822–1895)

The founder of microbiology, Louis Pasteur was professor of chemistry at the Sorbonne until he became director of the Pasteur Institute,
built by public subscription in 1889. His fame reached its dramatic
climax with his development of a method of inoculation of cattle
against anthrax. He had previously discovered that fermentation was
the result of microscopic organisms, and that harmful bacteria in
liquids such as milk could be killed by holding the fluid at a definite
temperature—the process now know as pasteurization. His discovery of the bacilli of two silkworm diseases saved the silk industry in France. He successfully treated hydrophobia by inoculation
with the attenuated bacilli of an artificial culture. Thus by proving
the efficacy of vaccination, Pasteur opened the way for the curative
and preventive treatment of many diseases, including diphtheria,
plague, tubercular infections and cholera.

THE GERM THEORY AND ITS APPLICATIONS
TO MEDICINE AND SURGERY

THE SCIENCES GAIN by mutual support. When, as the result
of my first communications on the fermentations in 1857-1858,
it appeared that the ferments, properly so-called, are living
beings, that the germs of microscopic organisms abound in
the surface of all objects, in the air and in water; that the
theory of spontaneous generation is chimerical; that wines,
beer, vinegar, the blood, urine and all the fluids of the body
undergo none of their usual changes in pure air, both Medicine
and Surgery received fresh stimulation. A French physician,
Dr. Davaine, was fortunate in making the first application of
these principles to Medicine, in 1863.

Our researches of last year, left the etiology of the putrid disease, or septicemia, in a much less advanced condition than that of anthrax. We had demonstrated the probability that septicemia depends upon the presence and growth of a microscopic body, but the absolute proof of this important conclusion was not reached. To demonstrate experimentally that a microscopic organism actually is the cause of a disease and the agent of contagion, I know no other way, in the present state of Science, than to subject the *microbe* (the new and happy term introduced by M. Sedillot) to the method of cultivation out of the body. It may be noted that in twelve successive cultures, each one of only ten cubic centimeters volume, the original drop will be diluted as if placed in a volume of fluid equal to the total volume of the earth. It is just this form of test to which M. Joubert and I subjected the anthrax bacteridium. Having cultivated it a great number of times in a sterile fluid, each culture being started with a minute drop from the preceding, we then demonstrated that the product of the last culture was capable of further development and of acting in the animal tissues by producing anthrax with all its symptoms. Such is—as we believe—the indisputable proof that *anthrax is a bacterial disease.*

Our researches concerning the septic vibrio had not so far been convincing, and it was to fill up this gap that we resumed our experiments. To this end, we attempted the cultivation of the septic vibrio from an animal dead of septicemia. It is worth noting that all of our first experiments failed, despite the variety of culture media we employed—urine, beer yeast water, meat water, etc. Our culture media were not sterile, but we found—most commonly—a microscopic organism showing no relationship to the septic vibrio, and presenting the form, common enough elsewhere, of chains of extremely minute spherical granules possessed of no virulence whatever. This was an impurity, introduced, unknown to us, at the same time as the septic vibrio; and the germ undoubtedly passed from the intestines—always inflamed and distended in septicemic animals —into the abdominal fluids from which we took our original cultures of the septic vibrio. If this explanation of the contamination of our cultures was correct, we ought to find a pure culture of the septic vibrio in the heart's blood of an animal recently dead of septicemia. This was what happened, but a new difficulty presented itself; all our cultures remained sterile. Furthermore this sterility was accompanied by loss in the culture media of (the original) virulence.

It occurred to us that the septic vibrio might be an obligatory anaërobe and that the sterility of our inoculated culture fluids might be due to the destruction of the septic vibrio by the atmospheric oxygen dissolved in the fluids. The Academy may remember that I have previously demonstrated facts of this nature in regard to the vibrio of butyric fermentation, which not only lives without air but is killed by the air.

It was necessary therefore to attempt to cultivate the septic vibrio either in a vacuum or in the presence of inert gases—such as carbonic acid.

Results justified our attempt; the septic vibrio grew easily in a complete vacuum, and no less easily in the presence of pure carbonic acid.

These results have a necessary corollary. If a fluid containing septic vibrios be exposed to pure air, the vibrios should be killed and all virulence should disappear. This is actually the case. If some drops of septic serum be spread horizontally in a tube and in a very thin layer, the fluid will become absolutely harmless in less than half a day, even if at first it was so virulent as to produce death upon the inoculation of the smallest portion of a drop.

Furthermore all the vibrios, which crowded the liquid as motile threads, are destroyed and disappear. After the action of the air, only fine amorphous granules can be found, unfit for culture as well as for the transmission of any disease whatever. It might be said that the air burned the vibrios.

If it is a terrifying thought that life is at the mercy of the multiplication of these minute bodies, it is a consoling hope that Science will not always remain powerless before such enemies, since for example at the very beginning of the study we find that simple exposure to air is sufficient at times to destroy them.

But, if oxygen destroys the vibrios, how can septicemia exist, since atmospheric air is present everywhere? How can such facts be brought in accord with the germ theory? How can blood, exposed to air, become septic through the dust the air contains?

All things are hidden, obscure and debatable if the cause of the phenomena be unknown, but everything is clear if this cause be known. What we have just said is true only of a septic fluid containing adult vibrios, in active development by fission: conditions are different when the vibrios are transformed into their germs, that is into the glistening corpuscles first described and figured in my studies on silk-worm disease, in dealing with worms dead of the disease called "flachérie." Only the adult vibrios disappear, burn up, and lose their virulence in contact with air: the germ corpuscles, under these conditions, remain always ready for new cultures, and for new inoculations.

All this however does not do away with the difficulty of understanding how septic germs can exist on the surface of objects, floating in the air and in water.

Where can these corpuscles originate? Nothing is easier than the production of these germs, in spite of the presence of air in contact with septic fluids.

If abdominal serous exudate containing septic vibrios actively growing by fission be exposed to the air, as we suggested above, but with the precaution of giving a substantial thickness to the layer, even if only one centimeter be used, this curious phenomenon will appear in a few hours. The oxygen is absorbed in the upper layers of the fluid—as is indicated by the change of color. Here the vibrios are dead and disappear. In the deeper layers, on the other hand, towards the bottom of this centimeter of septic fluid we suppose to be under observation, the vibrios continue to multiply by fission—protected from the action of oxygen by those that have perished above them: little by little they pass over to the condition of germ corpuscles with the gradual disappearance of the thread forms. So that instead of moving threads of varying length, sometimes greater than the field of the microscope, there is to be seen only a number of glittering points, lying free or surrounded by a scarcely perceptible amorphous mass. Thus is formed, containing the latent germ life, no longer in danger from the destructive action of oxygen, thus, I repeat, is formed the septic dust, and we are able to understand what has before seemed so obscure; we can see how putrescible fluids can be inoculated by the dust of the air, and how it is that putrid diseases are permanent in the world.

The Academy will permit me, before leaving these interesting results, to refer to one of their main theoretical consequences. At the very beginning of these researches, for they reveal an entirely new field, what must be insistently demanded? The absolute proof that there actually exist transmissible, contagious, infectious diseases of which the cause lies essentially and solely in the presence of microscopic organisms. The proof that for at least some diseases, the conception of spontaneous virulence must be forever abandoned—as well as the idea of contagion and an infectious element suddenly originating in the bodies of men or animals and able to originate diseases which propagate themselves under identical forms: and all of those opinions fatal to medical progress, which have given rise to the gratuitous hypotheses of spontaneous generation, of albuminoid ferments, of hemiorganisms, of archebiosis, and many other conceptions without the least basis in observation. What is to be sought for in this instance is the proof that along with our vibrio there does not exist an independent virulence belonging to the surrounding fluids or solids, in short that the vibrio is not merely an epiphenomenon of the disease of which it is the obligatory accompaniment. What then do we see, in the results that I have just brought out? A septic fluid, taken at the moment that the vibrios are not yet changed into germs, loses its virulence completely upon simple exposure to the air, but preserves this virulence, although exposed to air on the simple condition of being in a thick layer for some hours. In the first case, the virulence once lost by exposure to air, the liquid is incapable of taking it on again upon cultivation: but, in the second case, it preserves its virulence and can propagate, even after exposure to air. It is impossible, then, to assert that there is a separate virulent substance, either fluid or solid, existing, apart from the adult vibrio or its germ. Nor can it be supposed that there is a virus which loses its virulence at the moment that the adult vibrio dies; for such a substance should also lose its virulence when the vibrios, changed to germs, are exposed to the air. Since the virulence persists under these conditions it can only be due to the germ corpuscles—the only thing present. There is only one possible hypothesis as to the existence of a virus in solution, and that is that such a substance, which was present in our experiment in non-fatal amounts, should be continuously furnished by the vibrio itself, during its growth in the body of the living animal. But it is of little importance since the hypothesis supposes the forming and necessary existence of the vibrio.

I hasten to touch upon another series of observations which are even more deserving the attention of the surgeon than the preceding: I desire to speak of the effects of our microbe of pus when associated with the septic vibrio. There is nothing more easy to superpose—as it were—two distinct diseases and to produce what might be called a *septicemic purulent infection,* or a *purulent septicemia.* Whilst the microbe-producing pus, when acting alone, gives rise to a thick pus, white, or sometimes with a yellow or bluish tint, not putrid, diffused or enclosed by the so-called *pyogenic membrane,* not dangerous, especially if localized in cellular tissue, ready, if the expression may be used for rapid resorption; on the other hand the smallest abscess produced by this organism when associated with the septic vibrio takes on a thick gangrenous appearance, putrid, greenish and infiltrating the softened tissues. In this case the microbe of pus carried so to speak by the septic vibrio, accompanies it throughout the body: the highly-inflamed muscular tissues, full of serous fluid, showing also globules of pus here and there, are like a kneading of the two organisms.

812

By a similar procedure the effects of the anthrax bacteridium and the microbe of pus may be combined and the two diseases may be superposed, so as to obtain a purulent anthrax or an anthracoid purulent infection. Care must be taken not to exaggerate the predominance of the new microbe over the bacteridium. If the microbe be associated with the latter in sufficient amount it may crowd it out completely—prevent it from growing in the body at all. Anthrax does not appear, and the infection, entirely local, becomes merely an abscess whose cure is easy. The microbe-producing pus and the septic vibrio (not) being both anaërobes, as we have demonstrated, it is evident that the latter will not much disturb its neighbor. Nutrient substances, fluid or solid, can scarcely be deficient in the tissues from such minute organisms. But the anthrax bacteridium is exclusively aërobic, and the proportion of oxygen is far from being equally distributed throughout the tissues: innumerable conditions can diminish or exhaust the supply here and there, and since the microbe-producing pus is also aërobic, it can be understood how, by using a quantity slightly greater than that of the bacteridium it might easily deprive the latter of the oxygen necessary for it. But the explanation of the fact is of little importance: it is certain that under some conditions the microbe we are speaking of entirely prevents the development of the bacteridium.

Summarizing—it appears from the preceding facts that it is possible to produce at will, purulent infections with no elements of putrescence, putrescent purulent infections, anthracoid purulent infections, and finally combinations of these types of lesions varying according to the proportions of the mixtures of the specific organisms made to act on the living tissues.

These are the principal facts I have to communicate to the Academy in my name and in the names of my collaborators, Messrs. Joubert and Chamberland. Some weeks ago (Session of the 11th of March last) a member of the Section of Medicine and Surgery, M. Sedillot, after long meditation on the lessons of a brilliant career, did not hesitate to assert that the successes as well as the failures of Surgery find a rational explanation in the principles upon which the germ theory is based, and that

813

this theory would found a new Surgery—already begun by a celebrated English surgeon, Dr. Lister, who was among the first to understand its fertility. With no professional authority, but with the conviction of a trained experimenter, I venture here to repeat the words of an eminent *confrère*.

METHOD OF PREVENTING RABIES

Prophylaxy in rabies, as I announced it in my name and in the name of my collaborators, in some previous notes, surely constituted real progress in the study of this disease; scientific progress, however, rather than practical. Its application lay open to accidents. Of twenty dogs treated, I could not surely claim to have rendered more than 15 or 16 refractory to rabies.

It was, furthermore, expedient to end the treatment with a final very virulent inoculation, the inoculation of a control virus, so as to fortify and reinforce the refractory state. Besides, prudence required that one keep the dogs under observation during a period longer than the period of incubation of the disease produced by the direct inoculation of this last virus. From which it follows that no less than three or four months must pass before we can feel sure that the state is one of refractoriness toward rabies.

Such requirements would have limited greatly the application of the method.

Finally, only with difficulty could one apply the method to an immediate commencement of treatment, a condition made necessary by the element of the accidental and unforeseen in rabid dog bites.

What was needed, were it possible, was to effect a method more rapid and capable of conferring upon dogs what I would presume to term perfect security.

For how other than by advancing thus far dare one make any trial at all upon man?

After what might be called innumerable trials I achieved a prophylactic method, both prompt and practical, the success of which in dogs has been so frequent and so sure that I have confidence in the applicability of it generally to all animals and to man himself.

This method rests essentially on the following facts:

The inoculation into a rabbit by trepanation, under the dura mater, of a rabic spinal cord of a dog with street rabies, always gives to these animals a case of rabies after an average incubation period of around a fortnight.

If one passes the virus from this first rabbit to a second, from the second to a third, and so on, according to the foregoing procedure there soon is manifested a tendency, increasing in distinctness, toward a diminution of the incubation period of rabies in the rabbits successively inoculated.

After twenty to twenty-five passages from rabbit to rabbit one encounters incubation periods of eight days which remain during a new series of twenty to twenty-five passages. Then one attains an incubation period of seven days which recurs with striking regularity during a new series of up to ninety passages. At any rate it is at this figure that I am at the moment. And it is scarcely if at all that there at present appears a tendency toward an incubation period of a little less than seven days.

Experiments of this type, begun in November 1882, are already three years old, without the series ever having been interrupted and without our ever having recourse to a virus other than those of these rabbits successively dead of rabies. Nothing is easier, thus, than to have constantly at hand a rabic virus of perfect purity, always identical or practically so. Upon this hinges the *practicability* of the method.

Spinal cords of these rabbits are rabic throughout their entire length with constancy of virulence.

If one detaches portions of these cords several centimeters long, utilizing the greatest precautions for purity which it is possible to realize, and if one suspends these in dry air, gradually their virulence diminishes until it finally disappears entirely. The time for extinction of virulence varies very little with the thickness of the pieces, but markedly with the external temperature. The results constitute the *scientific* point in our method.

These facts established, here is a method for rendering a dog refractory to rabies in a relatively short time.

In a series of flasks in which the air is kept dry by pieces of potash placed on the bottom of the vessel, one suspends each day, a section of fresh rabic cord from a rabbit dead of rabies, developed after seven day's incubation. Likewise daily, one inoculates under the skin of a dog one full Pravaz syringe of sterilized bouillon in which one has dispersed a small fragment of one of these desiccated cords, commencing with a cord whose order number places it sufficiently far from the day of operation so that we are sure that it is not at all virulent. Previous experiments have established what may be considered safety in this matter. On the following days one proceeds in the same way with more recent cords, separated by an interval of two days, until one arrives at a last very virulent cord which has only been in the flask for a day or two.

At this time the dog is refractory to rabies. One is able to inoculate him with rabic virus under the skin or even on the surface of the brain without rabies declaring itself.

By applying this method, I finally had fifty dogs of every age and breed all refractory without encountering a single failure when unexpectedly there presented themselves at my laboratory upon the sixth of last July three persons from Alsace:

Theodore Vone, a petty merchant grocer of Meissengott near Schlestadt, bitten in the arm July 4th by his own dog which had gone mad;

Joseph Meister, aged nine years, likewise bitten on the 4th of July at 8 o'clock in the morning by the same dog. This child, thrown to the earth by the dog, had numerous bites on his hand, legs, and buttocks, some of them very deep and making walking difficult. The chief wounds had been cauterized with carbolic acid only twelve hours after the accident, at 8 in the evening of July 4th, by Dr. Weber of Ville;

The third person who had herself received no bites was the mother of little Joseph Meister.

At the autopsy of the dog, struck down by its master, the stomach of the dog was found full of straw, hay, bits of wood.

The dog had been quite mad. Joseph Meister had been dragged from under the dog covered with saliva and blood.

M. Vone had on his arm some marked contusions, but he assured me that his shirt had not been pierced by the fangs of the dog. Since he had nothing to fear I told him he could leave for Alsace the same day, and he did so. But I kept with me little Joseph Meister and his mother.

Now it happened that it was also on exactly July 6th that the Academy of Science was holding its weekly meeting; I saw there our colleague M. le Dr. Vulpian and told him what had happened. M. Vulpian, as well as Dr. Grancher, were good enough to accompany me at once to Joseph Meister and confirm the condition and number of his wounds. He had no less than fourteen of them.

The opinions of our colleague and of Dr. Grancher were to the effect that, from the intensity and number of his bites, Joseph Meister had been practically fatally exposed to the inception of rabies. I then communicated to M. Vulpian and M. Grancher the new results I had obtained in the study of rabies since my lecture in Copenhagen a year before.

The death of this child appearing to be inevitable, I decided, not without deep and acute anxiety, as you will well imagine, to try with Joseph Meister the method which had so often proved successful with dogs.

My fifty dogs, it is true, had not been bitten before I commenced to make them refractory, but I knew that this circumstance need not preoccupy me for I had previously already obtained the refractory state in dogs after their being bitten in a large number of cases. I had already presented evidence this year to the rabies Commission of this new and important forward step.

Therefore, on July 6th, at 8 in the evening, sixty hours after the bites of July 4th, and in the presence of Drs. Vulpian and Grancher, Joseph Meister was inoculated under the skin of the hypochondrium, right side, with one half of a Pravaz syringe of cord of a rabbit dead of rabies June 21st and since then preserved in a flask of dry air, namely, for fifteen days.

The days following, new inoculations were made, always in the hypochondrial region according to the conditions which I give in the following table:

July	Time	Cord taken	Dried for
7th	9 am	June 23rd	14 days
7th	6 pm	June 25th	12 days
8th	9 pm	June 27th	11 days
8th	6 pm	June 29th	9 days
9th	11 am	July 1st	8 days
10th	11 am	July 3rd	7 days
11th	11 am	July 5th	6 days
12th	11 am	July 7th	5 days
13th	11 am	July 9th	4 days
14th	11 am	July 11th	3 days
15th	11 am	July 13th	2 days
16th	11 am	July 15th	1 day

In this way I carried to 13 the number of inoculations and to 10 the number of days of treatment. I will explain later that a fewer number of inoculations would have sufficed. But you will understand that in this first attempt I felt obliged to act with the most particular circumspectness.

Each of the cords employed was also inoculated by trepanation into two new rabbits so as to follow the virulence of the materials we were injecting into the human subject.

Study of these rabbits made it possible to verify that the cords of July 6th, 7th, 8th, 9th, and 10th were not virulent, for they did not produce rabies in the rabbits. The cords of July 11th to 16th were all virulent, and the proportion of virulent substance present grew daily greater. Rabies declared itself after seven days' incubation for rabbits of July 15th and 16th; after eight days for those of the 12th and 14th; after fifteen days for those of July 11th.

During the last days, I had inoculated into Joseph Meister the very most virulent strain of rabies virus, a strain which taken from dogs and reinforced by many passages from rabbit gives rabies to rabbits in seven days, to dogs in eight to ten. I felt justified in undertaking to do so because of what happened to the fifty dogs to which I previously referred.

When the immune state has been attained one can without fear inoculate the strongest virus in any quantity whatever. It has always seemed to me that this would have no other effect than to consolidate the refractory state.

Thus, Joseph Meister escaped not only the rabies to which his bites might have given rise but also the virus which I injected as a control upon the immunity got by treatment, and the rabies which I injected was stronger than the street strain.

The final inoculation of this very virulent material has likewise the advantage of cutting down the time during which one need be apprehensive about the aftereffects of a bite. For if the rabies is going to be able to appear, then it will appear much sooner from the injected virus than from the weaker virus of the bite. After the middle of August, I looked forward with confidence toward the future soundness of Joseph Meister. Today as well, after a lapse of three months and three weeks since the accident, his health leaves nothing to be desired.

What interpretation is to be made of this new method which I have just made known for preventing rabies after the bite? I do not intend today to treat this question in a complete fashion. I wish to limit myself to some preliminary details having to do with the understanding of the meaning of the experiments which I am now pursuing in an effort to focus upon the best of the interpretation possible.

Returning now to the method for progressive attenuation of a fatal virus and the prophylaxy one can derive therefrom, the influence of air upon this attenuation being given, the first which presents itself in explanation of the effect of the method is that the sojourn of the cords in contact with dry air progressively diminishes the intensity of their virulence to the disappearing point.

From this, one would be persuaded that the prophylactic procedure in question rests upon the use first of a virus without appreciable virulence, next weak ones, and then stronger and stronger ones.

I will show finally that the facts do not agree with this way of looking at the matter. I will prove that the delays in the incubation period of the rabies given to rabbits day by day, such as I was speaking about above, given to check the state of the virulence of the cords desiccated in contact with air, are an effect of the impoverishment of the quantity of the virus present in these cords and not an effect of the impoverishment of the virulence.

Could one admit that the introduction of a virus of constant virulence would produce immunity—if one used very small quantities increasing them daily? This is an interpretation of my method which I have studied from the experimental point of view.

One can give the new method another interpretation, an interpretation certainly very foreign to the foregoing, but one which merits full consideration because it is in harmony with certain already achieved results in connection with vital phenomena in certain lower organisms, notably different pathogenic microbes.

Many microbes appear to give rise in their culture media to substances injurious to their own development.

In 1880, I began researches to establish that the microbe of chicken cholera produces a sort of self-poisoning substance. I did not succeed in demonstrating such a substance; but I feel today that the study should be taken up again—nor shall I fail to do so—operating in the presence of pure carbonic acid gas....

M. Raulin, my old teacher, now professor of the Faculty of Lyon, has established, in a very remarkable thesis which he defended at Paris, March 22, 1870, that the growth of *aspergillus niger* develops a substance which partially arrests the growth of this mold when the culture medium does not contain iron salts.

Could it not be that the rabies virus is composed of two distinct substances so that in addition to that which is living and able to reproduce in the nervous system, there is another having the faculty when present in suitable amounts of stopping the development of the foregoing? I will examine this third interpretation of the method of prophylaxy in rabies with all the attention it deserves in my next communication.

I scarcely need to mention in closing that perhaps the most important question to be resolved at this time is that of what interval to observe between the instant of the bite and the commencement of the treatment. That interval in the case of Joseph Meister was two and a half days. But we must be prepared for situations in which it is much longer.

Last Tuesday, October 20th, with the obliging assistance of MM. Vulpian and Grancher, I had to start treating a youth of 15 years, bitten six days before on both hands and in very serious condition.

I shall not delay in informing the Academy of the outcome from this new attempt.

Probably it will not be without emotion that the Academy will hear the account of the courageous act and presence of mind of this boy whom I started treating Tuesday last. He is a shepherd, fifteen years old, named Jean-Baptiste Jupille, from Villers-Farlay (Jura) who, on seeing a dog of suspicious actions and great size leap upon a group of six small friends of his, all younger than he was, lept forward, armed with his whip, in front of the animal. The dog seized Jupille's left hand in its mouth. At this, Jupille knocked the dog over, held it down, opened its mouth with his right hand, meanwhile receiving several new bites, and then, with the thong of his whip bound the dog's muzzle and dispatched the animal with one of his wooden shoes.

RESEARCHES ON THE MOLECULAR ASYMMETRY OF NATURAL ORGANIC PRODUCTS

III.

WHEN I began to devote myself to special work, I sought to strengthen myself in the knowledge of crystals, foreseeing the help that I should draw from this in my chemical researches. It seemed to me to be the simplest course, to take, as a guide, some rather extensive work on crystalline forms; to repeat all the measurements, and to compare my determinations with those of the author. In 1841, M. de la Provostaye, whose accuracy is well known, had published a beautiful piece of work on the crystalline forms of tartaric and paratartaric acids and of their salts. I made a study of this memoir. I crystallised tartaric acid and its salts, and investigated the forms of the crystals. But, as the work proceeded, I noticed that a very interesting fact had escaped the learned physicist. All the tartrates which I examined gave undoubted evidence of hemihedral faces.

This peculiarity in the forms of tartrates was not very obvious. This will be readily conceived, seeing that it had not been observed before. But when, in a species, its presence was doubtful, I always succeeded in making it manifest by repeating the crystallisation and slightly modifying the conditions. Sometimes the crystals bore all the faces demanded by the law of symmetry, but the hemihedry was still betrayed by an unequal development of one half of the faces. This is seen, for example in tartar emetic. It must be admitted that a circumstance which adds greatly to the difficulty in recognising hemihedry is the frequent irregularities of the crystals, which never develop quite freely. From this cause there arise deformations, arrestments of development in one direction or another, faces suppressed by accident, etc. Unless in circumstances of an almost exceptional character, the recognition of hemihedry, particularly in laboratory crystals, demands very attentive study. To this we must add the fact that, although hemihedry may be possible in a given form, and although it is a function of the internal structure of the substance, it may not be indicated externally, any more than one finds on every crystal of a cubic species all the forms compatible with the cube.

But however these things may be, I repeat that I found the tartrates hemihedral.

This observation would probably have remained sterile, without the following one.

Let a, b, c, be the parameters of the crystal form of any tartrate, and α, 6, γ, the angles of the crystallographic axes. The latter are ordinarily perpendicular, or slightly oblique. In addition, the ratio of two parameters, such as a and b, is almost the same in the various tartrates, whatever may be their composition, their quantity of water of crystallisation, or the nature of the bases; c alone shows sensible variations. There is a kind of semi-isomorphism among all the tartrates. One would imagine that the tartaric group dominated and stamped with similarity the forms of all the various substances in spite of the difference in the other constituent elements.

The results of this are, a resemblance in the forms of all tartrates, and the possibility of parallel orientation, taking, for example, as basis of orientation the position of the axes a and b.

Now if we compare the disposition of the hemihedral faces on all the prisms of the primitive forms of the tartrates, when they are oriented in the same manner, this disposition is found to be the same.

These results, which have been the foundation of all my later work, may be summed up in two words: the tartrates are hemihedral, and that in the same sense.

Guided then on the one hand by the fact of the existence of molecular rotary polarisation, discovered by Biot in tartaric acid and all its compounds, and on the other by Herschel's ingenious correlation, and yet again by the sagacious views of M. Delafosse, with whom hemihedry has always been a law of structure and not an accident of crystallisation, I believed that there might be a relation between the hemihedry of the tartrates and their property of deviating the plane of polarised light.

It is important thoroughly to grasp the development of the conceptions: —Haüy and Weiss observe that quartz possesses hemihedral faces and that these faces incline to the right on some specimens and to the left on others. Biot on his part finds that quartz crystals likewise separate themselves into two sets, in relation to their optical properties, the one set deviating the plane of polarised light to the right, the other to the left,

823

according to the same laws. Herschel in his turn supplies to these hitherto isolated facts the bond of union, and says:—Plagihedra of one kind deviated in the same sense; plagihedra of the other kind deviate in the opposite sense.

For my part I find that all tartrates are plagihedral, if I may so express myself, and that in the same sense; so that I might presume that here, as in the case of quartz, there was a relation between the hemihedry and the circular polarisation. At the same time the essential differences to which I have just referred between circular polarisation in quartz and in tartaric acid must not be neglected.

Thanks to the above discoveries, and to the relations which I have just enumerated, we are now in possession of a pre-conceived notion (for it is still nothing more than that) as to the possible inter-relations of the hemihedry and the rotative power of the tartrates.

Being very anxious to find by experiment some support for this still purely speculative view, my first thought was to see whether the very numerous crystallisable organic products which possess the molecular rotative property, have hemihedral crystalline forms, an idea which had not previously occurred to any one in spite of Herschel's correlation. This investigation met with the success which I anticipated.

I also occupied myself with the examination of the crystalline forms of paratartaric acid and its salts. These substances are isomeric with the tartaric compounds, but had all been found by Biot to be inactive towards polarised light. None of them exhibited hemihedry.

Thus the idea of the inter-relation of the hemihedry and the molecular rotary power of natural organic products gained ground.

I was soon enabled to establish it clearly by a wholly unexpected discovery. . . .

IV.

You will now understand why, being preoccupied, for the reasons already given, with a possible relation between the

824

hemihedry of the tartrates and their rotative property, Mitscherlich's note of 1844 should recur to my memory. I thought at once that Mitscherlich was mistaken on one point. He had not observed that his double tartrate was hemihedral while his paratartrate was not. If this is so, the results in his note are no longer extraordinary; and further, I should have, in this, the best test of my preconceived idea as to the interrelation of hemihedry and the rotatory phenomenon.

I hastened therefore to re-investigate the crystalline form of Mitscherlich's two salts. I found, as a matter of fact, that the tartrate was hemihedral, like all the other tartrates which I had previously studied, but, strange to say, the paratartrate was hemihedral also. Only, the hemihedral faces which in the tartrate were all turned the same way, were, in the paratartrate inclined sometimes to the right and sometimes to the left. In spite of the unexpected character of this result, I continued to follow up my idea. I carefully separated the crystals which were hemihedral to the right from those hemihedral to the left, and examined their solutions separately in the polarising apparatus. I then saw with no less surprise than pleasure that the crystals hemihedral to the right deviated the plane of polarisation to the right, and that those hemihedral to the left deviated it to the left; and when I took an equal weight of each of the two kinds of crystals, the mixed solution was indifferent towards the light in consequence of the neutralisation of the two equal and opposite individual deviations.

Thus, I start with paratartaric acid; I obtain in the usual way the double paratartrate of soda and ammonia; and the solution of this deposits, after some days, crystals all possessing exactly the same angles and the same aspect. To such a degree is this the case that Mitscherlich, the celebrated crystallographer, in spite of the most minute and severe study possible, was not able to recognize the smallest difference. And yet the molecular arangement in one set is entirely different from that in the other. The rotatory power proves this, as does also the mode of asymmetry of the crystals. The two kinds of crystals are isomorphous, and isomorphous with the corresponding tartrate.

But the isomorphism presents itself with a hitherto unobserved peculiarity; it is the isomorphism of an asymmetric crystal with its mirror image. This comparison expresses the fact very exactly. Indeed, if, in a crystal of each kind, I imagine the hemihedral facets produced till they meet, I obtain two symmetrical tetrahedra, inverse, and which cannot be superposed, in spite of the perfect identity of all their respective parts. From this I was justified in concluding that, by the crystallisation of the double paratartrate of soda and ammonia, I had separated two symmetrically isomorphous atomic groups, which are intimately united in paratartaric acid. Nothing is easier than to show that these two species of crystals represent two distinct salts from which two different acids can be extracted.

Using the treatment always employed in such cases, the purpose is served by precipitating each salt with a salt of lead or baryta, and then isolating the acids by means of sulphuric acid. . . .

VI.

Let us return to the two acids furnished by the two sorts of crystals deposited in so unexpected a manner in the crystallisation of the double paratartrate of soda and ammonia. I have already remarked that nothing could be more interesting than the investigation of these acids.

One of them, that which comes from crystals of the double salt hemihedral to the right, deviates to the right, and is identical with ordinary tartaric acid. The other deviates to the left, like the salt which furnishes it. The deviation of the plane of polarisation produced by these two acids is rigorously the same in absolute value. The right acid follows special laws in its deviation, which no other active substance had exhibited. The left acid exhibits them, in the opposite sense, in the most faithful manner, leaving no suspicion of the slightest difference.

That paratartaric acid is really the combination, equivalent for equivalent, of these two acids, is proved by the fact that, if somewhat concentrated solutions of equal weights of each of them are mixed, as I shall do before you, their combination

826

takes place with disengagement of heat, and the liquid solidifies immediately on account of the abundant crystallisation of para-tartaric acid, identical with the natural product.

In accord with their chemical and crystallographic proper-ties, all that can be done with one acid can be repeated with the other under the same conditions, and in each case we get identical, but not superposable products; products which re-semble each other like the right and left hands. The same forms, the same faces, the same angles, hemihedry in both cases. The sole dissimilarity is in the inclination to right or left of the hemihedral facets and in the sense of the rotatory power. . . .

IVAN PETROVICH PAVLOV

(1849–1936)

Ivan Pavlov received the Nobel prize for physiology and medicine in 1904, not for his famous analysis of the conditioned reflex, but for his researches into the physiology of the heart and secretory nerves of the pancreas and digestive glands. It was in 1907, as director of the department of physiology at the Institute of Experimental Medicine, that he began the study of the conditioned reflex, with his famous experiments on live dogs. Pavlov's work, involving the meticulous measurement of salivary activity and digestive juices, as well as brilliant operative techniques, established the importance of preserving normal situations in experimental research. Since he was a mechanist, tracing all action to the conditioned reflex, a principle he extended even to psychiatric research, his theory was gratefully taken over by the Marxists and made a central principle in their ideological canon.

THE CONDITIONED REFLEX

The conditioned reflex is now used as a separate physiological term to denote a certain nervous phenomenon, the detailed study of which has led to the creation of a new branch in the physiology of the higher nervous activity, as the first chapter in the physiology of the higher parts of the central nervous system. For many years empirical and scientific observations have been accumulated which show that a mechanical lesion or a disease of the brain, and especially of the cerebral hemispheres, causes a disturbance in the higher, most complex behaviour of the animal and man, usually referred to as psychical activity. At present hardly anyone with a medical education would doubt that our neuroses and psychoses are connected with the weakening or disappearance of the normal physiological properties of the brain, or with its greater or lesser destruction. But the following persistent, fundamental questions arise: what is the connection between the brain and the higher activity of the animal and man? With what and how must we begin the study of this activity? It would seem that psychical activity is the result of a certain mass of the brain and that physiology should investigate it in exactly the same way as the activity of all other parts of the organism is now being successfully investigated. However, this has not been done for a long time. Psychical activity has long (for thousands of years) been the object of study by a special branch of science—psychology. But physiology, strange as it may seem, only recently—in 1870—obtained with the help of its usual method of artificial stimulation the first precise facts relating to a certain (motor) physiological function of the cerebral hemispheres; with the help of its other usual method of partial destruction it acquired additional facts relating to the establishment of connections between other parts of the cerebral hemispheres and the most important receptors of the organism—the eye, the ear, etc. This raised hopes among physiologists, as well as psychologists, that close connection would be established between physiology and psychology. . . . But now even among psychologists and especially psychiatrists, there are many who are bitterly disappointed in the practical application of experimental psychology.

However, a new method of solving the fundamental question was already on the way. Was it possible to discover an elementary psychical phenomenon which at the same time could be fully and rightly regarded as a purely physiological phenomenon? Was it possible to begin with it, and by a strictly objective study (as generally done in physiology) of the conditions of its emergence, its various complexities and its disappearance, to obtain first of all an objective physiological picture of the entire higher nervous activity in animals, i.e., the normal functioning of the higher part of the brain, instead of the previous experiments involving its artificial irritation and destruction? Fortunately, such a phenomenon had long been observed by a number of re-

829

searchers; many of them paid attention to it and some even began to study it (special mention should be made of Thorndike), but for some reason or other they stopped the study at the very beginning and did not utilize the knowledge of this phenomenon for the purpose of elaborating a fundamental method of systematic physiological study of the higher activity in the animal organism. This was the phenomenon now termed the "conditioned reflex," thorough study of which has fully justified the previous experiments that can be successfully performed by all. We introduce into the mouth of a dog a moderate solution of some acid; the acid produces a usual defensive reaction in the animal: by vigorous movements of the mouth it ejects the solution, and at the same time an abundant quantity of saliva begins to flow first into the mouth and then overflows, diluting the acid and cleansing the mucous membrane of the oral cavity. Now let us turn to the second experiment. Just prior to introducing the same solution into the dog's mouth we repeatedly act on the animal by a certain external agent, say, a definite sound. What happens then? It suffices simply to repeat the sound, and the same reaction is fully reproduced—the same movements of the mouth and the same secretion of saliva.

Both of the above-mentioned facts are equally exact and constant. And both must be designated by one and the same physiological term—"reflex." Both disappear if we sever either the motor nerves of the mouth musculature and the secretory nerves of the salivary glands, i.e., the efferent drives, or the afferent drives going from the mucous membrane of the mouth and from the ear, and finally, if we destroy the central exchange where the nervous current (i.e., the moving process of nervous excitation) passes from the afferent to the efferent drives; for the first reflex this is the medulla oblongata, for the second it is the cerebral hemispheres.

In the light of these facts even the strictest judgement cannot raise any objection to such a physiological conclusion; at the same time, however, there is a manifest difference between the two reflexes. In the first place, their centres, as already mentioned, are different. In the second place, as is clear from the procedure of our experiments, the first reflex was reproduced without any preparation or special condition, while the second was obtained by means of a special method. This means that in the first case there took place a direct passage of the nervous current from one kind of drives to the other, without any special procedure. In the second case the passage demanded a certain preliminary procedure. The next natural assumption is that in the first reflex there was a direct conduction of the nervous current, while in the second it was necessary preliminarily to prepare the way for it; this concept had long been known to physiology and had been termed "Bahnung." Thus, in the central nervous system there are two different central mechanisms—one directly conducting the nervous current and the second—closing and opening it. There is nothing surprising in this conclusion. The nervous system is the most complex and delicate instrument on our planet, by means of which relations, connections are established between the numerous parts of the organism, as well as between the organism, as a highly complex system, and the innumerable, external influences. If the closing and opening of electric current is now regarded as an ordinary technical device, why should there be any objection to the idea that the same principle acts in this wonderful instrument? On this basis the *constant connection between the external agent and response of the organism, which it evokes, can be rightly called an unconditioned reflex, and the temporary connection—a conditioned reflex.*

The basic condition for the formation of a conditioned reflex is, generally speaking, a single or repeated coincidence of the indifferent stimulus with the unconditioned one. The formation of the reflex is quickest and meets with least difficulties when the first stimulus directly precedes the second, as shown in the above-mentioned auditory acid reflex. . . .

The conditioned reflex is formed on the basis of all unconditioned reflexes and from various agents of the internal medium and external environment both in their simplest and most complex forms, but with one limitation: it is formed only from those agents for the reception of which there are receptor elements in the cerebral hemispheres. Thus we have before us a very

831

extensive synthesizing activity effected by this part of the brain.

But this is not enough. The conditioned temporary connection is at the same time highly specialized, reaching the heights of complexity and extending to the most minute fragmentation of the conditioned stimuli as well as of some activities of the organism, particularly such as the skeletal movements and the speech movements. Thus we have before us a highly delicate analysing activity of the same cerebral hemispheres! Hence the enormous breadth and depth of the organism's adaptability, of its equilibration with the surrounding world. The synthesis is, apparently, a phenomenon of nervous coupling. What, then, is the analysis as a nervous phenomenon? Here we have several separate physiological factors. The foundation for the analysis is provided first of all by the peripheral endings of all the afferent nervous conductors of the organism, each one of which is specially adjusted to transform a definite kind of energy (both inside and outside the organism) in the process of nervous excitation; this process is then conducted to special, less numerous, cells of the lower parts of the central nervous system, as well as to the highly numerous special cells of the cerebral hemispheres. From there, however, the process of nervous excitation usually irradiates to various cells over a greater or lesser area. This explains why when the conditioned reflex has been elaborated, say, to one definite tone, not only all the other tones, but even many of the other sounds produce the same conditioned reaction. In the physiology of the higher nervous activity this is known as the generalization of conditioned reflexes. Consequently, here we simultaneously meet with phenomena of coupling and irradiation. But afterwards the irradiation gradually becomes more and more limited; the excitatory process concentrates in the smallest nervous point of the cerebral hemispheres, probably the group of corresponding special cells. This limitation is most rapidly effected by means of another basic nervous process known as inhibition. This is how the process develops. First we elaborate a conditioned generalized reflex to a definite tone. Then we continue our experiment with this reflex, constantly accompanying and reinforcing it with the unconditioned reflex;

but along with it we apply other, so to speak, spontaneously acting tones, but without any reinforcement. The latter gradually lose their effect, and, finally, the same thing takes place with the closest tone; for example, a tone of 500 oscillations per second will produce an effect, whereas the tone of 498 oscillations will not, i.e., it will be differentiated. These tones, which have now lost their effect, are inhibited. . . .

When the inhibitory process is intensified, it becomes concentrated. This leads to delimitation between the cortical point which is in a state of excitation and the points in a state of inhibition. And since there is a multitude of diverse points in the cortex, excitatory and inhibitory, relating both to the external world (visual, auditory and others) and to the internal world (motor, etc.), it represents a grandiose mosaic of intermittent points of various properties and various degrees of strength of the excitatory and inhibitory states. Thus, the alert working state of an animal or of a human being is a mobile and at the same time localized process of fragmentation of the excitatory and inhibitory states of the cortex, now in large, now in very small parts, it contrasts with the state of sleep when inhibition at the height of its intensity and extensity is spread evenly over the whole mass of the cerebral hemispheres, as well as down to a certain level. However, even then there may remain separate excitatory points in the cortex—which are, so to speak, on guard or on duty. Consequently, in the alert state both processes are in permanent mobile equilibration, as if struggling with each other. If the mass of external or internal stimulations falls off at once, a marked predominance of the inhibitory process takes place over the excitatory. Some dogs, in which the peripheral basic external receptors (visual, auditory and olfactory) are damaged, sleep twenty-three hours a day.

Along with the law of irradiation and concentration of the nervous processes, there is another permanently operating fundamental law—the law of reciprocal induction. According to this law, the effect of the positive conditioned stimulus becomes stronger when the latter is applied immediately or shortly after the concentrated inhibitory stimulus, just as the effect of the inhibitory stimulus proves to be more exact and profound after the concentrated positive stimulus. The reciprocal induction manifests itself both in the circumference of the point of excitation or inhibition simultaneously with their action, and in the point itself after the termination of the processes. . . .

The entire establishment and distribution in the cortex of excitatory and inhibitory states, taking place in a certain period under the action of external and internal stimuli, become more and more fixed under uniform, recurring conditions and are effected with ever-increasing ease and automatism. Thus, there appears a dynamic stereotype (systematization) in the cortex, the maintenance of which becomes an increasingly less difficult nervous task; but the stereotype becomes inert, little susceptible to change and resistant to new conditions and new stimulations. Any initial elaboration of a stereotype is, depending on the complexity of the system of stimuli, a difficult and often an extraordinary task. . . .

The most convincing proof that the study of the conditioned reflexes has brought the investigation of the higher part of the brain on to the right trail and that the functions of this part of the brain and the phenomena of our subjective world have finally become united and identical, is provided by the further experiments with conditioned reflexes on animals reproducing pathological states of the human nervous system—neuroses and certain psychotic symptoms; in many cases it is also possible to attain a rational deliberate return to the normal—recovery—i.e., a truly scientific mastery of the subject. Normal nervous activity is a balance of all the above-described processes participating in this activity. Derangement of the balance is a pathological state, a disease; and often there is a certain disequilibrium even in the so-called normal, or to be more precise, in the relative normal. Hence the probability of nervous illness is manifestly connected with the type of nervous system. Under the influence of difficult experimental conditions those of our dogs are quickly and easily susceptible to nervous disorders which belong to the extreme—excitable and weak—types. Of course, even in the strong equilibrated types the equilibrium can be deranged by applying very strong, extraordinary measures. The difficult conditions, which chronically violate the nervous equilibrium, include: overstrain of the excitatory process, overstrain of the inhibitory process and a direct collision of both opposite processes, in other words, overstrain of the mobility of these processes. We have a dog with a system of conditioned reflexes which are called forth stereotypically in one and the same order and at the same intervals. We sometimes apply exceptionally strong conditioned stimuli, sometimes we greatly prolong the duration of the inhibitory stimuli; we now elaborate a very delicate differentiation, now increase the quantity of inhibitory stimuli in the system of reflexes; finally, we either make the opposing processes follow each other immediately, or even simultaneously apply opposite conditioned stimuli, or at once change the dynamic stereotype, i.e., convert the established system of conditioned stimuli into an opposite series of stimuli. And we see that in all these cases the above-mentioned extreme types fall with particular ease into chronic pathological states differently manifesting themselves in these types. In the excitable type the neurosis is expressed in the following way. The inhibitory process, which even in a normal state constantly lags behind the excitatory process in relation to strength, now becomes very weak, almost disappearing: the elaborated, although not absolute, differentiations become fully disinhibited; the extinction assumes an extremely protracted character, the delayed reflex is converted into a short-delayed one, etc. In general, the animal becomes highly unrestrained and nervous during the experiments in the stand: it either behaves violently, or—which is much less frequent—falls into a state of sleep; this had not been observed before. In the weak type the neurosis is almost exclusively of a depressive character. The conditioned reflex activity becomes highly confused, and more often completely vanishes; in the course of the experiment the animal is in an almost continuous hypnotic state, manifesting its various phases (there are no conditioned reflexes at all, the animal even refuses food).

Experimental neuroses in most cases assume a lingering character lasting for months and even years. Some therapeutic remedies have been successfully tested in protracted neuroses.

The described neuroses in animals can best be compared with neurasthenia in human beings, especially since some neuropathologists insist on two forms of neurasthenia—excitatory and depressive. Besides, certain traumatic neuroses may correspond to them, as well as other reactive pathological states. It may be assumed that recognition of two signalling systems of reality in man will lead specially to an understanding of the mechanisms of two human neuroses—hysteria and pychasthenia. If, on the basis of the predominance of one system over the other, people can be divided into a predominantly thinking type and a predominantly artistic type, then it is clear that in pathological cases of a general disequilibrium of the nervous system, the former will become psychasthenics and the latter hysterics. . . .

In the course of the study of conditioned reflexes, along with general disorders of the cortex, there were frequently observed extremely interesting cases of disorders experimentally and functionally produced in very small points of the cortex. Let us take a dog with a system of various reflexes and among them conditioned reflexes to different sounds—a tone, a noise, the beat of a metronome, the sound of a bell, etc.; it is possible to induce a disorder only at one of the points of application of these conditioned stimuli, while all other points remain normal. The pathological state of an isolated cortical point is produced by the methods described above as morbific. The disorder manifests itself in different forms and degrees. The mildest change effected at this point is expressed in its chronic hypnotic state: instead of the normal relation between the strength of the effect induced by the stimulation and the physical inensity of the stimulus, the equalization and paradoxical phases develop at this point. Proceeding from the above, this, too, can be interpreted as a physiological preventive measure under a difficult state of a cortical point. When the pathological state develops further, the stimulus in some cases has no positive effect at all, provoking only inhibition. In other cases the opposite occurs. The positive reflex becomes unusually stable: its extinction proceeds more slowly than that of the normal reflexes; it is less susceptible to successive inhibition by other, inhibitory conditioned stimuli; it often stands out in bold relief for its strength among all other conditioned reflexes, which was not observed prior to the disorder. This signifies that the excitatory process at the given point has become chronically and pathologically inert. The stimulation of the pathological point sometimes remains indifferent to the points of other stimuli, and sometimes it is impossible to touch this point with its stimulus without deranging in one way or another the entire system of reflexes. There are grounds for assuming that in the case of disorder of isolated points, when now the inhibitory, now the excitatory processes predominate at the diseased point, the mechanism of the pathological state consists precisely in the derangement of equilibrium between the opposed processes: there takes place a considerable and predominant decrease now of one process, now of the other. In the case of pathological inertness of the excitatory process bromide (which reinforces the inhibitory process) often fully eliminates the inertness.

The following conclusion can hardly be considered fantastic. If stereotypy, iteration and perseveration, as is perfectly obvious, have their natural origin in the pathological inertness of the excitatory process of the different motor cells, then obsessional neurosis and paranoia must also have the same mechanism. This is simply a matter of other cells or of groups of cells connected with our sensations and notions. Thus, only one series of sensations and notions connected with the diseased cells becomes abnormally stable and resistant to the inhibitory influence of other numerous sensations and notions, which to a greater degree conform with reality because of the normal state of their cells. Another phenomenon, frequently observed in the study of pathological conditioned reflexes and having a direct bearing on human neuroses and psychoses, is circularity in the nervous activity. The disturbed nervous activity manifested more or less regular fluctuations. There was observed at first a period of extremely weakened activity (the conditioned reflexes were of a chaotic character, often fully disappeared or declined to the minimum); then, after several weeks or months, as if spontaneously, without any visible reason, there took place a greater or lesser, and even complete, return to the normal, which was again superseded by a period of pathological activity. Sometimes periods of weakened activity and abnormally increased activity alternated in this circularity. It is impossible not to see in these fluctuations an analogy with cyclothymia and the manic-depressive psychosis. The simplest way would be to ascribe this pathological periodicity to the derangement of normal relations between the excitatory and inhibitory processes, as far as their interaction is concerned. Since the opposite processes did not limit each other in due time and in the proper measure, but acted independently of each other and excessively, the result of their activity reached its maximum—and only then was one process superseded by the other. Thus, there developed a different, namely, exaggerated, periodicity, lasting a week or a month, instead of the short and very easy periodicity of one day. Finally, it is impossible not to mention a phenomenon which so far has manifested itself with exceptional force only in one dog. This is the extreme explosiveness of the excitatory process. Certain individual stimuli or all the conditioned stimuli produced an extremely violent and excessive effect (both motor and secretory), which, however, abruptly disappeared already during the action of the stimulus—when the alimentary reflex was reinforced, the dog did not take the food. Obviously, this was because of the high pathological lability of the excitatory process, which corresponds to the excitatory weakness of the human clinic. In certain conditions a weak form of this phenomenon is often observed in dogs.

All the pathological nervous symptoms described above are manifested in corresponding conditions both in normal dogs, i.e., not subjected to surgical operation, and (especially some of these symptoms, for example, circularity) in castrated animals, being, consequently, of an organic pathological nature. Numerous experiments have shown that the most fundamental property of the nervous activity in castrated animals is a considerable and predominant decline of the inhibitory process, which in the strong type, however, is greatly levelled out with the passage of time.

To sum up, we must emphasize once more that when we compare the ultra-paradoxical phase with the sense of possession and with inversion, and the pathological inertness of the excitatory process with obsessional neurosis and paranoia, we see how closely the physiological phenomena and the experiences of the subjective world are interconnected and how they merge.

MAX PLANCK

(1858–1947)

Nobel prize winner for physics in 1918, Max Planck is known today for his association with the quantum theory, which he began developing in 1901. Roughly speaking, a quantum is the smallest amount of energy that nature produces, and all energy changes can be expressed in units of quantum. Planck was led to his theory through the study of black-body radiation, when he observed through a spectroscope that the radiation did not flow, as physics had taught until that time, in a continuous stream, but in separate "bundles" or "quanta" like bullets from a gun. In order to determine quantum measurements, he evolved mathematically what is called Planck's constant. Planck was one of the most honored scientists in pre-Nazi Germany, but in 1944 one of his sons was executed for complicity in the anti-Hitler plot. His own home was destroyed by air raids on Berlin, and he was later rescued and given asylum by the Allies.

PHANTOM PROBLEMS IN SCIENCE

THE WORLD is teeming with problems. Wherever man looks, some new problem crops up to meet his eye—in his home life as well as in his business or professional activity, in the realm of economics as well as in the field of technology, in the arts as well as in science. And some problems are very stubborn; they just refuse to let us in peace. Our agonized thinking of them may sometimes reach such a pitch that our thoughts haunt us throughout the day, and even rob us of sleep at night. And if by lucky chance we succeed in solving a problem, we experience a sense of deliverance, and rejoice over the enrichment of our knowledge. But it is an entirely different story, and an experience annoying as can be, to find after a long time spent in toil and effort, that the problem which has been preying on one's mind is totally incapable of any solution at all—either because there exists no indisputable method to unravel it, or because considered in the cold light of reason, it turns out to be absolutely void of all meaning—in other words, it is a *phantom problem*, and all that mental work and effort was expended on a mere nothing. There are many such phantom problems—in my opinion, far more than one would ordinarily suspect—even in the realm of science.

There is no better safeguard against such unpleasant experiences than to ascertain in each instance, and at the very outset, whether the problem under consideration is a genuine or meaningful one, and whether a solution for it is to be expected. In view of this situation I will cite and examine a number of problems, in order to see whether they happen to be mere phantom problems. By doing so, I may be able to render a genuinely useful service to some of you. My selection of these problems to be exhibited as specimens is not based on any systematic viewpoint, and even less can it lay a claim to completeness in any respect. Most of them are taken from the realm of science, because this is the field in which the relevant factors are the most clearly discernible. However, this consideration will not deter me from touching upon other fields, too, whenever I can reasonably surmise that the subject holds an interest for you.

In order to decide whether or not a given problem is truly meaningful, we must first of all examine closely the assumptions contained in its wording. In many instances, these alone will immediately reveal the problem under consideration to be a phantom problem. The matter is simplest when an error is lurking in the assumptions. In this case, of course, it is immaterial whether the erroneous assumption was introduced deliberately or has just escaped detection. A lucid example is the famous problem of perpetual motion, i.e. the problem of devising a periodically functioning apparatus which will perform mechanical work perpetually without any other change in nature. Since the existence of such an apparatus would contradict the principle of the conservation of energy, such an apparatus cannot possibly occur in nature, so that this problem is a phantom problem. Of course, one may raise the following argument: "The principle of the conservation of energy, after all, is an experimental law. Accordingly, although today it is considered to be universal and all-embracing, its validity may one day have to be restricted— and in fact, such a curtailment of its universal applicability has been sometimes suspected in nuclear physics—and the problem of perpetual motion would then suddenly become genuine. Its meaninglessness is, therefore, by no means absolute."

This counter-argument may actually acquire practical significance, as is demonstrated especially clearly by the example of a no less well-known problem in chemistry: The ancient problem of changing base metal, for instance, mercury, into gold. Originally, prior to the birth of a scientific chemistry, this problem was considered to be pregnant with portentous meaning, and many a learned—and unlearned—mind was zealously occupied with it. But later, as the theory of chemical elements was developed and became universally accepted, the transmutation of metals turned into a phantom problem. In recent times, since the discovery of artificial radioactivity, the situation has again been reversed. The fact is that today it no longer seems to be fundamentally impossible to discover a process for removing a proton from the nucleus of the mercury atom and an electron from its shell. This operation would change the mercury atom into a gold atom. Therefore, at the present stage of science, the ancient quest of the alchemists no longer belongs to the class of phantom problems.

However, these examples must by no means be construed as indicating that the meaninglessness of a phantom problem is never absolute, but simply dependent on whether or not a certain theory is accepted as valid. There are also many phantom problems which are indubitably doomed to remain such forever. One of these, for instance, is the problem which used to keep many a great physicist busy for many years: The study of the mechanical properties of the luminiferous ether. The meaninglessness of this problem follows from its basic premise, which postulates that light vibrations are of a mechanical nature. This premise is erroneous, and must so remain forever.

Here is another example, taken from the field of physiology: It is a well known fact that the convex lens of the human eye projects an inverted image on the retina. When we see a tower, its image appears on the retina with the top of the tower pointing downward. When this phenomenon was established, a number of scientists tried to detect in the human organ of sight that particular mechanism which supposedly re-inverts the image on the retina. This is a phantom problem, and never can be anything else, for it is based on an erroneous premise, for which there can be no possible proof—namely, that in the organ of vision the image of an object must be upright rather than inverted.

Far more difficult than those cases in which, as in the examples just cited, the assumptions are mistaken, are problems whose presuppositions contain no error, but are so vaguely worded that they must remain phantom ones because they are inadequately formulated. Yet, it so happens that it is just such cases with which we shall be chiefly preoccupied.

My first example is a phantom problem, for the triviality of which I beg your forgiveness. The room in which we now sit, has two side walls, a right-hand one and a left-hand one. To you, *this* is the right side, to me, sitting facing you, *that* is the right side. The problem is: Which side is in reality the right-hand one? I know that this question sounds ridiculous, yet I dare call it typical of an entire host of problems which have been, and in part still are, the subject of earnest and learned debates, except that the situation is not always quite so clear. It demonstrates, right at the very outset, what great caution must be exercised in using the word, *real*. In many instances, the word has any sense at all only when the speaker first defines clearly the point of view on which his considerations are based. Otherwise, the words, *real* or *reality*, are often empty and misleading.

Another example: I see a star shining in the sky. What is *real* in it? Is it the glowing substance, of which it is composed, or is it the sensation of light in my eyes? The question is mean-

843

ingless so long as I do not state whether I am assuming a realistic or a positivistic point of view.

Still another example, this one from the realm of modern physics: When the behavior of a moving electron is studied through an electron microscope, the electron appears as a particle following a definite course. But when the electron is made to pass through a crystal, the image projected on the screen shows every characteristic of a refracted light wave. The question, whether the electron is in reality a particle, occupying a certain position in space at a certain time, or a wave, filling all of infinite space, will therefore constitute a phantom problem so long as we fail to stipulate which of the two viewpoints is applied in the study of the behavior of the electron.

The famous controversy between Newton's emission theory and Huygens' wave theory of light is also a phantom problem of science. For every decision for or against either of these two opposing theories will be a completely arbitrary one, depending on whether one accepts the point of view of the quantum theory or that of the classical theory.

In every one of the cases cited till now, we encountered a rather simple, easily appreciable situation. Now let us proceed to the consideration of a problem which was always regarded as one of central importance because of its meaning to human life —the famous body-mind problem. In this case, first of all we must try to ascertain the meaning of our problem. For there are philosophers who claim that mental processes need not be accompanied by physical processes at all, but can take place totally independently from the latter. If this view is right, mental processes are subject to entirely different laws than those applying to physical processes. If so, then, the body-mind problem splits into two separate problems—the body problem and the mind problem—thus losing its meaning, and degenerating into a phantom problem. With this finding, the case may be considered as good as closed, and we need only concern ourselves with the reciprocal interaction of mental and physical processes. Experience shows that they are very closely influenced by each other. For instance, somebody asks me a question. His question is introduced by a physical process, the propagation of the sound waves of the spoken words which, emitted by him, hit my ears and are transmitted to my brain through the sensory nerve paths. They then cause mental processes to take place in my brain, namely, a reflection on the meaning of the words perceived, followed by a decision as to the content of the answer to be given. Then another physical process operates my motor nerves and my larynx, to transmit the answer to the questioner by means of the physical process of propagating sound waves through the air.

Now then, what is the nature of the interrelation of the physical and mental processes? Are mental processes caused by physical ones? And if so, according to what laws? How can something material act on something immaterial, and *vice versa?* All these questions are difficult to answer. If we assume the existence of a causal interaction, a cause-and-effect relationship, between physical and mental processes, a continued, unrestricted applicability of the principle of the conservation of energy appears to be an indispensable premise. For one will not be disposed to sacrifice this universal foundation of exact science. But in that case, there would have to exist a numerically definite mechanical equivalent of psychic processes, as there is a definite equivalent of heat in thermodynamics, and there would be absolutely no method for measuring such a constant. For this reason, a solution has been attempted on the basis of the hypothesis that the mental forces contribute no perceptible energy to the physical processes, but act merely to liberate the latter, as a gentle breeze will start something that will grow into a mighty avalanche, or a tiny spark will blow up a huge powder magazine. However, this hypothesis does not solve the difficulty completely. Because in every case known to us, while the amount of energy expanded in liberating a process is very small in comparison with the energy released, yet it does exist, even though it may have just a microscopic magnitude. Even the very gentlest breeze and very tiniest spark possess an energy above zero— and this is what matters here.

However, it is well known that there are some forces which

produce a perceptible effect without any expenditure whatever of energy. These are what we may call "guiding forces," such as, for instance, the resistance due to the rigidity of railroad rails which forces the wheels of a train to follow a pre-determined curve, without any expenditure of energy. An attempt might be made to ascribe a similar role to the mental forces in the guiding of physical processes along pre-determined paths in the human brain. But this, too, involves grave and insurmountable difficulties. For the modern science of brain physiology is based on the very premise that it is possible to achieve a satisfactory understanding of the laws of biological processes without postulating the intervention of any particular mental force. Such a hypothesis avoids also the theory of parallelism which, in contrast to the theory of interaction, assumes that mental and physical processes must, necessarily, run side by side, each according to its own laws, without interfering with each other. Of course, it still remains incomprehensible just how this reciprocal interdependence of two such fundamentally different occurrences is to be conceived, and whether it perhaps requires the assumption of some form of pre-established harmony. In this respect, the theory of parallelism, too, is hardly satisfactory.

And now, in order to get to the bottom of the matter, let us ask ourselves this question of basic significance: Just what do we know about mental processes? In what circumstances and in what sense may we speak of mental processes? Let us consider first where we come across mental processes in this world. We must take it for granted that members of the higher animal kingdom as well as human beings have emotions and sensations. But as we descend to the lower animals—where is the borderline where sensation ceases to exist? Has a worm any sensation of pain as it is crushed under our feet? And may plants be considered capable of some kind of sensation? There are botanists who are disposed to answer this question affirmatively. But such a theory can never be put to the test, let alone proved, and the wisest course seems to be not to venture any opinion in this regard. Along the entire ladder of evolution, from the lowest order of life up to Man, there is no point at which one can establish a discontinuity in the nature of mental processes.

It is nevertheless possible to specify a quite definite border-line, of decisive importance for all that follows. This is the borderline between the mental processes within other individuals and the mental processes within one's own Ego. For everybody experiences his own emotions and sensations directly. They just simply exist for him. But we do not experience directly the sensations of any other individuals, however certain their existence may be, and we can only infer them in analogy to our own sensations. To be sure, there are physicians who solemnly claim to be able to perceive the emotions and moods of their patients no less clearly than the latter themselves. But such a claim can never be proved indisputably. Its questionability becomes most striking if we think of certain specific instances. Even the most sensitive dentist cannot feel the piercing pains which his patient at times has to suffer under his treatment. He can ascertain them only indirectly, on the basis of the moans or squirming of the patient. Or, to speak of a more pleasant situation, such as for instance a banquet, however clearly one may sense the pleasure of one's neighbor over the taste of his favorite wine, it is something quite different from tasting it on one's own tongue. What *you* feel, think, want, only *you* can know as first-hand information. Other people can conclude it only indirectly, from your words, conduct, actions and mannerisms. When such physical manifestations are entirely absent, they have no basis whatever to enable them to know your momentary mental state.

This contrast between first-hand, or direct, and second-hand, or indirect, experience is a fundamental one. Since our primary aim is to gain direct, first-hand experience, we shall now discuss the interrelation of our mental and physical states.

First of all, we find that we may speak of conscious states only. To be sure, many processes, perhaps even the most decisive ones, must be taking place in the subconscious mind. But these are beyond the reach of scientific analysis. For there exists no science of the unconscious, or subconscious, mind. It would be a contradiction in terms, a self-contradiction. One does not know that which is subconscious. Therefore, all problems concerning the subconscious are phantom problems.

Let us therefore take a simple conscious process involving body and mind. I prick my hand with a needle, and feel a sensation of pain. The wound made by the pin is the physical element, the sensation of pain is the mental element of the process. The wound is seen, the pain is felt. Is there, then, an indisputable method of throwing light upon the interrelation of the two elements of this process? It is easy to realize that this is absolutely impossible. For there is nothing here upon which light is to be thrown. The visual perception of the wound and the feeling of the pain are elementary facts of experience, but they are as different in nature as knowledge and feeling. Therefore, the question as to their essential interrelation represents no meaningful problem—it is just a phantom problem.

It is obvious that the two occurrences, the pin-prick and the sensation of pain, can be examined and analyzed most thoroughly, in every detail. But such an analysis calls for two different viewpoints. In the following I will refer to them, respectively, as the *psychological* and the *physiological* viewpoints. Observation based on the psychological viewpoint is rooted in self-consciousness; therefore, it is applicable directly only to the analysis of one's own mental processes. On the other hand, observation based on the physiological viewpoint is directed at the processes in the external world; therefore, its direct scope is limited to physical processes. These two viewpoints are incompatible. The adoption of one when the other one is called for, always leads to confusion. We cannot judge our mental processes directly from the physiological viewpoint any more than we can examine a physical process from the psychological viewpoint. This state of affairs makes the body-mind problem appear in a different light. For the examination of psychosomatic processes will yield entirely different results, according as the psychological or the physiological viewpoint is taken as the basis of observation. The psychological viewpoint will permit us to gain first-hand knowledge solely and exclusively of something that relates to our mental processes. The physiological viewpoint will produce first-hand information about physical processes only. It is therefore impossible to gain first-hand information about both physical and mental processes from any single viewpoint; and since in order to reach a clear conclusion, we must adhere to a given viewpoint, which automatically excludes the other, the search for the interrelation of physical and mental processes loses its meaning. In this case, there exist only physical processes *or* mental processes, but never processes which are physical *and* mental.

Therefore, it will do no harm to say that the physical and the mental are in no way different from each other. They are the selfsame processes, only viewed from two diametrically opposite directions. This statement is the answer to the riddle, which has been inseparable from the theory of parallelism, namely, how one is to conceive the fact that two types of processes so different from each other as the physical and the mental, are so closely interlinked. The link has now been disclosed. At the same time, the body-mind problem has been recognized as another phantom problem.

The cases heretofore discussed have dealt only with knowledge, and feeling. Physical states and processes are known, mental states and processes are felt. The situation is quite different, and more complicated, when cognition and feeling are joined by volition. For in that case we are confronted by the ancient dilemma of freedom of the will *versus* the law of causality. This problem holds a certain significance for ethics, too, and its discussion will be our immediate next step.

Is the will free, or is it causally determined? In order to be able to answer this question, first of all we must examine the methods which can be utilized for the study of the laws and regularity of volitional processes.

In this connection an important point must first be observed: In order to gain a correct insight into the regular course of a process, one must take every precaution lest the process be influenced by the method of observation used. Thus, for instance, when trying to ascertain the temperature of a body, we must not use any thermometer, the introduction of which would cause a change in the temperature under examination; similarly, in the microscopic observation of the processes taking place in a living cell, we must not employ illumination which might interfere with the normal course of those processes. All that holds true for physical and biological processes, applies naturally to the same extent to mental states and processes, too. It is one of the most elementary principles of experimental psychology that an observation may produce a totally false finding if the subject knows, or even suspects that he is being observed. For this reason, under certain circumstances, the observation itself will constitute a serious source of error.

Applying the above principle to the problem now before us, the most basic and elementary requirement which a scientifically perfect observation of the regular course of a volitional impulse must fulfill, is that it should not affect or influence that impulse. The automatic consequence of this requirement is that the choice of the acceptable viewpoint of the observation must, necessarily, be restricted. Namely, since the observation itself is no less a mental process than the volitional impulse which is to be observed, the observation may, under certain circumstances, influence the course of the volitional impulse, and thus distort the final finding. The only time when there is no reason to fear such interference is when you observe the will of another person without his knowledge, or when another person observes your will without your knowledge. On the other hand, this source of error will always be operative whenever you attempt to observe your own will. For in that case the mental process of the observation coincides in your unified self-consciousness with the mental process of the volitional impulse. Therefore, it is inadmissible to observe one's own will from the viewpoint of one's own Ego—and I am referring to the present as well as the future act of will, for the latter is co-determined by the present will, too. On the other hand, there is nothing to preclude a scientific observation of a volitional impulse of one's own past Ego. For past mental processes are not affected by a later analysis. In order to express this situation, I shall from now on make a distinction between an external and an internal viewpoint of observation. The external viewpoint is the one which permits the volitional processes to be observed without being disturbed, affected, or interfered with, by the observation. This viewpoint is adopted when observing the volitional processes of others, as well as when observing the *past* volitional processes of one's own Ego. The internal viewpoint is the one, from which the volitional processes cannot be observed without being thereby disturbed. This viewpoint is adopted when observing the present and future volitional processes of one's own Ego. The external viewpoint is suitable for a scientific examination of the laws governing volitional processes; the internal viewpoint is not admissible for this purpose. It is self-evident that these two viewpoints mutually preclude each other, and that it is senseless to apply both of them simultaneously.

Now then, if we adopt the external viewpoint—the only one admissible—as the basis of our scientific observation of volitional processes, every-day experience tells us that in our daily dealings with others we always presuppose certain motives, in other words, a causal determinism, in whatever they say and do, for otherwise their behavior would be inaccountable, and any orderly contact with them would be impossible. The same principle applies to scientific research, too. If a historian wanted to ascribe the decision of Julius Caesar to cross the Rubicon not to his political deliberations and to his innate temperament, but to free will, his view would be tantamount to a renunciation of scientific understanding. Therefore, we will have to conclude that from the external viewpoint of observation the will is to be assumed as causally determined.

The state of affairs is quite different as regards the internal viewpoint. As we have seen, the scientific method of observation fails to work here. On the other hand, however, this viewpoint opens up another source of information: Self-consciousness, which tells us immediately that we are able at any time to give any desired turn to our will as we can to our thoughts, whether as a result of mature deliberation, discretion, or even sheer whim. In this connection, it must be observed that this is by

851

no means a matter of an overt volitional act, which is often impeded by external circumstances, but solely giving the will an intended direction. In this domain we have absolute supreme command. Just think of the unspoken mental reservations which we are able to make with every word we speak. This is a real freedom, experienced at first hand, not a make-believe freedom, as it is claimed by many people who are unable to keep distinct the two opposite viewpoints. Of course, he who seeks to know the "real" freedom of will without reference to the viewpoint adopted, proceeds no differently than does the one who asks without further specification which side of this room is "really" the right side. On the present analysis, neither does the freedom of the will rest, as some have supposed, on a certain lack of intelligence. The degree of intelligence is of absolutely no significance here. Even the most intelligent person is no more capable of observing himself from the outside than is even the fastest runner of passing himself.

In summary, we can therefore say: Observed from without, the will is causally determined. Observed from within, it is free. This finding takes care of the problem of the freedom of the will. This problem came into being because people were not careful enough to specify explicitly the viewpoint of the observation, and to adhere to it consistently. This is a typical example of a phantom problem. Even though this truth is still being disputed time and again, there is no doubt in my mind that it is but a question of time before it will gain universal recognition.

JOSEPH PRIESTLEY

(1733–1804)

Joseph Priestley was a nonconformist English clergyman whose radical political and religious convictions led him to take flight to America, where he became a founder of Unitarianism. Although it was Lavoisier who contributed the name "oxygen," and established its importance in chemistry, Priestley is credited with isolating the gas and calling it "dephlogisticated air." (In actuality, the Swedish apothecary, Scheele, had prepared oxygen even earlier.) Priestley's original interest was electricity, on which he published *The History and Present State of Electricity* in 1767. He also isolated and described (under different names) the properties of nitrous oxide, hydrogen sulphide, carbon monoxide and ammonia. He is the author of a number of theological treatises.

EXPERIMENTS AND OBSERVATIONS ON DIFFERENT KINDS OF AIR

PRESENTLY, after my return from abroad, I went to work upon the *mercurius calcinatus*,which I had procured from Mr. Cadet; and with a very moderate degree of heat I got from about one fourth of an ounce of it an ounce measure of air, which I observed to be not readily imbibed, either by the substance itself from which it had been expelled (for I suffered them to continue a long time together before I transferred the air to any other place) or by water, in which I suffered this air to stand a considerable time before I made any experiment upon it.

In this air, as I had expected, a candle burned with a vivid flame; but what I observed new at this time (November 19), and which surprised me no less than the fact I had discovered before, was that, whereas a few moments' agitation in water will deprive the modified nitrous air of its property of admitting a candle to burn in it, yet, after more than ten times as much agitation as would be sufficient to produce this alteration in the nitrous air, no sensible change was produced in this. A candle still burned in it with a strong flame; and it did not in the least diminish common air, which I have observed that nitrous air, in this state, in some measure does.

But I was much more surprised when, after two days in which this air had continued in contact with water (by which it had diminished about one twentieth of its bulk), I agitated it violently in water about five minutes and found that a candle still burned in it as well as in common air. The same degree of agitation would have made phlogisticated nitrous air fit for respiration indeed, but it would certainly have extinguished a candle.

These facts fully convinced me that there must be a very material difference between the constitution of air from mercurius calcinatus, and that of phlogisticated nitrous air, notwithstanding their resemblance in some particulars. But though I did not doubt that the air from mercurius calcinatus was fit for respiration, after being agitated in water, as every kind of air without exception, on which I have tried the experiment, has been, I still did not suspect that it was respirable in the first instance; so far was I from having any idea of this air being, what it really was, much superior, in this respect, to the air of the atmosphere.

In this ignorance of the real nature of this kind of air I continued from this time (November) to the first of March following; having, in the meantime, been intent upon my experiments on the vitriolic acid air above recited, and the various modifications of air produced by spirit of niter, an account of which will follow. But in the course of this month I not only ascertained the nature of this kind of air, though very gradually, but was led to it by the complete discovery of the constitution of the air we breathe.

Till this first of March 1775 I had so little suspicion of the air from mercurius calcinatus, et cetera, being wholesome, that I had not even thought of applying it to the test of nitrous air; but thinking (as my reader must imagine I frequently must have done) on the candle burning in it after long agitation in water, it occurred to me at last to make the experiment; and putting one measure of nitrous air to two measures of this air, I found, not only that it was diminished, but that it was diminished quite as much as common air, and that the redness of the mixture was likewise equal to that of a similar mixture of nitrous and common air.

After this I had no doubt but that the air from mercurius calcinatus was fit for respiration, and that it had all the other properties of genuine common air. But I did not take notice of what I might have observed, if I had not been so fully possessed by the notion of there being no air better than common air, that the redness was really deeper, and the diminution something greater than common air would have admitted.

Moreover, this advance in the way of truth, in reality, threw me back into error, making me give up the hypothesis I had first formed, viz., that the mercurius calcinatus had extracted spirit of niter from the air; for I now concluded that all the constituent parts of the air were equally, and in their proper proportion, imbibed in the preparation of this substance, and also in the process of making red lead. For at the same time that I made the above-mentioned experiment on the air from mercurius calcinatus I likewise observed that the air which I had extracted from red lead, after the fixed air was washed out of it, was of the same nature, being diminished by nitrous air like common air; but at the same time I was puzzled to find that air from the red precipitate was diminished in the same manner, though the process for making this substance is quite different from that of making the two others. But to this circumstance I happened not to give much attention.

I wish my reader be not quite tired with the frequent repetition of the word "surprise," and others of similar import; but I must go on in that style a little longer. For the next day I was more surprised than ever I had been before with finding that, after the above-mentioned mixture of nitrous air and the air from mercurius calcinatus had stood all night (in which time the whole diminution must have taken place; and, consequently, had it been common air, it must have been made perfectly noxious and entirely unfit for respiration or inflammation), a candle burned in it, and even better than in common air.

I cannot, at this distance of time, recollect what it was that I had in view in making this experiment; but I know I had no expectation of the real issue of it. Having acquired a considerable degree of readiness in making experiments of this kind, a very slight and evanescent motive would be sufficient to induce me to do it. If, however, I had not happened, for some other purpose, to have had a lighted candle before me I should probably never have made the trial; and the whole train of my future experiments relating to this kind of air might have been prevented.

Still, however, having no conception of the real cause of this phenomenon, I considered it as something very extraordinary; but as a property that was peculiar to air that was extracted from these substances, and adventitious; and I always spoke of the air to my acquaintance as being substantially the same thing with common air.

I particularly remember my telling Dr. Price that I was myself perfectly satisfied of its being common air, as it appeared to be so by the test of nitrous air; though, for the satisfaction of others, I wanted a mouse to make the proof quite complete.

On the eighth of this month I procured a mouse and put it into a glass vessel, containing two ounce measures of the air from mercurius calcinatus. Had it been common air, a full-grown mouse, as this was, would have lived in it about a quarter of an hour. In this air, however, my mouse lived a full half hour; and though it was taken out seemingly dead, it appeared to have been only exceedingly chilled; for, upon being held to fire, it presently revived and appeared not to have received any harm from the experiment.

By this I was confirmed in my conclusion that the air extracted from mercurius calcinatus, et cetera, was at least as good as common air; but I did not certainly conclude that it was any better; because, though one mouse would live only a quarter of an hour in a given quantity of air, I knew it was not impossible but that another mouse might have lived in it half an hour; so little accuracy is there in this method of ascertaining the goodness of air; and indeed I have never had recourse to it for my own satisfaction, since the discovery of that most ready, accurate, and elegant test that nitrous air furnishes. But in this case I had a view to publishing the most generally satisfactory account of my experiments that the nature of the thing would admit of.

This experiment with the mouse, when I had reflected upon it some time, gave me so much suspicion that the air into which I had put it was better than common air that I was induced, the day after, to apply the test of nitrous air to a small part of that very quantity of air which the mouse had breathed so long; so that, had it been common air, I was satisfied it must have been very nearly, if not altogether, as noxious as possible, so as not to be affected by nitrous air; when, to my surprise again, I found that though it had been breathed so long it was still better than common air. For after mixing it with nitrous air, in the usual proportion of two to one, it was diminished in the proportion of four and one half to three and one half; that is, the nitrous air had made it two-ninths less than before, and this in a very short space of time; whereas I had never found that, in the longest time, any common air was reduced more than one fifth of its bulk by any proportion of nitrous air, nor more than one fourth by any phlogistic process whatever. Thinking of this extraordinary fact upon my pillow, the next morning I put another measure of nitrous air to the same mixture, and to my utter astonishment found that it was farther diminished to almost one half of its original quantity. I then put a third measure to it; but this did not diminish it any farther; but, however, left it one measure less than it was even after the mouse had been taken out of it.

Being now fully satisfied that this air, even after the mouse had breathed it half an hour, was much better than common air; and having a quantity of it still left, sufficient for the experiment, viz., an ounce measure and a half, I put the mouse into it; when

I observed that it seemed to feel no shock upon being put into it, evident signs of which would have been visible if the air had not been very wholesome; but that it remained perfectly at its ease another full half hour, when I took it out quite lively and vigorous. Measuring the air the next day, I found it to be reduced from one and one half to two thirds of an ounce measure. And after this, if I remember well (for in my register of the day I only find it noted that it was considerably diminished by nitrous air,) it was nearly as good as common air. It was evident, indeed, from the mouse having been taken out quite vigorous, that the air could not have been rendered very noxious.

For my further satisfaction I procured another mouse, and putting it into less than two ounce measures of air extracted from mercurius calcinatus and air from red precipitate (which, having found them to be of the same quality, I had mixed together), it lived three quarters of an hour. But not having had the precaution to set the vessel in a warm place, I suspect that the mouse died of cold. However, as it had lived three times as long as it could probably have lived in the same quantity of common air, and I did not expect much accuracy from this kind of a test, I did not think it necessary to make any more experiments with mice.

Being now fully satisfied of the superior goodness of this kind of air, I proceeded to measure that degree of purity with as much accuracy as I could, by the test of nitrous air; and I began with putting one measure of nitrous air to two measures of this air, as if I had been examining common air; and now I observed that the diminution was evidently greater than common air would have suffered by the same treatment. A second measure of nitrous air reduced it to two thirds of its original quantity, and a third measure to one half. Suspecting that the diminution could not proceed much farther, I then added only half a measure of nitrous air, by which it was diminished still more; but not much, and another half measure made it more than half of its original quantity; so that, in this case, two measures of this air took more than two measures of nitrous air and yet remained less than half of what it was. Five measures brought it pretty exactly to its original dimensions.

At the same time air from the red precipitate was diminished in the same proportion as that from mercurius calcinatus, five measures of nitrous air being received by two measures of this without any increase of dimensions. Now as common air takes about one half of its bulk of nitrous air before it begins to receive any addition to its dimensions from more nitrous air, and this air took more than four half measures before it ceased to be diminished by more nitrous air, and even five half measures made no addition to its original dimensions, I conclude that it was between four and five times as good as common air. It will be seen that I have since procured air better than this, even between five and six times as good as the best common air that I have ever met with.

OF THE RESTORATION OF AIR INFECTED WITH ANIMAL RESPIRATION, OR PUTREFACTION, BY VEGETATION

That candles will burn only a certain time, in a given quantity of air is a fact not better known, than it is that animals can live only a certain time in it; but the cause of the death of the animal is not better known than that of the extinction of flame in the same circumstances; and when once any quantity of air has been rendered noxious by animals breathing in it as long as they could, I do not know that any methods have been discovered of rendering it fit for breathing again. It is evident, however, that there must be some provision in nature for this purpose, as well as for that of rendering the air fit for sustaining flame; for without it the whole mass of the atmosphere would, in time, become unfit for the purpose of animal life; and yet there is no reason to think that it is, at present, at all less fit for respiration than it has ever been. I flatter myself, however, that I have hit upon one of the methods employed by nature for this great purpose. How many others there may be, I cannot tell.

When animals die upon being put into air in which other animals have died, after breathing in it as long as they could, it is plain that the cause of their death is not the want of any *pabulum vita*, which has been supposed to be contained in the air, but on account of the air being impregnated with something stimulating to their lungs; for they almost always die in convulsions, and are sometimes affected so suddenly, that they are irrecoverable after a single inspiration, though they may be withdrawn immediately, and every method has been taken to bring them to life again. They are affected in the same manner, when they are killed in any other kind of noxious air that I have tried, viz. fixed air, inflammable air, air filled with the fumes of sulphur, infected with putrid matter, in which a mixture of iron filings and sulphur has stood, or in which charcoal has been burned, or metals calcined, or in nitrous air, &c.

As it is known that *convulsions* weaken, and exhaust the vital powers, much more than the most vigorous *voluntary* action of the muscles, perhaps these universal convulsions may exhaust the whole of what we may call the *vis vitae* at once; at least that the lungs may be rendered absolutely incapable of action, till the animal be suffocated, or be irrecoverable for want of respiration.

If a mouse (which is an animal that I have commonly made use of for the purpose of these experiments) can stand the first shock of this stimulus, or has been habituated to it by degrees, it will live a considerable time in air in which other mice will die instantaneously. I have frequently found that when a number of mice have been confined in a given quantity of air, less than half the time that they have actually lived in it, a fresh mouse being introduced to them has been instantly thrown into convulsions, and died. It is evident therefore, that if the experiment of the Black Hole, at Calcutta, were to be repeated, a man would stand the better chance of surviving it, who should enter at first, than at the last hour.

I have also observed, that young mice will always live much longer than old ones, or than those which are full grown, when they are confined in the same quantity of air. I have sometimes known a young mouse to live six hours in the same circumstances in which an old mouse has not lived one. On these accounts, experiments with mice, and, for the same reason, no doubt, with other animals also, have a considerable degree of uncertainty attending them; and therefore, it is necessary to repeat them frequently, before the result can be absolutely depended upon. But every person of feeling will rejoice with me in the discovery of *nitrous air*, which supersedes many experiments with the respiration of animals; being a much more accurate test of the purity of air.

The discovery of the provision in nature for restoring air, which has been injured by the respiration of animals, having long appeared to me to be one of the most important problems in natural philosophy, I have tried a great variety of schemes in order to affect it. In these, my guide has generally been to consider the influences to which the atmosphere is, in fact, exposed; and, as some of my unsuccessful trials may be of use to those who are disposed to take pains in the farther investigation of this subject, I shall mention the principal of them.

The noxious effluvium with which air is loaded by animal respiration, is not absorbed by standing, without agitations, in fresh or salt water. I have kept it many months in fresh water, when, instead of being meliorated, it has seemed to become even more deadly, so as to require more time to restore it, by the methods which will be explained hereafter, than air which has been lately made noxious. I have even spent several hours in pouring this air from one glass vessel into another, in water, sometimes as cold, and sometimes as warm, as my hands could bear it, and have sometimes also wiped the vessels many times, during the course of the experiment, in order to take off that part of the noxious matter, which might adhere to the glass vessels, and which evidently gave them an offensive smell; but all these methods were generally without any sensible effect. The *motion*, also, which the air received in these circumstances, it is very evident, was of no use for this purpose. I had not then thought of the simple, but most effectual method of agitating air in water, by putting it into a tall jar and shaking it with my hand.

861

This kind of air is not restored by being exposed to the *light*, or any other influence to which it is exposed, when confined in a thin phial, in the open air, for some months.

Among other experiments, I tried a great variety of different *effluvia*, which are continually exhaling into the air, especially of those substances which are known to resist putrefaction; but I could not by these means effect any melioration of the noxious quality of this kind of air.

Having read, in the Memoirs of the Imperial Society, of a plague not affecting a particular village, in which there was a large sulphur-work, I immediately fumigated a quantity of this kind of air; or (which will hereafter appear to be the very same thing) air tainted with putrefaction, with the fumes of burning sulphur, but without any effect.

I once imagined, that the *nitrous acid* in the air might be the general restorative which I was in quest of; and the conjecture was favoured, by finding that candles would burn in air extracted from saltpetre. (This was the first instance of my finding dephlogisticated air, but without knowing it to be at all different from common air). I therefore spent a good deal of time in attempting, by a burning glass, and other means, to impregnate this noxious air with some effluvium of saltpetre, and, with the same view introduced into it the fumes of the smoking spirit of nitre; but both these methods were altogether ineffectual.

In order to try the effect of *heat*, I put a quantity of air, in which mice had died, into a bladder, tied to the end of the stem of a tobacco pipe, at the other end of which was another bladder, out of which the air was carefully pressed. I then put the middle part of the stem into a chafing-dish of hot coals, strongly urged with a pair of bellows; and, pressing the bladders alternately, I made the air pass several times through the heated part of the pipe. I have also made this kind of air very hot, standing in water before the fire. But neither of these methods were of any use.

Rarefaction and *condensation* by instruments were also tried, but in vain.

Thinking it possible that the *earth* might imbibe the noxious quality of the air, and thence supply the roots of plants with such putrescent matter as is known to be nutritive to them, I kept a quantity of air in which mice had died, in a phial, one half of which was filled with fine garden-mould; but, though it stood two months in these circumstances, it was not the better for it.

I once imagined that, since several kinds of air cannot be long separated from common air, by being confined in bladders, in bottles well corked, or even closed with ground stoppers, the affinity between this noxious air and the common air might be so great, that they would mix through a body of water interposed between them; the water continually receiving from the one, and giving to the other, especially as water receives some kind of impregnation from, I believe, every kind of air to which it is contiguous; but I have seen no reason to conclude, that a mixture of any kind of air with the common air can be produced in this manner.

I have kept air in which mice have died, air in which candles have burned out, and inflammable air, separated from the common air, by the slightest partition of water that I could well make, so that it might not evaporate in a day or two, if I should happen not to attend to them; but I found no change in them after a month or six weeks. The inflammable air was still inflammable, mice died instantly in the air in which other mice had died before, and candles would not burn where they had burned out before.

Since air tainted with animal or vegetable putrefaction is the same thing with air rendered noxious by animal respiration, I shall now recite the observations which I have made upon this kind of air, before I treat of the method of restoring them.

That these two kinds of air are, in fact, the same thing, I conclude from their having several remarkable common properties, and from their differing in nothing that I have been able to observe. They equally extinguish flame, they are equally noxious to animals, they are equally, and in the same way, offensive to the smell, they equally precipitate lime in lime water, and they are restored by the same means.

Since air which has passed through the lungs is the same thing with air tainted with animal putrefaction, it is probable that one use of the lungs is to carry off a putrid effluvium, without which, perhaps, a living body might putrefy as soon as a dead one.

Insects of various kinds live perfectly well in air tainted with animal or vegetable putrefaction, when a single inspiration of it would have instantly killed any other animal. I have frequently tried the experiment with flies and butterflies. The *aphides* also will thrive as well upon plants growing in this kind of air, as in the open air. I have been frequently obliged to take plants out of the putrid air in which they were growing, on purpose to brush away the swarms of these insects which infected them; and yet so effectually did some of them conceal themselves, and so fast did they multiply, in these circumstances, that I could seldom keep the plants quite clear of them.

When air has been freshly and strongly tainted with putrefaction, so as to smell through the water, sprigs of mint have presently died, upon being put into it, their leaves turning black; but if they do not die presently, they thrive in a most surprising manner. In no other circumstances have I ever seen vegetation so vigorous as in this kind of air, which is immediately fatal to animal life. Though these plants have been crowded in jars filled with this air, every leaf has been full of life; fresh shoots have branched out in various directions, and have grown much faster than other similar plants, growing in the same exposure in common air.

This observation led me to conclude, that plants, instead of affecting the air in the same manner with animal respiration, reverse the effects of breathing, and tend to keep the atmosphere sweet and wholesome, when it is become noxious, in consequence of animals either living and breathing, or dying and putrefying in it.

In order to ascertain this, I took a quantity of air, made thoroughly noxious, by mice breathing and dying in it, and

864

divided it into two parts; one of which I put into a phial immersed in water; and to the other (which was contained in a glass jar, standing in water) I put a sprig of mint. This was about the beginning of August, 1771, and after eight or nine days, I found that a mouse lived perfectly well in that part of the air, in which the sprig of mint had grown, but died the moment it was put into the other part of the same original quantity of air; and which I had kept in the very same exposure, but without any plant growing in it.

This experiment I have several times repeated; sometimes using air in which animals had breathed and died; and at other times using air tainted with vegetable or animal putrefaction; and generally with the same success.

Once, I let a mouse live and die in a quantity of air which had been noxious, but which had been restored by this process, and it lived nearly as long as I conjectured it might have done in an equal quantity of fresh air; but this is so exceedingly various, that it is not easy to form any judgment from it; and in this case the symptom of *difficult respiration* seemed to begin earlier than it would have done in common air.

Since the plants that I made use of manifestly grow and thrive in putrid air; since putrid matter is well known to afford proper nourishment for the roots of plants; and since it is likewise certain that they receive nourishment by their leaves as well as by their roots, it seems to be exceedingly probable, that the putrid effluvium is in some measure extracted from the air, by means of the leaves of plants, and therefore that they render the remainder more fit for respiration.

Towards the end of the year some experiments of this kind did not answer so well as they had done before, and I had instances of the relapsing of this restored air to its former noxious state. I therefore suspended my judgment concerning the efficacy of plants to restore this kind of noxious air, till I should have an opportunity of repeating my experiments, and giving more attention to them. Accordingly I resumed the experiments in the summer of the year 1772, when I presently had the most indisputable proof of the restoration of putrid air by vegetation; and as the fact is of some importance, and the subsequent variation in the state of this kind of air is a little remarkable, I think it necessary to relate some of the facts pretty circumstantially.

The air, on which I made the first experiments, was rendered exceedingly noxious by mice dying in it on the 20th of June. Into a jar nearly filled with one part of this air, I put a sprig of mint, while I kept another part of it in a phial, in the same exposure; and on the 27th of the same month, and not before, I made a trial of them, by introducing a mouse into a glass vessel, containing two ounce measures and a half, filled with each kind of air; and I noted the following facts.

When the vessel was filled with the air in which the mint had grown, a very large mouse lived five minutes in it, before it began to shew any sign of uneasiness. I then took it out, and found it to be as strong and vigorous as when it was first put in; whereas in the air which had been kept in the phial only, without a plant growing in it, a younger mouse continued not longer than two or three seconds, and was taken out quite dead. It never breathed after, and was immediately motionless. After half an hour, in which time the larger mouse (which I had kept alive, that the experiment might be made on both the kinds of air with the very same animal) would have been sufficiently recruited, supposing it to have received any injury by the former experiment, was put into the same vessel of air; but though it was withdrawn again, after being in it hardly one second, it was recovered with difficulty, not being able to stir from the place for near a minute. After two days, I put the same mouse into an equal quantity of common air, and observed that it continued seven minutes without any sign of uneasiness; and being very uneasy after three minutes longer I took it out. Upon the whole, I concluded that the restored air wanted about one fourth of being as wholesome as common air. The same thing also appeared when I applied the test of nitrous air.

In the seven days, in which the mint was growing in this jar of noxious air, three old shoots had extended themselves about

866

three inches, and several new ones had made their appearance in the same time. Dr. Franklin and Sir John Pringle happened to be with me, when the plant had been three or four days in this state, and took notice of its vigorous vegetation, and remarkably healthy appearance in that confinement.

On the 30th of the same month, a mouse lived fourteen minutes, breathing naturally all the time, and without appearing to be much uneasy, till the last two minutes, in the vessel containing two ounce measures and a half of air which had been rendered noxious by mice breathing in it almost a year before, and which I found to be most highly noxious on the 19th of this month, a plant having grown in it, but not exceedingly well, these eleven days: on which account I had deferred making the trial so long. The restored air was affected by a mixture of nitrous air, almost as much as common air.

That plants are capable of perfectly restoring air injured by respiration may, I think, be inferred with certainty from the perfect restoration, by this means, of air which had passed through my lungs, so that a candle would burn in it again, though it had extinguished flame before, and a part of the same original quantity of air still continued to do so. Of this one instance occurred in the year 1771, a sprig of mint having grown in a jar of this kind of air, from the 25th of July to the 17th of August following; and another trial I made, with the same success, the 7th of July, 1772, the plant having grown in it from the 29th of June preceding. In this case also I found that the effect was not owing to any virtue in the leaves of mint; for I kept them constantly changed in a quantity of this kind of air, for a considerable time, without making any sensible alteration in it.

These proofs of a partial restoration of air by plants in a state of vegetation, though in a confined and unnatural situation, cannot but render it highly probable, that the injury which is continually done to the atmosphere by the respiration of such a number of animals, and the putrefaction of such masses of both vegetable and animal matter, is, in part at least, repaired by the vegetable creation. And, notwithstanding the prodigious mass of air that is corrupted daily by the above-mentioned causes; yet, if we consider the immense profusion of vegetables upon the face of the earth, growing in places suited to their nature, and consequently at full liberty to exert all their powers, both inhaling and exhaling, it can hardly be thought, but that it may be a sufficient counterbalance to it, and that the remedy is adequate to the evil.

Dr. Franklin, who, as I have already observed, saw some of my plants in a very flourishing state, in highly noxious air, was pleased to express very great satisfaction with the result of the experiments. In his answer to the letter in which I informed him of it, he says,

"That the vegetable creation should restore the air which is spoiled by the animal part of it, looks like a rational system, and seems to be of a piece with the rest. Thus fire purifies water all the world over. It purifies it by distillation, when it raises it in vapours, and lets it fall in rain; and farther still by filtration, when, keeping it fluid, it suffers that rain to percolate the earth. We knew before that putrid animal substances were converted into sweet vegetables, when mixed with the earth, and applied as manure; and now, it seems, that the same putrid substances, mixed with the air, have a similar effect. The strong thriving state of your mint in putrid air seems to shew that the air is mended by taking something from it, and not by adding to it." He adds, "I hope this will give some check to the rage of destroying trees that grow near houses, which has accompanied our late improvements in gardening, from an opinion of their being unwholesome. I am certain, from long observation, that there is nothing unhealthy in the air of woods; for we Americans have everywhere in our country habitations in the midst of woods, and no people on earth enjoy better health, or are more prolific."

May not plants also restore air diminished by putrefaction, by absorbing part of the phlogiston with which it is loaded? The greater part of a dry plant, as well as of a dry animal substance, consists of inflammable air, or something that is capable of being converted into inflammable air; and it seems to be as probable that this phlogistic matter may have been imbibed by the roots and leaves of plants, and afterwards incorporated into their substance, as that it is altogether produced by the power of vegetation. May not this phlogistic matter be even the most essential part of the food and support of both vegetable and animal bodies?

Having discovered that vegetation restores, to a considerable degree of purity, air that had been injured by respiration or putrefaction, I conjectured that the phlogistic matter, absorbed by the water, might be imbibed by plants, as well as form other combinations with substances under the water. A curious fact, which has since been communicated to me, very much favours this supposition.

Mr. Garrick was so obliging as to give me the first intimation of it, and Mr. Walker, the ingenious author of a late English Dictionary, from whom he received the account, was pleased to take some pains in making farther inquiries into it for my use. He informed me that Mr. Bremner, who keeps a music-shop opposite to Somerset-house, was at Harwich, waiting for the packet; and observed that a reservoir at the principal inn was very foul on the sides. This made him ask the innkeeper why he did not clean it out; who immediately answered, that he had done so once, but would not any more; for that after cleansing the reservoir, the water which was caught in it grew fetid, and unfit for use; and that it did not recover its sweetness till the sides and bottom of the reservoir grew very foul again. Mr. Walker questioned Mr. Bremner, whether there were any vegetables growing at the sides and bottom of it; but of this he could not be positive. However, as he said it was covered with a *green substance*, which is known to be vegetable matter (and indeed nothing else could well adhere to the *sides*, as well as to the bottom of the reservoir) I think it will be deemed probable, that it was this vegetating matter that preserved the water sweet, imbibing the phlogistic matter that was discharged in its tendency to putrefaction.

I shall be happy, if the mention of this fact should excite an attention to things of this nature. Trifling as they seem to be, they have, in a philosophical view, the greatest dignity and importance; serving to explain some of the most striking phenomena in nature, respecting the general plan and constitution of the system, and the relation that one part of it bears to another.

CHANDRASEKHARA VENKATA RAMAN

(1888–)

This Indian physicist was awarded the Nobel prize in 1930 for his researches in the diffusion of light. The Raman effect concerns the frequency of scattered light waves produced by the impact of waves on molecules. Raman has also worked on the theory of musical instruments, is the author of many scientific papers, and has been highly honored both in his homeland and abroad.

THE SENSATIONS OF LIGHT AND COLOUR

AMONGST the means which Nature has provided for us to enable us to become conscious of our surroundings, the sensations of light and colour occupy a position of supreme importance. The Sun by day and the Stars by night are the power plants from which flow the streams of light which illuminate our surroundings. Not content with these natural sources, man likewise seeks to turn night into day by exercising his ingenuity and providing himself with artificial sources of light of various kinds. The radiations from the sun play a far greater role in our lives than merely enabling us to see our surroundings, but I shall not touch upon that topic now. No wonder, from the earliest times, the tremendous outpouring of energy from the sun has filled mankind with awe and made it the subject of adoration. The source of all that energy has naturally been one of the greatest problems of science.

The first real step towards an understanding of the nature of light is taken when we analyse light by means of a spectroscope. This instrument spreads out the light of the sun into a band of colours traversed by a great number of dark lines.

871

The colours in this band or spectrum, as it is called, vary continuously from one end to the other. The trained eye can easily appreciate fifty or even a hundred distinct tints in traversing the solar spectrum from the extreme violet to the extreme red end.

The spectroscope thus teaches us that the physical entity which we perceive as white light is essentially composite in its nature. To enable the characters of light to be defined in a precise way, we must consider the narrowest possible strip of the spectrum, which we may call monochromatic light. This is conveniently provided for us in the emission from certain gases and metallic vapours when excited by an electric discharge. The sodium vapour and the mercury vapour lamps which are now a feature of the street lighting in our great cities are seen on examination through a spectroscope to emit a small number of distinct monochromatic rays or sharp bright lines in the spectrum.

Various physical experiments, some of which are very simple, show that monochromatic light in its travel through space can be pictured as wave motion with a definite wavelength and frequency. The velocity of light in free space is the same as that of the electromagnetic waves sent out by radio stations. This by itself is sufficient proof that what we call light is essentially electromagnetic radiation, its wavelength being different from point to point in the visible spectrum, but everywhere only a minute fraction of the wavelength of even the shortest waves used in radio transmission. The physical basis of color is thus the difference, in wavelength and frequency of the electromagnetic waves corresponding to the different monochromatic rays in the spectrum. The wavelength of visible light diminishes from about 7,000 to about 4,000 Angstrom units as we pass from the red to the violet end of the spectrum. An Angstrom unit is a hundred millionth part of a centimetre.

Light is thus revealed to us as a minute strip in the whole tremendous possible range of wavelengths of electromagnetic radiation. It is natural to ask, "Why is it that we are able to perceive only this highly restricted part of the electromagnetic

872

spectrum as light?" The answer to this question is, I think, to be found in a study of the radiations of the sun which is our principal luminary. An examination of the nature of solar radiation shows that its spectrum extends well beyond the visible region both towards the longer and shorter wavelengths; such extension, however, is restricted on either side by absorption in the earth's atmosphere. The distribution of the solar energy within the spectrum is determined by what is called the effective temperature of the surface of the sun which is about 5,500°C. If one draws the energy curve of the heat radiations from a body at that temperature, one finds that it rises fairly rapidly with decreasing wavelengths and reaches a peak at a wavelength of about 5,500 Angstrom units and then drops very steeply for shorter wavelengths. If one were to draw a curve of the sensitivity of the human eye as dependent on the wavelength of the incident radiation for equal energies, one would find that the maximum sensitivity falls approximately at a wavelength of 5,500 Angstrom units. This coincidence between the wavelengths of maximum sensitiveness of the human eye and of maximum energy in the solar spectrum can hardly be considered accidental. If it is an accident, it certainly is a most remarkable coincidence. Indeed, it seems much more reasonable to suppose that the development of our visual sense during the long course of biological evolution has been such as to make the fullest possible use of the actual optical environment by the radiations of our sun.

Not merely are we conscious of light, but we also find ourselves in a position to obtain a reasonably accurate idea of our surroundings by means of our vision. Particularly remarkable is the fact that we get a three-dimensional picture of our surroundings and that we can at will fix our attention on any desired object either far or near. These powers rest on the constitution of the human eye as an optical instrument capable of forming a focussed image on the sensitive screen at its back known as the retina. Our stereoscopic sense of three-dimensional vision is possible because we possess two eyes and the retinal images formed by them are slightly different. It is really wonderful, when we come to think of it, that though two distinct pictures of the external world are formed on the retinae of our two eyes, we do not see double and are conscious only of a single external world. The perfect way in which we are able to direct our vision on any object either far or near and thereby scrutinise it in all its detail is also a remarkable example of how the structure of the organs of vision adapts itself to the demands made upon it.

One of the most remarkable features of our power of vision is its ability to adapt itself to the wide range of brightness in our surroundings. When we pass from the bright glare of sunshine in the open air to the dimly lit interior of a building, the intensity of illumination may fall by a factor of a million to one. If the eye is embarrassed by such a sudden drop in the intensity, it is only for a little while. Soon it adapts itself to the feeble illumination. After a long enough rest in the dark, objects that were invisible at first may appear insupportably bright. Under favourable conditions the sensitivity of the human eye is indeed amazing.

If the world we live in were just made up of whites and greys and blacks, it would indeed be a very dull world. Our capacity to appreciate differences in colour adds enormously to the pleasure with which we are conscious of our surroundings. As mentioned earlier, the physical basis of colour is the difference in wavelength and frequency corresponding to the different parts of the solar spectrum. But this statement covers but a very small part of our experience in regard to the actual sensations of colour. It is a question of great interest why a comparatively small change of wavelength or frequency should produce such profoundly different sensations in the human eye. We may also wonder what the physiological mechanism is which enables the eye to be conscious of such differences. In this connection it is very noteworthy that in actual practice we are but rarely concerned with the monochromatic tints of the spectrum. An object may appear vividly coloured, but on examination by a spectroscope may show all the colours of the spectrum. The blue colour of the sky is a typical illustration. Colour regarded

874

as a sensation is generally the result of a distribution of intensity in the spectrum different from that found in standard white light.

The study of colour regarded as a physiological sensation is a subject of great interest. It is also of much practical importance. As typical examples of the striking facts met with in the study of colour, we may mention the following: The colour of yellow light may be counterfeited by mixing spectral red and spectral green. White light may be counterfeited by mixing spectral yellow and spectral violet in a hundred to one ratio. Every known hue can be counterfeited by the appropriate mixture of three primary or spectral colours, one red, one green and one blue or violet. The wavelengths of the colours chosen as primary can be varied to a considerable extent and they may also be broad spectral bands instead of monochromatic rays.

No account of light and colour is complete which does not consider the visual phenomena coming under the general descriptions of illusion and visual fatigue. These play a great part in the sensations experienced by us when we view variously illuminated or coloured objects. They also play an important part in determining the effects known as contrast, visual harmony and clash which arise when different colours are placed adjacent to each other and play a vital part in visual aesthetics.

Some mention must also be made of the interesting condition known as colour blindness which afflicts some unfortunate individuals and prevents them from recognising differences of colour which are patent to normal sighted persons. To be colour-blind may be dangerous in certain types of employment. That is one of the reasons why its study has received much attention. It is also of interest as it throws some light on the phenomena of normal colour vision.

Of recent years, many exact studies have been made of the reactions of the eye to light. Attempts have also been made to translate the actual facts of vision into a theory of visual processes and sensations. Such theories largely rest on the known structure of the retina and the presence in it of certain hypothetical coloured materials which absorb the light falling on them and undergo certain temporary chemical changes. It is a fact that a coloured substance called visual purple can be extracted from the rods of the retina of the higher animals and that a solution of visual purple is bleached by strong light. It is this fact which forms the starting point of some of the newer theories of physiological optics.

WILHELM KONRAD ROENTGEN

(1845–1923)

Roentgen discovered the Roentgen or X ray in 1895, and was promptly rewarded by the Nobel prize for physics in 1901. A native of Holland, he studied in Switzerland and taught in numerous German universities. He discovered the X ray when he observed that certain crystals glowed when near an exhausted tube through which an electric charge was passing. The discovery was dramatically announced at a meeting of the Würzburg Physical and Medical Society, when Roentgen X-rayed the hand of the chairman and the bones showed up clearly in the photograph. The consequences of this discovery for medical diagnosis, surgery and the science of radiology are well known.

ABOUT A NEW TYPE OF RAYS

FIRST COMMUNICATION

1. If the discharge of a fairly large induction-coil be made to pass through a Hittorf vacuum-tube, or through a Lenard tube, a Crookes tube, or other similar apparatus, which has been sufficiently exhausted, the tube being covered with thin, black card-board which fits it with tolerable closeness, and if the whole apparatus be placed in a completely darkened room, there is observed at each discharge a bright illumination of a paper screen covered with barium platino-cyanide, placed in the vicinity of the induction-coil, the fluorescence thus produced being entirely independent of the fact whether the coated or the plain surface is turned towards the discharge-tube. This fluorescence is visible even when the paper screen is at a distance of two metres from the apparatus.

It is easy to prove that the cause of the fluorescence proceeds from the discharge-apparatus, and not from any other point in the conducting circuit.

2. The most striking feature of this phenomenon is the fact that an active agent here passes through a black card-board envelope, which is opaque to the visible and the ultra-violet rays of the sun or of the electric arc; an agent, too, which has the power of producing active fluorescence. Hence we may first investigate the question whether other bodies also possess this property.

We soon discover that all bodies are transparent to this agent, though in very different degrees. I proceed to give a few examples: Paper is very transparent; behind a bound book of about one thousand pages I saw the fluorescent screen light up brightly, the printers' ink offering scarcely a noticeable hindrance. In the same way the fluorescence appeared behind a double pack of cards; a single card held between the apparatus and the screen being almost unnoticeable to the eye. A single sheet of tin-foil is also scarcely perceptible; it is only after several layers have been placed over one another that their shadow is distinctly seen on the screen. Thick blocks of wood are also transparent, pine boards two or three centimetres thick absorbing only slightly. A plate of aluminum about fifteen millimetres thick, though it enfeebled the action seriously, did not cause the fluorescence to disappear entirely. Sheets of hard rubber several centimetres thick still permit the rays to pass through them. Glass plates of equal thickness behave quite differently, according as they contain lead (flintglass) or not; the former are much less transparent than the latter. If the hand be held between the discharge-tube and the screen, the darker shadow of the bones is seen within the slightly dark shadow-image of the hand itself. Water, carbon disulphide, and various other liquids, when they are examined in mica vessels, seem also to be transparent. That hydrogen is to any considerable degree more transparent than air I have not been able to discover. Behind plates of copper, silver, lead, gold, and platinum the fluorescence may still be recognized, though only if the thickness of the plates is not too great. Platinum of a thickness of 0.2 millimetre is still transparent; the silver and copper plates may even be thicker. Lead of a thickness of 1.5 millimetres is practically opaque; and on account of this property this metal is frequently most useful. A rod of wood with a square cross-section (20 $\times$ 20 millimetres), one of whose sides is painted white with lead paint, behaves differently according as to how it is held between the apparatus and the screen. It is almost entirely without action when the X-rays pass through it parallel to the painted side; whereas the stick throws a dark shadow when the rays are made to traverse it perpendicular to the painted side. In a series similar to that of the metals themselves their salts can be arranged with reference to their transparency, either in the solid form or in solution. . . .

6. The fluorescence of barium platino-cyanide is not the only recognizable effect of the X-rays. It should be mentioned that other bodies also fluoresce; such, for instance, as the phosphorescent calcium compounds, then uranium glass, ordinary glass, calcite, rock-salt, and so on.

Of special significance in many respects is the fact that photographic dry plates are sensitive to the X-rays. We are, therefore, in a condition to determine more definitely many phenomena, and so the more easily to avoid deception; wherever it has been possible, therefore, I have controlled, by means of photography, every important observation which I have made with the eye by means of the fluorescent screen.

In these experiments the property of the rays to pass almost unhindered through thin sheets of wood, paper, and tin-foil is most important. The photographic impressions can be obtained in a non-darkened room with the photographic plates either in the holders or wrapped up in paper. On the other hand, from this property it results as a consequence that undeveloped plates cannot be left for a long time in the neighborhood of the discharge-tube, if they are protected merely by the usual covering of paste-board and paper.

It appears questionable, however, whether the chemical action on the silver salts of the photographic plates is directly caused

879

by the X-rays. It is possible that this action proceeds from the fluorescent light which as noted above, is produced in the glass plate itself or perhaps in the layer of gelatin. "Films" can be used just as well as glass plates.

I have not yet been able to prove experimentally that the X-rays are able also to produce a heating action; yet we may well assume that this effect is present, since the capability of the X-rays to be transformed is proved by means of the observed fluorescence phenomena. It is certain, therefore, that all the X-rays which fall upon a substance do not leave it again as such.

The retina of the eye is not sensitive to these rays. Even if the eye is brought close to the discharge-tube, it observes nothing, although, as experiment has proved, the media contained in the eye must be sufficiently transparent to transmit the rays.

7. After I had recognized the transparency of various substances of relatively considerable thickness, I hastened to see how the X-rays behaved on passing through a prism, and to find whether they were thereby deviated or not.

Experiments with water and with carbon disulphite enclosed in mica prisms of about 30° refracting angle showed no deviation, either with the fluorescent screen or on the photographic plate. For purposes of comparison the deviation of rays of ordinary light under the same conditions was observed; and it was noted that in this case the deviated images fell on the plate about 10 or 20 millimetres distant from the direct image. By means of prisms made of hard rubber and of aluminium, also of about 30° refracting angle, I have obtained images on the photographic plate in which some small deviation may perhaps be recognized. However, the fact is quite uncertain; the deviation, if it does exist, being so small that in any case the refractive index of the X-rays in the substances named cannot be more than 1.05 at the most. With a fluorescent screen I was also unable to observe any deviation.

Up to the present time experiments with prisms of denser metals have given no definite results, owing to their feeble transparency and the consequently diminished intensity of the transmitted rays.

With reference to the general conditions here involved on the one hand, and on the other to the importance of the question whether the X-rays can be refracted or not on passing from one medium into another, it is most fortunate that this subject may be investigated in still another way than with the aid of prisms. Finely divided bodies in sufficiently thick layers scatter the incident light and allow only a little of it to pass, owing to reflection and refraction; so that if powders are as transparent to X-rays as the same substances are in mass—equal amounts of material being presupposed—it follows at once that neither refraction nor regular reflection takes place to any sensible degree. Experiments were tried with finely powdered rock-salt, with fine electrolytic silver-powder, and with zinc-dust, such as is used in chemical investigations. In all these cases no difference was detected between the transparency of the powder and that of the substance in mass, either by observation with the fluorescent screen or with the photographic plate.

From what has now been said it is obvious that the X-rays cannot be concentrated by lenses; neither a large lens of hard rubber nor a glass lens having any influence upon them. The shadow-picture of a round rod is darker in the middle than at the edge; while the image of a tube which is filled with a substance more transparent than its own material is lighter at the middle than at the edge. . . .

10. It is well known that Lenard came to the conclusion from the results of his beautiful experiments on the transmission of the cathode rays of Hittorf through a thin sheet of aluminum, that these rays are phenomena of the ether, and that they diffuse themselves through all bodies. We can say the same of our rays.

In his most recent research, Lenard has determined the absorptive power of different substances for the cathode rays, and, among others, has measured it for air from atmospheric pressure to 4.10, 3.40, 3.10, referred to 1 centimetre, according to the rarefaction of the gas contained in the discharge-apparatus. Judging from the discharge-pressure as estimated from the sparking distance, I have had to do in my experiments for the most part with rarefactions of the same order of magnitude, and only rarely with less or greater ones. I have succeeded in comparing by means of the L. Weber photometer—I do not possess a better one—the intensities, taken in atmospheric air, of the fluorescence of my screen at two distances from the discharge-apparatus—about 100 and 200 millimetres; and I have found from three experiments, which agree very well with each other, that the intensities vary inversely as the squares of the distances of the screen from the discharge-apparatus. Accordingly, air absorbs a far smaller fraction of the X-rays than of the cathode rays. This result is in entire agreement with the observation mentioned above, that it is still possible to detect the fluorescent light at a distance of 2 metres from the discharge-apparatus.

Other substances behave in general like air; they are more transparent to X-rays than to cathode rays.

11. A further difference, and a most important one, between the behavior of cathode rays and of X-rays lies in the fact that I have not succeeded, in spite of many attempts, in obtaining a deflection of the X-rays by a magnet, even in very intense fields.

The possibility of deflection by a magnet has, up to the present time, served as a characteristic property of the cathode rays; although it was observed by Hertz and Lenard that there are different sorts of cathode rays, "which are distinguished from each other by their production of phosphorescence, by the amount of their absortion, and by the extent of their deflection by a magnet." A considerable deflection, however, was noted in all of the cases investigated by them; so that I do not think that this characteristic will be given up except for stringent reasons.

12. According to experiments especially designed to test the question, it is certain that the spot on the wall of the discharge-tube which fluoresces the strongest is to be considered as the main centre from which the X-rays radiate in all directions. The X-rays proceed from that spot where, according to the data obtained by different investigators, the cathode rays strike the glass wall. If the cathode rays within the discharge-apparatus are deflected by means of a magnet, it is observed that the

X-rays proceed from another spot—namely, from that which is the new terminus of the cathode rays.

For this reason, therefore, the X-rays, which it is impossible to deflect, cannot be cathode rays simply transmitted or reflected without change by the glass wall. The greater density of the gas outside of the discharge-tube certainly cannot account for the great difference in the deflection, according to Lenard.

I therefore reach the conclusion that the X-rays are not identical with the cathode rays, but that they are produced by the cathode rays at the glass wall of the discharge-apparatus.

13. This production does not take place in glass alone, but, as I have been able to observe in an apparatus closed by a plate of aluminum 2 millimetres thick, in this metal also. Other substances are to be examined later.

14. The justification for calling by the name "rays" the agent which proceeds from the wall of the discharge-apparatus I derive in part from the entirely regular formation of shadows, which are seen when more or less transparent bodies are brought between the apparatus and the fluorescent screen (or the photographic plate).

I have observed, and in part photographed, many shadow-pictures of this kind, the production of which has a particular charm. I possess, for instance, photographs of the shadow of the profile of a door which separates the rooms in which, on one side, the discharge-apparatus was placed, on the other the photographic plate; the shadow of the bones of the hand; the shadow of a covered wire wrapped on a wooden spool; of a set of weights enclosed in a box; of a galvanometer in which the magnetic needle is entirely enclosed by metal; of a piece of metal whose lack of homogeneity becomes noticeable by means of the X-rays, etc.

Another conclusive proof of the rectilinear propagation of the X-rays is a pin-hole photograph which I was able to make of the discharge-apparatus while it was enveloped in black paper; the picture is weak but unmistakably correct.

15. I have tried in many ways to detect interference phe-

nomena of the X-rays; but, unfortunately, without success, perhaps only because of their feeble intensity.

16. Experiments have been begun, but are not yet finished, to ascertain whether electrostatic forces affect the X-rays in any way.

17. In considering the question what are the X-rays—which, as we have seen, cannot be cathode rays—we may perhaps at first be led to think of them as ultra-violet light, owing to their active fluorescence and their chemical actions. But in so doing we find ourserves opposed by the most weighty considerations. If the X-rays are ultra-violet light, this light must have the following properties:

(a) On passing from air into water, carbon disulphide, aluminium, rock-salt, glass, zinc, etc., it suffers no noticeable refraction.

(b) By none of the bodies named can it be regularly reflected to any appreciable extent.

(c) It cannot be polarized by any of the ordinary methods.

(d) Its absortion is influenced by no other property of substances so much as by their density.

That is to say, we must assume that these ultra-violet rays behave entirely different from the ultra-red, visible, and ultra-violet rays which have been known up to this time.

I have been unable to come to this conclusion, and so have sought for another explanation.

There seems to exist some kind of relationship between the new rays and light rays; at least this is indicated by the formation of shadows, the fluorescence and the chemical action produced by them both. Now, we have known for a long time that there can be in the ether longitudinal vibrations besides the transverse light-vibrations; and, according to the views of different physicists, these vibrations must exist. Their existence, it is true, has not been proved up to the present, and consequently their properties have not been investigated by experiment.

Ought not, therefore, the new rays to be ascribed to longitudinal vibrations in the ether?

I must confess that in the course of the investigation I have become more and more confident of the correctness of this idea, and so, therefore permit myself to announce this conjecture, although I am perfectly aware that the explanation given still needs further confirmation.

SECOND COMMUNICATION, MARCH 9, 1896

Since my work must be interrupted for several weeks, I take the opportunity of presenting in the following paper some new phenomena which I have observed.

18. It was known to me at the time of my first publication that X-rays can discharge electrified bodies; and I conjecture that in Lenard's experiments it was the X-rays, and not the cathode rays, which had passed unchanged through the aluminium window of his apparatus, which produced the action described by him upon electrified bodies at a distance. I have, however, delayed the publication of my experiments until I could contribute results which are free from criticism.

These results can be obtained only when the observations are made in a space which is protected completely, not only from the electrostatic forces proceeding from the vacuum-tube, from the conducting wires, from the induction apparatus, etc., but is also closed against air which comes from the neighborhood of the discharge-apparatus.

To secure these conditions I had a chamber made of zinc plates soldered together, which was large enough to contain myself and the necessary apparatus, which could be closed airtight, and which was provided with an opening which could be closed by a zinc door. The wall opposite the door was for the most part covered with lead. At a place near the discharge-apparatus, which was set up outside the case, the zinc wall, together with the lining of sheet-lead, was cut out for a width of 4 centimetres; and the opening was covered again air-tight with a thin sheet of aluminium. The X-rays penetrated through this window into the observation space.

I observed the following phenomena:

(a) Electrified bodies in air, charged either positively or negatively, are discharged if X-rays fall upon them; and this process goes on the more rapidly the more intense the rays are. The intensity of the rays was estimated by their action on a fluorescent screen or a photographic plate.

It is immaterial in general whether the electrified bodies are conductors or insulators. Up to the present I have not found any specific difference in the behavior of different bodies with reference to the rate of discharge; nor as to the behavior of positive and negative electricity. Yet it is not impossible that small differences may exist.

(b) If the electrified conductor be surrounded not by air but by a solid insulator, e.g., paraffin, the radiation has the same action as would result from exposure of the insulating envelope to a flame connected to the earth.

(c) If this insulating envelope be surrounded by a close-fitting conductor which is connected to the earth, and which, like the insulator, is transparent to X-rays, the radiation produces on the inner electrified conductor no action which can be detected by my apparatus.

(d) The observations noted under (a), (b), (c) indicate that air through which X-rays have passed possesses the power of discharging electrified bodies with which it comes in contact.

(e) If this is really the case, and if, further, the air retains this property for some time after it has been exposed to the X-rays, then it must be possible to discharge electrified bodies which have not been themselves exposed to the rays, by conducting to them air which has thus been exposed.

We may convince ourselves in various ways that this conclusion is correct. One method of experiment, although perhaps not the simplest, I shall describe.

I used a brass tube 3 centimetres wide and 45 centimetres long; at a distance of some centimetres from one end a part of the wall of the tube was cut away and replaced by a thin aluminium plate; at the other end, through an air-tight cap, a brass ball fastened to a metal rod was introduced into the tube in such a manner as to be insulated. Between the ball and the closed end of the tube there was soldered a side-tube which could be connected with an exhaust-apparatus; so that when this is in action the brass ball is subjected to a stream of air which on its way through the tube has passed by the aluminium window. The distance from the window to the ball was over 20 centimetres.

I arranged this tube inside the zinc chamber in such a position that the X-rays could enter through the aluminium window of the tube perpendicular to its axis. The insulated ball lay then in the shadow, out of the range of the action of these rays. The tube and the zinc case were connected by a conductor, the ball was joined to a Hankel electroscope.

It was now observed that a charge (either positive or negative) given to the ball was not influenced by the X-rays so long as the air remained at rest in the tube, but that the charge instantly decreased considerably if by exhaustion the air which had been subjected to the rays was drawn past the ball. If by means of storage cells the ball was maintained at a constant potential, and if the modified air was drawn continuously through the tube, an electric current arose just as if the ball were connected to the wall of the tube by a poor conductor.

(f) The question arises, How does the air lose the property which is given it by the X-rays? It is not yet settled whether it loses this property gradually of itself—i.e., without coming in contact with other bodies. On the other hand, it is certain that a brief contact with a body of large surface, which does not need to be electrified, can make the air inactive. For instance, if a thick enough stopper of wadding is pushed into the tube so far that the modified air must pass through it before it reaches the electrified ball, the charge on the ball remains unaffected even while the exhaustion is taking place.

If the wad is in front of the aluminium window, the result obtained is the same as it would be without the wad; a proof that it is not particles of dust which are the cause of the observed discharge.

Wire gratings act like wadding; but the gratings must be very

887

fine, and many layers must be placed over each other if the modified air is to be inactive after it is drawn through them. If these gratings are not connected to the earth, as has been assumed, but are connected to a source of electricity at a constant potential, I have always observed exactly what I had expected; but these experiments are not yet completed.

BERTRAND RUSSELL

(1872-   )

This English skeptic has made distinguished contributions to the philosophy of mathematics. With Whitehead, in *Principia Mathematica* (1910-13), he developed the idea of the unity of mathematics and formal logic. His extreme views have often brought him into conflict with conventional mores, and in the instance of his pacificism during World War I in conflict with the civil authorities. But his philosophical skepticism is based on a rigorous logical analysis. Among his many books, those touching on scientific subjects include: *Principles of Mathematics* (1903), *Introduction to Mathematical Philosophy* (1919), *The ABC of Relativity* (1925), and *The Analysis of Matter* (1927).

DEFINITION OF PURE MATHEMATICS

1. Pure Mathematics is the class of all propositions of the form "p implies q," where p and q are propositions containing one or more variables, the same in the two propositions, and neither p nor q contains any constants except logical constants. And logical constants are all notions definable in terms of the following: Implication, the relation of a term to a class of which it is a member, the notion of *such that,* the notion of relation, and such further notions as may be involved in the general notion of propositions of the above form. In addition to these, mathematics *uses* a notion which is not a constituent of the propositions which it considers, namely the notion of truth.

2. The above definition of pure mathematics is, no doubt, somewhat unusual. Its various parts, nevertheless, appear to be capable of exact justification—a justification which it will be

the object of the present work to provide. It will be shown that whatever has, in the past, been regarded as pure mathematics, is included in our definition, and that whatever else is included possesses those marks by which mathematics is commonly though vaguely distinguished from other studies. The definition professes to be, not an arbitrary decision to use a common word in an uncommon signification, but rather a precise analysis of the ideas which, more or less unconsciously, are implied in the ordinary employment of the term. Our method will therefore be one of analysis, and our problem may be called philosophical —in the sense, that is to say, that we seek to pass from the complex to the simple, from the demonstrable to its indemonstrable premises. But in one respect not a few of our discussions will differ from those that are usually called philosophical. We shall be able, thanks to the labours of the mathematicians themselves, to arrive at certainty in regard to most of the questions with which we shall be concerned; and among those capable of an exact solution we shall find many of the problems which, in the past, have been involved in all the traditional uncertainty of philosophical strife. The nature of number, of infinity, of space, time and motion, and of mathematical inference itself, are all questions to which, in the present work, an answer professing itself demonstrable with mathematical certainty will be given—an answer which, however, consists in reducing the above problems to problems in pure logic, which last will not be found satisfactorily solved in what follows.

3. The Philosophy of Mathematics has been hitherto as controversial, obscure and unprogressive as the other branches of philosophy. Although it was generally agreed that mathematics is in some sense true, philosophers disputed as to what mathematical propositions really meant: although something was true, no two people were agreed as to what it was that was true, and if something was known, no one knew what it was that was known. So long, however, as this was doubtful, it could hardly be said that any certain and exact knowledge was to be obtained in mathematics. We find, accordingly, that idealists have tended more and more to regard all mathematics as dealing with mere

appearance, while empiricists have held everything mathematical to be approximation to some exact truth about which they had nothing to tell us. This state of things, it must be confessed, was thoroughly unsatisfactory. Philosophy asks of Mathematics: What does it mean? Mathematics in the past was unable to answer, and Philosophy answered by introducing the totally irrelevant notion of mind. But now Mathematics is able to answer, so far at least as to reduce the whole of its propositions to certain fundamental notions of logic. At this point, the discussion must be resumed by Philosophy. I shall endeavour to indicate what are the fundamental notions involved, to prove at length that no others occur in mathematics, and to point out briefly the philosophical difficulties involved in the analysis of these notions. A complete treatment of these difficulties would involve a treatise on Logic, which will not be found in the following pages.

4. There was, until very lately, a special difficulty in the principles of mathematics. It seemed plain that mathematics consists of deductions, and yet the orthodox accounts of deduction were largely or wholly inapplicable to existing mathematics. Not only the Aristotelian syllogistic theory, but also the modern doctrines of Symbolic Logic, were either theoretically inadequate to mathematical reasoning, or at any rate required such artificial forms of statement that they could not be practically applied. In this fact lay the strength of the Kantian view, which asserted that mathematical reasoning is not strictly formal, but always uses intuition, *i.e.*, the *a priori* knowledge of space and time. Thanks to the progress of Symbolic Logic, especially as treated by Professor Peano, this part of the Kantian philosophy is now capable of a final and irrevocable refutation. By the help of ten principles of deduction and ten other premises of a general logical nature (*e.g.* "implication is a relation"), all mathematics can be strictly and formally deduced; and all the entities that occur in mathematics can be defined in terms of those that occur in the above twenty premises. In this statement, Mathematics includes not only Arithmetic and Analysis, but also Geometry, Euclidean and non-Euclidean, rational Dynamics, and an indefinite number of other studies still unborn or in their infancy. The fact that

all Mathematics is Symbolic Logic is one of the greatest discoveries of our age; and when this fact has been established, the remainder of the principles of mathematics consists in the analysis of Symbolic Logic itself.

5. The general doctrine that all mathematics is deduction by logical principles from logical principles was strongly advocated by Leibniz, who urged constantly that axioms ought to be proved and that all except a few fundamental notions ought to be defined. But owing partly to a faulty logic, partly to belief in the logical necessity of Euclidean Geometry, he was led into hopeless errors in the endeavour to carry out in detail a view which, in its general outline, is now known to be correct. The actual propositions of Euclid, for example, do not follow from the principles of logic alone; and the perception of this fact led Kant to his innovations in the theory of knowledge. But since the growth of non-Euclidean Geometry, it has appeared that pure mathematics has no concern with the question whether the axioms and propositions of Euclid hold of actual space or not: this is a question for applied mathematics, to be decided, so far as any decision is possible, by experiment and observation. What pure mathematics asserts is merely that the Euclidean propositions follow from the Euclidean axioms—*i.e.* it asserts an implication: any space which has such and such properties has also such and such other properties. Thus, as dealt with in pure mathematics, the Euclidean and non-Euclidean Geometrics are equally true: in each nothing is affirmed except implications. All propositions as to what actually exists, like the space we live in, belong to experimental or empirical science, not to mathematics; when they belong to applied mathematics, they arise from giving to one or more of the variables in a proposition of pure mathematics some constant value satisfying the hypothesis, and thus enabling us, for that value of the variable, actually to assert both hypothesis and consequent instead of asserting merely the implication. We assert always in mathematics that if a certain assertion p is true of any entity x, or of any set of entities x, y, z, . . . , then some other assertion q is true of those entities; but we do not assert either p or q separately of our entities. We

assert a relation between the assertion p and q, which I shall call *formal implications*.

6. Mathematical propositions are not only characterized by the fact that they assert implications, but also by the fact that they contain *variables*. The notion of the variable is one of the most difficult with which Logic has to deal, and in the present work a satisfactory theory as to its nature, in spite of much discussion, will hardly be found. For the present, I only wish to make it plain that there are variables in all mathematical propositions, even where at first sight they might seem to be absent. Elementary Arithmetic might be thought to form an exception: $1 + 1 = 2$ appears neither to contain variables nor to assert an implication. But as a matter of fact, as will be shown in Part II, the true meaning of this proposition is: "If x is one and y is one, and x differs from y, then x and y are two." And this proposition both contains variables and asserts an implication. We shall find always, in all mathematical propositions, that the words *any* or *some* occur; and these words are the marks of a variable and a formal implication. Thus the above proposition may be expressed in the form: "Any unit and any other unit are two units." The typical proposition of mathematics is of the form "$\phi(x, y, z, \ldots)$ implies $\psi(x, y, z, \ldots)$, whatever values $x, y, z, \ldots$ may have"; where $\phi(x, y, z, \ldots)$ and $\psi(x, y, z, \ldots)$, for every set of values of $x, y, z, \ldots$, are propositions. It is not asserted that ϕ is always true, nor yet that ψ is always true, but merely that, in all cases, when ϕ is false as much as when ϕ is true, ψ follows from it.

The distinction between a variable and a constant is somewhat obscured by mathematical usage. It is customary, for example, to speak of parameters as in some sense constants, but this is a usage which we shall have to reject. A constant is to be something absolutely definite, concerning which there is no ambiguity whatever. Thus $1, 2, 3, e, \pi$, Socrates, are constants; and so are *man*, and the human race, past, present and future, considered collectively. Proposition, implication, class, etc. are constants; but a proposition, any proposition, some proposition, are not constants, for these phrases do not denote one definite object. And thus what are called parameters are simply variables. Take, for example, the equation $ax + by + c = 0$, considered as the equation to a straight line in a plane. Here we say that x and y are variables, while a, b, c are constants. But unless we are dealing with one absolutely particular line, say the line from a particular point in London to a particular point in Cambridge, our a, b, c are not definite numbers, but stand for any numbers, and are thus also variables. And in Geometry nobody does deal with actual particular lines; we always discuss *any* line. The point is that we collect the various couples x, y into classes of classes, each class being defined as those couples that have a certain fixed relation to one triad (a, b, c). But from class to class, a, b, c also vary, and are therefore properly variables.

7. It is customary in mathematics to regard our variables as restricted to certain classes: in Arithmetic, for instance, they are supposed to stand for numbers. But this only means that *if* they stand for numbers, they satisfy some formula, *i. e.* the hypothesis that they are numbers implies the formula. This, then, is what is really asserted, and in this proposition it is no longer necessary that our variables should be numbers: the implication holds equally when they are not so. Thus, for example, the proposition "x and y are numbers implies $(x+y)^2 = x^2 + 2xy + y^2$" holds equally if for x and y we substitute Socrates and Plato: both hypothesis and consequent, in this case, will be false, but the implication will still be true. Thus in every proposition of pure mathematics, when fully stated, the variables have an absolutely unrestricted field: any conceivable entity may be substituted for any one of our variables without impairing the truth of our proposition.

8. We can now understand why the constants in mathematics are to be restricted to logical constants in the sense defined above. The process of transforming constants in a proposition into variables leads to what is called generalization, and gives us, as it were, the formal essence of a proposition. Mathematics is interested exclusively in *types* of propositions; if a proposition p containing only constants be proposed, and for a certain one of its terms we imagine others to be successively substituted, the result will in general be sometimes true and sometimes false.

Thus, for example, we have "Socrates is a man"; here we turn Socrates into a variable, and consider "x is a man." Some hypotheses as to x, for example, "x is a Greek," insure the truth of "x is a man"; thus "x is a Greek" implies "x is a man," and this holds for all values of x. But the statement is not one of pure mathematics, because it depends upon the particular nature of *Greek* and *man*. We may, however, vary these too, and obtain: If a and b are classes, and a is contained in b, then "x is an a" implies "x is a b." Here at last we have a proposition of pure mathematics, containing three variables and the constants *class*, *contained in*, and those involved in the notion of formal implications with variables. So long as any term in our proposition can be turned into a variable, our proposition can be generalized; and so long as this is possible, it is the business of mathematics to do it. If there are several chains of deduction which differ only as to the meaning of the symbols, so that propositions symbolically identical become capable of several interpretations, the proper course, mathematically, is to form the class of meanings which may attach to the symbols, and to assert that the formula in question follows from the hypothesis that the symbols belong to the class in question. In this way, symbols which stood for constants become transformed into variables, and new constants are substituted, consisting of classes to which the old constants belong. Cases of such generalization are so frequent that many will occur at once to every mathematician, and innumerable instances will be given in the present work. Whenever two sets of terms have mutual relations of the same type, the same form of deduction will apply to both. For example, the mutual relations of points in a Euclidean plane are of the same type as those of the complex numbers; hence plane geometry, considered as a branch of pure mathematics, ought not to decide whether its variables are points or complex numbers or some other set of entities having the same type of mutual relations. Speaking generally, we ought to deal, in every branch of mathematics, with any class of entities whose mutual relations are of a specified type; thus the class, as well as the particular term considered, becomes a variable, and the only true constants are

895

the types of relations and what they involve. Now a *type* of relation is to mean, in this discussion, a class of relations characterized by the above formal identity of the deductions possible in regard to the various members of the class; and hence a type of relations, as will appear more fully hereafter, if not already evident, is always a class definable in terms of logical constants. We may therefore define a type of relations as a class of relations defined by some property definable in terms of logical constants alone.

9. Thus pure mathematics must contain no indefinables except logical constants, and consequently no premisses, or indemonstrable propositions, but such as are concerned exclusively with logical constants and with variables. It is precisely this that distinguishes pure from applied mathematics. In applied mathematics, results which have been shown by pure mathematics to follow from some hypothesis as to the variable are actually asserted of some constant satisfying the hypothesis in question. Thus terms which were variables become constant, and a new premiss is always required, namely: this particular entity satisfies the hypothesis in question. Thus for example Euclidean Geometry, as a branch of pure mathematics, consists wholly of propositions having the hypothesis "S is a Euclidean space." If we go on to: "The space that exists is Euclidean," this enables us to assert of the space that exists the consequents of all the hypotheticals constituting Euclidean Geometry, where now the variable S is replaced by the constant *actual space*. But by this step we pass from pure to applied mathematics.

10. The connection of mathematics with logic, according to the above account, is exceedingly close. The fact that all mathematical constants are logical constants, and that all the premisses of mathematics are concerned with these, gives, I believe, the precise statement of what philosophers have meant in asserting that mathematics is *a priori*. The fact is that, when once the apparatus of logic has been accepted, all mathematics necessarily follows. The logical constants themselves are to be defined only by enumeration, for they are so fundamental that all the properties by which the class of them might be defined presuppose

some terms of the class. But practically, the method of discovering the logical constants is the analysis of symbolic logic, which will be the business of the following chapters. The distinction of mathematics from logic is very arbitrary, but if a distinction is desired, it may be made as follows. Logic consists of the premisses of mathematics, together with all other propositions which are concerned exclusively with logical constants and with variables but do not fulfil the above definition of mathematics (§ 1). Mathematics consists of all the consequences of the above premisses which assert formal implications containing variables, together with such of the premisses themselves as have these marks. Thus some of the premisses of mathematics, *e.g.* the principle of the syllogism, "if p implies q and q implies r, then p implies r," will belong to logic but not to mathematics. But for the desire to adhere to usage, we might identify mathematics and logic, and define either as the class of propositions containing only variables and logical constants; but respect for tradition leads me rather to adhere to the above distinction, while recognizing that certain propositions belong to both sciences.

ERNEST RUTHERFORD

(1871–1937)

One of the towering figures in twentieth-century physics is Lord Rutherford, who not only pioneered atomic research but actually disintegrated the nitrogen nucleus with radium alpha particles. Born in New Zealand, educated there and in England, he taught in Montreal and Manchester, and before his death was director of the Cavendish Laboratory at Cambridge. His early work was on radioactivity and electromagnetic waves. He discovered and named the alpha, beta and gamma rays emitted from radioactive substances, and received the Nobel prize for chemistry in 1908. Around 1911 he enunciated his atomic theory, of a positive nucleus surrounded by orbiting electrons, which led ultimately to the splitting of the atom, with all its ambiguous consequences for science and society. Works: *Radioactivity* (1904), *Radioactive Substances and Their Radiations* (1912), and *The Newer Alchemy* (1937).

THE ELECTRICAL STRUCTURE OF MATTER

ALL MEN deal with matter in the gross and our bodies are constructed of it. Mysteries of matter, therefore, have a fascination for thoughtful laymen as well as scientists and technologists. The atom has long been familiar as the ultimate unit of matter.

While the vaguest ideas were held as to the possible structure of atoms, there was a general belief among the more philosophically minded that the atoms could not be regarded as simple, unconnected units. For the clarifying of these somewhat vague ideas, the proof in 1897 of the independent existence of the electron as a mobile electrified unit of mass, minute compared with that of the lightest atom, was of extraordinary importance.

Our whole conception of the atom was revolutionized by the

study of radioactivity. The discovery of radium provided the experimenter with powerful sources of radiation specially suitable for examining the nature of the characteristic radiations emitted by the radioactive bodies in general. The wonderful succession of changes that occur in uranium, more than thirty in number, was soon disclosed.

It was early surmised that electricity was atomic in nature. This view was confirmed and extended by a study of the charges of electricity carried by electrons. Skillful experiments by physicists added to the knowledge of the subject. One of the main difficulties has been the uncertainty as to the relative part played by positive and negative electricity in the structure of the atom. The electron has a negative charge of one fundamental unit, while the charged hydrogen atom has a charge of one positive unit. There is the strongest evidence that the atoms of matter are built up of these two electrical units.

It may be of interest to try to visualize the conception of the atom we have so far reached by taking for illustration the heaviest atom, uranium. At the center of the atom is a minute nucleus surrounded by a swirling group of 92 electrons, all in motion in definite orbits, and occupying but by no means filling a volume very large compared with that of the nucleus. Some of the electrons describe nearly circular orbits round the nucleus; others, orbits of a more elliptical shape whose axes rotate rapidly round the nucleus. The motion of the electrons in the different groups is not necessarily confined to a definite region of the atom, but the electrons of one group may penetrate deeply into the region mainly occupied by another group, thus giving a type of interconnection or coupling between the various groups. The maximum speed of any electron depends on the closeness of the approach to the nucleus, but the outermost electron will have a minimum speed of more than 600 miles per second, while the innermost K electrons have an average speed of more than 90,000 miles per second, or half the speed of light.

The nucleus atom has often been likened to a solar system where the sun corresponds to the nucleus and the planets to the electrons. The analogy, however, must not be pressed too far.

899

Suppose, for example, we imagine that some large and swift celestial visitor traverses and escapes from our solar system without any catastrophe to itself or the planets. There will inevitably result permanent changes in the lengths of the month and year, and our system will never return to its original state. Contrast this with the effect of shooting an electron through the electronic structure of the atom. The motion of many of the electrons will be disturbed by its passage, and in special cases an electron may be removed from its orbit and hurled out of its atomic system. In a short time another electron will fall into the vacant place from one of the outer groups, and this vacant place in turn will be filled up, and so on until the atom is again reorganized. In all cases the final state of the electronic system is the same as in the beginning.

MANFRED SAKEL

(1900-1957)

Founder of the Insulin Shock Treatment which bears his name, Dr. Sakel was a Viennese psychiatrist who almost by accident initiated the modern biochemical revolution in the treatment of mental illness. From the early days of Freud little advance had been made in the cure of patients in mental hospitals, however effective Freudian therapy sometimes proved in the handling of neuroses. It was while experimenting with the use of insulin to calm alcoholics and drug addicts, shortly after his graduation from medical school in 1925, that Sakel noticed that patients who went into hypoglycemic coma enjoyed significant therapeutic results. It was not until 1933 that he got the chance to test his schock treatment of schizophrenia in the Vienna Clinic under Dr. Otto Poetzl. After the usual opposition from his profession, the Swiss Society for Psychiatry in 1937 announced that insulin "shock" was being taken up on an international scale. The selection which follows is from the introduction to Sakel's definitive book on *Schizophrenia* (1958), expounding the broad background of his work.

MAN AND HIS MIND

MAN IS the object of this investigation. He has to be considered as an indivisible unit on all levels, whether physical or abstract. All manifestations, physical and mental-emotional, can be traced to and must be considered as expressions of the undefinable Life Processes of this unit. The root of all of them can be found in the primordially prime objectives of maintaining the living unit intact—that is, of protecting it from injury, from hunger and thirst and thirdly, ensuring that it is neither blocked nor

901

prevented from gratifying the instincts which are expressed in desires leading to the preservation of the species. The non-attainment of these instincts leads to a discomfort almost equal to hunger or thirst, though, unlike the latter the denial of satisfaction does not lead to death. From this, it is possible to discern a few common primordial characteristics in all living matter. They are: the instinct of self-defense; the instinct of desire which fulfills the aim of the propagation of the species, the quest for WHY. All these characteristics seem to be universal.

Whereas the first two desires which serve the maintenance of the life of the individual have to be gratified at any cost at the peril of loss of life (by starvation, wounds, etc.) the third primary desire which serves the preservation of the race could be denied without incurring the catastrophe of death for the individual or the species because there are so many other members ready and willing to step into the gap.

Again, the instincts protecting the life of the individual, if blocked in their execution, provoke extreme discomfort and pain, but are of short duration because they can end in the extinguishing of desire through gratification. In contrast to this we see the apparent paradox in the discomfort arising from the denial of the third primary instinct. This discomfort lasts much longer and leads more readily to a permanent psychological change and lasting deviation. The individual can live with the third primary desire unfulfilled much longer than he can if the other two are denied gratification, and he is consequently molded by it. We see that the natural outcome of the third primary desire (sex and love) by far exceeds the other two in importance and predominance in the forming of the human "mind." It leads to almost equal passions to fulfill the desire and to compete with the fellow humans who could so easily replace the individual.

Man, who represents the highest development of the phylogenetic tree of life, acquired and is still acquiring new and almost unexplainable faculties which are seated in the brain—the organ which serves the purpose of generating the functions which defend and preserve life and continue the species on a conscious level. Homo Sapiens reached a state of such high development that he suddenly became aware of his lack of knowledge and understanding as to why he lives and has to maintain his existence and that of his species. In other words, Homo Sapiens acquired a fourth characteristic, apparently denied to the rest of living beings, which drove him to ask WHY. As a result of this, he acquired and developed the faculty of abstract thinking. It is undeniable that this was the highest of man's achievements. It can be added that it is equally undeniable that he had to pay the price for his desire for knowledge. That man was aware of this fact from the beginning of his civilized existence is apparent in the clear statement in the Old Testament embodied in the story of Adam and Eve "losing their Paradise and their innocence" and sacrificing their ease, contentment and animal comfort because they had trespassed beyond the animalistic limit and wanted to partake of the tree of knowledge.

One thing can be definitely accepted—that long prior to this development of abstract functions, man's first context of awareness must have been of disruptions or discomfort in the physiological and anatomical functions of his living processes. He suffered pain when hurt; he suffered great discomfort when hungry or thirsty; and he "suffered" the delight of performing the act of propagating his species. It can therefore be assumed that the organ containing the perception, recognition and regulation of emotions was developed eons before the abstract association of ideas and absolutes. This assumption can be substantiated by anatomical findings. The seat of the emotions is located in much deeper layers of the brain and belongs to much older developed strata of the cortex than the later and higher acquisition of the brain layers which serve abstractions and concepts of absolutes.

We have to assume that, as demonstrated above, the necessity for these human actions became little by little more subtle. Gradually these primordial emotional feelings became conscious and motivated primordial man in the execution of his various desires. High levels of the brain mass were developed which, with the separation of labor, began to take over certain functions. These brain levels which took over conscious actions had to grow layer by layer and supersede in the rank and exercise control

903

over those already in existence. The layers generating abstract thought developed to such a state of refinement that they apparently detached themselves from the lower layers from which they originally derived. An entirely new set of abstract conceptions was evolved which seemed to the multitude to be almost unrelated to underlying primordial drives. We should remember here the unassailable but frequently overlooked fact that the newer and more highly developed links in the chain of command of man's brain can inhibit but not control the lower and older and therefore more deeply ingrained ones, but not vice versa. Unfortunately, we do not pay much attention to the fact, in either scientific medical psychiatry or the general levels of human activities and behaviors (diplomacy, commerce, etc.) that the emotions can color the reason, but reason can never influence the emotions. . . .

The history of psychiatry abounds with theories, postulations, dogmatisms and persuasive treatments which are only rivaled in quantity by the lamentable lack of cures.

This may seem exaggerated but it can be documented in the overfilled mental hospitals. Patients remain there, unhelped in the gravest of human diseases, sometimes spending their entire lives incarcerated as has been the case for centuries. To be sure, their lot is now easier. They have better food, are better cared for; but they are still incarcerated. The physical improvements which we can and do count to our credit have made us, thanks to our increased efforts to achieve them, almost unaware of the fact that these patients still exist. Due to the force of habit and necessity, we appear to have forgotten them as well as the necessity to search for an experimental, scientific and medical cure for their illnesses.

Psychiatric diseases, contrary to diseases recognized as physical, have the common denominator of presenting dysfunctions in the realm of mentally perceivable actions alone. They must, therefore, be considered as the end-product of a deviation from the phylogenetically imprinted pattern of the nerve cell in its response to external or internal stimuli in a way established as normal since the beginning of the development of man. These responses constitute in toto a sequence of actions which are commonly referred to as "the mind" or "emotional content.". . .

There is great variety in the mental and emotional diseases which, as said before, are only perceived by the *mental* perceptions. The diseases can be as distinct from each other as a superficial scratch on the skin is distinct from a deadly cancer. For example, a too-intense anxious reaction due to a bona fide problematical condition confronting a patient is distinct in its nature from a complete schizophrenic confusion or a paranoid logical deduction from a delusional premise.

Psychiatry must therefore be conceived as an over-all term for a complex variety of diseased as well as overcharged distress reactions to complicated situations. . . .

This lack of distinction in connection with the causes of elusive and undefinable psychiatric manifestations has given an opportunity for speculators and formulators of postulations whose contentions did not have to be bound by objective tests. For example, although the clear-headed Hippocrates deduced with almost absolute logic that epileptic fits originate in maladies of the brain, it took centuries to accept this incontrovertible fact. The assumption that epileptics were either possessed by the Devil or the Holy Ghost, according to the particular frame of mind of the observer, succeeded for hundreds of years in erasing the clear facts of the disease. To illustrate man's tendency to follow the traditional pattern, even Socrates, who was certainly normal and clear-thinking, accepted lightning as being a demonstration of the wrath of the Gods because this was the long-imprinted pattern of the belief of his time. If today, over two thousand years later, someone were to expound such a simple fallacy which was valid to a man in 400 B.C., it would have to be accepted as a pathological disruption of a phylogenetically more recently imprinted pattern. . . .

Psychiatry became separated from experimental medicine partly because of its historical origin, partly because of the lack of any concrete knowledge or substance or remedial help. Generation after generation of psychiatrists continued in their scholastic adherence long after the other branches of medicine did

905

not even recall the time when dogmatism was considered a part of "doctoral science." Psychiatry had achieved nothing when the rest of medicine had already eliminated many of the other scourges of mankind. Psychiatrists debated and expounded explanations instead of cures. The only consolation available to them, which was relatively easy for their self-assertive personalities, was to preoccupy themselves with influencing and improving the condition of border-line psychiatric cases. People who were overwhelmed by the problems of life and who were also accessible to these procedures, were gradually brought within the compass of the appellation "psychiatry" and the number of "psychiatric" cases grew enormously. It was only human that these were finally elevated to being the prime objective and concern of the practicing psychiatrist. The psychiatrists stated the cures they achieved in these patients, and forgot to take into consideration the fact that they were curing patients who were not really sick but superficially emotionally disturbed people who at most needed moral support and perhaps only flattery and self-justification.

We can see how Mesmer was able to become pre-eminently successful in "treating" the prevailing hysteria of the idle of his time, and how he could establish his treatment as psychiatry. We can see how Charcot became world-famous for his hypnotic relief of hysterical fits (*arc de circle*) which is so seldom seen nowadays and which in patients of his time represented the core of what he thought was psychiatry.

The growth of the press and the printed word gave wide help to the preoccupation with such spurious "scientific" achievements. The descriptions in spectacular writings about such psychiatry were eagerly read and therefore more and more written about. Not only the specialists in this field but also the formulators and the pseudoscientific terminology of psychiatry started in our century to permeate the whole field of interpersonal human relations. The abyss between the experimental science of medicine and what came to be known as psychiatry became unbreachable. The value of the printed and spoken treatises about psychiatry as psychology started to overshadow the already painfully tangible fact of the distress and gravity of the real psychiatric problems of the

906

mentally sick. The core of psychiatric cases remained inmates of the growing number of mental homes, more humanely but not medically treated. That is not to say that the work of all these speculative investigators and writers must be considered as a complete loss. By investigating the mechanisms of patho-psychological behaviorisms, they added much to our knowledge though not to our understanding of deep psychological motivations.

If the medical profession had accepted this gain with its limitations, as it was originally meant to by the more scientific-minded successors of Charcot, like Freud and his disciples, a great contribution would have been added to the body of knowledge of man's motivation and would still not have hampered the development of experimental medical psychiatry. Unfortunately, the gain which we acquired from their investigations and their imparted knowledge was far overshadowed by the damage they did by not respecting their limitations. The subject matter became so fascinating, so intriguing, so plausible, that it was taken up to an overwhelming degree at the cost of neglecting the actual facts. It therefore seems necessary to delineate the hazy border lines between experimental medical cures and psychological medical tests and handling which are all absolutely vital for the purpose of diagnosis and important as adjuvants not only of psychiatric but of all other physical treatments as well.

In psychiatry, we can neither accept nor convey the clinical fact of abnormal or normal mental or emotional conditions without resorting to the accepted terminology of psychology. These terms have to convey some special condition of mental or emotional attitudes and reactions and responses to influences. It is therefore necessary to clarify—as much as the substance expressed by an abstract can be clarified—the field covered by the term psychology. We cannot proceed without agreement on what we are attempting to convey. We have to start at the beginning, at the root from which psychological attitudes and responses developed. It appears that they evolved according to a pattern which became imprinted on the nervous substrata and which was forced on it by selection or design in order to serve the purpose of preserving the individual and the species. For the purpose of elucidat-

907

ing this matter and in order to expound the by now very intricate superstructure of psychology, it is helpful to divide the subject into two parts.

The first half of the psychological domain (I call it domain for want of a better concrete expression of this abstract sequence of reactions and responses) is contained within the individual himself and can be independent of external interpersonal relationships.

The other half comes into play solely in response to and as the effect of actions and stimuli arising from interpersonal relationships. It evolved as the result of the necessity for the individual to live in the simplest unit of the family and later as a member of a tribe and finally a nation.

It should be recalled at this point that psychological actions are executed by reason but released by emotional imprints in Pavlov's reflex manner. These imprints were acquired and developed in the course of the long history of man's evolution. They were therefore characteristic, in general, of all men. However, the minute individual variations due to personality differentiations are very much more important in the particular behavior of each case than the common denominator of the original forced responses to primordial provocations.

To formulate psychological actions even broadly, it seems necessary to start with the speculation about their origin. As said before, we established three basic instincts in man: the instinct of preserving his life and well-being (animal comfort); the instinct of preserving the species; and the ultimately acquired desire to question the WHY of the necessity and origin of the two primary instincts (peace of mind and mental comfort). We will proceed now to classify the responses to these primordial instincts which alone can be brought under the appellation "emotion."

We can safely assume that the "emotional reaction" was a corollary of the first primary instinct of self-preservation and of its gratification. It must be concluded that the emotion was the mechanism which promoted this aim and which elicited the effort to accomplish it. In the course of an immense period of time, actions achieving this aim began to reach out into the abstract and even detached themselves from the original physical necessity to achieve it. Primordially, such actions were only meant to defend the individual against the immediate danger of external circumstances, that is to say, lack of food or water or human or circumstantial attacks.

Man's discovery of his newly acquired ability to play with abstract tools which were originally meant to serve as a means to an end, caused him to derive a great deal of pleasure from them. He came to devote so much time to this abstract "game" that gradually the means became an end in themselves. The release of the gratification of primordial urges was transferred from its habitual domicile in the lower instinctual centers to the higher levels which were not designed for this purpose but were developed for abstract functions only. This "achievement" permitted man to extend the "means" of securing gratification to the point where he detached them from his original primordial drives. In short, this transference led him ultimately to seek gratification in the acquisition of strength and excellence. He wanted to be superior to other men even though there was no longer a necessity for this in order for him to survive.

Secondary to defending his life by physical force, man had to seek food, not only to sustain his life but to acquire additional strength. He needed food unconditionally and he therefore sought for it irrespective of the needs of others. The desire to acquire the necessities of life beyond the immediate need with the aim of being provided indefinitely, led ultimately to premeditated planning. These new qualities of planning lent the individual a sense of security and power over those who were less well equipped. On the other hand, the need of the less fortunate gave them a feeling of insecurity and increased the sense of superiority on the part of the "possessors." It gave the latter a plus force bestowed on them by the others' acceptance of their inferiority and helplessness. This enabled the stronger ones to enforce their will. The fact that they were successful ensured their superiority. They acquired a feeling of omnipotence which counteracted the universal sense of impotence arising from the inability of man to control the influence of the forces of Nature. . . .

The slow but steady development of intricate human relations in an organized society which arose from the necessity of living close together, led to necessary modifications and adaptations. These came to be expressed in a new variety of psychological attitudes (different from primordial ones), for example, lust for power in the political and economic fields. These developed as a result of the congestion of living conditions and the essential division of labor. The deeply ingrained feeling of being rich or poor can be fitted in easily with this psychological development (living up to one's neighbor; hierarchical self-importance). The result of these changes in the psychological relations between men was a development from the primitive and basic principle of the survival of the fittest.

The second instinct of preserving the species, though as deeply ingrained as the first, is secondary in importance to it. It came to be regarded as almost equal in importance to the first when the growth and awareness of man's intellectual powers permitted him to achieve the gratification of the first instinct with ease. He therefore relegated it to a less important position. As the conquest of the problem of his survival became easier, he had more time to devote to sexual rivalry and love. The less time he needed to provide himself with food, the more time he had to dwell on his pleasures and fancies. I refer here to the mental preoccupation of evoking emotional charges, giving reign to the imagination and to the sublimation of creative thoughts in such fields as abstract thinking and the search for absolute values in art and literature. Whatever form these took, they still had their roots in primordial, brutal, sexual rivalry. Man's memory of the one-time need of this survived long after the necessity for it had become obsolete. The mechanics and the habits outlived the purpose for which they had been brought into being.

With them, the social aspects of man came into being. He wanted to excel in mind and body, to elevate and distinguish himself from the multitude. He wanted to be unique, attractive and desired as well as feared in his social and sexual context. As he progressed intellectually, he developed such easy means of satisfying his absolute minimum physical necessities that with the exception of emergencies, he forgot that the first primordial call upon him had been the search for the means to sustain life. The hardship of sustaining himself was gone. With the passing of generations, he lost his preoccupation with its importance. His mind was filled with other preoccupations; pleasures, diversions, competition for competition's sake. Conquests, physical and sexual, became a matter of mental deliberation instead of an instinctive necessity. . . .

The phenomenon of man's acquisition of the unique ability for abstract thought which led ultimately to his comprehension of absolutes came with acquisition of more highly developed and more specialized portions of his brain matter. Hitherto completely unknown fields of the quest for understanding the Whys and Wherefores of life in general and his own in particular were opened up. He reached the point where he "discovered or created" God. He started to meditate upon this new factor which became as important to him as his much older instincts and necessities. He endowed his discovered God with all the absolutes which he apprehended and felt compelled to abide by. Since he was not able to define this newly discovered force more closely, he accepted it as the Ultimate Unquestionable. This does not mean to say that he explained God in materialistic terms. Man was and is still not great enough to create anything that does not exist. The best that can be said is that he can apprehend and "discover" forces that he cannot explain.

This new spiritual adherence which embraces ethical and moral values seems at times on superficial examination to contradict the two purely animal instincts of the preservation of the individual and the species. This created new problems for man. His attempts to reconcile these two apparently diametrically contradictory wants and to fulfill both of them did not and do not work, because the formula for achieving this reconciliation is not yet invented.

We can see the demonstration of this conflict between the two as yet irreconcilable tendencies in man in the periodic excessive swings which occur in whole segments of mankind. These segments happen to be bound together through some common media of communication which pattern their way of thinking and enforce their adherence to certain concepts by means of traditional memories. Recorded history gives many examples of particular cultural traditions.

We can assume that most men are equipped with the potentiality of swinging to the extreme in either of these two directions. By giving way to the older, primordial tendencies, man can develop traits of selfishness, ruthlessness and self-indulgence. He may appear to have lost completely the phylogenetically newly acquired gravitation toward absolutes. He can become inconsiderate and insensitive to the needs of others and seek only his own benefit and pleasure.

Equally, we can see the opposite tendency in the cultural traditions, ideals and aims of a particular national group. What is apparent in the individual is absolutely unmistakable in a large group. A group may clearly show dedication to extreme physical force or, on the other hand, to extreme mysticism. Searching for this, we can discover that under normal circumstances the potential of being Good or Bad exists in every individual. The implication behind this is that training and education and imbuing the individual with an aim in life can make him Good, by suppressing the bad tendencies and cultivating the good ones, or vice versa.

The analysis of man's potentialities for Good and Bad must be carefully explored in order that the development and establishment of normal interpersonal behavior in man can be distinguished from on the surface similar but in reality pathological deviations. The pathological deviation in the interpersonal relationship can in one case be a sickness and be treated medically. In another case, it is the end result of psychological corruption or deformation of the personality and is therefore inaccessible and unresponsive to medical treatment.

The ability of man to live in a group, whether in the family, tribe or nation, was predetermined by the development of the factor of his inner need for adherence to the absolutes dictating his interpersonal relationships, the phylogenetically most recently acquired part of the total personality make-up, that is, man's impulsion toward interhuman relations, has therefore to be ac-

912

cepted as an integral part of the normal human being. Anger, hatred, jealousy, revenge, all psychological responses, can be explained by a combination of a variety of part factors of the primordial and the more recently acquired abstract impulses of man.

Since we have to deal in psychiatry with behaviors and responses to internal and external stimuli which do not always toe the line, we have to differentiate between sicknesses in the medical sense of the word and circumstantial personality maladjustments. A differentiation must be made between responses and behaviors which are generated either by emotional or by associative processes. For therapeutic purposes, utilizing our experimental medical knowledge, it is absolutely necessary in order to achieve a satisfactory result to formulate as clearly as possible a clear division between the two groups of abnormal and unusual human behavior.

One cause of maladjustment may be traced to the course of a particular patient's personal development, that is to say, that in his ontogenetic emotional or associative pattern some fault or trauma deviated him from a more normal course of development. These people will be in need of psychiatric help and the cause of their difficulties can rightly be assumed to be psychological in nature. Psychiatric traumas are usually incurred in the formative stages of the imprinting and ingraining of the responses and attitudes of these patients. They become frustrated, deviated, and may even present a picture of deeper seated, really nervous, dysfunctions but will have no break in the real phylogenetically anchored nervous intercellular patterns and pathways of responses acquired by selection in the long course of human development. This is the group to which patients belong who were badly molded but where the characteristic of their deformation is not the outcome of a biochemical and organic dysfunction but a personality psychological distortion. Medical physiological additional help will in this case reinforce the supportive psychological treatment.

The second group definitely belongs to the realm of experimental physical medicine. Its "abnormalcy" has its origin in entirely different mechanisms. A "break" in the phylogenetically ingrained patterns and pathways of nervous responses which normally flow in an enforced course is the outcome of a noxa. The enforced flow of responses in these established intercellular ruts which must follow rigidly, step by step, in a way similar to the constellation of the intercellular particles and electrons in a magnet, is suddenly disturbed.

The route on which the impulse should normally travel may be derailed by a disturbance in the intercellular pathways or patterns of transmission. The latter should not be thought of in neurological terms but as specific constellations of electromagnetic primary particles in the cell itself. These are not visible, even under a microscope but nevertheless they must exist. We cannot do without assuming their existence just as we cannot do without assuming electronic waves in which impulses travel. A stimulus releases an impulse in the nerve cell which is transmitted on these intercellular wave-lengths which I call intercellular pathways and patterns to the adjoining cellular unit through the synapsis until it reaches the normal end point of perception. This impulse which is converted from a stimulus will then be forced to continue its way in an insulated pattern or pathway until it reaches its destination. Under normal conditions, this impulse will not be able to "jump" the rail and elicit impulses which are not originally converted from stimuli in this chain of perception or "wave-lengths" nor create in the final destination point a perception which is unrelated to the original stimulus.

If the route is derailed, completely new phenomena, not normally experienced when this chain of pattern is insulated from the others and is strictly specific, will be evident. I refer here to hallucinations, delusions and the host of other unmotivated and uncalled for actions and reactions. This group of patients has definitely suffered a "structural" damage. As said before, this does not imply a structural damage in organic or microscopically visible implications, but a reversible damage in the biochemico-ionic or possible electro-magnetic constellations of the invisible particles in the nerve cells.

One can only visualize the process which ensures the insulation and isolation of the pathways and patterns on which impulses travel and the damage which causes them to "jump the rail." If this should happen in the intercellular pathways and patterns, and we have to assume that each specific neuronal cell has a number of abandoned and phylogenetically antiquated and inactive pathways, the stimulus converted into an impulse will travel on a nonaccustomed route. Conversely, the intercellular pathways which can be visualized as a fixed constellation of electromagnetic particles may be pathologically disturbed or rearranged and may thus create a completely abnormal pathway. We can compare this with the static or metallic interference in the electromagnetic tape which produces a cacophony of a symphonic and melodic harmony.

To express this in simpler terms, it may be advisable to bring the foregoing into line with hypotheses in the abstract sciences, and in particular, with physics. We know more about these other sciences, but we are still dealing with and perceiving the one and only universal energy which in a mental condition is translated into thoughts and emotions, and in physics, into measurable manifestations. In the latter we deal with hypotheses which are equally intangible but which have already been proved workable and helpful. I am referring specifically to the field of electronics and the magnetic constellations in the magnetized tape of a tape recorder. Though elusive and inconcrete, the theory behind this phenomenon demonstrates its soundness. The sound produced by a voice transmitted through a series of electronic tubes is capable of changing the originally polarized constellation of particles which are patterned in a certain direction in the tape and will produce a high fidelity recording and reproduction of the specific sound.

It is helpful to imagine the perception of psychic phenomena released by stimuli in the same way as the sound recording is perceived on the magnetic tape. Intercellular patterns and pathways are elicited by stimuli in human beings in the same way and with the end result of a conditioned reflex in Pavlov's sense of the word. These intercellular pathways and patterns become fixed and stable under normal circumstances and will remain so unless there is a cataclysmic interference in the cell structure.

915

Schizophrenia, the most grave and most widely spread single group of real psychiatric diseases (as opposed to functional ones) may appear in a variety of schizophrenic pictures and is the result of such a cataclysmic interference in the structure of the nerve cell.

In many schizophrenic patients, we may encounter a mirror reversal of the normal constellations of particles forming the intercellular pathways and patterns. Their reaction will appear logical but will be the exact opposite of their previous ones. The patient will hate the persons he formerly loved and love the persons he formerly hated. The same will frequently happen in the instinctual domain. The perfectly normal heterosexual may suddenly show a plausible performance of being a real homosexual. These cases are so common that they have given rise to the speculation in some schools of thought that paranoia, for example, is the end result of a repression of homosexual tendencies. The fact that the homosexual quality in these patients is only the most conspicuous of the other reversed or subverted emotional feelings is overlooked. All are symptoms of the basic schizophrenic primary process and disease. This can be proven without a doubt by those trained in the Classical Insulin Shock Treatment where, at a given moment in the course of the treatment, a "reversal or normalization" of the behavior of the patient can be seen for a short time. Such a patient will revert for shorter or longer moments, at a certain point during his hypoglycemia, to his previous normal personality pattern and voice distress and surprise about the feelings and drives he experienced a few moments before.

ERWIN SCHRÖDINGER

(1887-   )

Another important contributor to modern quantum theory is Erwin Schrödinger, whose wave theory of matter led him to evolve a theory of the atom based on wave mechanics. In addition to his work in this field he has made contributions to the theory of color and the study of radium. Winner (with Paul Dirac) of the Nobel prize for physics in 1933. Author of *Collected Papers on Wave-Mechanics* (1928), *Statistical Thermodynamics* (1945), and *What Is Life?* (1946). The selection which follows is from Schrödinger's Nobel prize address.

THE FUNDAMENTALS OF WAVE MECHANICS

WHEN A RAY of light passes through an optical instrument, such as a telescope or a photographic lens, it undergoes a change of direction as it strikes each refractive or reflective surface. We can describe the path of the light ray once we know the two simple laws which govern the change of direction. One of these is the law of refraction, which was discovered by Snell about three hundred years ago; and the other is the law of reflection, which was known to Archimedes nearly two thousand years before. . . .

From a much more general point of view, Fermat summed up the whole career of a light ray. In passing through media of varying optical densities light is propagated at correspondingly varying speeds, and the path which it follows is such as would have to be chosen by the light if it had the purpose of arriving within the shortest possible time at the destination which it actually reaches. (Here it may be remarked, in parentheses, that any two points along the path of the light ray can be chosen as

917

the points of departure and arrival respectively.) Any deviation from the path which the ray has actually chosen would mean a delay. This is Fermat's famous principle of least time. In one admirably concise statement it defines the whole career of a ray of light, including also the more general case where the nature of the medium does not change suddenly but alters gradually from point to point. The atmosphere surrounding our earth is an example of this. When a ray of light, coming from outside, enters the earth's atmosphere, the ray travels more slowly as it penetrates into deeper and increasingly denser layers. And although the difference in the speed of propagation is extremely small, yet under these circumstances Fermat's principle demands that the ray of light must bend earthward. . . .

Thus Fermat's principle directly appears as the *trivial quintessence* of the wave theory. Hence it was a very remarkable event when Hamilton one day made the theoretical discovery that the orbit of a mass point moving in a field of force (for instance, of a stone thrown in the gravitational field of the earth or of some planet in its course around the sun) is governed by a very similar general principle, which thenceforth bore the name of the discoverer and made him famous. Although Hamilton's principle does not precisely consist in the statement that the mass point chooses the quickest way, yet it states something so similar—that is to say, it is so closely analogous to the principle of minimum light time—that one is faced with a puzzle. It seemed as if nature had effected exactly the same thing twice, but in two very different ways—once, in the case of light, through a fairly transparent wave mechanism, and on the other occasion, in the case of mass points, by methods which were utterly mysterious, unless one was prepared to believe in some underlying undulatory character in the second case also. But at first sight this idea seemed impossible. . . .

The way out of the difficulty was actually (though unexpectedly) found in the possibility I have already mentioned, namely, that in the Hamiltonian principle we might also assume the manifestation of a "wave mechanism," which we supposed to lie at the basis of events in point mechanics, just as we have been long accustomed to acknowledge it in the phenomena of light and in the governing principle enunciated by Fermat. . . .

Let us now return from optics to mechanics and try to develop the analogy fully. The optical parallel of the old mechanics is the method of dealing with isolated rays of light, which are supposed not to influence one another. The new wave mechanics has its parallel in the undulatory theory of light. The advantage of changing from the old concept to the new must obviously consist in clearer insight into diffraction phenomena, or rather into something that is strictly analogous to the diffraction of light, although ordinarily even less significant; for otherwise the old mechanics could not have been accepted as satisfactory for so long a time. But it is not difficult to conjecture the conditions in which the neglected phenomenon must become very prominent, entirely dominate the mechanical process, and present problems that are insoluble under the old concept. This occurs inevitably whenever the entire mechanical system is comparable in its extension with the wave lengths of "material waves," which play the same role in mechanical processes as light waves do in optics.

That is the reason why, in the tiny system of the atom, the old concept is bound to fail. In mechanical phenomena on a large scale it will retain its validity as an excellent approximation, but it must be replaced by the new concept if we wish to deal with the fine interplay which takes place within regions of the order of magnitude of only one or a few wave lengths.

I would describe the present state of our knowledge as follows: The light ray, or track of the particle, corresponds to a longitudinal continuity of the propagating process (that is to say, in the direction of the spreading); the wave front, on the other hand, to a transverse one (that is to say, perpendicular to the direction of spreading). Both continuities are undoubtedly real.

919

BARUCH SPINOZA

(1632–1677)

The obscure lens grinder of Amsterdam who became the first great
philosopher of modern times, in spite of rejection by his own
church and the churches of Christendom, was firmly grounded in
mathematics and the physical sciences. Although he contributed no
startling inventions or innovations to posterity, he made use of mathematics in stating his philosophic formulations, and his thinking
had marked influence on many of the foremost thinkers who followed him, from Leibniz to Einstein. Because of the repressive times
in which he lived, his masterpiece, *The Ethics* (quoted here), was
never printed during his lifetime, though it was familiar in manuscript to the intellectual leaders of the seventeenth century.

IDEAS, THINGS, AND THE HUMAN MIND

By BODY I mean a mode or created form which expresses in
a certain determinate manner the essence of God, insofar as He
is considered as an extended thing. I consider as belonging to
the essence of a thing that which, being given, the thing is necessarily given also, and which, being removed, the thing is necessarily removed also; in other words, that without which the
thing, and which itself without the thing, can neither be nor be
conceived.

By idea, I mean the mental conception which is formed by the
mind as a thinking thing. I say conception rather than perception, because the word perception seems to imply that the mind
is passive in respect to the object; whereas conception seems to
express an activity of the mind.

By an adequate idea, I mean an idea which, insofar as it is
considered in itself, without relation to the object, has all the

920

properties or intrinsic marks of a true idea. I say intrinsic, in order to exclude that mark which is extrinsic, namely, the agreement between the idea and its object.

Duration is the indefinite continuance of existing. I say indefinite, because it cannot be determined through the existence itself of the existing thing, or by its efficient cause, which necessarily gives the existence of the thing, but does not take it away. Reality and perfection I use as synonymous terms.

By particular things, I mean things which are finite and have a conditioned existence; but if several individual things concur in one action, so as to be all simultaneously the effect of one cause, I consider them all, so far, as one particular thing.

Thought is an attribute of God, or God is a thinking thing.

Extension is an attribute of God, God is an extended thing.

The idea of God, from which an infinite number of things follow in infinite ways, can only be one.

Infinite intellect comprehends nothing save the attributes of God and his modifications. Now God is one. Therefore the idea of God, wherefrom an infinite number of things follow in infinite ways, can only be one.

The order and connection of ideas is the same as the order and connection of things.

Whatsoever can be perceived by the infinite intellect as constituting the essence of substance, belongs altogether only to one substance: consequently, substance *thinking* and substance *extended* are one and the same substance, comprehended now through one attribute, now through the other. So, also, a mode of extension and the idea of that mode are one and the same thing, though expressed in two ways. This truth seems to have been dimly recognized by those Jews who maintained that God, God's intellect, and the things understood by God are identical.

For instance, a circle existing in nature, and the idea of a circle existing, which is also in God, are one and the same thing displayed through different attributes. Thus, whether we conceive nature under the attribute of extension, or under the attribute of thought, or under any other attribute we shall find the same order, or one and the same chain of causes—that is, the same things following in either case.

I said that God is the cause of an idea—for instance, of the idea of a circle—insofar as he is a thinking thing; and of a circle, insofar as he is an extended thing, simply because the actual being of the idea of a circle can only be perceived as a proximate cause through another mode of thinking, and that again through another, and so on to infinity. So long as we consider things as modes of thinking, we must explain the order of the whole of nature, or the whole chain of causes, through the attribute of thought only. And, insofar as we consider things as modes of extension, we must explain the order of the whole of nature through the attribute of extension only; and so on, in the case of other attributes.

Wherefore of things as they are in themselves God is really the cause, inasmuch as he consists of infinite attributes.

The first element, which constitutes the actual being of the human mind, is the idea of some particular thing actually existing.

The human mind is part of the infinite intellect of God; thus when we say that the human mind perceives this or that, we make the assertion that God has this or that idea, not insofar as He is infinite, but insofar as He is displayed through the nature of the human mind or insofar as He constitutes the essence of the human mind; and when we say that God has this or that idea, not only insofar as He constitutes the essences of the human mind, but also insofar as He, simultaneously with the human mind, has the further idea of another thing, we assert that the human mind perceives a thing in part or inadequately.

The object of the idea constituting the human mind is the body, in other words a certain mode of extension which actually exists, and nothing else.

We comprehend, not only that the human mind is united to the body, but also the nature of the union between mind and body. However, no one will be able to grasp this adequately or distinctly unless he first has adequate knowledge of the nature

922

of our body. The propositions we have advanced hitherto have been entirely general, applying not more to men than to other individual things, all of which, though in different degrees, are animated. For of everything there is necessarily an idea in God, of which God is the cause, in the same way as there is an idea of the human body; thus whatever we have asserted of the idea of the human body must necessarily also be asserted of the idea of everything else. Still, on the other hand, we cannot deny that ideas, like objects, differ one from the other, one being more excellent than another and containing more reality, just as the object of one idea is more excellent than the object of another idea, and contains more reality.

Wherefore, in order to determine wherein the human mind differs from other things, and wherein it surpasses them, it is necessary for us to know the nature of its object, that is, of the human body. What this nature is, I am not able here to explain, nor is it necessary for the proof of what I advance, that I should do so. I will only say generally, that in proportion as any given body is more fitted than others for doing many actions or receiving many impressions at once, so also is the mind, of which it is the object, more fitted than others for forming many simultaneous perceptions; and the more the actions of one body depend on itself alone, and the fewer other bodies concur with it in action, the more fitted is the mind of which it is the object for distinct comprehension.

We may thus recognize the superiority of one mind over others, and may further see the cause, why we have only a very confused knowledge of our body, and also many kindred questions.

All bodies are either in motion or at rest.

Every body is moved sometimes more slowly, sometimes more quickly.

Bodies are distinguished from one another in respect of motion and rest, quickness and slowness, and not in respect of substance.

A body in motion or at rest must be determined to motion or

rest by another body, which other body has been determined to motion or rest by a third body, and that third again by a fourth, and so on to infinity.

A body in motion keeps in motion, until it is determined to a state of rest by some other body; and a body at rest remains so, until it is determined to a state of motion by some other body. This is indeed self-evident. For when I suppose, for instance, that a given body, A, is at rest, and do not take into consideration other bodies in motion, I cannot affirm anything concerning the body A, except that it is at rest. If it afterwards comes to pass that A is in motion, this cannot have resulted from its having been at rest, for no other consequence could have been involved than its remaining at rest. If, on the other hand, A be given in motion, we shall, so long as we only consider A, be unable to affirm anything concerning it, except that it is in motion. If A is subsequently found to be at rest, this rest cannot be the result of A's previous motion, for such motion can only have led to continued motion; the state of rest therefore must have resulted from something, which was not in A, namely, from an external cause determining A to a state of rest.

All modes wherein one body is affected by another body follow simultaneously from the nature of the body affected and the body affecting; so that one and the same body may be moved in different modes, according to the difference in the nature of the bodies moving it; on the other hand, different bodies may be moved in different modes by one and the same body.

When a body in motion impinges on another body at rest, which it is unable to move, it recoils, in order to continue its motion, and the angle made by the line of motion in the recoil and the plane of the body at rest, whereon the moving body has impinged, will be equal to the angle formed by the line of incidence and the same plane.

When any given bodies of the same or different magnitude are compelled by other bodies to remain in contact, or if they be moved at the same or different rates of speed, so that their mutual movements should preserve among themselves a certain

924

fixed relation, we say that such bodies are in union, and that altogether they compose one body or individual, which is distinguished from other bodies by this fact of union.

In proportion as the parts of an individual, or a compound body, are in contact over a greater or less superficies, they will with greater or less difficulty admit of being moved from their position; consequently the individual will, with greater or less difficulty, be brought to assume another form. Those bodies, whose parts are in contact over large superficies, are called *hard*; those, whose parts are in contact over small superficies, are called *soft*; those, whose parts are in motion among one another, are called *fluid*.

If certain bodies composing an individual be compelled to change the motion which they have in one direction for motion in another direction, but in such a manner that they be able to continue their motions and their mutual communication in the same relations as before, the individual will retain its own nature without any change of its actuality.

Furthermore, the individual thus composed preserves its nature, whether it be, as a whole, in motion or at rest, whether it be moved in this or that direction; so long as each part retains its motion, and preserves its communication with other parts as before.

A composite individual may be affected in many different ways, and preserve its nature notwithstanding. Thus far we have conceived an individual as composed of several individuals of diverse natures, other in respect of motion and rest, speed and slowness; that is, of bodies of the most simple character. If, however, we now conceive another individual composed of several individuals of diverse natures, we shall find that the number of ways in which it can be affected, without losing its nature, will be greatly multiplied. Each of its parts would consist of several bodies, and therefore each part would admit, without change to its nature, of quicker or slower motion, and would consequently be able to transmit its motions more quickly or more slowly to the remaining parts. If we further conceive a third kind of individuals composed of individuals of this second kind, we shall find that they may be affected in a still greater number of ways without changing their actuality.

We may easily proceed thus to infinity, and conceive the whole of nature as one individual, whose parts, that is, all bodies, vary in infinite ways, without any change in the individual as a whole.

The human mind is capable of perceiving a great number of things, and is so in proportion as its body is capable of receiving a great number of impressions.

The idea which constitutes the actual being of the human mind, is not simple, but compounded of a great number of ideas.

The idea of every mode, in which the human body is affected by external bodies, must involve the nature of the human body, and also the nature of the external body.

The human mind perceives the nature of a variety of bodies, together with the nature of its own.

The ideas which we have of external bodies indicate rather the constitution of our own body than the nature of external bodies.

If the human body is affected in a manner which involves the nature of any external body, the human mind will regard the said external body as actually existing, or as present to itself, until the human body be affected in such a way as to exclude the existence or the presence of the said external body.

The human mind does not perceive any external body as actually existing, except through the ideas of the modifications of its own body.

The human mind has no knowledge of the body, and does not know it to exist, save through the ideas of the modifications through which the body is affected.

The mind does not know itself, except insofar as it perceives the ideas of the modifications of the body.

The human mind does not involve an adequate knowledge of the parts composing the human body.

We can only have a very inadequate knowledge of the duration of our body.

All ideas, insofar as they are referred to God, are true.

All ideas which are in God agree in every respect with their objects; therefore they are all true.

Every idea, which in us is absolute or adequate and perfect, is true.

When we say that an idea in us is adequate and perfect, we say, in other words, that the idea is adequate and perfect in God, insofar as he constitutes the essence of our mind; consequently, we say that such an idea is true.

Falsity consists in the privation of knowledge, which inadequate, fragmentary, or confused ideas involve.

Inadequate and confused ideas follow by the same necessity, and adequate or clear and distinct ideas.

All ideas are in God, and insofar as they are referred to God are true and adequate; therefore there are no ideas confused or inadequate, except in respect to a particular mind; therefore all ideas, whether adequate or inadequate, follow by the same necessity.

Whatsoever ideas in the mind follow from ideas which are therein adequate, are also themselves adequate.

For when we say that an idea in the human mind follows from ideas which are therein adequate, we say, in other words, that an idea is in the divine intellect, whereof God is the cause, not insofar as He is infinite, nor insofar as He is affected by the ideas of very many particular things, but only insofar as He constitutes the essence of the human mind.

JOSEPH JOHN THOMSON

(1856–1940)

A fellow worker of Rutherford in the investigation of the atom, Sir Joseph John Thomson received the Nobel prize for physics in 1906, largely for his discovery of the electron. This discovery, which initiated the electrical theory of the atom, lends support to the claim that Thomson is the real founder of modern atomic physics. He organized the Cavendish research laboratory at Cambridge, and is the author of many books and papers, including: *Application of Dynamics to Physics and Chemistry* (1888), *The Conduction of Electricity Through Gases* (1903), *Rays of Positive Electricity and Their Application to Chemical Analysis* (1913), and *The Electron in Chemistry* (1923).

CATHODE RAYS

THE experiments discussed in this paper were undertaken in the hope of gaining some information as to the nature of the Cathode Rays. The most diverse opinions are held as to these rays; according to the almost unanimous opinion of German physicists they are due to some process in the aether to which—inasmuch as in a uniform magnetic field their course is circular and not rectilinear—no phenomenon hitherto observed is analogous: another view of these rays is that, so far from being wholly aetherial, they are in fact wholly material, and that they mark the paths of particles of matter charged with negative electricity. It would seem at first sight that it ought not to be difficult to discriminate between views so different, yet experience shows that this is not the case, as amongst the physicists who have most deeply studied the subject can be found supporters of either theory.

The electrified-particle theory has for purposes of research a great advantage over the aetherial theory, since it is definite and

928

its consequences can be predicted; with the aetherial theory it is impossible to predict what will happen under any given circumstances, as on this theory we are dealing with hitherto unobserved phenomena in the aether, of whose laws we are ignorant.

The following experiments were made to test some of the consequences of the electrified-particle theory.

CHARGE CARRIED BY THE CATHODE RAYS

If these rays are negatively electrified particles, then when they enter an enclosure they ought to carry into it a charge of negative electricity. This has been proved to be the case by Perrin, who placed in front of a plane cathode two coaxial metallic cylinders which were insulated from each other: the outer of these cylinders was connected with the earth, the inner with a gold-leaf electroscope. These cylinders were closed except for two small holes, one in each cylinder, placed so that the cathode rays could pass through them into the inside of the inner cylinder. Perrin found that when the rays passed into the inner cylinder the electroscope received a charge of negative electricity, while no charge went to the electroscope when the rays were deflected by a magnet so as no longer to pass through the hole.

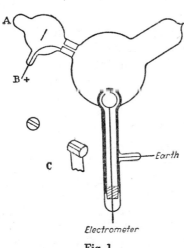

Fig. 1

This experiment proves that something charged with negative electricity is shot off from the cathode, travelling at right angles to it, and that this something is deflected by a magnet; it is open, however, to the objection that it does not prove that the cause of the electrification in the electroscope has anything to do with the cathode rays. Now the supporters of the aetherial theory do not deny that electrified particles are shot off from the cathode; they deny, however, that these charged particles have any more to do with the cathode rays than a rifle-ball has with the flash when a rifle is fired. I have therefore repeated Perrin's experiment in a form which is not open to this objection. The arrangement used was as follows:—Two coaxial cylinders (Fig. 1) with slits in them are placed in a bulb connected with the discharge-tube; the cathode rays from the cathode A pass into the bulb through a slit in a metal plug fitted into the neck of the tube; this plug is connected with the anode and is put to earth. The cathode rays thus do not fall upon the cylinders unless they are deflected by a magnet. The outer cylinder is connected with the earth, the inner with the electrometer. When the cathode rays (whose path was traced by the phosphorescence on the glass) did not fall on the slit, the electrical charge sent to the electrometer when the induction-coil producing the rays was set in action was small and irregular; when, however, the rays were bent by a magnet so as to fall on the slit there was a large charge of negative electricity sent to the electrometer. I was surprised at the magnitude of the charge; on some occasions enough negative electricity went through the narrow slit into the inner cylinder in one second to alter the potential of a capacity of 1.5 microfarads by 20 volts. If the rays were so much bent by the magnet that they overshot the slits in the cylinder, the charge passing into the cylinder fell again to a very small fraction of its value when the aim was true. Thus this experiment shows that however we twist and deflect the cathode rays by magnetic forces, the negative electrification follows the same path as the rays, and that this negative electrification is indissolubly connected with the cathode rays.

When the rays are turned by the magnet so as to pass through the slit into the inner cylinder, the deflexion of the electrometer connected with this cylinder increases up to a certain value, and then remains stationary although the rays continue to pour into the cylinder. This is due to the fact that the gas in the bulb becomes a conductor of electricity when the cathode rays pass through it, and thus, though the inner cylinder is perfectly insulated when the rays are not passing, yet as soon as the rays pass through the bulb the air between the inner cylinder and the outer one becomes a conductor, and the electricity escapes from the inner cylinder to the earth. Thus the charge within the inner cylinder does not go on continually increasing; the cylinder settles down into a state of equilibrium in which the rate at which it gains negative electricity from the rays is equal to the rate at which it loses it by conduction through the air. If the inner cylinder has initially a positive charge it rapidly loses that charge and acquires a negative one; while if the initial charge is a negative one, the cylinder will leak if the initial negative potential is numerically greater than the equilibrium value.

DEFLEXION OF THE CATHODE RAYS BY AN ELECTROSTATIC FIELD

An objection very generally urged against the view that the cathode rays are negatively electrified particles, is that hitherto no deflexion of the rays has been observed under a small electrostatic force, and though the rays are deflected when they pass near electrodes connected with sources of large differences of potential, such as induction-coils or electrical machines, the deflexion in this case is regarded by the supporters of the aetherial theory as due to the discharge passing between the electrodes, and not primarily to the electrostatic field. Hertz made the rays travel between two parallel plates of metal placed inside the discharge-tube, but found that they were not deflected when the plates were connected with a battery of storage-cells; on repeating this experiment I at first got the same result, but subsequent experiments showed that the absence of deflexion is due to the conductivity conferred on the rarefied gas by the cathode rays. On measuring this conductivity it was found that it diminished very rapidly as the exhaustion increased; it seemed then that on trying Hertz's experiment at very high exhaustions there might be a chance of detecting the deflexion of the cathode rays by an electrostatic force.

The apparatus used is represented in Fig. 2.

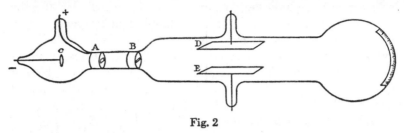

Fig. 2

The rays from the cathode C pass through a slit in the anode A, which is a metal plug fitting tightly into the tube and connected with the earth; after passing through a second slit in another earth-connected metal plug B, they travel between two parallel aluminum plates about 5 cm. long and 2 broad and at a distance of 1.5 cm. apart; they then fall on the end of the tube and produce a narrow well-defined phosphorescent patch. A scale pasted on the outside of the tube serves to measure the deflexion of this patch. At high exhaustions the rays were deflected when the two aluminum plates were connected with the terminals of a battery of small storage-cells; the rays were depressed when the upper plate was connected with the negative pole of the battery, the lower with the positive, and raised when the upper plate was connected with the positive, the lower with the negative pole. The deflexion was proportional to the difference of potential between the plates, and I could detect the deflexion when the potential-difference was as small as two volts. It was only when the vacuum was a good one that the deflexion took place, but that the absence of deflexion is due to the conductivity of the medium is shown by what takes place when the vacuum has just arrived at the stage at which the deflexion begins. At this stage there is a deflexion of the rays when the plates are first connected with the terminals of the battery, but if this connexion is maintained the patch of phosphorescence gradually creeps back to its undeflected position. This is just what would happen if the space between the plates were a conductor, though a very bad one, for then the positive and negative ions between the

932

plates would slowly diffuse, until the positive plate became coated with negative ions, the negative plate with positive ones; thus the electric intensity between the plates would vanish and the cathode rays be free from electrostatic force. Another illustration of this is afforded by what happens when the pressure is low enough to show the deflexion and a large difference of potential, say 200 volts, is established between the plates; under these circumstances there is a large deflexion of the cathode rays, but the medium under the large electromotive force breaks down every now and then and a bright discharge passes between the plates; when this occurs the phosphorescent patch produced by the cathode rays jumps back to its undeflected position. When the cathode rays are deflected by the electrostatic field, the phosphorescent band breaks up into several bright bands separated by comparatively dark spaces; the phenomena are exactly analogous to those observed by Birkeland when the cathode rays are deflected by a magnet, and called by him the magnetic spectrum.

A series of measurements of the deflexion of the rays by the electrostatic force under various circumstances will be found later on in the part of the paper which deals with the velocity of the rays and the ratio of the mass of the electrified particles to the charge carried by them. It may, however, be mentioned here that the deflexion gets smaller as the pressure diminishes, and when in consequence the potential-difference in the tube in the neighborhood of the cathode increases.

MAGNETIC DEFLEXION OF THE CATHODE RAYS IN DIFFERENT GASES

The deflexion of the cathode rays by the magnetic field was studied with the aid of the apparatus shown in Fig. 3. The cathode was placed in a side-tube fastened on to a bell-jar; the opening between this tube and the bell-jar was closed by a metallic plug with a slit in it; this plug was connected with the earth, and was used as the anode. The cathode rays passed through the slit in this plug into the bell-jar, passing in front of a vertical

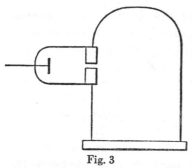

Fig. 3

plate of glass ruled into small squares. The bell-jar was placed between two large parallel coils arranged as a Helmholtz galvanometer. The course of the rays was determined by taking photographs of the bell-jar when the cathode rays were passing through it; the divisions on the plate enabled the path of the rays to be determined. Under the action of the magnetic field the narrow beam of cathode rays spreads out into a broad fan-shaped luminosity in the gas. The luminosity in this fan is not uniformly distributed, but is condensed along certain lines. The phosphorescence on the glass is also not uniformly distributed; it is much spread out, showing that the beam consists of rays which are not all deflected to the same extent by the magnet. The luminosity on the glass is crossed by bands along which the luminosity is very much greater than in the adjacent parts. These bright and dark bands are called by Birkeland, who first observed them, the magnetic spectrum. The brightest spots on the glass are by no means always the terminations of the brightest streaks of luminosity in the gas; in fact, in some cases a very bright spot on the glass is not connected with the cathode by any appreciable luminosity, though there may be plenty of luminosity in other parts of the gas. One very interesting point brought out by the photographs is that in a given magnetic field, and with a given mean potential-difference between the terminals, the path of the rays is independent of the nature of the gas. Photographs were taken of the discharge in hydrogen, air, carbonic acid, methyl iodide, i.e., in gases whose densities range from 1 to 70, and yet, not only were the paths of the most deflected rays the same in all cases, but even the details, such as the distribution of the bright and dark spaces, were the same; in fact, the photographs could hardly be distinguished from each other. It is to be noted that the pressures were not the same; the pressures in the different gases were adjusted so that the mean potential-differences between the cathode and the anode were the same in all the gases. When the pressure of a gas is lowered, the potential-difference between the terminals increases, and the deflexion of the rays produced by a magnet diminishes, or at any rate the deflexion of the rays when the phosphorescence is a maximum diminishes. If an airbreak is inserted an effect of the same kind is produced.

In the experiments with different gases, the pressures were as high as was consistent with the appearance of the phosphorescence on the glass, so as to ensure having as much as possible of the gas under consideration in the tube.

As the cathode rays carry a charge of negative electricity, are deflected by an electrostatic force as if they were negatively electrified, and are acted on by a magnetic force in just the way in which this force would act on a negatively electrified body moving along the path of these rays, I can see no escape from the conclusion that they are charges of negative electricity carried by particles of matter. The question next arises, What are these particles? are they atoms, or molecules, or matter in a still finer state of subdivision? To throw some light on this point, I have made a series of measurements of the ratio of the mass of these particles to the charge carried by it. To determine this quantity, I have used two independent methods. The first of these is as follows:—Suppose we consider a bundle of homogeneous cathode rays. Let m be the mass of each of the particles, e the charge carried by it. Let N be the number of particles passing across any section of the beam in a given time; then Q the quantity of electricity carried by these particles is given by the equation

$$Ne = Q.$$

We can measure Q if we receive the cathode rays in the inside of a vessel connected with an electrometer. When these rays strike against a solid body, the temperature of the body is raised; the kinetic energy of the moving particles being converted into heat; if we suppose that all this energy is converted into heat, then if we measure the increase in the temperature of a body of known thermal capacity caused by the impact of these rays, we can determine W, the kinetic energy of the particles, and if v is the velocity of the particles,

$$\tfrac{1}{2}Nmv^2 = W.$$

If p is the radius of curvature of the path of these rays in a uniform magnetic field H, then

$$\frac{mv}{e} = Hp = I,$$

where I is written for Hp for the sake of brevity. From these equations we get

$$\frac{1m}{2e}v^2 = \frac{W}{Q}$$

$$v = \frac{2W}{QI}$$

$$\frac{m}{e} = \frac{I^2Q}{2W}$$

Thus, if we know the values of Q, W, and I, we can deduce the values of v and m/e.

To measure these quantities, I have used tubes of three different types. The first I tried is like that represented in Fig. 2, except that the plates E and D are absent, and two coaxial cylinders are fastened to the end of the tube. The rays from the cathode C fall on the metal plug B, which is connected with the earth, and serves for the anode; a horizontal slit is cut in this plug. The cathode rays pass through this slit, and then strike against the two coaxial cylinders at the end of the tube; slits

936

are cut in these cylinders, so that the cathode rays pass into the inside of the inner cylinder. The outer cylinder is connected with an electrometer, the deflexion of which measures Q, the quantity of electricity brought into the inner cylinder by the rays. A thermo-electric couple is placed behind the slit in the inner cylinder; this couple is made of very thin strips of iron and copper fastened to very fine iron and copper wires. These wires passed through the cylinders, being insulated from them, and through the glass to the outside of the tube, where they were connected with a low-resistance galvanometer, the deflexion of which gave data for calculating the rise of temperature of the junction produced by the impact against it of the cathode rays. The strips of iron and copper were large enough to ensure that every cathode ray which entered the inner cylinder struck against the junction. In some of the tubes the strips of iron and copper were placed end to end, so that some of the rays struck against the iron, and others against the copper; in others, the strip of one metal was placed in front of the other; no difference, however, could be detected between the results got with these two arrangements. The strips of iron and copper were weighed, and the thermal capacity of

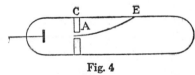

Fig. 4

the junction calculated. In one set of junctions this capacity was 5×10^{-3}, in another 3×10^{-3}. If we assume that the cathode rays which strike against the junction give their energy up to it the deflexion of the galvanometer gives us W or $\frac{1}{2}Nmv^2$.

The value of I, i.e., Hp, where p is the curvature of the path of the rays in a magnetic field of strength H was found as follows: —The tube was fixed between two large circular coils placed parallel to each other, and separated by a distance equal to the radius of either; these coils produce a uniform magnetic field, the strength of which is got by measuring with an ammeter the strength of the current passing through them. The cathode rays are thus in a uniform field, so that their path is circular. Suppose that the rays, when deflected by a magnet, strike against the

937

glass of the tube at E (Fig. 4), then, if p is the radius of the circular path of the rays,

$$2p = \frac{CE^2}{AC} + AC;$$

thus, if we measure CE and AC we have the means of determining the radius of curvature of the path of the rays.

The determination of p is rendered to some extent uncertain, in consequence of the pencil of rays spreading out under the action of the magnetic field, so that the phosphorescent patch of E is several millimetres long; thus values of p differing appreciably from each other will be got by taking E at different points of this phosphorescent patch. Part of this patch was, however, generally considerably brighter than the rest; when this was the case, E was taken as the brightest point; when such a point of maximum brightness did not exist, the middle of the patch was taken for E. The uncertainty in the value of p thus introduced amounted sometimes to about 20 percent; by this I mean that if we took E first at one extremity of the patch and then at the other, we should get values of p differing by this amount.

The measurement of Q, the quantity of electricity which enters the inner cylinder, is complicated by the cathode rays making the gas through which they pass a conductor, so that though the insulation of the inner cylinder was perfect when the rays were off, it was not so when they were passing through the space between the cylinders; this caused some of the charge communicated to the inner cylinder to leak away so that the actual charge given to the cylinder by the cathode rays was larger than that indicated by the electrometer.

To make the error from this cause as small as possible, the inner cylinder was connected to the largest capacity available, 1.5 microfarad, and the rays were only kept on for a short time, about 1 or 2 seconds, so that the alteration in potential of the inner cylinder was not large, ranging in the various experiments

938

from about .5 to 5 volts. Another reason why it is necessary to limit the duration of the rays to as short a time as possible, is to avoid the correction for the loss of heat from the thermo-electric junction by conduction along the wires; the rise in temperature of the junction was of the order 2°C.; a series of experiments showed that with the same tube and the same gaseous pressure Q and W were proportional to each other when the rays were not kept on too long.

Tubes of this kind gave satisfactory results, the chief draw-back being that sometimes in consequence of the charging up of the glass of the tube, a secondary discharge started from the cylinder to the walls of the tube, and the cylinders were surrounded by glow; when this glow appeared, the readings were very irregular; the glow could, however, be got rid of by pumping and letting the tube rest for some time. The results got with this tube are given in the Table under the heading Tube 1.

The second type of tube was like that used for photographing the path of the rays (Fig. 3); double cylinders with a thermo-electric junction like those used in the previous tube were placed in the line of fire of the rays, the inside of the bell-jar was lined with copper gauze connected with the earth. This tube gave very satisfactory results; we were never troubled with any glow round the cylinders, and the readings were most concordant; the only drawback was that as some of the connexions had to be made with sealing wax, it was not possible to get the highest exhaustions with this tube, so that the range of pressure for this tube is less than that for Tube 1. The results got with this tube are given in the Table under the heading Tube 2.

The third type of tube was similar to the first, except that the openings in the two cylinders were made very much smaller; in this tube the slits in the cylinders were replaced by small holes, about 1.5 millim. in diameter. In consequence of the smallness of the openings, the magnitude of the effects was very much reduced; in order to get measurable results it was necessary to reduce the capacity of the condenser in connexion with the inner cylinder to .15 microfarad, and to make the galvanometer exceedingly sensitive, as the rise in temperature of the thermo-

939

electric junction was in these experiments only about .5°C. on the average. The results obtained in this tube are given in the Table under the heading Tube 3.

[Tables omitted.]

It will be noticed that the value of m/e is considerably greater for Tube 3, where the opening is a small hole, than for Tubes 1 and 2, where the opening is a slit of much greater area. I am of opinion that the values of m/e got from Tubes 1 and 2 are too small, in consequence of the leakage from the inner cylinder to the outer by the gas being rendered a conductor by the passage of the cathode rays.

It will be seen from these tables that the value of m/e is independent of the nature of the gas. Thus, for the first tube the mean for air is $.40 \times 10^{-7}$, for hydrogen $.42 \times 10^{-7}$, and for carbonic acid gas $.4 \times 10^{-7}$; for the second tube the mean for air is $.52 \times 10^{-7}$, for hydrogen $.50 \times 10^{-7}$, and for carbonic acid gas $.54 \times 10^{-7}$.

Experiments were tried with electrodes made of iron instead of aluminum; this altered the appearance of the discharge and the value of v at the same pressure, the values of m/e were, however, the same in the two tubes; the effect produced by different metals on the appearance of the discharge will be described later on.

In all the preceding experiments, the cathode rays were first deflected from the cylinder by a magnet, and it was then found that there was no deflexion either of the electrometer or the galvanometer, so that the deflexions observed were entirely due to the cathode rays; when the glow mentioned previously surrounded the cylinders there was a deflexion of the electrometer even when the cathode rays were deflected from the cylinder.

Before proceeding to discuss the results of these measurements I shall describe another method of measuring the quantities m/e and v of an entirely different kind from the preceding; this method is based upon the deflexion of the cathode rays in an electrostatic field. If we measure the deflexion experienced by the rays when traversing a given length under a uniform electric intensity, and the deflexion of the rays when they traverse a given distance under a uniform magnetic field, we can find the values of m/e and v in the following way:—

Let the space passed over by the rays under a uniform electric intensity F be l, the time taken for the rays to traverse this space is l/v, the velocity in the direction of F is therefore

$$\frac{Fe}{m} \frac{l}{e},$$

so that θ, the angle through which the rays are deflected when they leave the electric field and enter a region free from electric force, is given by the equation

$$\theta = \frac{Fe}{m} \frac{l}{v^2}$$

If, instead of the electric intensity, the rays are acted on by a magnetic force H at right angles to the rays, and extending across the distance l, the velocity at right angles to the original path of the rays is

$$\frac{Hev}{m} \frac{l}{v},$$

so that ϕ, the angle through which the rays are deflected when they leave the magnetic field, is given by the equation

$$\phi = \frac{He}{m} \frac{l}{v}.$$

From these equations we get

$$v = \frac{\phi}{\theta} \frac{F}{H}$$

941

and

$$\frac{m}{e} = \frac{H^2\theta l}{F\phi^2}$$

In the actual experiments H was adjusted so that $\phi = \theta$, in this case the equations become

$$v = \frac{F}{H},$$

$$\frac{m}{m} = \frac{H^2 l}{F\theta}$$

The apparatus used to measure v and m/e by this means is that represented in Fig. 2. The electric field was produced by connecting the two aluminum plates to the terminals of a battery of storage-cells. The phosphorescent patch at the end of the tube was deflected, and the deflexion measured by a scale pasted to the end of the tube. As it was necessary to darken the room to see the phosphorescent patch, a needle coated with luminous paint was placed so that by a screw it could be moved up and down the scale; this needle could be seen when the room was darkened, and it was moved until it coincided with the phosphorescent patch. Thus when light was admitted, the deflexion of the phosphorescent patch could be measured.

The magnetic field was produced by placing outside the tube two coils whose diameter was equal to the length of the plates; the coils were placed so that they covered the space occupied by the plates, the distance between the coils was equal to the radius of either. The mean value of the magnetic force over the length l was determined in the following way: a narrow coil C whose length was l, connected with a ballistic galvanometer, was placed between the coils; the plane of the windings of C was parallel to the planes of the coils; the cross section of the coil was a rectangle 5 cm. by 1 cm. A given current was sent through the outer coils and the kick a of the galvanometer observed when this current was reversed. The coil C was then placed at the centre of two very large coils, so as to be in a field of uniform magnetic force: the current through the large coils was reversed and the kick B of the galvanometer again observed; by comparing a and B we can get the mean value of the magnetic force over a length l; this was found to be

$$60 \times l$$

where l is the current flowing through the coils.

A series of experiments was made to see if the electrostatic deflexion was proportional to the electric intensity between the plates; this was found to be the case. In the following experiments the current through the coils was adjusted so that the electrostatic deflexion was the same as the magnetic:

Gas	θ	H	F	l	m/e	v
Air..................	$8/110$	5.5	1.5×10^{10}	5	1.3×10^{-7}	2.8×10^{9}
Air..................	$9.5/110$	5.4	1.5×10^{10}	5	1.1×10^{-7}	2.8×10^{9}
Air..................	$13/110$	6.6	1.5×10^{10}	5	1.2×10^{-7}	2.3×10^{9}
Hydrogen.............	$9/110$	6.3	1.5×10^{10}	5	1.5×10^{-7}	2.5×10^{9}
Carbonic acid.........	$11/110$	6.9	1.5×10^{10}	5	1.5×10^{-7}	2.2×10^{9}
Air..................	$8/110$	5	1.8×10^{10}	5	1.3×10^{-7}	3.6×10^{9}
Air..................	$7/110$	3.6	1×10^{10}	5	1.1×10^{-7}	2.8×10^{9}

The cathode in the first five experiments was aluminum, in the last two experiments it was made of platinum; in the last experiment Sir William Crooke's method of getting rid of the mercury vapour by inserting tubes of pounded sulphur, sulphur iodide, and copper filings between the bulb and the pump was adopted. In the calculation of m/e and v no allowance has been made for the magnetic force due to the coil in the region outside the plates; in this region the magnetic force will be in the opposite direction to that between the plates, and will tend to bend the cathode rays in the opposite direction: thus the

943

effective value of H will be smaller than the value used in the equations, so that the values of m/e are larger, and those of v less than they would be if this correction were applied. This method of determining the values of m/e and v is much less laborious and probably more accurate than the former method; it cannot, however, be used over so wide a range of pressures.

From these determinations we see that the value of m/e is independent of the nature of the gas, and that its value 10^{-7} is very small compared with the value 10^{-4}, which is the smallest value of this quantity previously known, and which is the value for the hydrogen ion in electrolysis.

Thus for the carriers of the electricity in the cathode rays m/e is very small compared with its value in electrolysis. The smallness of m/e may be due to the smallness of m or the largeness of e, or to a combination of these two. That carriers of the charges in the cathode rays are small compared with ordinary molecules is shown, I think, by Lenard's results as to the rate at which the brightness of the phosphorescence produced by these rays diminishes with the length of path travelled by the ray. If we regard this phosphorescence as due to the impact of the charged particles, the distance through which the rays must travel before the phosphorescence fades to a given fraction (say $1/e$, where $e = 2.271$) of its original intensity, will be some moderate multiple of the mean free path. Now Lenard found that this distance depends solely upon the density of the medium, and not upon its chemical nature or physical state. In air at atmospheric pressure the distance was about half a centimetre, and this must be comparable with the mean free path of the carriers through air at atmospheric pressure. But the mean free path of the molecules of air is a quantity of quite a different order. The carrier, then, must be small compared with ordinary molecules.

The two fundamental points about these carriers seem to me to be (1) that these carriers are the same whatever the gas through which the discharge passes, (2) that the mean free paths depend upon nothing but the density of the medium traversed by these rays.

EVANGELISTA TORRICELLI

(1608–1647)

Assistant to the blind Galileo a few months preceding his death, Torricelli succeeded him as professor at the Florentine Academy. Torricelli's major contribution to hydromechanics was the invention of the barometer from an inverted column of mercury (1643), and his discovery that water will not rise above 33 feet in a suction pump. He made improvements on the telescope, constructed a primitive microscope, and worked on the cycloid.

THE BAROMETER

(To Michelangelo Ricci in Rome)

Florence, June 11, 1644

Most Illustrious Sir and
Most Learned Patron

Several weeks ago I sent Sig. Antonio Nardi several of my demonstrations of the areas of cycloids, and asked him that after he had examined them he would send them on at once to yourself or to Sig. Magiotti. I have already called attention to the fact that there are in progress certain philosophical experiments, I do not know just what, relating to vacuum, designed not simply to make a vacuum but to make an instrument which will show the changes in the atmosphere, as it is now heavier and more gross and now lighter and more subtle. Many have said that a vacuum does not exist, others that it does exist in spite of the repugnance of nature and with difficulty; I know of no one who has said that it exists without difficulty and

945

without a resistance from nature. I argued thus: If there can be found a manifest cause from which the resistance can be derived which is felt if we try to make a vacuum, it seems to me foolish to try to attribute to vacuum those operations which follow evidently from some other cause; and so by making some very easy calculations, I found that the cause assigned by me (that is, the weight of the atmosphere) ought by itself alone to offer a greater resistance than it does when we try to produce a vacuum. I say this because a certain philosopher, seeing that he cannot escape the admission that the weight of the atmosphere causes the resistance which is felt in making a vacuum, does not say that he admits the operation of the heavy air, but persists in asserting that nature also concurs in resisting the vacuum. We live immersed at the bottom of a sea of elemental air, which by experiment undoubtedly has weight, and so much weight that the densest air in the neighborhood of the surface of the earth weighs about one four-hundredth part of the weight of water. Certain authors have observed after twilight that the vaporous and visible air rises above us to a height of fifty or fifty-four miles, but I do not think it is so much, because I can show that the vacuum ought to offer a much greater resistance than it does, unless we use the argument that the weight which Galileo assigned applies to the lowest atmosphere, where men and animals live, but that on the peaks of high mountains the air begins to be more pure and to weigh much less than the four-hundredth part of the weight of water. We have made many vessels of glass like those shown as A and B (Fig. 1) and with tubes two cubits long. These were filled with quicksilver, the open end was closed with the finger, and they were then inverted in a vessel where there was quicksilver C; then we saw that an empty space was formed and that nothing happened in the vessel where this space was formed; the tube between A and D remained always full to the height of a cubit and a quarter and an inch over. To show that the vessel was entirely empty, we filled the bowl with pure water up to D and then, raising the tube little by little, we saw that, when the opening of the tube reached the water, the quicksilver fell out of the

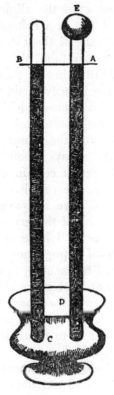

Fig. 1

tube and the water rushed with great violence up to the mark *E*. It is often said in explanation of the fact that the vessel *AE* stands empty and the quicksilver, although heavy, is sustained in the tube *AC*, as has been believed hitherto, the force which prevents the quicksilver from falling down, as it would naturally do, is internal to the vessel *AE*, arising either from the vacuum or from some exceedingly rarefied substance; but I asserted that it is external and that the force comes from without. On the surface of the liquid which is in the bowl there rests the weight of a height of fifty miles of air; then what wonder is it if into the vessel *CE*, in which the quicksilver has no inclination

947

and no repugnance, not even the slightest, to being there, it should enter and should rise in a column high enough to make equilibrium with the weight of the external air which forces it up? Water also in a similar tube, though a much longer one, will rise to about 18 cubits, that is, as much more than quicksilver does as quicksilver is heavier than water, so as to be in equilibrium with the same cause which acts on the one and the other. This argument is strengthened by an experiment made at the same time with the vessel A and with the tube B in which the quicksilver always stood at the same horizontal line AB. This makes it almost certain that the action does not come from within; because the vessel AE, where there was more rarefied substance, should have had a greater force, attracting much more actively because of the greater rarefaction than that of the much smaller space B. I have endeavored to explain by this principle all sorts of repugnances which are felt in the various effects attributed to vacuum, and I have not yet found any with which I cannot deal successfully. I know that your highness will perceive many objections, but I hope if you think them over they will be resolved. My principal intention I was not able to carry out, that is, to recognize when the atmosphere is grosser and heavier and when it is more subtle and lighter, because the level AB in the instrument EC changes for some other reason (which I would not have believed) especially as it is sensible to cold or heat, exactly as if the vessel AE were full of air.

Your devoted and obliged Servant,

E. TORRICELLI

ANDREAS VESALIUS

(1514-1564)

The first man to become really acquainted with the interior of the human body—and hence the discoverer of countless new biological facts—was the Flemish anatomist, Vesalius. His seven-volume work, *De Humani Corporis Fabrica* (*The Anatomy of the Human Body*) published in 1543, became a cornerstone of modern anatomy. Because he discovered so many errors in the long-revered Galen, and was reputed to resort to "body-snatching" to obtain material for his researches, he ran into the usual ecclesiastical opposition. Driven from Italy to Spain, where he served Charles V, he was eventually hauled before the Inquisition and, in commutation of the death sentence, ordered on a pilgrimage to Jerusalem. He died on the way home.

THE PREFACE OF ANDREAS VESALIUS
to
His Own Books on the Anatomy of the Human Body
addressed to
The Most Great and Invincible Emperor
THE DIVINE CHARLES V

THOSE engaged in the arts and sciences, Most Gracious Emperor Charles, find many serious obstacles to the exact study and successful application of them. In the first place, no slight inconvenience results from too great separation between branches of study which serve for the perfection of one art. But much worse is the mischievous distribution among different practitioners of the practical applications of the art. This has been carried so far that those who have set before themselves the attainment of an art embrace one part of it to the neglect of

949

the rest, although they are intimately bound up with it and can by no means be separated from it. Such never achieve any notable result; they never attain their goal or succeed in basing their art upon a proper foundation.

I shall pass over all the other arts in silence and confine myself to a few remarks on that which presides over the health of mankind. This, of all the arts which the mind of man has discovered, is by far the most beneficial, necessary, abstruse, and laborious. But in bygone times, that is to say [in the West] after the Gothic deluge and [in the East] after the reign of Mansor at Bochara in Persia, under whom, as we know, the Arabs still lived as was right on terms of familiarity with the Greeks, medicine began to be sore distempered. Its primary instrument, the employment of the hand in healing, was so neglected that it was relegated to vulgar fellows with no instruction whatsoever in the branches of knowledge that subserve the art of medicine.

In ancient times there were three medical sects, to wit, the Dogmatic, the Empirical, and the Methodical, but the exponents of each of these embraced the whole of the art as the means to preserve health and war against disease. To this end they referred all that they individually thought necessary in their particular sects, and employed the service of a threefold aid to health: first, a theory of diet; secondly, the whole use of drugs; and thirdly, manual operation. This last, above the rest, nicely proves the saying that medicine is the addition of that which is defective and the removal of that which is in excess; as often as we resort to the art of medicine for the treatment of disease we have occasion to employ it; and time and experience have taught, by the benefits it has conferred, that it is the greatest aid to human health.

This triple manner of treatment was equally familiar to the doctors of each sect; and those who applied manual operation according to the nature of the affection expended no less care in training their hands than in establishing a theory of diet, or in learning to recognize and compound drugs. This, not to mention his other books, is clearly shown by those most perfect of the compositions of Hippocrates: "On the Function of the Doctor," "On Fractures of Bones," "On Dislocations of Joints and Similar Ailments." Nay, more, Galen, after Hippocrates the prince of medicine, in addition to the fact that he boasts from time to time that the care of the gladiators of Pergamum was entrusted to his sole charge, and that when age was now becoming a burden he was reluctant for the monkeys he had for dissection to be skinned by the help of slaves, frequently impresses on us his joy in manual dexterity and how zealously he, in common with the other doctors of Asia, employed it. Indeed, there is no one of the ancients who does not seem as solicitous to hand down to posterity the method of cure which is effected by the hand as those methods which depend on diet and drugs.

But it was especially after the ruin spread by the Goths, when all the sciences, which before had flourished gloriously and were practiced as was fitting, went to ruin, that more fashionable doctors, first in Italy, in imitation of the old Romans, despising the work of the hand, began to delegate to slaves the manual attentions which they judged needful for their patients, and themselves merely to stand over them like master builders. Then, when all the rest also who practiced the true art of healing gradually declined the unpleasant duties of their profession, without, however, abating any of their claim to money or honor, they quickly fell away from the standard of the doctors of old. Methods of cooking, and all the preparation of food for the sick, they left to nurses; compounding of drugs they left to the apothecaries; manual operation to barbers. Thus in course of time the art of healing has been so wretchedly rent asunder that certain doctors, advertising themselves under the name of physicians, have arrogated to themselves alone the prescription of drugs and diet for obscure diseases, and have relegated the rest of medicine to those whom they call surgeons and scarcely regard as slaves, disgracefully banishing from themselves the chief and most ancient branch of the medical art, and that which principally (if indeed there be any other) bases itself upon the investigation of nature. Yet among the Indians today

951

it is the kings that chiefly exercise this [surgical] art; the Persians hand it down as an obligatory inheritance to their children, as formerly did the whole family of the Asclepiads; the Thracians, with many other nations, cultivate and honor it above other arts, to the neglect almost of that part of the art [the prescription of drugs] which formerly many proscribed from the state, as devised for the deception and destruction of men; for it, refusing the aid of nature, gives no deep relief, but rather, endeavoring to help nature while it is in any case overwrought by the effort to cast off the disease, it often destroys it quite and utterly distracts it from its normal function. Consequently it is to it in particular we owe the fact that so many scoffs are wont to be cast at doctors, and this most holy art is made a mock, though all the time one part of it, which those trained in liberal studies allow basely to be torn from them, could adorn it forever with peculiar praise.

For when Homer, that wellspring of genius, declares that a man that is a doctor is better than a host, and together with all the poets of Greece celebrates Podalyrius and Machaon, truly these divine sons of Aesculapius are thus praised not for the reason that they banished a touch of fever or other ailments which nature usually cures, unaided, and without the assistance of the doctor more easily than with his aid, nor because they pandered to the appetites of men in obscure and desperate affections, but because they devoted themselves in particular to the cure of dislocations, fractures, bruises, wounds, and other breaches of continuity, and to fluxions of blood, and because they freed the noble warriors of Agamemnon from javelins, darts, and other evils of that kind, which wars particularly occasion, and which always demand the careful attention of the doctor.

But it was not at all my purpose to set one instrument of medicine above the rest, since the triple art of healing, as it is called, cannot at all be disunited and wrenched asunder, but belongs in its entirety to the same practitioner; and for the due attainment of this triple art, all the parts of medicine have been established and prepared on an equal footing, so that the individual parts are brought into use with a success proportioned to the degree in which one combines the cumulative force of all. How rarely indeed a disease occurs which does not at once require the triple manner of treatment; that is to say, a proper diet must be prescribed, some service must be rendered by medicine, and some by the hand. Therefore the tyros in this art must by every means be exhorted to follow the Greeks in despising the whisperings of those physicians (save the mark!), and, as the fundamental nature and rational basis of the art prescribes, to apply their hands also to the treatment, lest they should rend the body of medicine and make of it a force destructive of the common life of man.

And they must be urged to this with all the greater earnestness because men today who have had an irreproachable training in the art are seen to abstain from the use of the hand as from the plague, and for this very reason, lest they should be slandered by the masters of the profession as barbers before the ignorant mob, and should henceforth lack equal gain and honor with those less than half doctors, losing their standing both with the uneducated commonalty and with princes. For it is indeed above all other things the wide prevalence of this hateful error that prevents us even in our age from taking up the healing art as a whole, makes us confine ourselves merely to the treatment of internal complaints, and, if I may utter the blunt truth once for all, causes us, to the great detriment of mankind, to study to be healers only in a very limited degree.

For when, in the first place, the whole compounding of drugs was handed over to the apothecaries, then the doctors promptly lost the knowledge of simple medicines which is absolutely essential to them; and they became responsible for the fact that the druggists' shops were filled with barbarous terms and false remedies, and also that so many elegant compositions of the ancients were lost to us, several of which have not yet come to light; and, finally, they prepared an endless task for the learned men, not only of our own age, but for those who preceded it by some years, who devoted themselves with indefatigable zeal to research in simple medicines; so much so that they may be regarded as having gone far to restore the knowledge of them to its former brilliance.

But this perverse distribution of the instruments of healing among a variety of craftsmen inflicted a much more odious shipwreck and a far more cruel blow upon the chief branch of natural philosophy [anatomy], to which, since it comprises the natural history of man and should rightly be regarded as the firm foundation of the whole of medicine and its essential preliminary, Hippocrates and Plato attached so much importance that they did not hesitate to put it first among the parts of medicine. For though originally it was the prime object of the doctors' care, and though they strained every nerve to acquire it, it finally began to perish miserably when the doctors themselves, by resigning manual operations to others, ruined anatomy. For when the doctors supposed that only the care of internal complaints concerned them, considering a mere knowledge of the viscera as more than enough for them, they neglected the structure of the bones and muscles, as well as of the nerves, veins, and arteries which run through bones and muscles, as of no importance for them. And further, when the whole conduct of manual operations was entrusted to barbers, not only did doctors lose the true knowledge of the viscera, but the practice of dissection soon died out, doubtless for the reason that the doctors did not attempt to operate, while those to whom the manual skill was resigned were too ignorant to read the writings of the teachers of anatomy.

It is thus utterly impossible for this class of men to preserve for us a difficult art which they have acquired only mechanically. And equally inevitably this deplorable dismemberment of the art of healing has introduced into our schools the detestable procedure now in vogue, that one man should carry out the dissection of the human body, and another give the description of the parts. These latter are perched up aloft in a pulpit like jackdaws, and with a notable air of disdain they drone out information about facts they have never approached at first hand, but which they merely commit to memory from the books of others, or of which they have descriptions before their eyes;

the former are so ignorant of languages that they are unable to explain their dissections to the onlookers and botch what ought to be exhibited in accordance with the instruction of the physician, who never applies his hand to the dissection, and contemptuously steers the ship out of the manual, as the saying goes. Thus everything is wrongly taught, days are wasted in absurd questions, and in the confusion less is offered to the onlooker than a butcher in his stall could teach a doctor. I omit all mention of those schools in which there is scarcely even a thought of opening a human body to exhibit its structure. So far had ancient medicine fallen some years ago from its pristine glory.

But when medicine in the great blessedness of this age, which the gods will to entrust to the wise guidance of your divine power, had, together with all studies, begun to live again and to lift its head up from its utter darkness (so much so, indeed, that it might without fear of contradiction be regarded in some academies as having well-nigh recovered its ancient brilliance); and when there was nothing of which the need was now so urgently felt as the resurrection of the science of anatomy, then I, challenged by the example of so many eminent men, insofar as I could and with what means I could command, thought I should lend my aid. And lest, when all others for the sake of our common studies were engaged in some attempt and with such great success, I alone should be idle, or lest I should fall below the level of my forebears, doctors to be sure not unknown to fame, I thought that this branch of natural philosophy should be recalled from the dead, so that if it did not achieve with us a greater perfection than at any other place or time among the old teachers of anatomy, it might at least reach such a point that one could with confidence assert that our modern science of anatomy was equal to that of old, and that in this age anatomy was unique both in the level to which it had sunk and in the completeness of its subsequent restoration.

But this effort could by no manner of means have succeeded if, when I was studying medicine at Paris, I had not myself applied my hand to this business, but had acquiesced in the casual and superficial display to me and my fellow students by certain barbers of a few organs at one or two public dissections. For in such a perfunctory manner was anatomy then treated in the place where we have lived to see medicine happily reborn that I myself, having trained myself without guidance in the dissection of brute creatures, at the third dissection at which it was my fortune ever to be present (this, as was the custom there, was concerned exclusively or principally with the viscera), led on by the encouragement of my fellow students and teachers, performed in public a more thorough dissection than was wont to be done. Later I attempted a second dissection, my purpose being to exhibit the muscles of the hand together with a more accurate dissection of the viscera. For except for eight muscles of the abdomen, disgracefully mangled and in the wrong order, no one (I speak the simple truth) ever demonstrated to me any single muscle, or any single bone, much less the network of nerves, veins, and arteries.

Subsequently at Louvain, where I had to return on account of the disturbance of war, because during eighteen years the doctors there had not even dreamed of anatomy, and in order that I might help the students of that academy, and that I myself might acquire greater skill in a matter both obscure and in my judgment of prime importance for the whole of medicine, I did somewhat more accurately than at Paris expound the whole structure of the human body in the course of dissecting, with the result that the younger teachers of that academy now appear to spend great and very serious study in acquiring a knowledge of the parts of man, clearly understanding what invaluable material for philosophizing is presented to them from this knowledge. Furthermore at Padua, in the most famous gymnasium of the whole world, I had been charged with the teaching of surgical medicine five years by the illustrious Senate of Venice, which is far the most liberal in the endowment of the higher branches of learning. And since the carrying out of anatomical inquiry is of importance for surgical medicine, I devoted much effort to the investigation of the structure of man, and so directed my inquiries, and, exploding the ridiculous fashion of the schools, so taught the subject that we could not find in my procedure anything that fell short of the tradition of the ancients.

However, the supineness of the medical profession has seen to it only too well that the writings of Eudemus, Herophilus, Marinus, Andreas, Lycus, and other princes of anatomy should not be preserved to us, since not even a fragment of any page has survived of all those famous writers whom Galen mentions, to the number of more than twenty, in his second commentary to the book of Hippocrates on "The Nature of Man." Nay, even of his own anatomical writings scarcely the half has been saved from destruction. But those who followed Galen, among whom I place Oribasius, Theophilus, the Arabs, and all our own writers whom I have read to date, all of them (and they must pardon me for saying this), if they handed on anything worth reading, borrowed it from him. And, believe me, the careful reader will discover that there is nothing they were further from attempting than the dissection of bodies. They placed an absolute trust in I know not what quality of the writing of their chief, and in the neglect of dissection of the rest, and shamefully reduced Galen to convenient summaries, never departing from him by so much as the breadth of a nail, that is, supposing they succeed in arriving at his meaning. Nay, they place it in the forefront of their books that their own writings are pieced together from the teachings of Galen, and that all that is theirs is his. And so completely have all surrendered to his authority that no doctor has been found to declare that in the anatomical books of Galen even the slightest error has ever been found, much less could now be found; though all the time (apart from the fact that Galen frequently corrects himself, and in later books, after acquiring more experience, removes oversights that he had committed in earlier books, and sometimes teaches contradictory views) it is quite clear to us, from the revival of the art of dissection, from a painstaking perusal of the works of Galen, and from a restoration of them in several places, of which we have no reason to be ashamed, that Galen himself never dissected a human body lately dead. Nay, more, deceived by his

957

monkeys (although it is admitted that human bodies dried, and prepared as it were for an inspection of the bones, did come under his observation), he frequently wrongly controverts the ancient doctors who had trained themselves by dissecting human corpses.

And again, how many false observations you will find him to have made even on his monkeys. I shall say nothing about the astonishing fact that in the manifold and infinite divergences of the organs of the human body from those of the monkey Galen hardly noticed anything except in the fingers and the bend of the knee—which he would certainly have passed over with the rest, if they had not been obvious to him without dissection. But at the moment I do not propose to criticize the false statements of Galen, easily the foremost among the teachers of anatomy; and much less would I wish to be regarded now in the beginning as disloyal to the author of all good things and lacking in respect for his authority. For I am not unaware how the medical profession (in this so different from the followers of Aristotle) are wont to be upset when in more than two hundred instances, in the conduct of the single course of anatomy I now exhibit in the schools, they see that Galen has failed to give a true description of the interrelation, use, and function of the parts of man—how they scowl at times, and examine every inch of the dissection in their determination to defend him. Yet they too, drawn by the love of truth, gradually abandon that attitude and, growing less emphatic, begin to put faith in their own not ineffectual sight and powers of reason rather than in the writings of Galen. These true paradoxes, won not by slavish reliance on the efforts of others, nor supported merely by masses of authorities, they eagerly communicate in their correspondence to their friends; they exhort them so earnestly and so friendly-wise to examine them for themselves, and to come at last to a true knowledge of anatomy, that there is ground for hope that anatomy will ere long be cultivated in all our academies as it was of old in Alexandria.

And that the muses might the more smile upon this hope, I have, so far as in me lay, and in addition to my other publications on this subject—which certain plagiarists, thinking me far away from Germany, have put out there as their own—made a completely fresh arrangement in seven books of my information about the parts of the human body in the order in which I am wont to lay the same before that learned assembly in this city, as well as at Bologna and at Pisa. Thus those present at the dissections will have a record of what was there demonstrated, and will be able to expound anatomy to others with less trouble. And also the books will be by no means useless to those who have no opportunity for personal examination, for they relate with sufficient fullness the number, position, shape, substance, connection with other parts, use and function of each part of the human body, together with many similar facts which we are wont to unravel during dissection concerning the nature of the parts, and also the method of dissection applicable to dead and living animals. Moreover, the books contain representations of all the parts inserted in the text of the discourse, in such a way that they place before the eyes of the student of nature's works, as it were, a dissected corpse.

Thus in the first book I have described the nature of all bones and cartilages, which, since the other parts are supported by them, and must be described in accordance with them, are the first to be known by students of anatomy. The second book treats of the ligaments by which bones and cartilages are linked one with another, and then the muscles that affect the movements that depend upon our will. The third comprises the close network of veins which carry to the muscles and bones and the other parts the ordinary blood by which they are nourished, and of arteries which control the mixture of innate heat and vital spirit. The fourth treats of the branches not only of the nerves which convey the animal spirit to the muscles, but of all the other nerves as well. The fifth explains the structure of the organs that subserve nutrition effected through food and drink; and furthermore, on account of the proximity of their position, it contains also the instruments designed by the Most High Creator for the propagation of the species. The sixth is devoted to the heart, the *fomes* of the vital faculty, and the parts that subserve it. The seventh describes the harmony between the structure of the brain and the organs of sense, without, however, repeating from the fourth book the description of the network of nerves arising from the brain. . . .

But here there comes into my mind the judgment of certain men who vehemently condemn the practice of setting before the eyes of students, as we do with the parts of plants, delineations, be they never so accurate, of the parts of the human body. These, they say, ought to be learned not by pictures but by careful dissection and examination of the things themselves. As if, forsooth, my object in adding to the text of my discourse images of the parts, which are most faithful, and which I wish could be free from the risk of being spoiled by the printers, was that students should rely upon them and refrain from dissecting bodies; whereas my practice has rather been to encourage students of medicine in every way I could to perform dissections with their own hands. Assuredly, if the practice of the ancients had lasted down to our day, namely, to train boys at home in carrying out dissections, just as in making their letters and in reading, I would gladly consent to our dispensing not only with pictures but with all commentaries. For the ancients only began to write about dissection when they decided that honor demanded that they should communicate the art not only to their children but to strangers whom they respected for their virtue. For, as soon as boys were no longer trained in dissection, the inevitable consequence at once followed that they learned anatomy less well, since the training had been abolished with which they had been wont to begin in youth. So much so that when the art had deserted the family of the Asclepiads, and had been now for many centuries on the decline, books were needed to preserve a complete view of it. Yet how greatly pictures aid the understanding of these things, and how much more accurately they put the things before the eyes than even the clearest language, nobody can have failed to experience in geometry and the other mathematical disciplines.

But, however that may be, I have done my best to this single end, namely, in an equally recondite and laborious matter, to aid as many as possible, and truly and completely to describe the structure of the human body—which is built up not of some ten or twelve parts (as seems to those who give it a passing glance) but of some thousands of different parts—and to bring to students of medicine a substantial contribution toward the understanding of those books of Galen treating of this branch of learning, which of all his writings most require the assistance of a teacher.

Moreover, I am aware [first] how little authority my efforts will carry by reason of my youth (I am still in my twenty-eighth year); and [secondly] how little, on account of the frequency with which I draw attention to the falsity of Galen's pronouncements, I shall be sheltered from the attacks of those who have not—as I have done in the schools of Italy—applied themselves earnestly to anatomy, and who, being now old men devoured by envy at the true discoveries of youth, will be ashamed, together with all the other sectaries of Galen, that they have been hitherto so purblind, failing to notice what I now set forth, yet arrogating to themselves a mighty reputation in the art— [I know, I say, how little authority my efforts will carry] unless they come forth auspiciously into the light, commended by the great patronage of some divine power. And, inasmuch as it cannot be more safely sheltered or more splendid adorned than by the imperishable name of the Divine Charles, the Most Great and Invincible Emperor, I beseech Your Majesty to allow this work of mine, which on many accounts and for many reasons is dangerous to itself, to circulate for a short time under Your Majesty's auspices, glory, and patronage, until through experience of the facts, through judgment which matures with time, and through learning, I may make the fruit of my toil worthy of the Most High and Best Prince, or may offer another gift worthy of acceptance on another subject chosen from our art.

LEONARDO DA VINCI

(1452–1519)

Symbol of the rebirth of learning and the scientific spirit at the close of the Dark Ages, Leonardo still stands as the first man of the Renaissance. His artworks have stood the test of time better than his scientific notions, which foreshadowed later discoveries, but are in themselves often quite primitive. The only record we have of most of them lies in the half-sketched pages of his notebooks. Nevertheless he was a pioneer, if incomplete, thinker in many areas, including, of course, aviation, hydraulics, mechanics, anatomy, astronomy and geology. His known works of a scientific nature include the engineering of a great canal and various military installations.

ON FLIGHT

A BIRD is an instrument working according to mathematical law, which instrument it is within the capacity of man to reproduce with all its movements, but not with a corresponding degree of strength, though it is deficient only in the power of maintaining equilibrium. We may therefore say that such an instrument constructed by man is lacking in nothing except the life of the bird, and this life must needs be supplied from that of man.

The life which resides in the bird's members will without doubt better conform to their needs than will that of man, which is separated from them, and especially in the most imperceptible movements which preserve equilibrium. But since we see that the bird is equipped for many obvious varieties of movements, we are able from this experience to declare that the most rudimentary of these movements will be capable of being comprehended by man's understanding; and that he will to a great extent be able to provide against the destruction of that instrument of which he has himself become the living principle and the propeller.

The slanting descent of birds made against the wind will always be made beneath the wind, and their reflex movement will be made upon the wind.

But if this falling movement is made to the east when the wind is blowing from the north, then the north wing will remain under the wind and it will do the same in the reflex movement, wherefore at the end of this reflex movement the bird will find itself with its front to the north.

And if the bird descends to the south while the wind is blowing from the north it will make this descent upon the wind, and its reflex movement will be below the wind; but this is a vexed question which shall be discussed in its proper place, for here it would seem that it could not make the reflex movement.

When the bird makes its reflex movement facing and upon the wind it will rise much more than its natural impetus requires, seeing that it is also helped by the wind which enters underneath it and plays the part of a wedge. But when it is at the end of its ascent it will have used up its impetus and therefore will depend upon the help of the wind, which as it strikes it on the breast would throw it over if it were not that it lowers the right or left wing, for this will cause it to turn to the right or left, dropping down in a half circle.

The bird maintains itself in the air by imperceptible balancing when near to the mountains or lofty ocean crags; it does this by means of the curves of the winds which, as they strike against the projections, being forced to preserve their first impetus, bend their straight course toward the sky with divers revolutions, at the beginning of which the birds come to a stop with their wings open, receiving underneath themselves the continual buffetings of the reflex courses of the winds, and by the angle of their bodies acquiring as much weight against the wind as the wind makes force against this weight. And so by such a condition of equilibrium the bird proceeds to employ the smallest beginnings of every variety of power that can be produced.

The man in a flying machine has to be free from the waist upward in order to be able to balance himself as he does in a boat, so that his center of gravity and that of his machine may oscillate and change where necessity requires through a change in the center of its resistance.

The movement of the [man-made] bird ought always to be above the clouds so that the wing may not be wetted, and in order to survey more country and to escape the danger caused by the revolutions of the winds among the mountain defiles which are always full of gusts and eddies of winds. And if, moreover, the bird should be overturned you will have plenty of time to turn it back again, following the instructions I have given, before it falls down again to the ground.

If the point of the wing is struck by the wind and the wind enters underneath the point the bird will then find itself liable to be overturned unless it employs one of two remedies; that is, either it suddenly enters with this point under the wind or lowers the opposite wing from the middle forward.

The [mechanical] bird I have described ought to be able by the help of the wind to rise to a great height, and this will prove to be its safety; since even if all the above-mentioned revolutions were to befall it, it would still have time to regain a condition of equilibrium; provided that its various parts have a great power of resistance, so that they can safely withstand the fury and violence of the descent, by the aid of the defenses which I have mentioned; and its joints should be made of strong tanned hide, and sewn with cords of strong raw silk. And let no one encumber himself with iron bands, for these are very soon broken at the joints or else they become worn out, and consequently it is well not to encumber oneself with them.

THE PARACHUTE

If a man have a tent made of linen of which the apertures have all been stopped up, and it be twelve braccia across [over

964

twenty-five feet] and twelve in depth, he will be able to throw himself down from any height without sustaining any injury.

OF THE SEA WHICH GIRDLES THE EARTH

I perceive that the surface of the earth was from of old entirely filled up and covered over in its level plains by the salt waters, and that the mountains, the bones of the earth, with their wide bases, penetrated and towered up amid the air, covered over and clad with much high-lying soil. Subsequently, the incessant rains have caused the rivers to increase, and by repeated washing, have stripped bare part of the lofty summits of these mountains, leaving the site of the earth, so that the rock finds itself exposed to the air, and the earth has departed from these places. And the earth from off the slopes and the lofty summits of the mountains has already descended to their bases, and has raised the floors of the seas which encircle these bases, and caused the plain to be uncovered, and in some parts has driven away the seas from there over a great distance.

WHY WATER IS SALT

. . . The saltness of the sea is due to the numerous springs of water, which, in penetrating the earth, find the salt mines, and dissolving parts of these carry them away with them to the ocean and to the other seas, from whence they are never lifted by the clouds which produce the rivers. So the sea would be more salt in our times than it has ever been at any time previously. . . .

CHANGES OF EARTH AND SEA

The destruction of marshes will be brought about when turbid rivers flow into them. This is proved by the fact that where the river flows swiftly it washes away the soil, and where it delays there it leaves its deposit, and both for this reason, and because water never travels so slowly in rivers as it does in the marshes of the valleys, the movement of the waters there is imperceptible. But in these marshes the river has to enter through a low, narrow, winding channel, and it has to flow out over a large area of but little depth; and this is necessary because the water flowing in the river is thicker and more laden with earth in the lower than in the upper part; and the sluggish water of the marshes also is the same, but the variation between the lightness and heaviness of the upper and lower waters of the marshes far exceeds that in the currents of rivers, in which the lightness of the upper part differs but little from the heaviness of the part below.

So the conclusion is that the marsh will be destroyed because it is receiving turbid water below, while above, on the opposite side of the same marsh, only clear water is flowing out; and, consequently, the bed of the marsh will of necessity be raised by means of the soil which is being continually discharged into it.

The shells of oysters and other similar creatures which are born in the mud of the sea, testify to us of the change in the earth round the centre of our elements. This is proved as follows:—the mighty rivers always flow turbid because of the earth stirred up in them through the friction of their waters upon their bed and against the banks; and this process of destruction uncovers the tops of the ridges formed by the layers of these shells, which are embedded in the mud of the sea where they were born when the salt waters covered them. And these same ridges were from time to time covered over by varying thicknesses of mud which had been brought down to the sea by the rivers in floods of varying magnitude; and in this way these shells remained walled up and dead beneath this mud, which became raised to such a height that the bed of the sea emerged into the air. And now these beds are of so great a height that they have become hills or lofty mountains, and the rivers, which wear away the sides of these mountains, lay bare the strata of the shells, and so the light surface of the earth is continually raised, and the antipodes draw nearer to

the centre of the earth, and the ancient beds of the sea become
chains of mountains.

ORIGIN AND MEANING OF FOSSILS

Of the Flood and of Marine Shells. If you should say that the
shells which are visible at the present time within the borders of
Italy, far away from the sea and at great heights, are due to the
Flood having deposited them there, I reply that, granting this
Flood to have risen seven cubits above the highest mountain, as
he has written who measured it, these shells which always inhabit
near the shores of the sea ought to be found lying on the mountain
sides, and not at so short a distance above their bases, and all at
the same level, layer upon layer.

Should you say that the nature of these shells is to keep near
the edge of the sea, and that as the sea rose in height the shells
left their former place and followed the rising waters up to their
highest level:—to this I reply that the cockle is a creature incapable of more rapid movement than the snail out of water, or
is even somewhat slower, since it does not swim, but makes a
furrow in the sand, and supporting itself by means of the sides
of this furrow it will travel between three and four braccia in a
day; and therefore with such a motion as this it could not have
travelled from the Adriatic sea as far as Monferrato in Lombardy,
a distance of two hundred and fifty miles in forty days,—as he
has said who kept a record of that time.

And if you say that the waves carried them there—they could
not move by reason of their weight except upon their base. And
if you do not grant me this, at any rate allow that they must have
remained on the tops of the highest mountains, and in the lakes
which are shut in among the mountains, such as the lake of Lario
or Como, and Lake Maggiore, and that of Fiesole and of Perugia
and others.

If you should say that the shells were empty and dead when
carried by the waves, I reply that where the dead ones went the
living were not far distant, and in these mountains are found all

967

living ones, for they are known by the shells being in pairs and by their being in a row without any dead, and a little higher up is the place where all the dead with their shells separated have been cast up by the waves, near where the rivers plunged in mighty chasm into the sea. So it was with the Arno, which fell from the Gonfolina near to Monte Lupo and there left gravel deposits, which deposits are still to be seen welded together and forming one concrete mass of various kinds of stones from different localities and of varying colour and hardness. And a little further on, where the river turns towards Castel Fiorentino, the hardening of the sand has formed tufa stone; and below this it has deposited the mud in which the shells lived; and the mud has risen by degrees as the floods of the Arno poured their turbid waters into this sea. So from time to time the floor of the sea was raised, and this caused these shells to be in layers.

This is seen in the cutting of Colle Gonzoli, which has been made precipitous by the action of the Arno wearing away its base, in which cutting the aforesaid layers of shells are plainly to be seen in the bluish clay, and there are also to be found other things from the sea.

As for those who say that the shells are found over a wide area and produced at a distance from the sea by the nature of the locality and the disposition of the heavens which moves and influences the place to such a creation of animal life,—to them it may be answered that, granted such an influence over these animals, they could not happen all in one line, save in the case of those of the same species and age; and not one old and another young, one with an outer covering and another without, one broken and another whole, nor one filled with sea sand, and the fragments great and small of others inside the whole shells which stand gaping open; nor the claws of crabs without the rest of their bodies; nor with the shells of other species fastened on to them, like animals crawling over them and leaving the mark of their track on the outside where it has eaten its way like a worm in wood; nor would there be found among them bones and teeth of fish which some call arrows, others serpents' tongues; nor would so many parts of different animals be found joined together, unless they had been thrown up there upon the borders of the sea.

And the Flood could not have carried them there, because things which are heavier than water do not float high in the water, and the aforesaid things could not be at such heights unless they had been carried there floating on the waves, and that is impossible on account of their weight.

Where the valleys have never been covered by the salt waters of the sea, there the shells are never found.

Since things are far more ancient than letters, it is not to be wondered at if in our days there exists no record of how the aforesaid seas extended over so many countries; and if moreover such record ever existed, the wars, the conflagrations, the deluges of the waters, the changes in speech and habits have destroyed every vestige of the past. But sufficient for us is the testimony of things produced in the salt waters and now found again in the high mountains far from the seas.

Shells and the Reason of Their Shape. The creature that resides within the shell constructs its dwelling with joints and seams and roofing and the other various parts, just as man does in the house in which he dwells; and this creature expands the house and roof gradually in proportion as its body increases and as it is attached to the sides of these shells. Consequently the brightness and smoothness which these shells possess on the inner side is somewhat dulled at the point where they are attached to the creature that dwells there, and the hollow of it is roughened, ready to receive the knitting together of the muscles by means of which the creature draws itself in when it wishes to shut itself up within its house.

When nature is on the point of creating stones, it produces a kind of sticky paste, which, as it dries, forms itself into a solid mass together with whatever it has enclosed there, which, however, it does not change into stone but preserves within itself in the form in which it has found them. This is why leaves are found whole within the rocks which are formed at the bases of the mountains, together with a mixture of different kinds of things, just as they have been left there by the floods from the rivers which have occurred in the autumn seasons; and there

969

the mud caused by the successive inundations has covered them over, and then this mud grows into one mass together with the aforesaid paste, and becomes changed into successive layers of stone which correspond with the layers of the mud.

Of Creatures Which Have Their Bones on the Outside, Like Cockles, Snails, Oysters, Scollops, "Bouoli" and the Like, which are of Innumerable Kinds. When the floods of the rivers which were turbid with fine mud deposited this upon the creatures which dwelt beneath the waters near the ocean borders, these creatures became embedded in this mud, and finding themselves entirely covered under a great weight of mud they were forced to perish for lack of a supply of the creatures on which they were accustomed to feed.

In course of time the level of the sea became lower, and as the salt water flowed away this mud became changed into stone; and such of these shells as had lost their inhabitants became filled up in their stead with mud; and consequently, during the process of change of all the surrounding mud into stone, this mud also which was within the frames of the half-opened shells, since by the opening of the shell it was joined to the rest of the mud, became also itself changed into stone; and therefore all the frames of these shells were left between two petrified substances, namely that which surrounded them and that which they enclosed.

These are still to be found in many places, and almost all the petrified shell fish in the rocks of the mountains still have their natural frame round them, and especially those which were of a sufficient age to be preserved by reason of their hardness, while the younger ones which were already in great part changed into chalk were penetrated by the viscous and petrifying moisture.

Of Shells in Mountains. And if you wish to say that the shells are produced by nature in these mountains by means of the influence of the stars, in what way will you show that this influence produces in the very same place shells of various sizes and varying in age, and of different kinds?

ALESSANDRO VOLTA

(1745–1827)

Pioneer of electricity and professor of natural philosophy at Padua, Volta developed the theory of current electricity, discovered the electric decomposition of water, invented the electrophorus and an electroscope. His most important work was his discovery that electricity can be produced by the juncture of metals, leading to the invention of an electric battery and the famous voltaic pile. The volt, unit of electrical measurement, is of course named after him.

ON THE ELECTRICITY EXCITED BY THE MERE CONTACT OF CONDUCTING SUBSTANCES OF DIFFERENT KINDS

Como, in the Milanais
March 20th, 1800

AFTER A LONG silence, which I do not attempt to excuse, I have the pleasure of communicating to you, Sir, and through you to the Royal Society, some striking results to which I have come in carrying out my experiments on electricity excited by the simple mutual contact of metals of different sorts, and even by the contact of other conductors, also different among themselves, whether liquids or containing some liquid, to which property they owe their conducting power. The most important of these results, which includes practically all the others, is the construction of an apparatus which, in the effects which it produces, that is, in the disturbances which it produces in the arms etc., resembles Leyden jars, or better still electric batteries feebly charged, which act unceasingly or so that their charge after each discharge reestablishes itself; which in a word provides an unlimited charge or

971

imposes a perpetual action or impulsion on the electric fluid; but which otherwise is essentially different from these, both because of this continued action which is its property and because, instead of being made, as are the ordinary jars and electric batteries, of one or more insulating plates in thin layers of those bodies which are thought to be the only electric bodies, coated with conductors or bodies called non-electrics, this new apparatus is formed altogether of several of these latter bodies, chosen even among the best conductors and therefore the most remote, according to what has always been believed, from the electric nature. Yes! the apparatus of which I speak, and which will doubtless astonish you, is only an assemblage of a number of good conductors of different sorts arranged in a certain way. 30, 40, 60, pieces or more of copper, or better of silver, each in contact with a piece of tin, or what is much better, of zinc and an equal number of layers of water or some other liquid which is a better conductor than pure water, such as salt-water or lye and so forth, or pieces of cardboard or of leather, etc. well soaked with these liquids; when such layers are interposed between each couple or combination of the two different metals, such an alternative series of these three sorts of conductors always in the same order, constitutes my new instrument; which imitates, as I have said, the effects of Leyden jars or of electric batteries by giving the same disturbances as they; which in truth, are much inferior to these batteries when highly charged in the force and noise of their explosions, in the spark, in the distance through which the charge can pass, etc., and equal in effect only to a battery very feebly charged, but a battery nevertheless of an immense capacity; but which further infinitely surpasses the power of these batteries in that it does not need, as they do, to be charged in advance by means of an outside source; and in that it can give the disturbance every time that it is properly touched, no matter how often. . . .

I proceed to give a more detailed description of this apparatus and of some other analogous ones, as well as the most remarkable experiments made with them.

I provided myself with several dozen small round plates or

discs of copper, of brass, or better of silver, an inch in diameter more or less (for example, coins) and an equal number of plates of tin, or which is much better, of zinc, approximately of the same shape and size; I say approximately because precision is not necessary, and in general the size as well as the shape of the metallic pieces is arbitrary: all that is necessary is that they may be arranged easily one above the other in a column. I further provided a sufficiently large number of discs of cardboard, of leather, or of some other spongy matter which can take up and retain much water, or the liquid with which they must be well soaked if the experiment is to succeed. These pieces, which I will call the moistened discs, I make a little smaller than the metallic discs or plates, so that when placed between them in the way that I shall soon describe, they do not protrude.

Now having in hand all these pieces in good condition, that is to say, the metallic discs clean and dry, and the other non-metallic ones well soaked in water or which is much better, in brine, and afterwards slightly wiped so that the liquid does not come out in drops, I have only to arrange them in the proper way; and this arrangement is simple and easy.

I place horizontally on a table or base one of the metallic plates, for example, one of the silver ones, and on this first plate I place a second plate of zinc; on this second plate I lay one of the moistened discs; then another plate of silver, followed immediately by another of zinc, on which I place again a moistened disc. I thus continue in the same way coupling a plate of silver with one of zinc, always in the same sense, that is to say, always silver below and zinc above or *vice versa*, according as I began, and inserting between these couples a moistened disc; I continue, I say, to form from several of these steps a column as high as can hold itself up without falling (Figs. 2, 3, 4). . . .

Coming back to the mechanical construction of my apparatus, which admits of several variations, I proceed to describe here not all those which I have thought out and constructed either on a large or small scale, but some only which are either more curious or more useful or which present some real advantage, such as being easier or quicker to construct, more certain in their effects or keeping in good condition longer. To begin with one of these which unites almost all of these advantages, which in its form differs the most from the columnar apparatus described before but which has the disadvantage of being a much larger apparatus, I present this new apparatus which I call the crown of cups in the next figure.

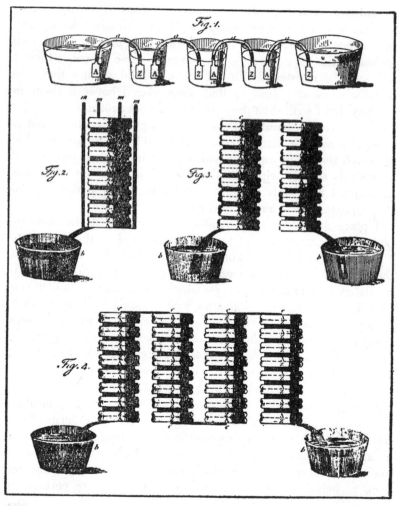

We set up a row of several cups or bowls made of any material whatever except the metals, cups of wood, of shell, of clay, or better of crystal (small drinking glasses or goblets are very suitable) half-full of pure water, or better of brine or of lye; and we join them all together in a sort of chain by means of metallic arcs of which one arm Aa or only the end A which is placed in one of the goblets is of red or yellow copper, or better of silvered copper, and the other Z, which is placed in the next goblet is of tin or better of zinc. I may observe here in passing that lye and the other alkaline liquids are preferable when one of the metals which is immersed in them is tin; brine is preferable when it is zinc. The two metals of which each arc is composed are soldered together somewhere above the part which is immersed in the liquid and which ought to touch it with a sufficiently large surface: for this purpose it is suitable that this part should be an inch square or very little less; the rest of the arc may be as much narrower as we please, and may even be a simple metallic wire. It may also be made of a third metal different from the two which are immersed in the liquid of the goblets; since the action on the electric fluid which results from all the contacts of several metals which are in immediate contact, the force with which this fluid is driven at the end, is the same absolutely or nearly as that which it would have received by the immediate contact of the first metal with the last without any of the intermediate metals, as I have verified by direct experiment, of which I shall have occasion to speak elsewhere.

Now then a train of 30, 40, 60 of these goblets joined up in this manner and arranged either in a straight line or in a curve or set round in any way forms the whole of this new apparatus, which fundamentally and in substance is the same as the other one of the column tried before; the essential feature, which consists in the immediate connection of the different metals which form each pair and the mediate connection of one couple with another by the intermediary of a damp conductor, appears in this apparatus as well as in the other.

975

ACKNOWLEDGMENT

Acknowledgment is gratefully made to the following publishers and authors for permission to reprint from their works:

Abelard-Schuman Ltd.: *Nobel Prize Winners in Physics* by Niels H. de V. Heathcote; *Nobel Prize Winners in Medicine and Physiology* by Lloyd G. Stevenson.

George Allen & Unwin Ltd.: "The Fundamental Idea of Wave Mechanics" by Erwin Schroedinger, translated by Dr. James Murphy and W. H. Johnston, in *Science and the Human Temperament*.

Cambridge University Press: *The Theory of Spectra and Atomic Constitution—Three Essays* by Niels Bohr.

The Clarendon Press: *Early Theories of Sexual Generation* by F. J. Cole; *Quantum Theory* by Max Planck, translated by H. T. Clarke and L. Silberstein.

P. F. Collier & Son Company: *The Harvard Classics*, edited by Charles W. Eliot.

J. M. Dent & Sons Ltd.: *Greek Medicine*, edited and translated by A. J. Brock.

Doubleday & Company: *The Autobiography of Science*, edited by Forest Ray Moulton and Justus J. Schifferes; *Masterworks of Science*, edited by John Warren Knedler, Jr.

E. P. Dutton & Company: *Memories of My Life* by Francis Galton.

John F. Fulton: Translation of "Concerning Electrical Forces in Muscular Movement," by Luigi Galvani.

Harcourt, Brace and Company: *The Notebooks of Leonardo da Vinci*, translated by Edward MacCurdy.

Harvard University Press and the President and Fellows of Harvard College: *A Source Book in Animal Biology* by Thomas S. Hall; *A Source Book in Astronomy* by Harlow Shapley and Helen E. Howarth; *A Source Book in Chemistry* by Henry M. Leicester and Herbert S. Klickstein; *A Source Book in Geology* by Kirtley F. Mather and Shirley L. Mason; *A Source Book in Physics* by William Francis Magie.

Paul B. Hoeber, Inc.: *The Life and Times of Ambroise Paré* by Francis R. Packard.

International Publishers: *Lectures on Conditioned Reflexes* by Ivan P. Pavlov.

The Johns Hopkins Press: "The Hippocratic Oath," translated by Ludwig Edelstein in *Bulletin of the History of Medicine*.

Macmillan & Company Ltd. and St. Martin's Press, Inc.: *The Miscellaneous Papers of Heinrich Hertz*.

Mining Publications, Ltd.: *On Metals* by Agricola, translated by Mr. and Mrs. Herbert Hoover.

W. W. Norton & Company: *Principles of Mathematics* by Bertrand Russell.

Princeton University Press: *A Critique of the Theory of Evolution* by Thomas Hunt Morgan

The Ray Society of the British Museum and Bernard Quaritch Ltd.: *Critica Botanica* by Carolus Linnaeus, translated by Sir Arthur Holt.

The Royal Aeronautical Society: *The Flight of Birds* by Giovanni Borelli.

The Royal Horticultural Society of London: "Experiments in Plant Hybridization" by Gregor Mendel.

The Honorary Editors of the *Proceedings of the Royal Society of Medicine*: *Anatomy of the Human Body* by Andreas Vesalius, translated by B. Farrington.

Justus J. Schifferes: "A Personal Story of Invention" by Daniel Gabriel Fahrenheit; "Little Animals in Rain Water" by Anton van Leeuwenhoek.

The Smithsonian Institution: "Memoir on Mechanical Flight" by Samuel P. Langley.

Charles C. Thomas, Publishers: *Readings in the History of Physiology*.

Helen G. Thompson: "Treatise on Light" by Christian Huygens, translated by Silvanus P. Thompson.

United Engineering Trustees, Inc.: *Popular Research Narratives*, edited by Alfred D. Flinn.

University of Chicago Press: *The Physical Principles of the Quantum Theory* by Werner Heisenberg, translated by Carl Eckart and Frank C. Hoyt.

University of Pennsylvania Press: *The Opus Majus of Roger Bacon*, translated by Robert Belle Burke.

William H. Wise & Company: *The World's Greatest Books*.